Structural Analysis

**PRENTICE-HALL INTERNATIONAL SERIES
IN CIVIL ENGINEERING AND ENGINEERING MECHANICS**

W. J. Hall, Editor

Structural Analysis

Tung Au
Professor of Civil Engineering
Carnegie-Mellon University

Paul Christiano
Professor and Head of Civil Engineering
Carnegie-Mellon University

Prentice-Hall, Inc., Englewood Cliffs, New Jersey 07632

Library of Congress Cataloging-in-Publication Data

AU, TUNG, (date)
  Structural analysis.

  Bibliography: p.
  Includes index.
1. Structures, Theory of. I. Christiano, Paul,
(date) II. Title.
TA645.A87 1987   624.1'7   86-12261
ISBN 0-13-853383-0

Editorial/production supervision: Gretchen K. Chenenko
Cover design: Lundgren Graphics
Cover photo: David Steidl
  Steidl-Balzer Productions, Inc.
Manufacturing buyer: Rhett Conklin

Printed in the United States of America

10 9 8 7 6 5 4 3 2 1

ISBN 0-13-853383-0 025

PRENTICE-HALL INTERNATIONAL (UK) LIMITED, *London*
PRENTICE HALL OF AUSTRALIA PTY. LIMITED, *Sydney*
PRENTICE-HALL CANADA INC., *Toronto*
PRENTICE-HALL HISPANOAMERICANA, S.A., *Mexico*
PRENTICE-HALL OF INDIA PRIVATE LIMITED, *New Delhi*
PRENTICE-HALL OF JAPAN, INC., *Tokyo*
PRENTICE-HALL OF SOUTHEAST ASIA PTE. LTD., *Singapore*
EDITORA PRENTICE-HALL DO BRASIL, LTDA., *Rio de Janeiro*

Contents

*Special topics may be left out at the discretion of the instructor.

Preface

This book is written as a text for a two-semester course in structural analysis. It deals with both statically determinate and indeterminate structures, and provides unity and depth in the application of concepts and principles of mechanics to structural analysis. Approximately two thirds of the text deals with classical structural analysis, while the remainder deals with matrix analyses, including an introduction to the finite element method.

Throughout the entire text, emphasis is placed on the application of the principles of mechanics to the analysis of structures rather than the routine solution of certain types and classes of existing structures. By stressing the difference between real structures and their mathematical models at the very beginning, the text brings home to the student the significance of intuitive perception and gives a broad insight beyond that obtained through a formal mathematical solution. However, troublesome details of application are by no means neglected. Ample examples are completely worked out to illustrate the methods of approach for a great variety of problems. Numerous homework problems with varying degrees of difficulty are given to challenge the students' facility and improve their proficiency in problem solving. Most problems associated with matrix methods are amenable to hand computation although the instructor might wish to make computer programs available to students to facilitate matrix operations. Problems requiring large-scale computations and general-purpose computer codes have been deliberately avoided to emphasize basic concepts and procedures.

A substantial part of this book is devoted to the review of mechanics of rigid and deformable solids, which may be omitted if such a review is deemed unnecessary. On the other hand, some of the special topics, as noted by asterisks in the Contents, may be left out if much time must be spent in the review of basic principles. By providing a thorough treatment of a large number of topics, the book permits unusual flexibility in selection of the course content at the discretion of the instructor.

This book represents a joint undertaking of the authors. The first ten chapters were written by the first author who drew heavily from materials in his earlier work, *Elementary Structural Mechanics*, published by Prentice-Hall, Inc. The last four chapters were written by the second author. However, the entire manuscript has been critically reviewed and modified by both authors for clarity, continuity, and consistency. The development of this book has been influenced by many previous publications by others in this field to whom the authors are greatly indebted. The References at the end of the book list important works.

The authors wish to acknowledge their indebtedness to their colleagues at Carnegie-Mellon University during the preparation of the manuscript, particularly to Dr. Steven Fenves, who offered numerous valuable suggestions, and to Drs. Jacobo Bielak, Irving J. Oppenheim, James P. Romualdi, and William L. Whittaker, who used an earlier version of this book in their classes. The laboratory model for demonstrating the deflected shapes of beams in Chapter 2 was constructed by Charles H. Heaton, Jr., with the assistance of Lawrence G. Cartwright, and the photographs of various deflected beams were taken by Dr. Daniel R. Rehak. Their efforts have helped to produce a set of marvelous illustrations. Thomas Siller kindly provided solutions for the finite element examples and homework assignments in Chapter 14, and Godofredo Camacho and Teresa Adams furnished solutions for many of the problems for homework assignments in Chapters 11 through 13. The authors also wish to thank Frances Kastner and Margaret Faulkner for their painstaking efforts in typing the manuscript.

Appreciation is especially due to Dr. William J. Hall of the University of Illinois who reviewed the manuscript and made a number of constructive suggestions.

Tung Au
Paul Christiano

Structural Analysis

1

Introduction

1-1 ENGINEERING STRUCTURES

Throughout human history, engineering structures have been constructed for specific purposes to serve individual and societal needs. The pyramids in Egypt and the Great Wall in China are only two examples of many monuments that remind us of the accomplishments of ancient builders. In more recent times, the art of construction has been supplemented by new scientific discoveries and innovative technologies. Today, we are witnessing the proliferation of structures of all types, forms and sizes to serve and support a variety of human activities. Without exception, the art and science of building reflect the cultural developments in various eras of civilization.

The evolution of engineered structures can indeed be traced to the ingenuity and resourcefulness of their builders, as well as the available materials and technological advances of the times in which they were built. Many monumental structures of our time represent the triumph of new conquests over natural barriers and the fulfillment of the hopes and dreams of mankind. In the past century, many structures established new records of all kinds—in span length, in height, and in use of new structural forms, among other advances—only to be surpassed by yet more imposing structures built a short time later. The story of the accomplishments of engineers and builders never ceases.

A striking example which embodies both technological breakthrough and aesthetic quality of a structure is the Brooklyn Bridge over the East River in New York City, illustrated in Fig. 1-1. At the time of its completion in 1883, this suspension bridge had a span 50% longer than that of any other bridge. It

1

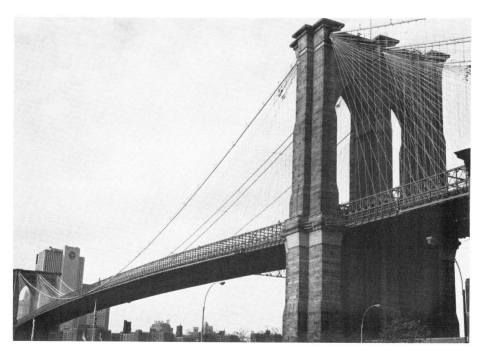

Figure 1-1 Brooklyn Bridge, NYC, NY. Photo by Daina Romualdi.

was the crowning achievement of John A. Roebling, culminating his lifelong contributions to the art and science of bridge building until his death following a job-site accident in 1869. Washington A. Roebling, who succeeded his father as chief engineer of the project, was disabled physically during the construction of a pneumatic caisson, and his wife Emily has been credited for playing the important role of emissary between him and the assistant engineers at the job site during 11 of the 14 years of the project. The story of the Brooklyn Bridge is an inspiring human drama, revealing the vision, spirit, and dedication of its builders.

Incidentally, John A. Roebling's first highway suspension bridge was the Smithfield Street Bridge over the Monongahela River in Pittsburgh, Pennsylvania, which was built in 1846 and torn down in 1882. The present lenticular truss–type structure at the same site, illustrated in Fig. 1-2, which was opened to traffic in 1883 while still under construction, was engineered by Gustav Lindenthal, another renowned bridge builder. Lindenthal later designed the Hell Gate Bridge over the East River in Long Island Sound, New York, which was the longest arch span at the time of its completion in 1916, and the Sciotoville Bridge over the Ohio River between Ohio and Kentucky, which broke all records for continuous bridges in 1917.

The structural design of skyscrapers offers another example of the triumph of innovation in overcoming the barrier of high costs for tall buildings. The most revolutionary concept in skyscraper design was introduced in 1965 by Fazlur Khan who argued that, for a building of a given height, there is an

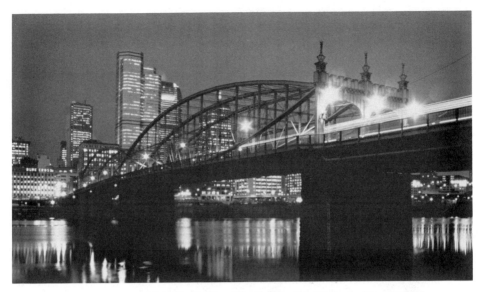

Figure 1-2 Smithfield St. Bridge, Pittsburgh, PA. Photo by David Steidl, © Steidl/Balzer Productions, Inc., Pittsburgh, PA.

appropriate structural system that would produce the most efficient use of materials, as exemplified by the skyscrapers designed by him. Based on this new concept, he used a truss tube structural system for the 100-story John Hancock Center in Chicago, illustrated in Fig. 1-3, requiring only half of the steel per floor area as that needed for a rigid frame structure of comparable height. He also adopted the tubular building concept for the 50-story One Shell Plaza in Houston, illustrated in Fig. 1-4, which reigned as the tallest concrete building in the world for nearly a decade. This revolution in skyscraper design

Figure 1-3 John Hancock Center, Chicago, IL (Skidmore, Owings & Merrill, Architects/Engineers). Photo by Bill Engdahl, © Hedrich-Blessing, Chicago, IL.

Figure 1-4 One Shell Plaza, Houston, TX (Skidmore, Owings & Merrill, Architects/Engineers). Photo by Ezra Stoller, © Esto Photographics, Inc., Mamaroneck, NY.

was made possible, not only by Kahn's intellectual effort, but also by the availability of the electronic computer which could process the enormously complicated structural analysis associated with his conceptualization.

Clearly, a structural engineer should gain a broad appreciation of the problems associated with the design of a structure as well as the skill in structural analysis and design. Even though only the latter is the primary responsibility of a structural engineer, innovative design requires the cultivation of a mind which refuses to restrict itself to a well-defined area of specialization.

1-2 STRUCTURAL ENGINEERING

Structural engineering is defined as the process of utilizing the art and science in the planning, analysis, design, and construction of structures. *Planning* consists of the conceptualization and development of a general layout of a structure that satisfies functional, economical, and esthetic requirements.

Analysis refers to the modeling of the real structure and the solution of the idealized problem. *Design* involves the selection of proper materials for the structure and the determination of the shapes and sizes of its components. *Construction* pertains to fabrication, erection, and inspection of the structure. The final completion of a safe but efficient and economical structure depends on the satisfactory execution of the project through all stages.

It should be noted, however, that these basic steps are by no means distinct but rather are interdependent. Some of them involve mathematical analysis; others require judgement based on experience. Quite frequently it is necessary to have a balanced combination of both, depending on the degree of complexity of the structure. We shall examine each step in detail in order to gain a better understanding of the overall approach to a structural engineering problem.

Planning. This is the initial phase of a project that requires, above all, creative imagination and sound judgement. If the structure is a highway bridge, for instance, the topography, soil conditions, and traffic patterns near the bridge site must be studied. Next the type of structure most suitable for the crossing must be considered. A girder, truss, arch, or suspension bridge are common alternatives. Experience with similar problems is often a guide for selecting the type of structure. However, the existing standard structural forms may fail to satisfy all the requirements and new ones must be developed. Here the engineer needs both an innovative spirit and traditional conservatism. Otherwise, he or she may be too absorbed in the existing types of structure to recognize that a new approach is possible. On the other hand, she or he may see all the virtues and none of the weaknesses of the new form so that only later experience may reveal its undesirable or even disastrous aspects. It is important, therefore, that a structural engineer acquires a broad understanding of the principles of mechanics and sound judgement derived from practical experience.

For purposes of comparison, it is often necessary to make preliminary designs and cost estimates for several structural schemes. As a matter of practical necessity, crude approximations may be introduced in the analysis. Once a particular structure is chosen, however, more precise data and methods are used to obtain better and more reliable solutions. Such operations are usually carried out through several iterations until a satisfactory solution is obtained.

Analysis. The analysis of structural systems is founded on the principles of mechanics. Before the formulation and solution of a problem, however, the system is usually idealized and simplified so that the conceptual model will be simple enough to analyze and yet not too different from the real structure. A great deal of judgement is involved in making simplifying assumptions, which can be verified only by experiment or justified by experience. At this stage, three distinct phases should be recognized. First, the real structure may be divided into appropriate component systems that can be analyzed separately—one part at a time if necessary and possible. In a steel-framed building, for example, the beams and columns at each level can be considered as separate elements. Second, we must determine the loads that are transmitted and resisted by each system, considering not only the magnitude, location, and distribution of these loads, but also the frequency of their occurrence and the nature of their action. Third, it is necessary to examine the characteristics of the system against the consequences of failure or unserviceability of the structure; thus, the concept of structural safety will not be lost in the idealization. These three phases are closely related to each other, and all three of them affect the method of analysis. Although the analysis itself is a rather mechanical procedure, the consideration of these factors involves a great deal of judgement.

As an example, consider the effect of a trailer truck traversing a highway bridge. It is customary to replace the dynamic effect by an equivalent stationary load. Under such circumstances, the mathematical model will be the same as that for a static load and the problem can be solved by statics. On the other hand, if the dynamic effect is not approximated by static loads, the mass of the bridge must be included in the idealized system to analyze the vibration of the bridge.

Design.   This phase involves the proportioning of the components or members of the structural system. The choice of materials for the structure depends not only on the suitability of the materials but also on their availability; for this reason the materials should be determined in the early planning stage. This is especially true if the choice of materials may influence the form of the structure, or vice versa. For example, in the design of a mill building, a steel skeleton frame may be selected because a similar frame in reinforced concrete will limit the span of the structure owing to the unfavorable ratio of resistance to weight of the material. However, if a thin-shelled roof is adopted, reinforced concrete may prove to be more suitable than steel. Again, the interplay of these factors definitely affects the structural system, and a thorough knowledge of the properties of materials is indispensable in selecting the proper materials for specific structures.

The proportions of the component members of a structure must be so chosen that the structure as a whole can safely and economically perform the intended services under the prescribed loading conditions. Failure in certain parts of a structure may have only local effects, but in other cases it may cause the complete collapse of the structure. For this reason, no member or connection in a structure should be overlooked. Because of the elements of uncertainty and perhaps ignorance of the expected loads, the material properties, and the criteria for failure, a *factor of safety* is introduced in proportioning the structural members. This may be accomplished either by providing a comfortable margin below the yield strengths of materials in specifying the allowable stresses or by adopting design loads higher than the loads expected in the lifetime of the structure.

It should be observed that design is almost inseparable from analysis. The exact sizes of structural members can be determined only after a complete analysis of the structure. On the other hand, there are certain items in analysis that depend on the results of design. One example is the weight of the structure, which cannot be determined exactly until all members of the structure are proportioned. Hence, the procedure of analysis and design may involve cycles of successive corrections.

Construction.   As the project reaches its final stage, the work shifts from design office to plant and field, where the structure is fabricated and erected. The structural engineer may no longer have direct control over the job, but he should provide adequate supervision to ensure that the structure is satisfactorily completed. It is also important that an engineer be familiar with the various techniques of construction and their limitations because this will certainly influence his thinking in planning as well as in analysis and design.

The cost of construction, for instance, is affected by the availability of materials and skilled labor trained for the work at the location of the structure. Hence, an ideal structure for one locality may not be the best solution in another situation. The techniques of construction also have direct effects in analysis and design. One of the most striking examples is the computation of erection stresses for a long-span bridge. During construction, a part of the structure first erected may sometimes be used to support derricks and other construction equipment for the erection of an adjacent unit. The stresses in the members of the partially completed structure may exceed those in the completed structure under the most severe loading condition. It is imperative, therefore, to design the structure properly to withstand the expected loads at various stages of construction. This also applies to falsework and formwork used in construction.

1-3 LOADS ON STRUCTURES

The term *loads* is broadly defined as the environmental demands on structures. These demands, both natural and man-made, may appear in the form of *forces* such as wind, snow, or weights of people and traffic, or in the form of *displacements* such as earthquake motions, mine subsidences, or change in the length of a structural member due to thermal expansion or misfit.

The loads on structures may be classified in many ways. For example, the sources of such loads can be classified broadly into two major categories: the *body forces* and the *surface forces*. Forces distributed over the body of a structure, such as gravitational forces, magnetic forces, or inertia forces, are called body forces. Forces distributed over the surface of a structure, such as traffic loads, hydrostatic pressure, or wind pressure, are called surface forces. Furthermore, these forces may either be *stationary* or *movable,* depending on whether or not the position of the loads may be changed. From another point of view, these forces may be classified as *static loads* and *dynamic loads*. The former includes forces that are applied steadily, such as the weight of the structure, or furniture or people in a building. The latter refers to forces which produce dynamic effects on a structure, such as the impact of moving trucks, the aerodynamic phenomena of wind, or the aftershock of a blast. In order to simplify the analysis, we often attempt to approximate the effects of dynamic loads by the use of *equivalent static* loads.

The intensities of static loads and equivalent static loads that must be imposed on a structure for design purposes may be found in codes and specifications developed by national professional organizations and trade associations involved in various aspects of structural design. Even with these guidelines, the determination of loads on structures is not a simple matter. First of all, we must consider the magnitude, location, and distribution of loads that may act on a structure. However, from the standpoint of design, we must be ready to answer several other questions. For instance, what are the combinations of loads that will have the most severe effect? What is the likelihood or probability of the occurrence of such combinations? Should a structure be designed to resist the worst possible loads that may occur only a few times during its life of service, or to support loads under normal conditions? These questions will be addressed later.

In this section, we shall describe only briefly the nature and occurrence of various types of loads and their representations as static or equivalent static loads.

Dead loads.   The weight of the basic frame of a structure and other immovable parts attached to it is called *dead load*. Although the actual weight of a structure can be accurately computed only after the sizes of all structural members are determined, the dead loads must be estimated for the purpose of analysis at a very early stage. It may be observed that the ratio of dead load to total load on a structure is an important factor in influencing the dead load calculation. In short-span structures, for example, such a ratio is small and the dead load is relatively unimportant. Then, a reasonably good estimate of the dead weight is usually sufficient. For long-span structures, however, such a ratio is relatively large and the dead load becomes predominant. Hence, an accurate appraisal of the actual weight of the structure becomes necessary.

Live loads.   Broadly speaking, all loads that are movable or moving are called *live loads*. In a narrower sense, however, the term is usually reserved for moving gravity loads excluding the dynamic effects due to vibratory motion or other causes. The dynamic effects are usually taken into consideration by an *impact factor,* which is the percentage increase in weight over the same load at rest. Thus, the equivalent static load in this case is equal to the stationary vertical load times the sum of one plus the impact factor. The external horizontal loads are usually referred to as *lateral* or *longitudinal* forces, depending on the direction of the force with respect to the structure. Horizontal loads may be caused by wind or hydrostatic pressure, or by the acceleration or swaying motion of the moving vehicles. Some of these forces are dynamic in nature but are often replaced by equivalent static loads.

Building occupancy loads. Within the live load category, the weights associated with people, furniture, movable equipment, etc. in buildings are referred to as occupancy loads. These loads should be positioned to give maximum effect on each of the members on the floor directly supporting these loads; however, only partial loading may be considered in determining the load effect on columns at the lower floors of a multi-story building.

Bridge moving loads. Motor vehicles on highway bridges and locomotives and rolling stock on railroad bridges are included in this category. Because of wide variations in the distribution of highway traffic, a rational loading pattern is usually adopted as standard truck loads or lane loads. The loadings for railroads and mass transit vehicles on bridges are usually based on the heaviest type of trains and other vehicles crossing the bridges.

Snow loads. The weight of snow on building roofs may be treated as vertical live load whose magnitude, of course, depends on the climate of the locality. For flat roofs, the full weight of the snow should be used in design; for pitched roofs the intensity may be reduced. Snow is seldom considered in the design of bridges, since a heavy snowfall would either slow the speed of the traffic and reduce the impact on the bridge or make the bridge impassable.

Wind loads. The actions of wind on structures represent rather complicated aerodynamic phenomena that involve the velocity of wind and the orientation, area, and shape of structures and structural elements. For ordinary enclosed structures, such as conventional buildings, the wind pressure on a plane surface normal to the direction of the wind may be treated as equivalent static load because the relationship between the time variation of the wind and the natural frequency of the structure is such as to cause essentially static response. However, the wind may not only exert positive pressure on the windward side but may also create negative pressure or suction on the leeward side of a building. For buildings with pitched roofs spanning large areas, such as hangars, auditoriums, or mill buildings, the pressure on the windward side and that on the leeward side of the roof should be treated separately.

Water pressure. The pressure exerted by a fluid at rest is normal to the surface of a submerged object. The magnitude of the pressure depends on the density of the fluid and the vertical distance from the point in question to the free surface of the fluid. Thus, a linear pressure distribution occurs from the free surface of a liquid of constant density to points below the surface.

Soil pressure. Structures that retain earth horizontally or vertically are subjected to soil pressure. This pressure depends on a number of variables such as the unit weight, cohesion and angle of internal friction of the soil, the geologic conditions under which the soil was deposited, and the rigidity and construction procedure of the structure. In some cases, the structure may deflect slightly under the soil pressure, and thus reduce the effective pressure on the structure.

Earthquake motions.   The behavior of structures subjected to earthquakes has generally been recognized as a transient vibration phenomenon. Although an earthquake causes vertical as well as horizontal movements, the horizontal component of acceleration is usually the most threatening. The response of a structure to an earthquake depends on a great number of factors, such as the acceleration patterns of the ground motion and the natural period of vibration and damping of the structure. If the fundamental period of natural vibration of a structural system lies in the range of dominant earthquake acceleration periods, the structure will produce a magnified response or resonance. When the natural period of the system is remote from the range, its response will be relatively small. A rational method for establishing the design forces on a structure involves the determination of the total lateral force or the base shear transmitted to the structure from the ground, and the distribution of that shear as equivalent forces applied to the structure.

Blast loads.   A structure may be subjected to a strong pressure that radiates from the center of a violent explosion, such as occurs during a nuclear blast. Very shortly after the detonation, the pressure wave advances to a neighboring point and almost instantaneously increases its pressure from atmospheric pressure, depending on the distance from the center of explosion. The pressure at the wave front is called the frontal or peak over-pressure. The advancing wave is called the *shock wave,* which drops to atmospheric pressure very rapidly after the wave front passes and leaves a trailing strong wind. When the shock wave is obstructed by a structure in its path, the pressure in the wave is increased owing to reflection but the reflected over-pressure drops off rapidly as the shock wave moves on. This is followed by the trailing wind that creates a drag as it passes the structure. Although the phenomenon is dynamic in nature, a design procedure essentially based on equivalent static loading is available.

Loads due to temperature changes.   The members of a structure expand or contract due to temperature changes in proportion to the coefficient of expansion of the material. When such members are subjected to differential changes in temperature, they tend to move relative to each other. If these movements are prevented by connections or supporting conditions, stresses will be developed in the members.

Loads due to forced fit.   When a member is forced into place due to construction misfits, it will be strained if prevented from adjusting itself to avoid forced fit. A similar problem is created by nonuniform settlement of the foundation of a structure with redundant supports. The stresses caused by the unintentional straining of a member may be quite high for certain types of structures and therefore cannot be ignored.

1-4 PERFORMANCE OF STRUCTURES

The final test of a well–designed engineering structure lies in its performance, which is usually indicated by its conformity with the requirements of serviceability and safety. Serviceability requires that the structure be free from excessive deformation or vibration under loads, and safety is characterized by the structural resistance against failure or the ultimate load-carrying capacity of the structure. A satisfactory design for serviceability will usually result in adequate safety if the relation between load and deformation is linear. When the load-deformation relation is nonlinear, an adequate design for one does not assure a satisfactory answer for the other.

From the standpoint of analysis, to which the greater part of this book is devoted, we are concerned only with choosing a mode of behavior of the structure that will cause either unserviceability or failure so that we can analyze it. From the standpoint of design, however, the problem is interwoven with many intricate factors that are not immediately obvious. Many of these are obscurely incorporated in the design codes and specifications or completely bypassed by these codes so that we may not be fully aware of their significance. We shall bring these factors to light by further examining the criteria for serviceability and safety of structures.

In order to satisfy both criteria, a structure must be so designed that it has sufficient strength and suffers no excessive deformation. Although the serviceability of a structure is governed by the elastic limit of the material, its ultimate load-carrying capacity may be characterized by one of the following modes of behavior:

1. *Plastic deformation of ductile materials.* For structural members of ductile material such as mild steel, large plastic deformation with increasing load-carrying capacity precedes rupture. In such a case, usually the appearance of excessive deformation will give sufficient warning of impending danger. Furthermore, the ultimate collapse loads on a structure may be predicted by the method of plastic analysis. Thus, this type of failure may be prevented by the removal of the overload or by temporary shoring.
2. *Buckling of compression members.* Large lateral deflection may result from the buckling of a compression member. Since the deflection appears suddenly at the critical load, this mode of failure usually occurs rather abruptly. For long slender members subjected to compression, buckling may occur even if the stresses in the entire member are below the elastic limit of the material. Such a phenomenon is called *elastic buckling*. Thus, a compression member must be designed against buckling.

3. *Brittle fracture under static loads.* For brittle materials such as concrete, rupture may occur without apparent deformation. Therefore, it is a good practice to proportion reinforced concrete beams so that the ultimate strength of the beam is governed by the yielding of the reinforcing steel rather than by crushing or diagonal tension in concrete. Even for normally ductile materials, brittle fracture may occur as a result of a combination of adverse factors such as low temperature, combined tensile stresses, or cracks of critical size in the material. Many metals exhibit a range of transition temperature under which the material becomes susceptible to brittle fracture. This is especially true if a flaw is present in the area where the state of stress is biaxial or triaxial. Once a crack is formed near the flaw, it propagates rapidly and a brittle fracture occurs in the member. Extensive research has been conducted to study the exact cause of crack formations and methods to arrest them. There has been some success in arresting these cracks for specific types of structural members, but generally speaking, no sure method has been discovered for preventing their formation.

4. *Fatigue fracture under dynamic repeated loads.* When a structural member is subjected to a large number of cycles of loading and unloading, rupture may occur at a stress level considerably lower than the ultimate strength of the material under static load. Since repeated loads are usually applied to the structure by dynamic means, such as locomotives or machinery that produces unbalanced driving forces, the dynamic effect should be separated from the effect arising from repeated loads. The former is classified as *impact,* whereas the latter is known as *fatigue.* For reinforced concrete structures, there is some evidence that the bond and shear strengths of concrete may be considerably reduced after a relatively small number of cycles of reversal of stress. On the other hand, steel structures are found to be unaffected, except at welded joints, geometry changes, and flaws, by relatively large number of cycles of loading and unloading for the type of moving loads that normally travel on bridges. However, steel members may suffer fatigue failure if severe vibration is present. Even plastic fatigue is possible in the case of aeolian vibration of transmission lines.

From the study of these modes of failure, it is obvious that elastic strength alone does not always give a complete picture of either the safety or serviceability of a structure. Whenever the situation indicates that this is the case, we must safeguard against other possibilities of failure or unserviceability.

The factor of safety plays a very important role in this regard. In order to ensure elasticity in a structure, the maximum stress permitted in any part of the structure under expected loads must be below the yield stress of the material by a certain margin. If the term *factor of serviceability* is defined as the ratio of yield stress to allowable stress, then the *margin of serviceability* equals this ratio minus one. Even if the actual load on the structure is slightly greater than the expected load, the structure will still behave elastically as long as the maximum stress in the structure does not exceed the yield stress. If the overload is so large that the structure begins to deform plastically, there is still no imminent danger of failure since ductility and work-hardening properties of the material provide reserve strength that cannot be predicted by the elastic analysis. On the other hand, structures designed for a criterion of ultimate load-carrying capacity usually carry only a fraction of the ultimate load under operating or service conditions. The ratio of ultimate load to operation load is called the *load factor* or *factor of safety*. However, the term "factor of safety" is commonly used in a broader sense to mean either load factor or factor of serviceability. By adopting a generous load factor, the structure will behave elastically under operating conditions although the maximum stress in the structure under such conditions cannot readily be obtained. Thus, one approach can be used to obtain the elastic behavior of the structure under operating conditions but not to predict its ultimate load-carrying capacity. The other approach will lead to the ultimate load-carrying capacity of the structure without considering its elastic behavior.

These two concepts of design are by no means contradictory. As a matter of fact, such dichotomy leads to a more sophisticated philosophy of design. In the light of different design criteria, it is possible to consider the loading conditions on structures more intelligently. For instance, the analysis of a structure under ordinary operating loads may be based on the elastic criterion, but the same structure under some possible but highly improbable loads or combinations of loads may be analyzed on the basis of the plastic criterion. In other words, a structure is expected to be serviceable under normal loading conditions, but under unusual circumstances of a disastrous nature, such as earthquakes or blasts of a highly improbable magnitude, it may be sufficient to design the structure to survive imminent danger of collapse without concern for large deformation. Hence, the serviceability and load factors can be adjusted for the situation.

It is difficult for the student to realize the importance of the role of design specifications. Actually many major decisions, including the nature and magnitude of applied loads, the properties of materials, the factors of safety, the design criteria, and sometimes even the methods of analysis, are dictated by the specifications. The student should acquire some of these specifications and investigate the reasoning behind the requirements. An engineer should learn to reach professional decisions based upon experience and should never be content to follow blindly the provisions of the specifications. In actual practice, an engineer is often called upon to solve new problems that lie beyond the scope of existing specifications, and must decide what the design requirements are under those circumstances—and often must convince the client.

Many national organizations as well as local authorities assume the responsibility for public safety by recommending specifications and requirements for design. These recommendations are based on the best evidence and judgement currently available and are revised periodically to keep up with the latest research and development. Some of the codes and specifications most frequently encountered by civil engineers include the following:

1. *The Basic Building Code,* Building Officials and Code Administrators, International (BOCA).
2. *The Standard Building Code,* South Building Code Congress, International (SBCC).
3. *The Uniform Building Code,* International Conference of Building Officials (ICBO).
4. *Requirements for Minimum Design Loads in Building and Other Structures,* American National Standards Institute (ANSI).
5. *Building Code Requirements for Reinforced Concrete,* American Concrete Institute (ACI).
6. *Specifications for the Design Fabrication and Erection of Structural Steel for Buildings,* American Institute of Steel Construction (AISC).
7. *National Design Specification for Stress-Grade Lumber and Its Fastenings,* National Forest Products Association (NFPA).
8. *Specifications for Aluminum Structures,* The Aluminum Association (AA).
9. *Standard Specifications for Highway Bridges,* The American Association of State Highway and Transportation Officials (AASHTO).
10. *Specifications for Steel Railway Bridges,* American Railway Association (AREA).
11. *ASTM Standards in Building Codes,* American Society for Testing Materials (ASTM).

1-5 STRUCTURAL ANALYSIS

After discussing various aspects of structural engineering, we shall discuss broadly the procedure of structural analysis which includes the following steps:

1. Recognize the actual problem.
2. Formulate the idealized problem.
3. Solve the idealized problem.
4. Interpret the solution of the idealized problem judiciously to draw conclusions about the actual problem.

Although the first and the last steps depend to a very large extent on judgement based on experience, an effort is made from time to time to emphasize the important factors involved. For example, the idealization of structures is illustrated by the pairwise comparison of an actual structure and its idealized counterpart in Figs. 1-5 through 1-8. In the remaining chapters, we shall

(a)

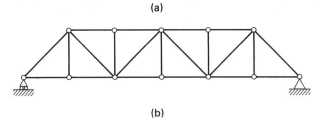

(b)

Figure 1-5 (a) A single-span railroad bridge. (b) An idealized simple truss.

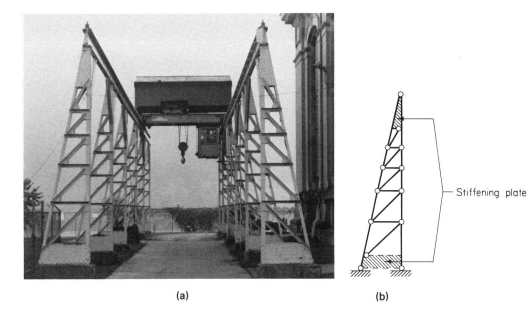

(a)

(b)

Stiffening plate

Figure 1-6 (a) A crane runway supported by trusses. (b) An idealized supporting truss.

Sec. 1-5 Structural Analysis

15

(a)

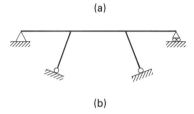

(b)

Figure 1-7 (a) A three-span highway bridge. (b) An idealized continuous rigid frame.

(a)

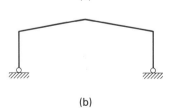

(b)

Figure 1-8 (a) A gabled-frame industrial building under construction. (b) An idealized gabled rigid frame.

Introduction   Chap. 1

concentrate mainly on the second and third steps, i.e., the formulation and solution of the problems.

The basic considerations in the formulation of such problems may be outlined as follows:

1. Analyze the forces and the conditions of equilibrium.
2. Study the deformations and the requirements of geometrical compatibility.
3. Establish the force-deformation relations from the properties of materials.

These principles may be applied to formulate a structural problem of any degree of complexity although it is sometimes preferable to tackle more complicated problems by means of the principles of work and energy.

For certain simple systems, however, the reactions and internal forces in the system can be completely analyzed from the conditions of equilibrium. Then, the deformations can be derived from the known internal forces and the given load-deformation characteristics of the material. Such systems are classified as *statically determinate structures*. For other systems, in which the reactions and internal forces cannot be determined from the conditions of equilibrium alone, the requirements of geometrical compatibility and the load-deformation relations will be needed to furnish additional conditions for the complete solution of a problem. These latter systems are called *statically indeterminate structures*.

Since the dynamic effects on structures involve mass, displacement, velocity, acceleration, and energy in the system, we must base our preliminary analysis on an assumed structure with characteristics sufficiently similar to the final structure. By using equivalent static loads and other simplified concepts, a reasonable structure may be selected without too many complications. If this is done intelligently, further dynamic analysis will be only a process of confirming the preliminary choice of the structure. Thus, analysis based on equivalent static loads has its place in structural design but it also has its limitations. If we are not aware of all the important factors in a situation, we cannot properly provide for variation and generalization in those factors. For this reason, concepts of equivalent static loads for dynamic problems must be used judiciously.

The foregoing discussion clearly indicates the importance of an integrated knowledge of structural engineering in order to obtain the best possible solution of a structural problem. Inasmuch as engineering is an art, it cannot be completely replaced by an exact science. Engineers have learned to rely more and more on the methodology of science but they cannot entirely dispense with judgement. Paradoxically, a good understanding of the basic principles in structural analysis can often lead to a better appreciation of the actual behavior of structures if the mathematical analysis is kept in proper perspective and proportion. Intuitive perception and insight are invaluable but not infallible. Hence, judgement based on experience must be tempered by rational analysis.

A proper balance of theoretical preparation and practicality based on a sense of judgement is essential to a successful structural engineer.

1-6 SYSTEMS OF UNITS IN STRUCTURAL MECHANICS

Since the American system (formerly English system) of units is the legal standard of weights and measures in the United States, it is used throughout this text including all examples and problems. However, the student should also be familiar with the International System (SI) of units, which has been adopted by most countries. Consequently, we will discuss briefly the conversion of these systems of units pertaining to structural analysis.

Basically, the units of measures used in structural analysis represent a subset of units adopted for mechanics, and only such units will be discussed here. From Newton's second law of motion, it is known that

$$F = ma \tag{1-1}$$

where force F is a vector, acceleration a also a vector, and mass m a scalar quantity. The mass of a body represents the *force per unit acceleration,* which is often described qualitatively by the term *inertia.* There are four base units for the quantities in Eq. (1-1), i.e., force, length, time, and mass; only three are independent and the fourth is a derived unit. Thus, if force, length, and time are selected as independent base units, the mass will have a unit derived from $m = F/a$ as follows:

$$\text{mass} = \frac{\text{force}}{\text{length/time}^2} = \frac{\text{force-time}^2}{\text{length}}$$

On the other hand, if mass, length, and time are chosen as independent base units, the force will be a derived unit as follows:

$$\text{force} = (\text{mass})(\text{length/time}^2) = \frac{\text{mass-length}}{\text{time}^2}$$

It is important to note that the mass is an invariant whether force or mass is selected as the base unit. Any system based on mass, length, and time is absolute because it is independent of the gravitational acceleration g. A system based on force, length, and time is referred to as a gravitational system, since force or weight depends on the value g which in turn varies with location, i.e., elevation, latitude, and longitude.

The American system of units is a gravitational system built upon the independent base units of force, length, and time, while the International System (SI) of units is an absolute system based on the independent base units of mass, length, and time. A comparison of the units of the basic elements for the two systems and the conversion factors based on specified standard gravitation are shown in Table 1-1.

Table 1-1 BASE UNITS OF SYSTEMS OF UNITS

Base unit	American	SI	Conversion factors	
force	pound (lb)	newton (N)	1 lb = 4.448 N;	1 N = 0.2248 lb
length	foot (ft)	meter (m)	1 ft = 0.3048 m;	1 m = 3.2808 ft
time	second (sec)	second (sec)	—	
mass	slug	kilogram (kg)	1 slug = 0.4536 kg;	1 kg = 2.2046 slug

In the American system, the unit of force is the pound (lb) which is defined in terms of the pull of gravity on a given mass at a specified (standard) location. At standard gravitation of $g_0 = 32.174$ ft/sec^2, the body having a pull of gravity of one pound has a one-pound mass. At any other location with gravity g ft/sec^2 instead of g_0, the mass of a body remains constant but the force or weight varies, i.e., a one-pound mass weighs g/g_0 lb. Generally, the force or weight of a body having a M-lb mass is given by

$$F = M\frac{g}{g_0} = \frac{Mg}{32.174} \qquad \text{(in pounds)} \qquad (1\text{-}2)$$

The slug is a derived unit of mass, defined as the amount of mass that is accelerated one foot per second per second by a force of one pound, i.e.,

$$1 \text{ slug} = 1 \frac{\text{lb-sec}^2}{\text{ft}}$$

which is independent of g.

In the International System (SI), the unit of mass is the kilogram (kg), which is defined as the invariant amount of mass that is accelerated one meter per second per second by a unit force. The newton (N) is a derived unit of force which refers to a pull of gravity on a body having a given mass at standard gravitation of $g_0 = 9.8066$ m/sec^2. Thus, the unit force corresponding to a pull on a one-kilogram mass at standard gravitation is

$$1 \text{ N} = 1 \frac{\text{kg-m}}{\text{sec}^2}$$

At any other location with gravity g m/sec^2 instead of g_0, a one-kilogram mass weighs g/g_0 N. Generally, the force or weight of a body having a M-kg mass is given by

$$F = M\frac{g}{g_0} = \frac{Mg}{9.8066} \qquad \text{(in newtons)} \qquad (1\text{-}3)$$

Because of the fundamental difference between the gravitational system and the absolute system, the conversion factors between the American system and International System (SI) of units at standard gravitation are sometimes stated as follows:

$$1 \text{ lb} = 4.448 \text{ N} = 4.448 \text{ kg force}$$

$$1 \text{ kg} = 2.2046 \text{ slug} = 2.2046 \text{ lb mass}$$

These expressions clearly imply that

$$1 \text{ lb} = 4.448 \ \frac{\text{kg-m}}{\text{sec}^2}$$

$$1 \text{ kg} = 2.2046 \ \frac{\text{lb-sec}^2}{\text{ft}}$$

In the American system, some convenient multiples or fractions of base units commonly used in structural analysis are kilopounds or its abbreviation kips (k) for forces or weights, and feet (ft) or inches (in.) for lengths. The units for cross-sectional areas are usually expressed in square feet (ft^2) or square inches (in.^2). The units of stresses are expressed either in pounds per square inch (psi) or kips per square inch (ksi), while the units for moments may be expressed in foot-pounds (ft-lb), foot-kips (ft-k) or inch-pounds (in.-lbs).

For the International System (SI), the multiples or fractions of base units usually involve a factor of 1000 or 10^3. The prefixes commonly attached to the base units are given in Table 1-2.

Table 1-2 MULTIPLICATION FACTORS FOR SI BASE UNITS

Prefix	Symbol	Factor
giga	G	10^9
mega	M	10^6
kilo	K	10^3
milli	m	10^{-3}
micro	μ	10^{-6}
nano	n	10^{-9}

Thus, in the international system (SI), the units for forces and weights are newtons (N) or kilonewtons (KN), and the units for lengths are meters (m). The units for cross-sectional areas are usually expressed in square meter (m^2) or square millimeters (mm^2). The unit of stresses is newtons per square meter (N/m^2), which is called a pascal (Pa). Since pascal is a very small unit (1 psi = 6895 Pa), the most convenient SI unit for stresses is the mega-pascal (MPa), which is equivalent to MN/m^2 or N/mm^2. The unit for moments can be conveniently expressed in meter newton (mN) or meter kilonewtons (mKN).

2

Structural Systems

A *structural system* may be defined as an assembly of members such as bars, cables, arches, etc. with the purpose of transmitting external loads to the surrounding environment or foundation. A structural system cut away from a larger structural system—or from its foundation—is called a *free body*. To replace the influence of the members or supports that have been cut away, constraining forces are introduced at the supporting points of the isolated system; such forces are known as *reactions*. In order to determine the internal resistance of a structural system, imaginary sections may be passed through typical elements or members of the system. The portion of the system thus isolated from the rest of the system is also a free body in which the surrounding influences are replaced by *internal forces*. If a structural system is in static equilibrium, the free body isolated from any portion of the system must also be in equilibrium.

An internal force is sometimes called a *stress resultant*, which represents the total effect of stress components acting on the cross-sectional area of a member intersected by an imaginary plane. An internal couple is also known as a *stress couple* and refers to the couple resulting from these stress components. *Stress* is defined as the intensity of *force per unit area*, and in general varies over the cross-sectional area of a member. The components of stress may include *normal stress*, which is perpendicular to the section, and *shearing stress*, which is tangential to the section. Accordingly, a stress resultant may be either a *normal force* or a *shearing force*, depending on whether it is acting normal or tangential to the plane of the section. Similarly, a stress couple may be a *bending moment* resulting from the normal stress components, or a *twisting moment* resulting from the shearing stress components. A twisting moment is also called a *torque*. Broadly speaking, the term "force" is sometimes used to imply either force or couple. Hence, the term "applied load" may refer to either external force or external couple, and the term "stress resultant" may be used to designate either internal force or internal couple.

A structural member subjected to the action of external forces or couples experiences certain deformations that usually include translational and rotational displacements. In a narrower sense, however, the term *displacement* refers only to translational movement, and the term *rotation* is used to denote rotational movement. Displacements and rotations are the outward indications of the strain in a member. *Strain* is defined as the *deformation per unit length*, and has a dimensionless unit. The components of strain may include axial strain normal to the section, called *normal strain*, and angular distortion in the plane of the section, called *shearing strain*. Thus, the geometry of a deformed structure is specified by the displacements and rotations resulting from the normal and shearing strains in its members.

The deformations tolerated in engineering structures are in general very small. Hence, the analysis of internal forces may be based on the dimensions of the undeformed shape without appreciable error, and the computation of the displacements may in turn be based on the internal forces thus obtained. This approach to the solution of structural systems is called the *small deflection theory*. Within the limitation of small deflection, structural systems are usually stressed below the elastic limit of the material. Hence, the small deflection theory is also known as the *elastic theory*. For unusually flexible structures in which displacements are large in comparison with the cross-sectional dimensions of the member although small in comparison with the length of the member, such as the cable of a long-span suspension bridge, the dimensions of the deformed structure must be used for more accurate analysis. Such an approach is known as the *large deflection theory* or *deflection theory*. Although only small deflection theory will be considered in this book, the deformations are usually exaggerated in illustrations solely for the sake of clarity.

The simultaneous positions of all particles of a system are called the *configuration* of the system. For structural systems consisting of slender members, the configuration is specified by centerlines passing through the centroids of the cross sections of the members. The centerline of a member is sometimes referred to as the *axis* of the member. When a structure is treated as a rigid system, the configuration is assumed to remain unchanged upon application of loads. On the other hand, when a structure is considered as a deformable system, the structure changes from one configuration to another as loads are applied.

The selection of a suitable structural form for a given situation is one of the most important steps in structural analysis. New structural forms are developed constantly to satisfy ever-increasing needs. Buildings, bridges, towers, hangars, and the like represent but a few of the manifestations of diversified structural forms. The development of structural forms is also influenced by the properties of new materials. Thin shell structures, for example, have become popular in recent years because reinforced concrete can be utilized more efficiently in this type of structure than in framed structures. High-strength steels with large ductility have made possible many new applications in bridge design.

From the point of view of efficiency, the structural forms may be classified into two broad categories: the *uniform stress* form and the *varying stress* form. In the former every element is subjected to a uniform stress. Thus, if the stress at a point of the structure becomes critical, the stresses in all parts of the structure will be critical. In the latter nonuniform stress distribution prevails. As a result, even if the stresses at certain points of the structure approach the critical value, the stresses in other parts of the same structure may still be much below the critical value. It is obvious that the uniform stress form makes more efficient use of the material.

Strictly speaking, no real structural form or member has uniform stress throughout because in reality the edges or ends of the member are so fastened that stress concentrations are introduced at such locations. However, this does not alter the fact that the state of uniform stress exists in the member at distances removed from the regions near fastened edges or ends. Such a conclusion is based on *Saint-Venant's principle*, which states that if the forces acting on a small portion of the surface of an elastic body are replaced by another statically equivalent system of forces at the same portion of the surface, this redistribution of loading produces substantial changes in stresses locally but has a negligible effect on the stresses at distances that are large in comparison with the linear dimensions of the surface on which the forces are changed.* Thus, the practical utility of the concept of uniform stress is unimpaired.

The simplest example of the uniform stress form is a member subjected to an axial force. Fig. 2-1(a) shows a bar of uniform cross section that is acted on by a tensile force distributed uniformly over the cross section. The state of stress at every point of the bar, therefore, is uniaxial tension. Fig. 2-1(b) shows a plate of uniform thickness, that is acted on by tensile forces S_1 and S_2 distributed uniformly over the respective parallel edges of the plate. Then, the state of stress at every point of the plate is biaxial tension.

When a slender member is supported and loaded laterally, as shown in

---

* See, for instance, S. Timoshenko and J. N. Goodier, *Theory of Elasticity,* 2nd ed. (New York: McGraw-Hill Book Co., Inc., 1951, p. 33).

(a) Bar

(b) Plate

Figure 2-1

Fig. 2-2(a), it is subjected to shear and bending and is called a *beam*. Under such circumstances, the shearing and bending stresses vary from point to point at a cross section as well as along the length of the member. If a plate is supported and loaded laterally, in general it will be subjected to shear, bending, and twisting, and is called a *slab*, as shown in Fig. 2-2(b). Again, the stresses due to shear, bending, and twisting vary from point to point along the width as well as along the length of the slab.

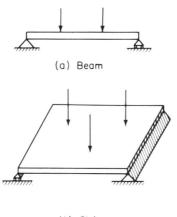

(a) Beam

(b) Slab

Figure 2-2

For flexible structural forms which can resist neither compression, shear, nor bending, only tensile forces will result in the system even if lateral forces are applied. In this case, the magnitude and location of the applied forces dictate the shape of the flexible structure. For example, consider a cable subjected to vertical loads uniformly distributed along the horizontal span of the cable. It can be demonstrated that the cable takes the shape of a parabola, as shown in Fig. 2-3(a). Since the slope of the cable varies and the *horizontal component* of the tension in the cable remains constant along its length, the tensile force along the cable varies from point to point along its length. How-

(a) Cable

(b) Membrane   **Figure 2-3**

ever, the distribution of this tensile force at a particular cross section is uniform owing to the absence of shear and bending, and theoretically at least, the state of stress can be made uniform throughout the entire length if the cross-sectional area of the cable varies in the same proportion as the tensile force acting on it. The cable may, therefore, be considered as a *pseudo-uniform* stress form. Similarly, a circular membrane subjected to a uniform pressure, as shown in Fig. 2-3(b), will be stretched like a balloon. In general, however, the tensile stresses in the membrane are not uniform because the inflated shape may be any surface of revolution. The membrane therefore represents a pseudo-uniform stress form and the tensile stresses are called *membrane stresses*. In the special case of a spherical surface, the membrane stresses are uniform in all directions.

On the other hand, inflexible curved structural forms that are properly constrained may also be subjected to direct stresses only under certain loading conditions. Fig. 2-4(a) shows a parabolic arch with three hinges. If the vertical loads are uniformly distributed along the horizontal span of the arch, the arch will be subjected only to an axial compressive force, usually called *thrust*, along its curved length. For any other loading, shear and bending as well as thrust exist at a section normal to the axis of the arch. Thus, the parabolic arch acts as a pseudo-uniform stress form under one loading condition and becomes a varying stress form under other loading conditions. Similarly, only membrane stresses exist in a shell of revolution whose bottom edge is completely unrestrained and on which the loading is axisymmetrical, as shown in Fig. 2-4(b). If the bottom edge of the shell is fixed or otherwise restrained, however, the structure will be subjected to shear and bending as well as membrane stresses. Again, this structure acts as a pseudo-uniform stress form for one edge condition and becomes a varying stress form for another edge condition.

Uniform stress forms of structures can be built up from a number of uniform stress elements. Pin-connected trusses are typical examples. Fig.

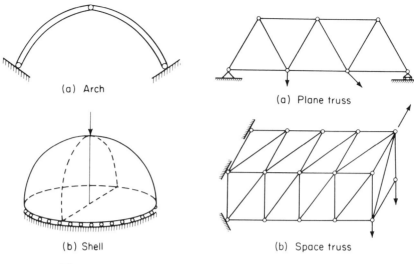

(a) Arch

(b) Shell

Figure 2-4

(a) Plane truss

(b) Space truss

Figure 2-5

2-5(a) shows a plane truss subjected to external loads. However, each of the members in the truss is subjected to a uniform stress even though the truss as a whole tends to bend under the action of the loads. Fig. 2-5(b) shows a space truss which is subjected to twisting as well as bending. Nevertheless, the stress in each member is uniform.

Quite frequently, the efficiency of varying stress members may be improved by reducing the bending at the critical section while increasing the bending in other parts of the same member. This concept leads to the development of rigid frames in which the bending effects in the center part of its members are reduced owing to the presence of the rigid joints that resist bending. Fig. 2-6(a) indicates a rigid frame with all elements lying in the same plane, and Fig. 2-6(b) shows a rigid frame in space. In the former the members

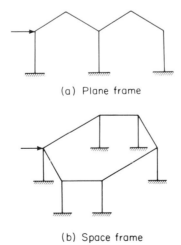

(a) Plane frame

(b) Space frame

Figure 2-6

Structural Systems   Chap. 2

of the frame are subjected to axial force, shear, and bending only, but in the latter the members of the frame are also subjected to twisting.

2-3 IDEALIZATION OF STRUCTURAL SYSTEMS

Actual structures exist in three dimensions and generally consist of an assembly of intricate elements and connections. In order to effectively analyze such structures, it is convenient to break up the structure into component parts of manageable order and to convert these parts into conceptual models. Because of such simplifying assumptions, the results of analysis should be subjected to judicious interpretations.

In order to compare results of theoretical analysis with the behavior of the actual structure, we rely on experience or experiment. For conventional structures we can exercise our judgment based on experience. On the other hand, unusual structures for which no previous experience is available will require experiment. The latter approach underlines the importance of research in an ever-expanding industrial world in which we are confronted with many problems and situations that are completely new and unexplored.

A general principle for idealizing a structure is that, whenever possible, the actual three-dimensional structure should be reduced to component two-dimensional systems because the techniques of analyzing three-dimensional structures are rather complicated. Of course, there are structures for which the variation of stresses and strains in three dimensions is important and that cannot be reduced to simpler systems. Consider, for example, the arch dam shown in Fig. 2-7. This structure transmits the upstream hydrostatic pressure to the canyon wall by arch action as well as to the foundation by cantilever action. Thus, the state of stress at any point in the dam must be treated as a three-dimensional problem in elasticity.

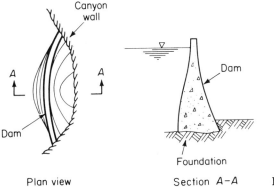

Plan view   Section *A–A*   **Figure 2-7**

However, a reasonable simplification may be accomplished for thin structural systems of uniform thickness, such as the plate shown in Fig. 2-8(a), for which the external forces applied at the edges are distributed uniformly over the thickness. Since no force is acting in the direction transverse to the plate,

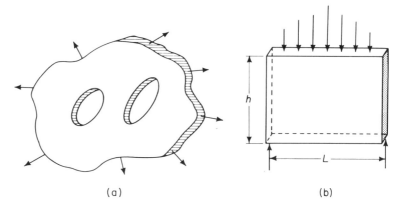

(a)   (b)

Figure 2-8

it may be assumed that the stress components in that direction are zero and the stress components in directions parallel to the faces of the plate do not vary through the thickness. Problems such as this are called *plane stress* problems. An example of a plane stress problem is a deep beam as shown in Fig. 2-8(b). On the other hand, a similar simplification is possible for long structures, such as retaining walls, culverts, tunnels, and so forth, for which the applied forces as well as the shape of the cross section do not vary along the length. In such cases, it may be assumed that the end sections are confined between two fixed rigid planes such that the displacement and hence the strain in the long direction is prevented. Since all cross sections are in the same condition in regard to loading and geometry of the cross section, it is necessary to consider only a slice between two sections at a unit distance apart, as shown in Fig. 2-9. Problems of this type are called *plane strain* problems. It can be demonstrated that the plane strain problem, like the plane stress problem, reduces to the determination of stress components in two dimensions only.

(a) Retaining wall   (b) Culvert

Figure 2-9

There are other structures in the form of surfaces whose thickness, although not necessarily uniform, is small in comparison with the other two dimensions, but the applied forces in general do not lie in the middle surface. The middle surface is that surface that everywhere bisects the thickness of the element. This group of structures can be further classified into two categories: slabs and shells.* In the case of slabs, i.e., flat plates subjected to lateral loads, a satisfactory approximate theory may be developed by neglecting the normal stresses in the direction transverse to the middle surface of the plate. For thin shells, i.e., curved surfaces whose thicknesses are small in comparison with their radii of curvature as well as with the other dimensions, the bending stresses are usually small and the stresses due to strains in the middle surface are more important except in the vicinity of restrained edges. If the edge conditions of a shell are such that bending can be neglected, the problem is greatly simplified. The theory of shells based on the omission of bending stresses is called the *membrane theory*.

Structures may also consist of slender members, not necessarily of uniform cross section, whose length is large in comparison with the other two dimensions, but the applied forces may vary along the length of the member. Cables, arches, beams, frames, and trusses belong to this category. Although cables, arches, and beams are generally classified as two-dimensional systems, frames and trusses may be either two-dimensional or three-dimensional.

Two-dimensional structures are by far the most common systems encountered in structural analysis. As a practical matter, we shall deal primarily with two-dimensional systems consisting of slender members, with occasional reference to three-dimensional frames and trusses. We shall therefore consider a few conventional structures and examine how they are idealized in the light of experience. Fig. 2-10(a) illustrates a through-truss railroad bridge. The structure may be separated into several structural units: the main trusses, the lateral bracing systems, and the floor framing. The main trusses are designed

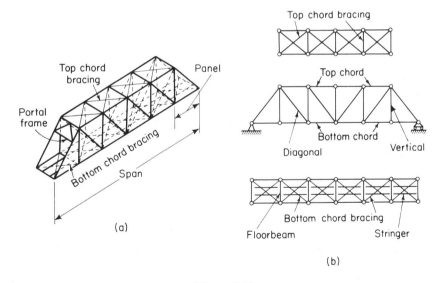

Figure 2-10

*See, for instance, S. Timoshenko and S. Woinowsky-Krieger, *Theory of Plates and Shells*, 2nd ed. (New York: McGraw-Hill Book Co., Inc., 1959).

primarily to carry vertical loads that are transmitted to the trusses through the floor framing (stringers and floor beams). The portal frame, the top chord bracings, and the bottom chord bracings are designed to resist the horizontal or lateral forces and are known as *lateral bracing systems*. In addition to transmitting floor loads to the joints of the trusses, the floor beams also act as part of the bottom chord bracing. Fig. 2-10(b) shows the idealized plane truss, the analysis of which is usually based on the following assumptions:

1. The members of the truss are connected together by smooth pins at their ends.
2. The weight of the truss as well as the imposed loads and reactions will act only at the joints.
3. The members are straight.

The first assumption can be well justified if the members consist of eye-bars with pin-connected joints. Even then, the pins are not perfectly smooth, and rough pins lead to friction between the pin and the eyebar. In modern practice, the connections of truss members are usually either bolted or welded. Furthermore, the top and bottom chords of the truss usually are made up of members continuous over several panels instead of shorter members connected at the joints. However, errors due to neglect of these end restraints are usually not serious, and the secondary effects due to restraint at the joints can be evaluated later if greater refinement is necessary. The second assumption is usually valid for imposed loads since the floor beams are connected to the bottom chords of the trusses at the joints. For all practical purposes, the weight of the truss can be apportioned as loads at the joints of the truss; the error due to such practice is small. The third assumption implies that no bending exists in any member of the truss.

Fig. 2-11(a) shows the framing plan of a highway bridge deck, the longitudinal and transverse sections of which are shown in Fig. 2-11(b) and 2-11(c), respectively. (Note that Fig. 2-11(c) is drawn in a different scale.) The concrete deck is considered as a separate unit if no adequate bond is provided between the concrete slab and the steel plate girders. On the other hand, if suitable devices are used to ensure the bonding of the concrete to the steel, the floor system can be designed as a composite unit. The idealized model in this case is a group of simply supported beams subjected to vertical loads, whereas the diaphragm bracings are counted on to resist horizontal or lateral forces. The analysis of the system based on the elementary theory of flexure involves the following approximations:

1. The girder is straight and prismatic, and its cross section has at least one axis of symmetry.
2. The loads are applied along the axis of symmetry of the girder section.
3. The girder is adequately braced and stiffened to avoid buckling in the flange or the web of the girder.

Figure 2-11

The first two assumptions can be easily justified. In order to justify the third assumption, we count on the concrete slab to guard against lateral buckling of the top flange as indicated in Fig. 2-11(c) and add vertical stiffeners as shown in Fig. 2-11(d) to prevent buckling of the web of the girder. The diaphragms shown in Fig. 2-11(a) and (c) are provided to maintain alignment of the girders and lateral transmission of loads, thus permitting even distribution of deformation. If the girder is continuous over two or more spans, however, the diaphragms will also serve the purpose of providing lateral supports against buckling of the bottom flange of the girder.

A suspended bridge can also be divided into component parts by separating the main span from the side spans as shown in Fig. 2-12. Since the cable is flexible, a stiffening system is tied to the traffic deck so that the cable will not change shape while a load is moving on the bridge. The stiffening system may be a girder or a truss known as a *stiffening girder* or *stiffening truss,* as the case may be. The cable and the stiffening system for the main span can be isolated as shown in Fig. 2-12(c). In idealizing the structure, the following assumptions are usually made:

1. If the load is uniformly distributed along the horizontal span, such as the weight of the floor system, it will be carried entirely by the cable.

2. If the load on the bridge is not uniform, as in the case of moving vehicles, it will be distributed among the hangers through the stiffening system, which may be a girder or a truss.

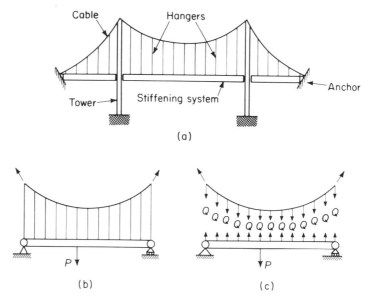

Figure 2-12

3. Since the hangers are closely and uniformly spaced and the hanger loads are approximately equal, the shape of the cable may be assumed to be parabolic.

Fig. 2-13 shows an arch bridge in which the main girders are continuous over the vertical supports and are prevented from horizontal movement by the links at the right end of the girders. If the joints at the ends of the vertical posts

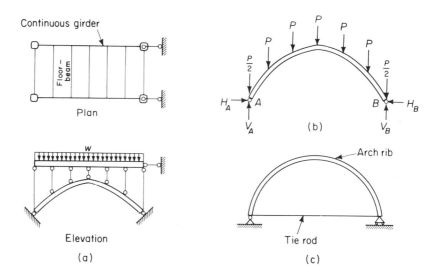

Figure 2-13

are assumed to be pin-connected, the girders can be analyzed as continuous beams with multiple supports. Thus, the uniform load shown in Fig. 2-13(a) will eventually be transmitted to the arch rib through the vertical posts, and the resulting concentrated loads acting on the arch rib may be represented by Fig. 2-13(b).

Another important characteristic of an arch is that there will be horizontal components of reactions at supports as a result of the arch action—even if all applied loads are vertical. Hence, we can take full advantage of an arch structure only if the foundation is such that it offers resistance to horizontal thrust. Occasionally, however, especially in the design of arch roofs, the horizontal thrust at the supports of the arch are provided by a tie-rod as shown in Fig. 2-13(c). In actual construction the tie-rod is hidden below the floor in a building, but the necessity for its existence should not escape the attention of the student.

Consider next a typical framing plan for a steel-framed office building, as shown in Fig. 2-14(a). The idealized model of the girder at the center of the framing plan is given in Fig. 2-14(b). Since the girder is assumed to be simply supported, the connection from girder to column shown in Fig. 2-14(c) is designed to transmit only the vertical reaction of the girder. The end restraint of the connection for rotation is negligibly small. In cases where such a simplification is not assumed, the end of the girder may be subjected to a moment and the connection must be designed accordingly. A similar situation exists for the gable frames supporting the roof of the mill building shown in Fig. 2-15(a). The conceptual model of the gable frame shown in Fig. 2-15(b) is assumed to have fixed supports because the ends of the columns are embedded in heavy concrete footings. Since large deformation of the frame is undesirable, the joints connecting the members of the frame are made to be as rigid as possible, permitting practically no *relative* rotation between connecting members at the joints. Fig. 2-15(c) illustrates a welded connection of this type. Frames consisting only of rigid connections between members are called *rigid frames*.

In determining the span length of an idealized beam or frame, there is always the question of whether the distance from centerline to centerline of

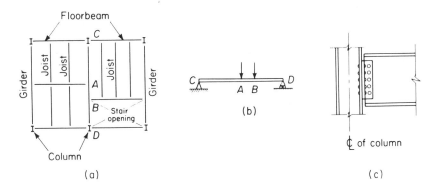

(a)

(b)

(c)

Figure 2-14

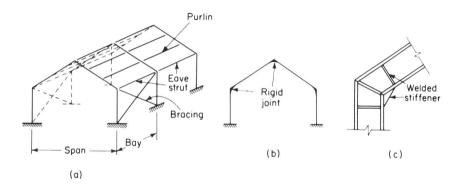

(a)

(b)

(c)

Figure 2-15

columns or the clear dimension should be used. Similarly, the same problem arises in determining the column height between floors. In general, the distance from centerline to centerline is considered sufficiently accurate for analysis. If further refinement is necessary, modifications may be made later, as is often done in the analysis of continuous frames.

2-4 EQUILIBRIUM AND KINEMATIC STABILITY

A structural system is in a state of equilibrium if the constraints permit no rigid-body movement upon application of loads. The system is assumed to be rigid in the sense that displacements due to deformation are negligible in comparison with the dimensions of the structure. The necessary and sufficient conditions to ensure equilibrium of an isolated system are that the resultant force in any direction and the resultant moment about any point be zero. Expressing these conditions for a space structure in a rectangular Cartesian coordinate shown in Fig. 2-16(a), we obtain the following set of equations of equilibrium:

$$\sum F_x = 0, \qquad \sum F_y = 0, \qquad \sum F_z = 0$$
$$\sum M_x = 0, \qquad \sum M_y = 0, \qquad \sum M_z = 0 \tag{2-1}$$

For a right-handed coordinate system, note that the positive direction of the moment with respect to the axis of rotation follows the right-hand rule. For example, if M_x represents the direction of rotation of a right-hand screw when tightened, the positive direction of the x-axis represents the direction of the advance of the screw.

For the case of a plane structure lying in the xy-plane of the coordinate system shown in Fig. 2-16(b), the set of equations reduces to

$$\sum F_x = 0, \qquad \sum F_y = 0, \qquad \sum M_z = 0 \tag{2-2}$$

(a)

(b)

Figure 2-16

Note that the z-axis in space becomes a point when projected on the xy-plane. Thus, in the analysis of plane structures, the moment about a point is synonymous with the moment about an axis normal to the xy-plane passing through that point. Furthermore, in order to be consistent with the right-handed coordinate system in space, we consider counterclockwise moments as positive in coplanar systems.

The conditions of equilibrium may also be expressed in other forms. Usually, one or more of the equations involving the summation of forces may be replaced by an equation or equations involving the summation of moments, provided that the resulting equations are independent. In general, six independent equations are available for the equilibrium of structural system in space whereas three independent equations are available for a coplanar system. In the case of a coplanar system, for example, Eqs. (2-2) may be replaced by

$$\sum M_a = 0, \qquad \sum M_b = 0, \qquad \sum M_c = 0$$

in which a, b, and c represent points on the xy-plane not lying on the same straight line.

Several important and useful conclusions may be drawn from the simple cases of equilibrium. If a structural member is in equilibrium under the action of two forces, these two forces must be equal, opposite, and colinear, as shown in Fig. 2-17(a). If a member in equilibrium is acted on by three forces, these forces must be coplanar and their lines of action must be either concurrent or parallel, as shown in Figs. 2-17(b) and 2-17(c) respectively.

Since the existence of the state of equilibrium of a system is based on the tacit assumption that the system is properly constrained internally as well as (a)　　　　　　　　(b)　　　　　　　(c)　　　　**Figure 2-17**

externally, a structural system that satisfies this requirement is said to be in a position of *stable equilibrium*. If a system does not have a sufficient number of internal or external constraints, it will undergo a rigid-body movement upon the application of a small displacement. Such a system is said to be *kinematically unstable*, and is usually referred to as a *mechanism*.

Occasionally, we may encounter some unconventional structural systems that are stable under one loading condition but unstable under another. Such systems are said to be in a state of *unstable equilibrium* when the precarious balance is maintained. Although this situation is undesirable for ordinary structures such as buildings and bridges, it may be necessary for certain special-purpose structures. A precariously balanced bicycle might be cited as an example of a coplanar system in a state of unstable equilibrium. Trusses supporting the screen of a radar antenna and resting on roller bearings are typical examples of space structures that may be in a state of unstable equilibrium. The roller bearings can be locked in a fixed position if desired. When the supports are unlocked, the structure is then in a state of unstable equilibrium.

For a stable system, we can formulate the unknown forces in terms of external loads and the conditions of equilibrium. If the unknown forces in the system can be solved by the equations of equilibrium alone, the system is said to be a *statically determinate structure*. When there are more unknown forces in a stable system than there are equations of equilibrium available for their solution, these forces cannot be solved by statics alone and the system is known as a *statically indeterminate* or *redundant structure*. The latter can further be classified into two categories. If the redundant forces appear when the structure as a whole is considered as a free body, the system is *externally* redundant. If such redundant forces occur when a part of the structure is taken as a free body, the system is *internally* redundant.

Let us consider a few simple illustrations. The beams shown in Fig. 2-18 are rigid systems fixed in position by external constraints. Beam (a) is inadequately restrained and is kinematically unstable, beam (b) is sufficiently restrained and is statically determinate, and beam (c) is over restrained and is externally redundant. However, if a vertical load is applied to beam (a) instead

(a)　　　　　　　　(b)　　　　　　　(c)

Figure 2-18

of an inclined load, the system will be in unstable equilibrium. Similar conclusions may be drawn from the systems in Fig. 2-19. If a small lateral displacement is applied to the member in Fig. 2-19(a), it will return to its original position. On the other hand, Fig. 2-19(b) shows a system that is inherently unstable. Theoretically speaking, the member would be able to resist the external axial load if there were absolutely no disturbance in the lateral direction. In reality, however, some small lateral disturbance will exist and the member will tend to move away from the original position even if the disturbing force is later removed. Hence, the system is unstable.

(a)   (b)   **Figure 2-19**

We may also analyze the internal rigidity of a system by the simple examples in Fig. 2-20. Truss (a) is nonrigid and therefore kinematically unstable, truss (b) is just rigid and statically determinate, whereas truss (c) is overrigid and internally redundant. If we consider only part of truss (c) as a free body, as shown in part (d), we find that there are four unknown internal forces although only three equations of equilibrium are available for a coplanar system. Thus, truss (c) is statically indeterminate.

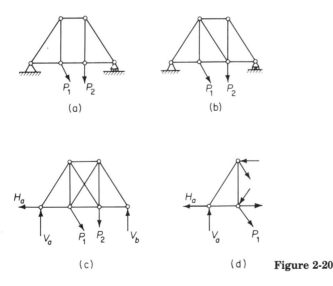

(a)   (b)

(c)   (d)   **Figure 2-20**

We shall now consider some simple, statically determinate, structural systems. Such systems are internally rigid and are properly constrained externally by a sufficient number of components of reaction. These components of reaction can therefore be completely specified by the equations of equilibrium.

A plane structure may in general be completely restrained from rigid-body movement by three components of reaction defined by three equations of equilibrium. A support that can prevent rotation as well as horizontal and vertical displacements in a plane structure is called a *fixed support*. If the support can resist only horizontal and vertical displacements but not rotation, it is said to be a *hinge* or *pin*. If the support is permitted to slide in one direction as well as to rotate, it may be represented by a roller, which provides a constraining force normal to the direction of sliding. The term *roller* is used in a broad sense to allow the constraining force to act either *upward* or *downward* relative to the surface of sliding.

Similarly, a structure in space can be completely restrained by six components of reaction specified by six equations of equilibrium. A fixed support for a space structure can prevent displacements along any of the three coordinate axes as well as rotation about any of them. A ball-and-socket joint can resist only displacements along the three coordinate axes but not rotations; hinges and rollers may also be used for supports of space structures.

The components of reaction may be described figuratively by links, each of which is used to represent one component in a specific direction. Consider, for example, the cantilever beam in Fig. 2-21(a). The components of reaction are represented by links 1, 2, and 3, as shown in Fig. 2-21(b). The rotation and the horizontal displacement at the fixed support are resisted by links 1 and 2, while the vertical displacement at the support is resisted by link 3. Similarly, for the simply supported beam in Fig. 2-22(a), the pin or hinge at support A is

(a)   (b)   **Figure 2-21**

(a)

(b)

Figure 2-22

replaced by two links while the roller at support B is equivalent to a vertical link, as shown in Fig. 2-22(b). Since the number of links equals the number of equations of equilibrium, the components of reaction can be obtained by statics. However, there are restrictions on the arrangement of the links in order to insure complete constraint of a system. If all three links supporting a system are concurrent or parallel, as shown in Figs. 2-23(a) and 2-23(b), respectively, the system will not be completely restrained. In case (a), the components of reaction cannot resist the moment developed by the external forces about support A. In case (b), the system is unstable and will swing to the right. Systems that collapse under external loads because of the geometrical orientation of links or members are also said to be *kinematically unstable*.

(a) (b)

Figure 2-23

The idea of representing components of reaction by links may also be applied to structures in space. Consider, for instance, the rigid system in space in Fig. 2-24(a), which is subjected to external forces F_x, F_y, and F_z, and external moments M_x, M_y, and M_z. The fixed support may be replaced by six links as indicated in Fig. 2-24(b). Thus, the displacements and rotations of the support will be prevented by these links. Similarly, for the system in Fig. 2-25(a), the ball-and-socket joint at support A can be represented by three links, whereas the pin at support B and the roller at support C can, respectively, be replaced by two links and one link, as shown in Fig. 2-25(b). Since the number of links equals the number of equations of equilibrium, the components of reaction can be determined by statics. As in the case of plane structures, there are restrictions on the orientation or arrangement of the links supporting a system

(a) (b)

Figure 2-24

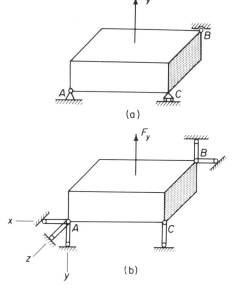

(a)

(b)

Figure 2-25

in space in order to avoid kinematic instability. If all links have lines of action which intersect a straight line, as shown in Fig. 2-26(a), there is no resistance to the moment developed by external forces about that line. Similarly, if all links are parallel, as shown in Fig. 2-26(b), the system will swing to the right upon the application of external loads. On the other hand, if all links lie on parallel planes, as shown in Fig. 2-26(c), the system is partially restrained. However, since the system must move a small distance to the right before restraining forces can be developed in the links, it is not completely restrained.

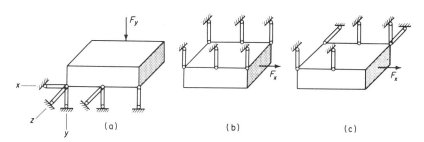

(a)   (b)   (c)

Figure 2-26

Example 2-1. Find the reactions of the simply supported beam in Fig. 2-27(a). The beam is first isolated from its supports as shown in Fig. 2-27(b), in which the components of the reactions are indicated by H_a, V_a, and V_b. If the applied load is resolved into vertical and horizontal components of 8 kips and 6 kips, respectively, the components of reaction may be obtained from the equations of equilibrium. Thus,

$$\sum M_a = 0, \qquad 8V_b - (8)(2) = 0, \qquad V_b = 2 \text{ kips}$$

(a)

(b)

(c)

(d)

Figure 2-27

$$\sum F_x = 0, \qquad H_a = 6 \text{ kips}$$

$$\sum F_y = 0, \qquad V_a + V_b = 8, \qquad V_a = 8 - 2 = 6 \text{ kips}$$

The same result may be obtained if we choose to use the condition that the moment of all forces be zero about any three arbitrary points not lying on the same line. Thus, from Fig. 2-27(b)

$$\sum M_a = 0, \qquad 8V_b - (8)(2) = 0, \qquad V_b = 2 \text{ kips}$$

$$\sum M_b = 0, \qquad 8V_a - (8)(6) = 0, \qquad V_a = 6 \text{ kips}$$

$$\sum M_c = 0, \qquad 8V_b - H_a d = 0$$

From the relation of similar triangles $d/2 = \frac{4}{3}$ and $d = \frac{8}{3}$. Hence,

$$H_a = \frac{(2)(8)}{\frac{8}{3}} = 6 \text{ kips}$$

If the resultant of the components of reaction at support A is desired, it may be obtained from the geometrical relation shown in Fig. 2-27(c). Then,

$$R_a = \sqrt{V_a^2 + H_a^2} = \sqrt{36 + 36} = 8.48 \text{ kips}$$

$$\theta_a = \tan^{-1} \frac{V_a}{H_a} = \tan^{-1} 1 = 45°$$

This result would have been obtained directly if the free-body diagram in Fig. 2-27(d) had been used. It should be noted that the number of unknowns in the system remains the same since θ_a as well as R_a must be determined in this case. From the standpoint of minimizing numerical computation, however, the solution involving vertical and horizontal components of reaction is usually preferred.

Example 2-2. Compute the reactions for the beam in Fig. 2-28(a).

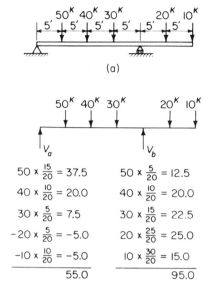

(a)

$$50 \times \frac{15}{20} = 37.5 \qquad 50 \times \frac{5}{20} = 12.5$$
$$40 \times \frac{10}{20} = 20.0 \qquad 40 \times \frac{10}{20} = 20.0$$
$$30 \times \frac{5}{20} = 7.5 \qquad 30 \times \frac{15}{20} = 22.5$$
$$-20 \times \frac{5}{20} = -5.0 \qquad 20 \times \frac{25}{20} = 25.0$$
$$-10 \times \frac{10}{20} = -5.0 \qquad 10 \times \frac{30}{20} = 15.0$$
$$\overline{55.0} \qquad \overline{95.0}$$

(b)

Figure 2-28

Since the beam is horizontal and there is no horizontal forces acting on it, the equation of equilibrium $\Sigma\, F_x = 0$ immediately leads to the conclusion that the horizontal component of reaction at support A must be zero. Thus, only vertical components of reactions at supports A and B need to be considered and they can be determined from the remaining two equations of equilibrium:

$$\Sigma\, M_a = 0, \qquad 20V_b - (50)(5) - (40)(10) - (30)(15) - (20)(25) - (10)(30) = 0$$
$$V_b = 95 \text{ kips}$$

$$\Sigma\, M_b = 0, \qquad -20V_a + (50)(15) + (40)(10) + (30)(5) - (20)(5) - (10)(10) = 0$$
$$V_a = 55 \text{ kips}$$

It is always desirable to provide independent checks on the computations by considering another condition of equilibrium. For example,

$$\Sigma\, F_y = 0, \qquad 95 + 55 - 50 - 40 - 30 - 20 - 10 = 0 \text{ (checked)}$$

There are numerous ways in which we may keep track of our computations and check them in order to avoid mistakes. As long as the solution is carried out in an orderly and systematic manner, the detail of execution is only a matter of personal preference. Fig. 2-28(b) shows computations in which the total reactions are obtained by summing up the reactions due to each external load.

Example 2-3. Compute the reactions at supports A and B of the system in Fig. 2-29(a).
Since the cable can resist only tension, the reaction A must have the same

(a)

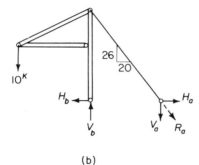

(b)   Figure 2-29

line of action as member AC. For the free-body diagram in Fig. 2-29(b), the vertical and horizontal components of reaction at A must bear a ratio of $V_a/H_a = 26/20$. Hence, there are only three independent unknowns that can be solved by the equations of equilibrium.

$$\sum M_b = 0, \qquad -20V_a + (10)(20) = 0, \qquad V_a = 10 \text{ kips}$$

$$\sum F_y = 0, \qquad V_b - V_a - 10 \quad = 0, \qquad V_b = 20 \text{ kips}$$

$$\sum F_x = 0, \qquad H_a - H_b \qquad = 0, \qquad H_a = H_b = (\tfrac{20}{26})V_a = 7.7 \text{ kips}$$

Example 2-4. Determine the reactions at supports D, E, and F of the system in Fig. 2-30(a).

In drawing the free-body diagram for a system, it is sometimes impossible to detect the correct sense of direction of a reaction. In such a case the sense may be arbitrarily assumed. If the result obtained on such a basis is positive, the assumed sense is correct; otherwise, the actual sense of direction of the reaction is opposite the assumed sense. Considering the free-body diagram in Fig. 2-30(b), we assume the senses of direction of the reactions as indicated. Although six components of reaction are shown in the figure, there are only three independent unknowns because each of the reactions must have a line of action corresponding to the axis of the member it supports. Thus, the vertical and horizontal components of each reaction are related to each other as follows:

$$V_d/H_d = \tfrac{4}{3} \qquad \text{or} \qquad H_d = 0.75V_d$$

$$V_e/H_e = \tfrac{2}{1} \qquad \text{or} \qquad H_e = 0.5V_e$$

$$V_f/H_f = \tfrac{2}{1} \qquad \text{or} \qquad H_f = 0.5V_f$$

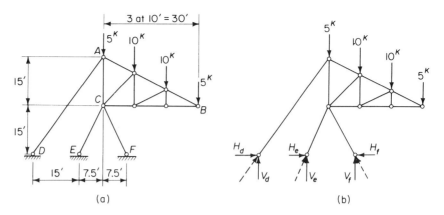

Figure 2-30

In order to simplify the solution, it is advisable to take moments about points that represent the intersections of some unknown components of reaction. For example,

$$\sum M_c = 0, \qquad 15H_d - 22.5V_d - (10)(10) - (10)(20) - (5)(30) = 0$$

$$(15)(0.75V_d) - 22.5V_d = 450$$

$$V_d = -40 \text{ kips} \quad \text{and} \quad H_d = -30 \text{ kips}$$

$$\sum M_f = 0, \qquad -(-40)(30) - 15V_e + (5)(7.5) - (10)(2.5 + 12.5)$$

$$- (5)(22.5) = 0$$

$$V_e = 65 \text{ kips} \quad \text{and} \quad H_e = 32.5 \text{ kips}$$

$$\sum M_e = 0, \qquad -(-40)(15) + 15V_f - (5)(7.5 + 37.5)$$

$$- (10)(17.5 + 27.5) = 0$$

$$V_f = 5 \text{ kips} \quad \text{and} \quad H_f = 2.5 \text{ kips}$$

As a check, we may consider

$$\sum F_y = 0, \qquad (-40) + 65 + 5 - 5 - 10 - 10 - 5 = 0$$

Note that the sense of the reaction at D has been erroneously assumed. Hence, the result is negative, and the negative sign must be consistently carried through the entire problem unless a new free-body diagram indicating the correct sense of the reaction is drawn.

Example 2-5. Find the reactions of the angle frame shown in Fig. 2-31(a). The components of the reactions H_a, V_a, and V_c are indicated in the free-body diagram in Fig. 2-31(b), from which the following equations of equilibrium are obtained:

(a)

(b)

Figure 2-31

$$\sum M_a = 0, \qquad 8V_c - (17.32)(6) = 0, \qquad V_c = 12.99 \text{ kips}$$

$$\sum F_y = 0, \qquad V_a + V_c = 17.32, \qquad V_a = 4.33 \text{ kips}$$

$$\sum F_x = 0, \qquad H_a = 10 \text{ kips}$$

As a check,

$$\sum M_d = 0, \qquad (12.99)(2) - (4.33)(6) = 0$$

2-6 COMPOUND SYSTEMS

A *compound system* is defined as a statically determinate system formed by interconnecting two or more simple systems. Since extra components of reaction are usually introduced in such a system, the interconnections must be so constructed that they provide additional conditions for the solution of the reactions. These additional conditions are called the *conditions of inter-connection*. Consider the compound systems shown in Fig. 2-32. The compound beam in Fig. 2-32(a) is obtained by combining the simple beam *AD* with the cantilever beam *DC*. At the interconnection point *D* a hinge is provided so that no moment is transmitted through that point. The components of reaction of the system may be solved by considering beam *AD* and beam *DC* as separate

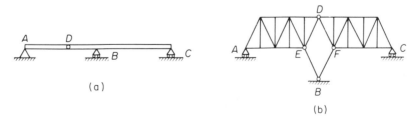

(a)

(b)

Figure 2-32

free bodies. Similarly, the compound truss in Fig. 2-32(b) is considered a combination of simple trusses *ADE* and *CDF*. The components of reaction can again be computed by isolating the simple trusses as free bodies.

A compound system may also be thought of as a statically determinate system formed by introducing releases to an otherwise statically indeterminate structure. A *release* is defined as a discontinuity in a structural member that is incapable of transmitting a stress resultant. If we refer again to Fig. 2-32(a), the compound beam may be regarded as a continuous beam, with its resistance to moment disrupted by the introduction of a hinge at point *D*. Similarly in Fig. 2-32(b), the compound truss may be considered as a continuous truss, the continuity of which has been released by the removal of member *BD*. The introduction of the hinge *D* in the former, or the removal of member *BD* in the latter, represents the condition of construction that produces the desired release in the structure. Hence, the conditions of interconnection may also be called the *conditions of release*.

Compound systems are especially susceptible to kinematic instability owing to the orientation of certain members or reactions. Consider, for example, the systems shown in Fig. 2-33. Whereas systems (a) and (b) in the figure are stable, system (c) is unstable because each member tends to rotate about the adjacent end hinge. The movement in system (c) can be arrested only after both members have yielded or stretched enough to cause large deformation of the center hinge. In that case, the structural system can no longer be treated as a rigid system.

In the case of the compound truss in Fig. 2-34(a), the system becomes

(a)   (b)   (c)

Figure 2-33

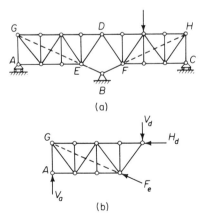

(a)

(b)

Figure 2-34

kinematically unstable when members *BE* and *BF* are oriented in such a manner that their lines of action pass through points *G* and *H*, respectively. This can be seen from the free-body diagram representing the left half of the truss in which all forces except V_d pass through point *G*. Thus, nothing will prevent the rotation of this part of the truss under the action of V_d when we take the moment of all forces about point *G*.

Example 2-6. Compute the reactions of the compound system shown in Fig. 2-35(a).
Since a cable can take tension only, the directions of the reactions at supports *A* and *B* must be in line with members *AE* and *BE*, respectively. The reaction at support *D* can be resolved into vertical and horizontal components. When the system as a whole is taken as a free body, there are four unknown reaction components in three equations of equilibrium. However, a fourth equation may be obtained from the condition of release that no horizontal resistance be provided at point *C*. Hence, the components of reaction can be completely determined.

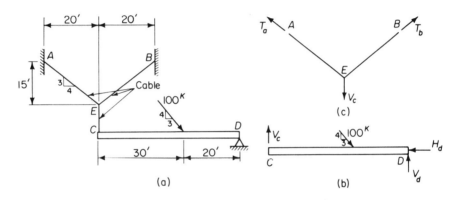

(a)   (b)   (c)

Figure 2-35

This problem can be readily solved by isolating the system into two parts, as shown in Fig. 2-35(b) and (c). From the former, we obtain

$$\sum F_x = 0, \qquad H_d = (\tfrac{3}{5})(100) = 60 \text{ kips}$$

$$\sum M_c = 0, \qquad V_d = (\tfrac{1}{50})(\tfrac{4}{5})(100)(30) = 48 \text{ kips}$$

$$\sum F_y = 0, \qquad V_c = (\tfrac{4}{5})(100) - 48 = 32 \text{ kips}$$

From the latter is it obvious that

$$T_a = T_b = (\tfrac{1}{2})(32)(\tfrac{5}{3}) = 26.7 \text{ kips}$$

Example 2-7. Compute the reactions of the compound beam shown in Fig. 2-36(a).
In this structure there are theoretically six components of reaction since two of the supports are on rollers and the other two are hinged. There are also three

(c)   (b)   (d)   **Figure 2-36**

equations resulting from the releases since $\Sigma\ M_c = 0$ at hinge C, and $\Sigma\ M_d = 0$ and $\Sigma\ F_x = 0$ at link DD'. Therefore, there are six equations for six unknown components of reaction. Actually, the problem can be greatly simplified since there is no horizontal load acting on the structure and thus the horizontal components of reaction become zero from the consideration of $\Sigma\ F_x = 0$. Four unknown vertical components of reaction V_a, V_b, V_e and V_f remain and must satisfy the equations of equilibrium $\Sigma\ F_y = 0$ and $\Sigma\ M_z = 0$, and the conditions of release $\Sigma\ M_c = 0$ and $\Sigma\ M_d = 0$. For this problem, the procedure can best be illustrated by separating the beam segments into free bodies as shown in Fig. 2-36(b), (c), and (d). Starting with Fig. 2-36(b), for which there are only two unknowns,

$$\Sigma\ M_c = 0, \qquad (V_d)(20) - (50)(12) = 0, \qquad V_d = 30 \text{ kips}$$

$$\Sigma\ F_y = 0, \qquad V_c + V_d = 50, \qquad V_c = 20 \text{ kips}$$

From Fig. 2-36(c), for $\Sigma\ M_a = 0$,

$$(20)(28) + (10)(24) + (1)(20)(\tfrac{20}{2}) - (V_b)(20) = 0, \qquad V_b = 50 \text{ kips}$$

For $\Sigma\ F_y = 0$,

$$V_a + V_b = (1)(20) + 10 + 20, \qquad V_a = 0$$

From Fig. 2-36(d), for $\Sigma\ M_f = 0$,

$$(30)(30) + (1)(30)(\tfrac{30}{2}) - (V_e)(20) = 0, \qquad V_e = 67.5 \text{ kips}$$

For $\Sigma\ F_y = 0$,

$$V_e + V_f = 30 + (1)(30), \qquad V_f = -7.5 \text{ kips}$$

It should be pointed out that the result for $V_a = 0$ is purely a coincidence. For other loads, it may be a positive or negative quantity. If it turns out to be positive, the assumed sense of direction of the reaction is correct; if it is negative, the assumed sense of the reaction should be reversed. Thus $V_f = -7.5$ kips means that the reaction should be directed downward.

Example 2-8. Compute the reactions of the three-hinged arch shown in Fig. 2-37(a).

The components of reaction of the arch, shown dotted in Fig. 2-37(a), can be related to the applied loads as follows:

$$\sum M_c = 0, \qquad (V_a)(140) + (80)(3.75) - (30)(80) - (20)(40) + (H_a)(26.25) = 0$$

or

$$140V_a + 26.25H_a = 2{,}900$$

$$\sum F_x = 0, \qquad H_a + H_c = 80$$

$$\sum F_y = 0, \qquad V_a + V_c = 30 + 20$$

Since there are four unknowns and only three equations of equilibrium, an additional equation must be obtained from the condition of release $\sum M_b = 0$. Thus, by taking moments of all the forces to the left of hinge B about B, we have

$$(H_a)(60) - (80)(30) - (30)(20) + (V_a)(80) = 0$$

or

$$80V_a + 60H_a = 3{,}000$$

This last equation is equivalent to one of the equations of equilibrium, $\sum M_b = 0$, for the free body shown in Fig. 2-37(b). Solving these four equations simultaneously, we obtain $H_a = 29.8$ kips, $V_a = 15.1$ kips, $H_c = 50.2$ kips, and $V_c = 34.9$ kips. The reactions H_b and V_b at the hinge can also be obtained from the other two equations of equilibrium for Fig. 2-37(b).

$$\sum F_x = 0, \qquad H_b = 80 - 29.8 = 50.2 \text{ kips}$$

$$\sum F_y = 0, \qquad V_b = 30 - 15.1 = 14.9 \text{ kips}$$

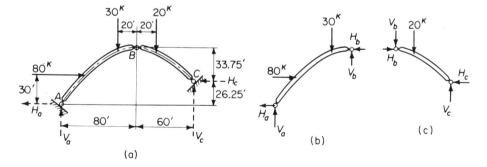

Figure 2-37

By considering the free body shown in Fig. 2-37(c), these reactions can be checked. For $\Sigma M_b = 0$,

$$(20)(20) + (50.2)(33.75) - (34.9)(60) = 400 + 1,694 - 2,094 = 0$$

Example 2-9. Determine the components of reaction of the structure shown in Fig. 2-38(a).

(a)

(b)   (c)   **Figure 2-38**

If we consider the structure as a whole, the following equations of equilibrium are obtained:

$$\Sigma F_x = 0, \qquad H_c - 40 = 0 \tag{a}$$

$$\Sigma F_y = 0, \qquad V_a + V_b + V_c = 100 \tag{b}$$

$$\Sigma M_c = 0, \qquad 100V_b + (40)(40) - 100V_a - (100)(40) = 0 \tag{c}$$

Since there are four unknown components of reaction V_a, V_b, V_c, and H_c, an additional equation must be obtained from the condition of release. This may be accomplished by considering support C as a free body as shown in Fig. 2-38(b). Thus,

$$\Sigma F_x = 0, \qquad \frac{\sqrt{2}}{2} F_{cd} - \frac{4}{5} F_{ce} + H_c = 0 \tag{d}$$

$$\Sigma F_y = 0, \qquad -\frac{\sqrt{2}}{2} F_{cd} - \frac{3}{5} F_{ce} + V_c = 0 \tag{e}$$

from which we may obtain

$$F_{ce} = \frac{V_c + H_c}{1.4}$$

If we now consider the right half of the truss as a free body as shown in Fig. 2-38(c), an expression relating V_b, V_c, and H_c may be obtained by taking moments about point F. Note that the force F_{ce} may be resolved into components at point G so that its horizontal component passes through point F. Then,

$$\sum M_f = 0, \qquad 100V_b + \frac{3}{5}F_{ce}\left(\frac{160}{3}\right) - (100)(40) = 0$$

or

$$100V_b + (32)\left(\frac{V_c + H_c}{1.4}\right) - (100)(40) = 0 \qquad \text{(f)}$$

Finally, all components of the reactions may be obtained from the simultaneous solution of Eqs. (a), (b), (c), and (f) as follows:

$$H_c = 40 \text{ kips}, \qquad V_a = 29.25 \text{ kips}, \qquad V_b = 53.25 \text{ kips}, \qquad V_c = 17.50 \text{ kips}$$

Identical results would have been obtained if F_{cd} were solved from Eqs. (d) and (e) so that an additional equation is obtained by considering the left half of the structure as a free body.

Example 2-10. Compute the reactions of the structure shown in Fig. 2-39(a). Since there are four unknown components of reaction and only three equations of equilibrium, an additional equation must be obtained from the condition of release $\sum M_c = 0$. However, we can simplify the computation by isolating the structure into two parts as shown in Fig. 2-39(b) and (c). From the former, we have

$$\sum M_c = 0, \qquad 80V_b = \frac{100}{\sqrt{2}}(160), \qquad V_b = 141.4 \text{ kips}$$

(a)

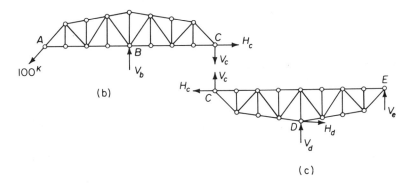

(b)

(c)

Figure 2-39

$$\sum F_x = 0, \qquad H_c = \frac{100}{\sqrt{2}} = 70.7 \text{ kips}$$

$$\sum F_y = 0, \qquad 141.4 - \frac{100}{\sqrt{2}} - V_c = 0, \qquad V_c = 70.7 \text{ kips}$$

From the latter, we obtain

$$\sum M_d = 0, \qquad 80V_e + (70.7)(30) - (70.7)(80) = 0, \qquad V_e = 44.2 \text{ kips}$$

$$\sum F_x = 0, \qquad H_d = 70.7 \text{ kips}$$

$$\sum F_y = 0, \qquad V_d + 44.2 + 70.7 = 0, \qquad V_d = -114.9 \text{ kips}$$

Note that the negative sign for V_d indicates that the reaction at D is downward instead of upward.

2-7 REDUNDANT SYSTEMS

From the point of view of static equilibrium, structural systems may be classified as statically determinate or indeterminate. The basic approach in identifying the typical characteristics of these systems is to check first whether there are sufficient reaction components and members to maintain the equilibrium of the structure. If so, further checks should be made to insure that all reaction components and members are properly oriented so that the structure will be kinematically stable. When there are more reaction components or internal restraints than necessary, remove the redundances until the structure becomes statically determinate. Then, the number of redundances removed is known as the *degree of statical indeterminacy* or *degree of redundancy*.

In general, if a structure is internally stable without redundancy, the degree of statical indeterminacy depends only on the number of external redundances, i.e., the extra components of reaction that can be removed in order to make the structure statically determinate. Let d be the degree of statical indeterminacy, r be the number of independent components of reaction, and e be the number of equations of equilibrium for the structure as a whole. Then,

$$d = r - e \qquad (2-3)$$

where $e = 3$ for a plane structure and $e = 6$ for a space structure. A structure is said to be statically determinate when $d = 0$.

Consider, for example, the plane structures shown in Fig. 2-40. In each case there are three independent equations of equilibrium when the structure as a whole is taken as a free body. The reactions at the supports are the only unknown forces acting on the structure. Since the statical indeterminacy in each case is caused by the extra components of reaction that can be removed without causing the collapse of the structure, the number of components of reaction in excess of three is the degree of indeterminacy or redundancy of the system. Since the number of independent components of reaction is four, five,

(a) (b) (c) **Figure 2-40**

and six for the structures in Figs. 2-40(a), (b), and (c) respectively, the corresponding degrees of indeterminacy are therefore equal to one, two and three.

When a structure is internally unstable or internally redundant, Eq. (2-3) may not be applicable. First, we should rule out cases that are kinematically unstable such as the systems shown in Figs. 2-41(a) and (b) respectively. Furthermore, Fig. 2-41(a) also contains internal redundances since there are more bars than necessary to make the structure statically determinate even though one of the panels lacks sufficient restraint to provide stability.

(a)

(b)

Figure 2-41

On the other hand, the actual degree of indeterminacy of a system may be smaller than the *nominal* number obtained from Eq. (2-3). Consider, for instance, the cases shown in Figs. 2-42(a), (b), and (c), with the corresponding free-body diagrams in Figs. 2-42(d), (e), and (f). In the example of Fig. 2-42(a), the structure is statically indeterminate to the first degree as the above criterion would indicate, but the structures in Figs. 2-42(b) and (c) may be considered as only statically indeterminate to the first and second degrees, respectively, for practical purposes, provided that the vertical displacement of the structure will not cause significant horizontal displacement in each case.

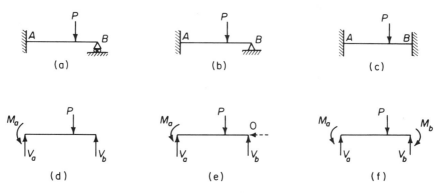

(a) (b) (c)

(d) (e) (f)

Figure 2-42

This assumption of negligible horizontal displacement is quite accurate in most cases. Thus, no horizontal reaction is included in the free-body diagrams in Figs. 2-42(e) and (f).

Continuous beams. If a section is passed through a beam bending in a single principal plane, there will be at the most three stress resultants, i.e., axial force, shearing force and bending moment. Since there is no internal redundancy in a beam, we are only concerned with the external redundancy in the analysis of a continuous beam. Generally, the total number of unknowns in a continuous beam without releases is $3m + r$ where m is the number of spans and r is the number of independent components of reaction. If j denotes the number of supports, a total of $3j$ equations of equilibrium may be obtained theoretically by considering each of these supports as a free-body diagram, even though some of these equations are identically zero when there is no horizontal load. Hence, the degree of statical indeterminacy of a continuous beam is given by

$$d = 3m + r - 3j \qquad (2\text{-}4)$$

while the criterion for statical determinacy is

$$d = 3m + r - 3j = 0 \qquad (2\text{-}5)$$

In practice, all vertical supports of a continuous beam except one are assumed to move freely in the horizontal direction. Consequently, the number of independent components of reaction can be determined accordingly. For example, a continuous beam with $m = 5$ spans has $j = 6$ supports. Suppose that the left support of the continuous beam is fixed, i.e., no rotation as well as no horizontal and vertical displacements, while all other supports are restrained in the vertical direction only. Then, the number of independent components of reaciton is $r = 3 + 5 = 8$ in this case. According to Eq. (2-4),

$$d = (3)(5) + 8 - (3)(6) = 5$$

For continuous beams with releases, such as internal hinges, the degree of statical determinacy is reduced by one for each hinge to account for the loss of resistance to rotation at the hinge. Thus, if the same continuous beam with five spans contains two internal hinges, the degree of statical indeterminacy becomes $d = 5 - 2 = 3$.

Rigid frames. An over-all criterion for statical determinacy may be established for rigid frames. For plane frames, there are in general three stress resultants for a section passing through each member of the frame. Thus, the total number of unknowns in the frame is equal to $3m + r$, in which m is the number of members and r is the number of independent components of reaction. If j denotes the number of joints *including the points of reaction*, a total of $3j$ equations of equilibrium may be obtained by considering each of these joints as a free body. Hence, the degree of statical indeterminacy of a plane rigid frame is also given by

$$d = 3m + r - 3j \qquad (2\text{-}6)$$

while the criterion for statical determinacy is

$$d = 3m + r - 3j = 0 \qquad (2\text{-}7)$$

Note that a rigid frame may have internal as well as external redundances. Consequently, Eq. (2-6) is intended to include both types of redundances. This can be illustrated by the multistoried frame in Fig. 2-43(a) in which $m = 12$, $r = 12$, and $j = 11$. From Eq. (2-6),

$$d = (3)(12) + 12 - (3)(11) = 15.$$

On the other hand, it may observed that the structure has nine degrees of external redundancy because there are twelve components of reaction, as shown in Fig. 2-43(b). A section at the second level indicates that there are nine unknown forces and moments and only three equations of equilibrium if the top part of the structure is taken as a free body. Thus, the structure has six degrees of internal redundancy. The total number of redundances is therefore $9 + 6 = 15$.

(a)   (b)

Figure 2-43

If hinges are introduced in the members of a plane rigid frame, each hinge will provide an extra equation $\Sigma M = 0$ at the point of the hinge. Let the number of hinges in a rigid frame be denoted by n; then the criterion of statical determinacy will become

$$3m + r - 3j - n = 0$$

For the structure shown in Fig. 2-44(a), the degree of statical indeterminacy is $36 + 12 - 33 - 5 = 10$. However, if the hinges are introduced at a joint, the rotational restraints of all members meeting at the joint will be released. On the other hand, the equilibrium condition that the algebraic sum of the moments from all members meeting at the joint be zero becomes a repetitive statement in view of the existence of the hinge. Thus, the actual reduction of

(a)

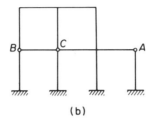

(b)   **Figure 2-44**

redundancy due to the introduction of a hinge at a joint equals the number of
the members meeting at the joint minus one. For the structure shown in Fig.
2-44(b), the hinge at joint A reduces the redundancy by one, the hinge at joint
B reduces the redundancy by two, and the hinge at C reduces the redundancy
by three. Hence the degree of statical indeterminacy of the structure becomes
$36 + 12 - 33 - 1 - 2 - 3 = 9$.

For rigid frames in three dimensions, there are in general six stress
resultants for a section passing through each member of the frame, and thus
a total number of $6m$ unknowns from all members. The total number of equations of equilibrium from all joints including the points of reaction is equal to
$6j$. If r is the number of independent components of reaction, the degree of
statical indeterminacy of a space frame is given by

$$d = 6m + r - 6j \tag{2-8}$$

while the criterion for statical determinacy is

$$d = 6m + r - 6j = 0 \tag{2-9}$$

Pin-connected trusses. In the case of trusses, the problem is simplified
by the fact that the joints of the trusses are assumed to be pin-connected. This
assumption leads to the simplification that there is only one stress component
at a section passing through each member and that the joints can resist only
direct forces but not moments. Thus, for a plane truss, the total number of
unknowns in the truss is equal to $m + r$, in which m is the number of the
members and r is the number of independent components of reaction. If j
denotes the number of joints including the points of reaction, a total of $2j$
equations of equilibrium may be obtained by considering each of these joints as

a free body. Thus, the degree of statical indeterminacy of a plane truss is given by

$$d = m + r - 2j \qquad (2\text{-}10)$$

while the criterion for statical determinacy is

$$d = m + r - 2j = 0 \qquad (2\text{-}11)$$

This rule may be applied to the structures shown in Figs. 2-45 and 2-46. In Fig. 2-45(a), $m = 18$, $r = 3$, $j = 10$. Since $m + r - 2j = 1$, the structure is statically indeterminate to the first degree. In Fig. 2-45(b), $m = 20$, $r = 3$, and $j = 10$. Since $m + r - 2j = 3$, the structure is statically indeterminate to the third degree. In Fig. 2-46(a), $m = 39$, $r = 4$, and $j = 20$. Thus

$$m + r - 2j = 3$$

and the structure is statically indeterminate to the third degree. In Fig. 2-46(b), $m = 25$, $r = 4$, and $j = 14$. Since $m + r - 2j = 1$, the structure is statically indeterminate to the first degree.

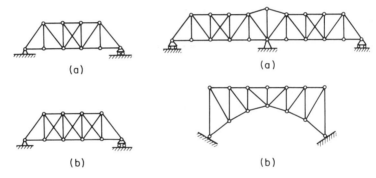

<table>
<tr><td>(a)</td><td>(a)</td></tr>
<tr><td>(b)</td><td>(b)</td></tr>
<tr><td>Figure 2-45</td><td>Figure 2-46</td></tr>
</table>

For plane trusses, the releases in structures are accomplished by omitting certain members such as those shown dotted in Figs. 2-47(a) and (b). Thus, m is reduced by one in Fig. 2-47(a) and is reduced by two in Fig. 2-47(b). Since the reduction of each of these members is accompanied by the introduction of an additional component of reaction in the respective structures, the criterion of $m + r - 2j = 0$ may still be used. For the structure in Fig. 2-47(a), $m = 24$,

(a)   (b)

Figure 2-47

$r = 4$, and $j = 14$; for the structure in Fig. 2-47(b), $m = 59$, $r = 5$, and $j = 32$. Hence, both structures are statically determinate.

For space trusses, a total of $3j$ equations of equilibrium may be obtained by considering each of the joints as a free-body. Then, the degree of statical indeterminacy of a space truss is given by

$$d = m + r - 3j \tag{2-12}$$

while the criterion for statical determinacy is

$$d = m + r - 3j = 0 \tag{2-13}$$

Suspension bridges. The center span of a suspension bridge may be idealized as a cable that carries a uniform horizontal load from the roadway through a set of uniformly spaced vertical hangers. The roadway may be stiffened by a girder or a truss as shown by the structures in Fig. 2-48. For these cases, there are four known components of reaction in each system, if the stiffening girder or truss is subjected to vertical loads only. This is true because the directions of the cable reactions must be in line with the tangents of the cable at supports A and B, and the hangers are so flexible that they can transmit only vertical loads. Hence, each system is statically determinate because an additional condition of release is present in the system. In Fig. 2-48(a), the condition of release is provided by the center hinge C' in the girder, whereas in Fig. 2-48(b) no moment can be transmitted from truss $A'C'$ to truss $B'C'$. Thus, joint C' in Fig. 2-48(b) has the same effect as hinge C' in Fig. 2-48(a).

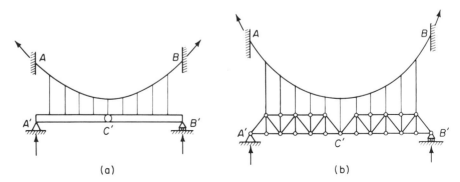

(a)   (b)

Figure 2-48

If no release is introduced in the stiffening girder or truss in a suspension bridge, then each system will be statically indeterminate to the first degree under the specified assumptions.

2-8 DEFLECTED SHAPES OF STRUCTURES

Structural members deform in accordance with the force-deformation properties of the material when they are subjected to internal forces and moments. Hence, the deflected shapes of structures are influenced by the constraints at supports and the applied loads. For the purpose of illustration, the deflected shape of a structure can be sketched in a scale that would exaggerate the significant features even though the deflections in the elastic range generally are too small to be visible. For example, before finding the moments at various sections of a beam, it is possible to detect the directions of these moments by observing the curvatures of the beam at these sections from its approximate deflected shape. On the other hand, if the moment diagram is found first, the deflected shape of the beam can be accurately sketched by noting the moment-curvature relationship.

The exaggerated deflected shapes of beams can best be illustrated by laboratory models made of elastic material shown in the photographs from Figs. 2-49 through 2-56. In these models, the simply supported ends are allowed to rotate freely while the fixed ends are clamped. Concentrated loads are applied by lowering the pointers to produce the desired deflections.

In Fig. 2-49(a), a single-span beam with two concentrated loads is simply supported; by contrast, a single-span beam with the same loading in Fig. 2-49(b) is fixed at both ends which are characterized by the horizontal slopes at the supports. Note the single convex curvature of the simple beam in Fig. 2-49(a) and the change of curvature at the points of inflection of the fixed-end beam in Fig. 2-49(b). The deflected shapes of a single span beam with overhangs at both ends under different loading conditions are shown in Fig. 2-50(a), (b) and (c). The overhangs in Fig. 2-50(a) remain straight because of absence of bending moments; so are portions of the overhangs beyond the concentrated loads toward the free ends in Fig. 2-50(b) and (c). However, the deflected beam

(a)

(b)

Figure 2-49

(a)

(b)

(c)

Figure 2-50

in Fig. 2-50(b) has a single concave curvature between supports while the deflected beam in Fig. 2-50(c) contains two points of inflection between supports. Both Figs. 2-51(a) and (b) show a single-span beam with a load on the right overhang, the difference being that the left support in Fig. 2-51(a) is simply supported while the left suppport in Fig. 2-51(b) is fixed. Note again the point of inflection and the horizontal slope at the left support of the deflected beam in Fig. 2-51(b).

A three-span beam with two internal hinges in the center span is shown in Figs. 2-52(a) and (b). Note the kinks in the deflected shapes of the beam where the internal hinges are located. In Fig. 2-52(a), these kinks are accentuated by the load in the center span, whereas in Fig. 2-52(b), the portion of the

(a)

(b)

Figure 2-51

(a)

(b)

Figure 2-52

Sec. 2-8   Deflected Shapes of Structures

61

beam between the internal hinges is horizontal since it is not affected by the loads on the side spans. The three-span beams in Figs. 2-53(a) and (b) are, respectively, simply supported and fixed at both exterior supports. However, each beam has an internal hinge at the center span so that a kink occurs in the deflected shape of the beam at that point.

(a)

(b)

Figure 2-53

Figure 2-54(a) shows a two-span continuous beam with a fixed exterior left support and a simply supported exterior right support. When a load is applied to the left span only, the deflected shape of the right span is concave upward, and that of the left span is affected by the fixed condition of the exterior left support. Fig. 2-54(b) shows a two-span continuous beam which has

(a)

Figure 2-54

(b)

Figure 2-54 (cont.)

fixed supports at both exterior ends. Because of beam geometry and loading conditions, the deflected shape shows symmetry with respect to the center support.

Figures 2-55(a) and (b) show a three-span continuous beam with simple exterior supports under different loading conditions, while Fig. 2-55(c) shows a three-span continuous beam with fixed exterior supports under a load at the center span. In each case, the deflected shape reflects the symmetry of beam geometry and loading conditions. Note also the deflections of the unloaded spans and the effects of the fixed supports on the slopes of the deflected shapes. In Fig. 2-56, the four-span continuous beam with simple exterior support is loaded at the right span only. It can be seen how the deflected shape of the unloaded spans is affected by the load on the right span.

(a)

(b)

Figure 2-55

Sec. 2-8   Deflected Shapes of Structures

(c)

Figure 2-55 (*cont.*)

Figure 2-56

After we have acquired some understanding of the deflected shapes of beams under different loadings and support conditions, it will be possible for us to sketch the deflected shape of a beam with greater confidence. For example, we can envision a positive moment or a negative moment in a certain portion of a beam by pointing to the respective concave curvature or convex curvature in the deflected beam. Similarly, we can expect that at a point of inflection corresponding to the transition from concave to convex curvature, the moment equals zero since it can neither be positive nor negative.

The deflected shape of a rigid frame can also be sketched by using the same principle. However, greater caution must be exercised in determining the curvatures of the members meeting at a joint since the free-body diagram of an isolated rigid joint must be in equilibrium. Two examples of the deflected shapes of statically determinate rigid frames are shown in Figs. 2-57 and 2-58.

Figure 2-57

Figure 2-58

Since the members of a truss are subjected to axial forces only, the shape of a deflected truss represents the accumulated changes in lengths of the members which are consistent with the geometry of the truss configuration. Thus, the angle changes at the joints of a truss will result from the changes in lengths of the members. For the truss shown in Fig. 2-59(a) in which the horizontal chord members are 30 ft long and the verticals are 40 ft long, the changes in lengths are noted along the members. The deflected shape of the truss resulting from the such changes is exaggerated as shown in Fig. 2-59(b).

(a)

(b)   **Figure 2-59**

The importance of a good understanding of the force-displacement relationships of structures cannot be overemphasized. Although we are primarily interested in finding the internal forces and moments in Chapters 3 through 5, the force-displacement relationships will be discussed in detail in Chapters 6 and 7. Students should refer to the deflected shapes of structures in this section and study carefully the underlying force-displacement relationships when they encounter similar problems in subsequent chapters.

Example 2-11. Find the relationship between the load P and the deflection of v of point C in Fig. 2-60, assuming that both members AC and CB have a cross-sectional area A and a modulus of elasticity E.

This is a special case which shows nonlinear relationship between force and deformation even though the material is linearly elastic. The structural system in Fig. 2-60 is in a position of unstable equilibrium because no horizontal reactions will be developed until the structure has deformed excessively. As a result, the

Figure 2-60

force-deformation relation of the system is nonlinear. Let us consider the system in its deformed position as indicated by the dotted lines when the material remains in the elastic range. Because of symmetry, the internal forces in bars AC and BC are equal. Let F be the bar force when the system is in the deformed position. Then,

$$\sum F_y = 0, \qquad 2F \sin \alpha = P$$

For small angles of α, we can use the approximation

$$\sin \alpha = \tan \alpha = v/L$$

Hence,

$$\frac{2Fv}{L} = P \quad \text{or} \quad F = \frac{PL}{2v}$$

The strain in each bar can be obtained from

$$\epsilon = \frac{1}{L}(\sqrt{L^2 + v^2} - L) = \left[1 + \frac{v^2}{L^2}\right]^{1/2} - 1 \approx \frac{1}{2}\frac{v^2}{L^2}$$

Then, from Hooke's law, we have $\sigma = F/A = \epsilon E$, or

$$F = A\epsilon E = \frac{AEv^2}{2L^2}$$

Hence, the relation between the load P and the displacement v is given by

$$P = \frac{2Fv}{L} = \frac{AEv^3}{L^3}$$

The internal force F in each bar may also be expressed in terms of the load P and the geometrical and material properties of the bar. Since $v = 2F/PL$, we have

$$F = \frac{AE\left(\dfrac{2F}{PL}\right)^2}{2L^2} = \frac{4AEF^2}{2P^2L^4}$$

Then,

$$F = \frac{P^2L^4}{2AE}$$

Hence, the relationship between F and P is nonlinear as indicated in this equation.

PROBLEMS

2-1 to 2-14. In each of the systems in Figs. P2-1 to P2-14, compute the components of reaction.

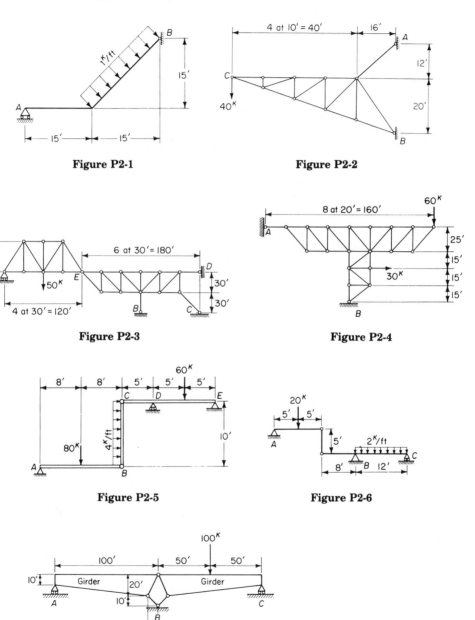

Figure P2-1

Figure P2-2

Figure P2-3

Figure P2-4

Figure P2-5

Figure P2-6

Figure P2-7

Figure P2-8

Figure P2-9

Figure P2-10

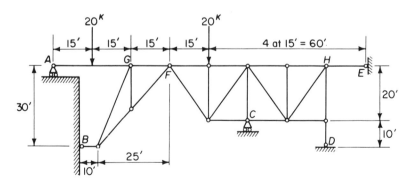

Figure P2-11

Structural Systems   Chap. 2

Figure P2-12

Figure P2-13

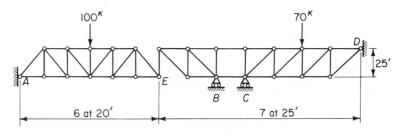

Figure P2-14

2-15 to 2-20. In each of the systems in Figs. P2-15 to P2-20, determine whether the structure is statically determinate or indeterminate. If it is statically indeterminate, state the degree of static indeterminacy.

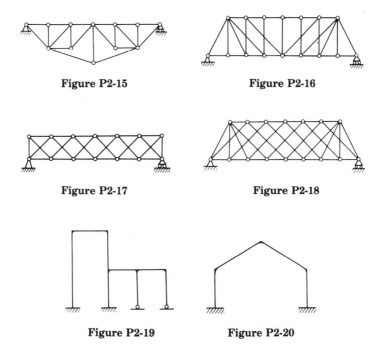

Figure P2-15

Figure P2-16

Figure P2-17

Figure P2-18

Figure P2-19

Figure P2-20

3

Forces and Moments in Beams and Frames

3-1 SIMPLE PLANE STRUCTURES

The analysis of simple structures usually begins with the determination of reactions. After the reactions of a structure are obtained, the internal forces and moments in the desired locations of the structure may be studied by passing imaginary sections through those locations. The variations of the internal forces and moments in various members of a structure—and especially their maximum values—are of utmost importance for design purposes.

We begin with simple plane structures that are statically determinate and consist of relatively few members. In this category we include simple beams and rigid frames. The stress resultants acting on a section through a member of a plane structure can in general be resolved into an axial force, a transverse shear force, and a bending moment. Plane trusses, which are widely used as structural systems, represent a special class because of the assumption of smooth pin connections for all their members, and therefore they will be treated separately in Chapter 4. Cables and arches that consist of curved members will be discussed in Chapter 5.

For plane structures that are statically indeterminate, the internal forces and moments as well as reactions cannot be determined by statics alone. However, these stress resultants may be obtained by the same procedure after the number of unknowns in the system has been reduced to that which may be solved by statics. Many of the simple structures used as examples in this chapter do not represent common real structures, but are the simplified versions of more complicated structures. Thus, the student should be well aware of the possibilities of other applications of the principles presented here.

3-2 AXIAL FORCES, SHEARS, AND MOMENTS

Let us consider a section passing through a structural member normal to the axis of the member, as shown in Fig. 3-1(a). The stress resultants acting at the section include an axial force N, a transverse shear force S, and a bending moment M. The transverse shear force and the bending moment will henceforth be abbreviated as "shear" and "moment," respectively, in the analysis of plane structures. If a small element such as the portion shown dotted to the left of the section in Fig. 3-1(a) is cut off from the member, equal but opposite forces should be added to the left face of the element in order to maintain the equilibrium of the free body since no external forces are acting on the element. Looking from the front of the element, these internal forces and moments can be represented as shown in Fig. 3-1(b). Looking from the back of the element, however, a mirror image as shown in Fig. 3-1(c) is obtained. Although the directions of N and M remain the same in Fig. 3-1(c) as in Fig. 3-1(b), the direction of S is reversed. It is necessary therefore to adopt a sign convention so that the situation at a section can be defined more clearly and systematically.

(a) (b) (c)

Figure 3-1

The selection of a particular convention is a matter of convenience. Figure 3-2 shows the sign convention that is most convenient from the viewpoint of structural design and is referred to as the *designer's sign convention*. Except for Chapters 11 to 14 in which the sign convention is a natural consequence of matrix methods, this sign convention will be used throughout this book. As shown in Fig. 3-2(a), the pair of axial forces is considered as positive when it

(a) (b) (c)

Figure 3-2

produces tension in a member, and is negative when it causes compression in the member. In Fig. 3-2(b), the pair of shears is designated as positive if it tends to push the left side of a member upward, and is negative if it pushes the left side of the member downward. In Fig. 3-2(c), the pair of moments is said to be positive if it tends to bend a member into a concave curvature causing tension in the bottom of a member, and is negative if it causes the member to bend into a convex curvature causing tension in the top of a member. It should be pointed out that the position of the member is assumed to be horizontal when such a sign convention is introduced. If the member is vertical, such as member BC in Fig. 3-3(a), it can be looked upon from the right or the left of the member. Under such circumstances, it can be specified that either the right-hand side of member BC is to be considered as the bottom or that all members will be viewed from the inside of the structure. Although the former viewpoint is definitely more general, the latter also has some merits. For the structure in Fig. 3-3(b), for instance, it is impossible to differentiate which side of the vertical member is the inside of the structure. For that reason, the latter viewpoint cannot be applied to structures with more than one span or one story. The former convention will therefore be used for multispan or multistory rigid frames. On the other hand, for structures such as arches, rings, and simple frames with inclined legs such as the one shown in Fig. 3-3(c), it is much easier to view the member from the inside of the structure. The latter convention is used for such cases despite its limitations.

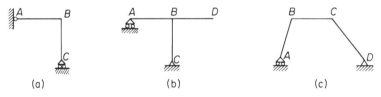

Figure 3-3

It may be well to mention other sign conventions and to discuss briefly their advantages or disadvantages in the analysis of structural problems. Figure 3-4(a) shows a convention for axial force that defines a positive force as one whose sense of direction points in the positive direction of the coordinate axis. Although the signs of these forces are consistent with the direction of the coordinate axis, it is not possible to determine from the sign whether a force is tensile or compressive. However, if the section on which an axial force acts is defined as positive when its outwardly directed normal is pointing in the

Figure 3-4

Forces and Moments in Beams and Frames   Chap. 3

direction of the positive coordinate axis and as negative when the outward normal points the other way, the state of stress can be correctly obtained. Thus, the area of a section may be considered as $+A$ or $-A$ accordingly. For $+N$ and $+A$ on the right end of the member, $\sigma = N/A$ represents tensile stress in the member. For $-N$ and $-A$ on the left end of the member $\sigma = (-N)/(-A) = N/A$ also indicates tensile stress. Figure 3-4(b) shows a convention for shear that is the complete reverse of that of Fig. 3-2(b). Whereas the convention in Fig. 3-2(b) is more convenient to apply, that of Fig. 3-4(b) has the merit of being positive in the same direction as positive shearing stress defined for the general state of stress acting on an element in a right-handed coordinate system. Figure 3-4(c) shows a convention for moment that defines positive moment as one which rotates in the counter-clockwise direction at the ends of the member. In summing up moments, this convention simplifies the operation, but it is impossible to determine from the sign of the moment whether the member is bent concave upward or downward.

The determination of axial force, shear, and moment at any section of a structure is based on the consideration of static equilibrium of the free body on either side of the section. These stress resultants acting on the free body at one side of the section are equal in magnitude but opposite in sense to the respective stress resultants acting on the free body at the other side. Thus, for a plane structure, the axial force N acting normal to any transverse section of a member may be obtained by summing up algebraically the components in that direction of all external forces and reactions acting on a free body. The shear S at any transverse section of a member is the algebraic sum of the components in the transverse direction of all external forces and reactions acting on the free body. The bending moment is the algebraic sum of the moments in the plane of the structure, taken about the intersection of the axis of the member and the transverse section, of all external loads and reactions acting on the free body. It is customary to start from the left end of the structure as the origin of the coordinate axis and to use the left-hand side of the section as a free body. However, the use of the right-hand side of the section as a free body sometimes involves less computation if there are fewer external loads and reactions on that portion of the structure.

The senses of direction of the axial force N, shear S, and moment M at any section of a structure are not always immediately obvious. If the correct senses of direction of these forces and moment cannot be detected by inspection, they can always be assumed to act in the positive direction of the sign convention. In that case, a positive result will indicate that the assumed sense of direction is correct, and a negative result means that the actual sense of direction is the reverse of the assumed direction. The variations of the axial force, shear, and moment along the length of a member can be expressed algebraically or graphically as a function of the distance x along the length of the member. We shall consider here the formulation of the algebraic expressions for these quantities.

Example 3-1. For the beam shown in Fig. 3-5(a), write a general expression for the axial force, shear, and moment at typical sections of the beam.

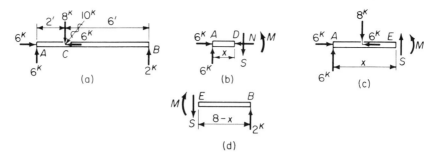

Figure 3-5

The inclined load of 10 kips is resolved into vertical and horizontal components of 8 kips and 6 kips, respectively. The components of reaction H_a, V_a, and V_b are obtained from the equations of equilibrium.

$$\sum M_a = 0, \qquad 8 \, V_b - (8)(2) = 0, \qquad V_b = 2 \text{ kips}$$

$$\sum F_y = 0, \qquad V_a + V_b = 8, \qquad V_a = 8 - 2 = 6 \text{ kips}$$

$$\sum F_x = 0, \qquad H_a = 6 \text{ kips}$$

As a check, $\Sigma M_b = 0$, $(8)(6) - 8V_a = 0$, $V_a = 6$ kips.

In obtaining the stress resultants, a section is first passed through a point D between A and C at a distance x from A. Then the free body on the left-hand side of the section will be as shown in Fig. 3-5(b). Since the correct senses of direction of forces and moment in this case are rather obvious, they have been assigned proper directions in the figure. Thus, all the results are positive.

$$\sum F_x = 0, \qquad N = 6 \text{ kips}$$

$$\sum F_y = 0, \qquad S = 6 \text{ kips}$$

$$\sum M_d = 0, \qquad M = 6x \text{ ft-kips}$$

Note that the moment M is a function of x, the distance from the left support. The axial force N and the shear S are independent of the distance x as long as it is smaller than the distance AC.

If a section is passed through point E of the same beam as shown in Fig. 3-5(c), the same procedure may be repeated.

$$\sum F_x = 0, \qquad N = 0$$

$$\sum F_y = 0, \qquad S = 8 - 6 = 2 \text{ kips}$$

$$\sum M_e = 0, \qquad M = 6x - 8(x - 2) = 16 - 2x \text{ ft-kips}$$

It can be seen that the same results may also be obtained from the free-body diagram in Fig. 3-5(d). Note that M and S shown in Fig. 3-5(d) are equal and opposite to those shown in Fig. 3-5(c). Thus,

$$\sum F_y = 0, \qquad S = 2 \text{ kips}$$

$$\sum M_e = 0, \qquad M = 2(8 - x) = 16 - 2x \text{ ft-kips}$$

Example 3-2. For the portal frame shown in Fig. 3-6(a), write a general expression for the axial force, shear, and moment at typical sections of the beam.

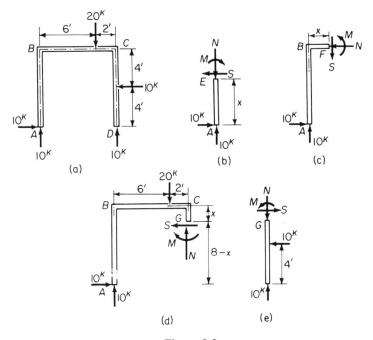

Figure 3-6

The reaction components H_a, V_a, and V_d for the frame are obtained as follows:

$$\sum M_a = 0, \qquad 8V_d + (10)(4) - (20)(6) = 0, \qquad V_d = 10 \text{ kips}$$

$$\sum F_y = 0, \qquad V_a + V_d = 20, \qquad V_a = 10 \text{ kips}$$

$$\sum F_x = 0, \qquad H_a = 10 \text{ kips}$$

As a check,

$$\sum M_d = 0, \qquad (10)(4) + (20)(2) - 8V_a = 0, \qquad V_a = 10 \text{ kips}.$$

When a section is passed through point E, a free-body diagram as shown in Fig. 3-6(b) is obtained. Let x be the coordinate axis along the length of the member. Then,

$$\sum F_x = 0, \qquad N = 10 \text{ kips}$$

$$\sum F_y = 0, \qquad S = 10 \text{ kips}$$

$$\sum M_e = 0, \qquad M = 10x \text{ ft-kips}$$

For a section passed through point F, the free body representing the left-hand side is shown in Fig. 3-6(c).

$$\sum F_x = 0, \qquad N = 10 \text{ kips}$$

$$\sum F_y = 0, \qquad S = 10 \text{ kips}$$

$$\sum M_f = 0, \qquad M = (10)(x) - (10)(8) = 10x - 80 \text{ ft-kips}$$

For a section passed through point G, the free-body diagram to the left of the section is shown in Fig. 3-6(d).

$$\sum F_x = 0, \qquad N = 10 \text{ kips}$$

$$\sum F_y = 0, \qquad S = 10 \text{ kips}$$

$$\sum M_g = 0, \qquad M = (20)(2) + (10)(8 - x) - (10)(8) = 40 - 10x \text{ ft-kips}$$

The free-body diagram to the right of the section passed through point G may also be used. Such a diagram is shown in Fig. 3-6(e), and the results thus obtained check with those from Fig. 3-6(d).

$$\sum F_x = 0, \qquad N = 10 \text{ kips}$$

$$\sum F_y = 0, \qquad S = 10 \text{ kips}$$

$$\sum M_g = 0, \qquad M = (10)(8 - x - 4) = 40 - 10x \text{ ft-kips}$$

Example 3-3. For the cantilever beam shown in Fig. 3-7(a), write a general expression for the axial force, shear, and moment at typical sections of the beam. The reaction components of the beam are obtained as follows:

$$\sum M_f = 0, \qquad (30)(30) + (1)(30)(\tfrac{30}{2}) - 20V_e = 0, \qquad V_e = 67.5 \text{ kips}$$

$$\sum F_y = 0, \qquad V_e - V_f = 30 + (1)(30), \qquad V_f = 7.5 \text{ kips}$$

Since there is no horizontal force acting on the beam, there will be no axial

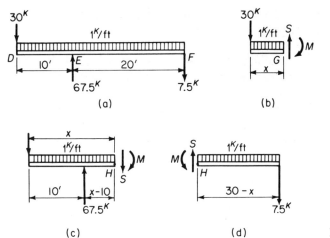

Figure 3-7

force acting on any section normal to the length of the beam. Thus, for a section passed through point G, the free body at the left-hand side of the section will be as shown in Fig. 3-7(b).

$$\sum F_y = 0, \qquad S = 30 + (1)(x) = 30 + x \text{ kips}$$

$$\sum M_g = 0, \qquad M = (30)(x) + (1)(x)(x/2) = 30x + x^2/2 \text{ ft-kips}$$

For a section passed through point H, the free body at the left-hand side of the section may be represented by Fig. 3-7(c).

$$\sum F_y = 0, \qquad S = 67.5 - 30 - (1)(x) = 37.5 - x \text{ kips}$$

$$\sum M_h = 0, \qquad M = (30)(x) + (1)(x)(x/2) - (67.5)(x - 10)$$

$$= x^2/2 - 37.5x + 675 \text{ ft-kips}$$

As a check, the right-hand side of the section passed through G may also be used as a free body as shown in Fig. 3-7(d).

$$\sum F_y = 0, \qquad S = (1)(30 - x) + 7.5 = 37.5 - x \text{ kips}$$

$$\sum M_h = 0, \qquad M = (7.5)(30 - x) + (1)(30 - x)^2/2$$

$$= x^2/2 - 37.5x + 675 \text{ ft-kips}$$

3-3 DIFFERENTIAL RELATIONSHIPS IN BEAMS

Since the variation of axial forces in a beam is usually rather simple, we can dismiss it without further discussion. The variations of shears and moments can be expressed as functions of the position x along a beam, as explained in the previous section. However, they can also be obtained through successive integrations of the loading function.

Consider a beam with applied loads as shown in Fig. 3-8(a). If a differential element of length δx is isolated from the beam by two parallel sections at x and $x + \delta x$, the forces and moments acting on the free body are as shown in Fig. 3-8(b), in which the positive directions of applied loads, shears, and moments are indicated. The intensity of load q can be considered as uniformly distributed over the length δx since the variation of q leads to higher-order terms of δx which are negligibly small compared to δx. Since the element represents a free body in equilibrium, the following conditions must be fulfilled:

$$\sum F_y = 0, \qquad S + q\delta x - (S + \delta S) = 0$$

or

$$q = \frac{dS}{dx} \tag{3-1}$$

$$\sum M_c = 0, \qquad (M + \delta M) - M - (S + \delta S)\delta x + q\delta x \frac{\delta x}{2} = 0$$

As δx approaches 0 as a limit, the higher-order terms become negligible. Thus,

$$(M + \delta M) - M - S\delta x = 0$$

or

$$S = \frac{dM}{dx} \tag{3-2}$$

Equation (3-1) states that the rate of change of the shear along the beam is equal to the intensity of the applied load, and Eq. (3-2) indicates that the rate

(a)

(b)　　　　(c)　　　　(d)　　　　**Figure 3-8**

　　　　Forces and Moments in Beams and Frames　　　Chap. 3

of change of the moment along the beam is equal to the shear. These two equations are important because the critical values of moment and shear along the beam may be determined from them. Thus, if S is a continuous function of x for an interval $a \leqq x \leqq b$ in which the derivative dS/dx exists, the maximum or minimum shear occurs at a point where $q = dS/dx = 0$. Similarly, if M is a continuous function of x for an interval $a \leqq x \leqq b$ in which the derivative dM/dx exists, the maximum or minimum moment occurs at a point where $S = dM/dx = 0$. From a practical point of view, however, the second statement is far more useful than the first because the shear function S is seldom continuous for beams under ordinary loads. For example, if a concentrated load P is acting at point D of the beam in Fig. 3-8(a), there is a sudden change in shear between a section just to the left and another section just to the right of the load P as shown in Fig. 3-8(c). Hence, the derivative dS/dx does not exist at point D and Eq. (3-1) does not apply at this point. The moment function M may also be discontinuous as a result of applied loads such as the couple M_e at point E of the beam in Fig. 3-8(a). This couple causes a sudden change in moment from one section to another adjacent section, as shown in Fig. 3-8(d). In such a case, the derivative dM/dx does not exist, and Eq. (3-2) cannot be used for point E.

Conversely, if the loading function q is known, Eqs. (3-1) and (3-2) can be integrated and expressed in the following form:

$$S = \int q \, dx + C_1 \tag{3-3}$$

and

$$M = \int S \, dx + C_2 \tag{3-4}$$

Equation (3-3) indicates that the shear at any section of the beam is an integral of the applied loads or the *area under the loading curve*. The constant of integration C_1 can be determined from the conditions of shear at the supports of the beam. Thus, Eq. (3-3) represents the variation of shears or the *shear curve* along the length of the beam. Equation (3-4) means that the moment at any section normal to the beam is an integral of the shear forces or the *area under the shear curve*. The constant of integration C_2 can be evaluated from the conditions of moment at the supports of the beam. Hence Eq. (3-4) represents the variation of moments or the *moment curve* along the length of the beam. The conditions of shear and moment at the supports of the beam by which the constants of integration are evaluated are called the *force boundary conditions,* or simply *boundary conditions.*

As examples, consider two beams, one cantilever and the other simply supported, subjected to downward uniformly distributed load w_0 as shown in Figs. 3-9 and 3-10. Since $q = -w_0$, where the negative sign indicates the downward direction and w_0 is a constant, then for both beams,

$$S = \int -w_0 \, dx + C_1 = -w_0 x + C_1$$

and

$$M = \int S \, dx + C_2 = -\frac{w_0 x^2}{2} + C_1 x + C_2$$

For the cantilever beam shown in Fig. 3-9(a), the boundary conditions are as follows: $S = 0$ at $x = 0$ and $M = 0$ at $x = 0$. Hence the constants of integration C_1 and C_2 are both zero. Then,

$$S = -w_0 x$$

Figure 3-9

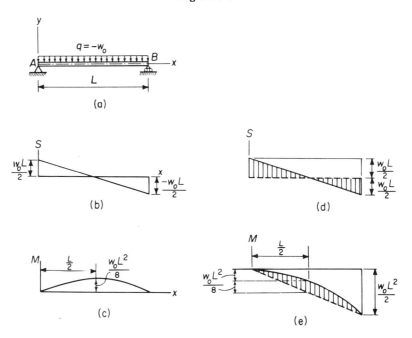

Figure 3-10

Forces and Moments in Beams and Frames   Chap. 3

and

$$M = -\frac{w_0 x^2}{2}$$

The shear and moment curves from these two equations are plotted in Figs. 3-9(b) and (c), respectively. For the simply supported beam shown in Fig. 3-10(a), the boundary conditions may be taken as $S = V_a$ at $x = 0$ and $M = 0$ at $x = 0$ if the reaction V_a is obtained first. However, the boundary conditions $M = 0$ at $x = 0$ and at $x = L$ may also be used without obtaining the reaction V_a. It can easily be seen in this case that $V_a = w_0 L/2$. Thus, from the former set of conditions, we get $C_1 = w_0 L/2$ and $C_2 = 0$, or

$$S = \frac{w_0 L}{2} - w_0 x$$

and

$$M = \frac{w_0 L x}{2} - \frac{w_0 x^2}{2}$$

The shear and moment curves from these two equations are plotted in Figs. 3-10(b) and (c) respectively. From the latter set of conditions, the constants of integration can be obtained as follows:

at $x = 0$, $M = 0$: $\qquad C_2 = 0$

at $x = L$, $M = 0$: $\qquad -\frac{w_0 L^2}{2} + C_1 L + C_2 = 0, \qquad C_1 = \frac{w_0 L}{2}$

Thus the same results for shear and moment may be obtained.

In examining Eqs. (3-3) and (3-4) further, we observe that in general

$$S = \int q \, dx + C_1$$

and

$$M = \int S \, dx + C_2 = \int \left(\int q \, dx \right) dx + C_1 x + C_2$$

Hence, the *shape* of the shear and moment curves is defined by the corresponding integral independent of the boundary conditions. The *ordinates* of the points on the curves, of course, are influenced by the boundary conditions that are expressed in the constants of integration C_1 and C_2. The equation of the shear curve may be considered as the superposition of a diagram of

$$S = \int q \, dx \qquad \text{for } C_1 = 0$$

and a vertical translation of the x-axis equal to $S = C_1$. The equation of the moment curve may be considered as the superposition of

$$M = \int \left(\int q \, dx \right) dx \qquad \text{for } C_1 = C_2 = 0$$

and a combination of vertical translation and rotation of the x-axis equivalent to $M = C_1 x + C_2$. For the special case where $C_2 = 0$, the movement of x-axis becomes pure rotation as represented by $M = C_1 x$. Since the cantilever beam in Fig. 3-9 represents the case $C_1 = C_2 = 0$, and the simply supported beam in Fig. 3-10 has $C_1 = w_0 L/2$ and $C_2 = 0$, the ordinates of the shear and moment curves of the latter may be obtained by superimposing $S = C_1$ and $M = C_1 x + C_2$ respectively to those of the former, as shown in Figs. 3-10(d) and (e) respectively. Diagrams showing proper *ordinates* as well as the *shape* of the shear curve are known as *shear diagrams*; similar diagrams showing proper *ordinates* as well as the *shape* of the moment curve are called *moment diagrams*. Thus, the shear and moment diagrams for the beam in Fig. 3-10(a) are either represented by Figs. 3-10(b) and (c) respectively, or by the *shaded portions* in Figs. 3-10(d) and (e) respectively.

In connection with the construction of shear and moment diagrams, we should first clarify several terms. The *area under a curve* is defined as the area between the curve and the coordinate axis involved. This is literally true if the curve has positive ordinates in the interval under consideration but actually means the area above the curve if the curve has negative ordinates in that interval. When a reference axis in a diagram is rotated, the *ordinates* of the curve are assumed to move *normal to the original direction of the reference axis*. Thus, if a horizontal axis is being rotated, the ordinates of the curve will still be measured vertically. The *maximum* or *minimum* point on a curve may be considered relative only to the points on the curve in the immediate vicinity. When a function assumes its largest value algebraically in the range, the term *maximum positive* is used to denote such an absolute maximum point if it is positive. Similarly, a point representing the least value algebraically in the range is termed *maximum negative* if such an absolute minimum point is negative.

Equations (3-3) and (3-4) can also be expressed in the form of definite integrals for the interval of $a < x < b$ as follows:

$$S_b - S_a = \int_a^b q\,dx \tag{3-5}$$

and

$$M_b - M_a = \int_a^b S\,dx \tag{3-6}$$

Equation (3-5) states that the shear at any section of a beam is equal to the shear at a previous section plus the area of the loading diagram between the two sections in the positive direction of the coordinate axis. Similarly, according to Eq. (3-6), the moment at any section of a beam is equal to the moment at a previous section plus the area of the shear diagram between the two sections in the positive direction of the coordinate axis. Thus the construction of shear and moment diagrams becomes a process of summation starting from an initial point of known shear and moment.

In the previous section, we observed that the shear and moment in a beam can be easily obtained by integrations from Eqs. (3-3) and (3-4), or from Eqs. (3-5) and (3-6), if the loading functions are continuous. For beams with concentrated loads or distributed loads having sudden changes along its length, the loading functions may contain a number of discontinuities or singularities. It is possible to develop a general procedure for the direct integration of such loading functions if a concise notation is adopted for the treatment of the singularity functions.

The basic types of singularity functions that may appear as applied loads on a beam are shown in Fig. 3-11, and the corresponding loading functions are given in Fig. 3-12. The actual loading function on a beam may be obtained from the superposition of these basic cases. Before considering the application of

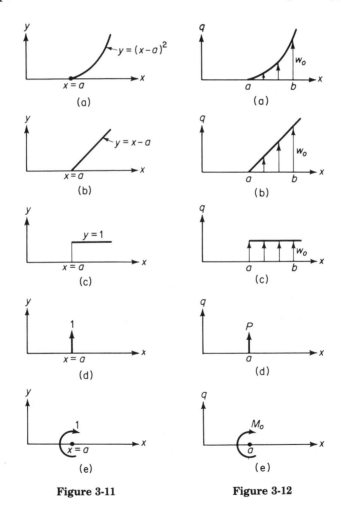

Figure 3-11 **Figure 3-12**

these functions, however, we shall study their properties and their integration relations.

The family of singularity functions in Fig. 3-11 may be defined by a notation

$$y_n = \langle x - a \rangle^n \qquad\qquad (3\text{-}7)$$

in which n is a number associated with a particular function. The bracket notation has different meanings for $n \geq 0$ and for $n < 0$. When $n \geq 0$, it is defined as follows:

$$y_n = 0 \qquad\qquad \text{for } x < a$$

$$y_n = (x - a)^n \qquad \text{for } x \geq a$$

Thus, the functions in Figs. 3-11(a), (b), and (c) may respectively be represented by

$$y_2 = \langle x - a \rangle^2$$

$$y_1 = \langle x - a \rangle^1$$

$$y_0 = \langle x - a \rangle^0$$

The integration of these functions is given by

$$\int_{-\infty}^{x} \langle x - a \rangle^n \, dx = \frac{\langle x - a \rangle^{n+1}}{n + 1}, \qquad n \geq 0 \qquad\qquad (3\text{-}8)$$

When $n < 0$, the bracket notation is defined as

$$y_n = 0 \qquad \text{for } x \neq a$$

$$y_n = 1 \qquad \text{for } x = a$$

in which $y_n = 1$ is a unit concentrated force when $n = -1$ and it refers to a unit couple at $x = a$ when $n = -2$. Thus, the functions in Fig. 3-11(d) and (e) are exceptional cases that may be expressed in the bracket notation as follows:

$$y_{-1} = \langle x - a \rangle^{-1}$$

$$y_{-2} = \langle x - a \rangle^{-2}$$

These two functions are zero everywhere except at $x = a$ where they are finite. Hence, their integrations are obtained as follows:

$$\int_{-\infty}^{x} \langle x - a \rangle^{-2} \, dx = \langle x - a \rangle^{-1} \qquad\qquad (3\text{-}9)$$

$$\int_{-\infty}^{x} \langle x - a \rangle^{-1} \, dx = \langle x - a \rangle^{0} \qquad\qquad (3\text{-}10)$$

If the loading functions are individually represented by the curves shown in Fig. 3-12, the corresponding mathematical expressions are given by

$$q = \frac{w_0}{(b - a)^2} \langle x - a \rangle^2$$

$$q = \frac{w_0}{(b-a)}\langle x - a \rangle^1$$

$$q = w_0 \langle x - a \rangle^0$$

$$q = P_0 \langle x - a \rangle^{-1}$$

$$q = M_0 \langle x - a \rangle^{-2}$$

Note that for the first loading function, which represents a second-degree parabola starting at $x = a$, the function continues beyond $x = b$ to $x = +\infty$. The abscissa b is given only to define the shape of the parabola such that $q = w_0$ at $x = b$. The same is true for the second loading function, which is an inclined line starting at $x = a$ and continues until $x = +\infty$. The third loading function is a horizontal line representing $q = w_0$ from $x = a$ to $x = +\infty$ since $(x - a)^0 = 1$. In order to stop either of these functions at $x = b$, we must subtract the portion of the area under the curve beyond $x = b$. No such complication is encountered in the last two loading functions, which are nonzero only at $x = a$.

As an example, let us consider the beam shown in Fig. 3-8(a). The loading function for the beam may be written according to the bracket notation as follows:

$$q(x) = \frac{w_0}{c}\langle x \rangle^1 - \frac{w_0}{c}\langle x - c \rangle^1 - w_0\langle x - c \rangle^0 + P\langle x - c - d \rangle^{-1}$$

$$+ M_e\langle x - c - d - e \rangle^{-2}$$

The first three terms on the right-hand side of the equation represent the triangular loading acting on the beam. The first term indicates

$$q = 0 \quad \text{for } x < 0; \qquad q = \frac{w_0}{c}x \quad \text{for } x \geq 0$$

The second and third terms represent, respectively, a triangular area and a rectangular area beyond $x = c$ that must be subtracted from the first term in order to stop the triangular loading at point $x = c$. Thus, the second term means

$$q = 0 \quad \text{for } x < c; \qquad q = -\frac{w_0}{c}(x - c) \quad \text{for } x \geq c$$

and the third term indicates that

$$q = 0 \quad \text{for } x < c; \qquad q = -w_0(x - c)^0 = -w_0 \quad \text{for } x \geq c$$

The fourth and fifth terms on the right-hand side of the equation represent the concentrated load P and the couple M_e respectively as follows:

$$q = 0 \quad \text{for } x \neq c + d; \qquad q = P \quad \text{for } x = c + d$$

$$q = 0 \quad \text{for } x \neq c + d + e; \qquad q = M_e \quad \text{for } x = c + d + e$$

For the purpose of obtaining the shear and moment equations in a beam, it is convenient to include the reactions as concentrated forces in the loading function. These reactions can be computed first from the external loads. Thus, the loading function including the reactions R_a and R_b for the beam in Fig. 3-8(a) is given by

$$q(x) = -R_a \langle x \rangle^{-1} + \frac{w_0}{c} \langle x \rangle^1 - \frac{w_0}{c} \langle x - c \rangle^1 - w_0 \langle x - c \rangle^0$$

$$+ P \langle x - c - d \rangle^{-1} + M_e \langle x - c - d - e \rangle^{-2} - R_b \langle x - L \rangle^{-1}$$

in which the reaction terms are negative since the reactions are acting downward. For a beam of finite length, we have the conditions $S = 0$ and $M = 0$ at $x = -\infty$. Then, according to Eqs. (3-7) and (3-8), the shear and moment functions may be obtained by successive integrations as follows:

$$S(x) = \int_{-\infty}^{x} q \, dx = -R_a \langle x \rangle^0 + \frac{w_0}{2c} \langle x \rangle^2 - \frac{w_0}{2c} \langle x - c \rangle^2 - w_0 \langle x - c \rangle^1$$

$$+ P \langle x - c - d \rangle^0 + M_e \langle x - c - d - e \rangle^{-1} - R_b \langle x - L \rangle^0$$

$$M(x) = \int_{-\infty}^{x} S \, dx = -R_a \langle x \rangle^1 + \frac{w_0}{6c} \langle x \rangle^3 - \frac{w_0}{6c} \langle x - c \rangle^3 - \frac{w_0}{2} \langle x - c \rangle^2$$

$$+ P \langle x - c - d \rangle^1 + M_e \langle x - c - d - e \rangle^0 - R_b \langle x - L \rangle^1$$

This method of treating singularity functions makes possible the generalization of the concept of obtaining shears and moments in beams by successive integrations. Thus, the integration formulas represented by Eqs. (3-3) to (3-6) are, theoretically at least, no longer limited to continuous functions only. On the other hand, solutions of problems involving discontinuous functions are rather lengthy in spite of the simplified technique introduced in this section so we shall not elaborate further on its application. For the actual solutions of problems involving irregular loadings, a numerical procedure is suggested in Sections 3-7 and 3-8.

3-5 SHEAR AND MOMENT DIAGRAMS FOR BEAMS

For beams or girders, the variations of shears and moments along the length of a member may be represented graphically by the shear and moment diagrams, respectively, for the member. It is convenient to make these diagrams directly below the loading diagram of the member, using the same horizontal scale in the direction of the member. Shears and moments at the critical points may be computed directly from the equilibrium of the free body, or by the summation process as represented by Eqs. (3-5) and (3-6).

The summation process is rather straightforward and can be used to great advantage. However, each integration means raising the degree of the equation representing the curve by one. For instance, if the loading intensity is uniform, the equation representing such intensity is a horizontal line that can be conceived as involving the zero power of x. The integral for the shear diagram will be an inclined line that is a linear function of x. Similarly, the equation for a uniformly varying load is linear, but the resulting curve in the shear diagram is a second-degree parabola. So long as the elements of areas composing the loading and shear diagrams involve only rectangles, triangles, and second-degree parabolas, the summation process is very effective. For irregular loadings, however, approximations must be made in order to obtain a reasonable answer by the summation process.

Example 3-4. Construct shear and moment diagrams for the beam shown in Fig. 3-13(a).

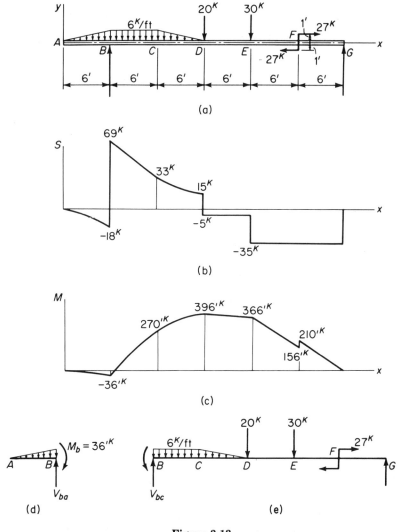

Figure 3-13

The reactions of the beam are obtained from the conditions of equilibrium as follows:

$$\sum M_b = 0, \qquad 30V_g - (27)(2) - (30)(18) - (20)(12) - (\tfrac{1}{2})(6)(6)(8)$$

$$- (6)(6)(3) + (\tfrac{1}{2})(6)(6)(2) = 0$$

or

$$V_g = 35.0 \text{ kips}$$

$$\sum F_y = 0, \qquad V_b + 35 = (\tfrac{1}{2})(6)(6) + (6)(6) + (\tfrac{1}{2})(6)(6) + 20 + 30$$

or

$$V_b = 87.0 \text{ kips}$$

The reactions should always be checked in order to avoid carrying the errors to subsequent steps.

$$\sum M_g = 0, \qquad 30V_b - (\tfrac{1}{2})(6)(6)(32) - (6)(6)(27) - (\tfrac{1}{2})(6)(6)(22) - (20)(18)$$

$$- (30)(12) + (27)(2) = 0$$

or

$$V_b = 87.0 \text{ kips}$$

Shears at various sections of the beam are obtained by the summation of the area of the loading diagram, starting from point A. Where there are vertical forces acting, such as points B, D, and E, sections should be cut just to the left and just to the right of the force since each of these sections may represent critical values of shear. The horizontal forces forming an external couple at point F do not contribute to vertical shears. We shall use a single subscript to denote the function at a point if the function is continuous at that point, and use double subscripts if the function is discontinuous at the point. In the latter case, the second subscript indicates whether we refer to the left or the right of the point in question.

$$S_a = 0 \text{ from the given boundary condition}$$

$$S_{ba} = -(\tfrac{1}{2})(6)(6) = -18 \text{ kips}$$

$$S_{bc} = -18 + 87 = 69 \text{ kips}$$

$$S_c = 69 - (6)(6) = 33 \text{ kips}$$

$$S_{dc} = 33 - (\tfrac{1}{2})(6)(6) = 15 \text{ kips}$$

$$S_{de} = 15 - 20 = -5 \text{ kips}$$

$$S_{ed} = -5 + 0 = -5 \text{ kips}$$

$$S_{eg} = -5 - 30 = -35 \text{ kips}$$

The curves joining the critical points in Fig. 3-13(b) are drawn in accordance with the differential relationship given by Eq. (3-1). Since the loading diagram between

A and B indicates a negative distributed load of varying intensity that increases in magnitude with the positive x-axis, the slope of the shear diagram from A to B is negative and increases in magnitude in the positive direction of the x-axis. Thus the resulting curve is concave downward. From B to C, the loading intensity is uniform and negative, and so is the slope in the shear diagram. From C to D, the loading intensity is negative and decreases in magnitude in the positive x-axis. Thus, the shear diagram between C and D is represented by a curve concave upward. Since there is no vertical load between D and E, or between E or G, each of these intervals is represented by a horizontal line in the shear diagram.

Moments at various sections of the beam are obtained by the summation of the area of the shear diagram, starting again from point A. For the external couple at point F, there is a sudden change in moment from the left to the right of the section. Hence,

$$M_a = 0 \text{ from the given boundary condition}$$

$$M_b = -(\tfrac{1}{3})(6)(18) = -36 \text{ ft-kips}$$

$$M_c = -36 + (6)(33) + (\tfrac{1}{2})(6)(69 - 33) = 270 \text{ ft-kips}$$

$$M_d = 270 + (6)(15) + (\tfrac{1}{3})(6)(33 - 15) = 396 \text{ ft-kips}$$

$$M_e = 396 + (6)(-5) = 366 \text{ ft-kips}$$

$$M_{fe} = 366 + (6)(-35) = 156 \text{ ft-kips}$$

$$M_{fg} = 156 + (27)(2) = 210 \text{ ft-kips}$$

The curves joining the critical points in Fig. 3-13(c) are drawn in accordance with the differential relationship given by Eq. (3-2). It should be pointed out that the curve segments from A to B and from C to D are cubical parabolas, but the curve segment from B to C is a second-degree parabola. Note also that the maximum positive and negative moments occur at points D and B, respectively, where the vertical forces at D and B intersect the x-axis in the shear diagram.

We may digress to point out that the beam in Fig. 3-13(a) can be isolated into free bodies as shown in Figs. 3-13(d) and (e). The moment at B can easily be determined from the free body in Fig. 3-13(d) and can be applied to the free body in Fig. 3-13(e) as a known moment. This does not alter the shear and moment diagrams of the original beam. However, the reaction R_b of the original beam is equal to the sum of V_{ba} and V_{bc} in Figs. 3-13(d) and (e) respectively. The reaction V_{ba} in Fig. 3-13(d) corresponds to the shear S_{ba} just to the left of point B of the original beam and the reaction V_{bc} in Fig. 3-13(e) corresponds to the shear S_{bc} just to the right of point B of the beam. Neither of them is equal to its reaction R_b. This point is important because very often we may wish to simplify a problem as given in Fig. 3-13(a) to equivalent systems as shown in Figs. 3-13(d) and (e). In that case, we should realize that the reaction at point B of the original beam must be obtained from the shears at *both* sides of point B.

Example 3-5. Draw the shear and moment diagrams for the beam shown in Fig. 3-14(a).

The reactions of the beam are first obtained as follows:

$$\sum M_b = 0, \qquad 200 - 100 + 30V_a - (2)(16)(8 + 7 + 7) - (80)(7) = 0$$

(a)

(b)

(d)

(c)

(e)

Figure 3-14

$$V_a = 38.8 \text{ kips}$$

$$\sum F_y = 0, \qquad V_b = (2)(16) + 80 - 38.8 = 73.2 \text{ kips}$$

Thus, the shear and moment diagrams may be plotted as shown in Figs. 3-14(b) and (c), respectively.

However, we may also obtain the shear and moment diagrams by the principle of superposition if the external loads are applied to the beam separately. For example, we can consider first the vertical loads on the beam without the end moments. Then, the reactions become

$$\sum M_b = 0, \qquad 30V_a - (2)(16)(8 + 7 + 7) - (80)(7) = 0$$

$$V_a = 42.1 \text{ kips}$$

$$\sum F_y = 0, \qquad V_b = (2)(16) + 80 - 42.1 = 69.9 \text{ kips}$$

The shear and moment diagrams for the beam due to the vertical loads alone are indicated by the solid lines in Figs. 3-14(d) and (e), respectively. Next we consider only the end moments acting on the beam without the vertical loads. Thus, the reactions are obtained as follows:

$$\sum M_b = 0, \qquad 30V_a + 200 - 100 = 0, \qquad V_a = -3.3 \text{ kips}$$

$$\sum F_y = 0, \qquad V_a + V_b = 0, \qquad V_b = 3.3 \text{ kips}$$

This indicates that a pair of forces, equal and opposite, is acting at the supports to balance the external end moments. The shear and moment diagrams for the beam due to the end moments alone are indicated by the dotted lines in Figs. 3-14(d) and (e), respectively. Note that the shear and moment diagrams resulting from vertical loads are plotted with *positive* ordinates above the horizontal base line whereas those due to end moments are plotted with *negative* ordinates above the horizontal base line. When the diagrams resulting from vertical loads are superimposed on those due to end moments, the overlapping areas will be cancelled and the remaining shaded areas represent the final diagrams due to vertical loads and end moments.

In comparing Figs. 3-14(b) and (c) with Figs. 3-14(d) and (e), it can be seen that the results are identical although the diagrams may appear slightly different because of different base lines for measuring the ordinates. We may also view the case with vertical loads only as a beam with boundary conditions $M_a = 0$ and $M_b = 0$. With the given boundary conditions $M_a = -100$ ft-kips and $M_b = -200$ ft-kips, the shapes of shear and moment curves remain the same but the ordinates of the shear and moment diagrams are different from those of the beam with no end moments. The reason is that the base line of the shear diagram for the beam without end moments is translated upward, and the base line of the moment diagram is both translated upward and rotated in a counterclockwise direction as a result of the end moments. Thus, in the analysis of a beam acted on by end moments as well as vertical loading, the effect of end moments may be superimposed upon that of an identical beam having the same vertical loading but no end moments.

3-6 SHEAR AND MOMENT DIAGRAMS FOR RIGID FRAMES

For rigid frames consisting of straight members, the variations of shears and moments along the length of a member can be treated in the same manner as that for beams. However, the positive directions of the ordinates of the shear and moment diagrams for each member of the frame should be clearly indicated since different sign conventions may be used as explained in Section 3-2.

Example 3-6. Construct shear and moment diagrams for the rigid frame shown in Fig. 3-15(a).

The reactions of the frame are first obtained as follows:

$$\sum M_d = 0, \qquad 20V_a - (5)(8)(16) - (30)(12) + (2)(10)(5) + (10)(10)$$

$$+ (20)(15) + (\tfrac{1}{2})(4)(15)(15) = 0$$

$$V_a = 17.5 \text{ kips}$$

$$\sum F_y = 0, \qquad V_d = (5)(8) + 30 + (2)(10) + 10 - 17.5 = 82.5 \text{ kips}$$

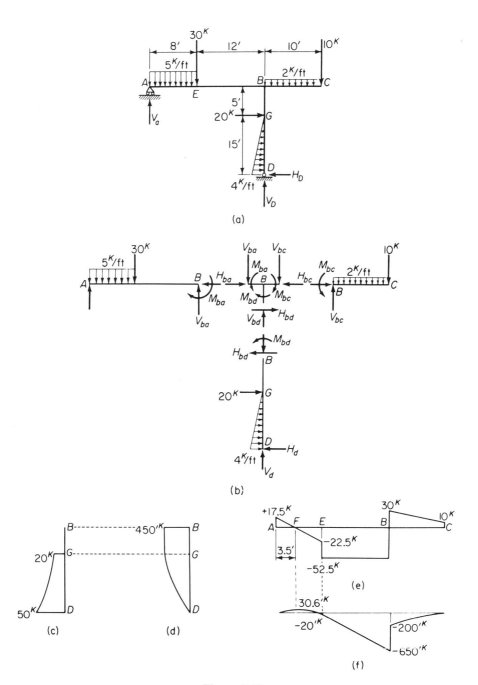

Figure 3-15

$$\sum F_x = 0, \qquad H_d = (\tfrac{1}{2})(4)(15) + 20 = 50 \text{ kips}$$

$$\sum M_a = 0, \qquad (5)(8)(4) + (30)(8) + (2)(10)(25) + (10)(30) - (20)(5)$$

$$- (\tfrac{1}{2})(4)(15)(15) - (82.5)(20) + (50)(20) = 0 \qquad \text{(checked)}$$

In constructing the shear and moment diagrams, we can first isolate all the members meeting at joint B as free bodies as shown in Fig. 3-15(b). The members may be thought of being cut just outside of the joint, and joint B is held in equilibrium by forces and moments equal but opposite to those at the ends of the members. The senses of forces and moments at point B are arbitrarily assumed. If the sense of a force or moment is correct, the result will have the same sign as assumed; otherwise, the result will be of opposite sign. In general, the unknowns at end B of each member may be obtained from the conditions of equilibrium of that member. Their results can be checked by the consideration of equilibrium of joint B. With the assumed senses of forces and moment as shown, we have

$$\sum F_x = 0, \qquad H_{bc} - H_{ba} - H_{bd} = 0$$

$$\sum F_y = 0, \qquad V_{bc} + V_{ba} - V_{bd} = 0$$

$$\sum M_b = 0, \qquad M_{ba} - M_{bd} - M_{bc} = 0$$

Since no external horizontal forces act on members AB and BC, H_{ba} and H_{bc} are obviously zero. In such a case, we can easily consider members AB and BC together.

The shear and moment diagrams for the vertical member DB are shown in Figs. 3-15(c) and (d), respectively. Shears at the critical sections of the vertical member are obtained by the summation of the area in the loading diagram.

$$S_d = 50 \text{ kips from the boundary condition}$$

$$S_{gd} = 50 - (\tfrac{1}{2})(4)(15) = 20 \text{ kips}$$

$$S_{gh} = 20 - 20 = 0$$

Moments at the critical sections of the member are obtained from the summation of the area in the shear diagram.

$$M_d = 0 \text{ from the boundary condition}$$

$$M_g = (15)(20) + (\tfrac{1}{3})(15)(50 - 20) = 450 \text{ ft-kips}$$

$$M_b = 450 + 0 = 450 \text{ ft-kips}$$

The curves joining the critical points in the shear and moment diagrams are plotted according to the differential relationships given by Eqs. (3-1) and (3-2).

The shear and moment diagrams of the horizontal member AC are shown in Figs. 3-15(e) and (f), respectively. Shears at various sections of the girder are determined as follows:

$$S_a = 17.5 \text{ kips from the boundary condition}$$

$$S_{ea} = 17.5 - (5)(8) = -22.5 \text{ kips}$$

$$S_{eb} = -22.5 - 30 = -52.5 \text{ kips}$$

$$S_{bc} = -52.5 + 82.5 = 30 \text{ kips}$$

$$S_{cb} = 30 - (2)(10) = 10 \text{ kips}$$

Point F of zero shear in the shear diagram corresponds to the point of maximum moment in the moment diagram. The distance AF can be obtained from the relation of similar triangles, or $AF = (17.5)(8)/(40) = 3.5$ ft. Then, moments at various sections of the girders can also be obtained from the summation of the area in the shear diagram.

$$M_a = 0 \text{ from the boundary condition}$$

$$M_f = (\tfrac{1}{2})(3.5)(17.5) = 30.6 \text{ ft-kips}$$

$$M_e = 30.6 + (\tfrac{1}{2})(4.5)(-22.5) = -20 \text{ ft-kips}$$

$$M_{be} = -20 + (12)(-52.5) = -650 \text{ ft-kips}$$

$$M_{bc} = -650 + 450 = -200 \text{ ft-kips}$$

It should be pointed out that there is a sudden change in moment along the girder at point B owing to the moment of 450 ft-kips introduced at joint B by the vertical member DB. As shown in Fig. 3-15(b), the algebraic sum of moments from all members meeting at joint B must be zero, i.e.,

$$M_{ba} - M_{bd} - M_{bc} = 650 - 450 - 200 = 0$$

The moment M_{bc} can also be obtained from the consideration of the portion BC of the girder as a free body. Thus,

$$M_{bc} = -(10)(10) - (2)(10)^2/2 = -200 \text{ ft-kips}$$

Example 3-7. Draw shear and moment diagrams for the gable frame with pitched roof as shown in Fig. 3-16(a).

To simplify the solution of the problem, the loads are resolved into vertical and horizontal components. The reactions are obtained as follows:

$$\sum M_a = 0, \qquad (2)(20)^2/2 + (\tfrac{5}{13})(26)(25 + 30) + (\tfrac{12}{13})(26)(12 + 24)$$

$$+ (20)(46) - 56V_e = 0$$

$$V_e = 48.8 \text{ kips}$$

$$\sum F_x = 0, \qquad H_a = (\tfrac{5}{13})(26)(2) + (2)(20) = 60 \text{ kips}$$

$$\sum F_y = 0, \qquad V_a = (\tfrac{12}{13})(26)(2) + 20 - 48.8 = 19.2 \text{ kips}$$

$$\sum M_e = 0, \qquad (19.2)(56) + (2)(20)^2/2 - (\tfrac{12}{13})(26)(44 + 32)$$

$$+ (\tfrac{5}{13})(26)(25 + 30) - (20)(10) = 0 \qquad \text{(checked)}$$

Figure 3-16

From the free-body diagrams of the individual members in Fig. 3-16(b), it can easily be seen that $H_b = 20$ kips, $H_c = 0$, and $H_d = 0$; $V_b = 19.2$ kips, $V_c = 28.8$ kips, and $V_d = 48.8$ kips. Furthermore,

$$M_b = (60)(20) - (40)(10) = 800 \text{ ft-kips}$$

$$M_c = 800 + (19.2)(36) + (20)(15) - (26)(26 + 13) = 778 \text{ ft-kips}$$

$$M_d = 778 - (28.8)(20) - (20)(10) = 0$$

For the vertical members, the steps of computing axial force, shear, and moment in the member are obvious. For the inclined members, however, only the horizontal and vertical components of the axial force and shear are given with the moment at the rigid joints. Thus, the axial force and shear for the free-body diagrams shown in Fig. 3-16(c) must be obtained from the horizontal and vertical components. For the free body on the left-hand side of the figure,

$$N_b = (20)(\tfrac{12}{13}) - (19.2)(\tfrac{5}{13}) = 11.1 \text{ kips}$$

$$S_b = (20)(\tfrac{5}{13}) + (19.2)(\tfrac{12}{13}) = 25.4 \text{ kips}$$

$$N_{cb} = 11.1 \text{ kips}$$

$$S_{cb} = (2)(26) - 25.4 = 26.6 \text{ kips}$$

For the free body on the right-hand side of the figure,

$$N_d = (48.8)(\tfrac{3}{5}) = 29.3 \text{ kips}$$

$$S_d = (48.8)(\tfrac{4}{5}) = 39.1 \text{ kips}$$

$$N_{cd} = 29.3 - (\tfrac{3}{5})(20) = 17.3 \text{ kips}$$

$$S_{cd} = 39.1 - (\tfrac{4}{5})(20) = 23.1 \text{ kips}$$

Finally, the shear and moment diagrams are plotted in Figs. 3-16(d) and (e), respectively.

3-7 GIRDERS SUPPORTING FLOOR BEAMS

In many structures, the external loads are applied to a floor system that in turn transmits these loads to the main member or main system of the structure. As an example, a girder supporting floor beams is shown in Fig. 3-17(a). In gen-

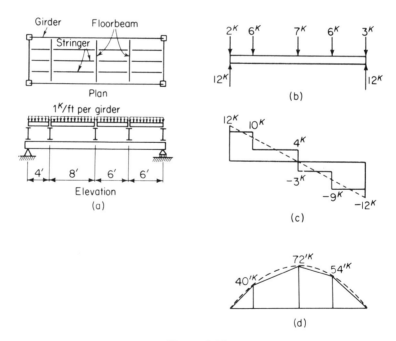

Figure 3-17

eral, the span lengths of the stringers need not be equal and thus the floor beams are irregularly spaced. The locations of the floor beams are called *panel points* whereas the distances between them are considered as the panels of the girder. The load transmission from stringers to floor beams and then to the girder is straightforward since the reactions of the stringers are the applied loads on the girder. Thus, the concentrated loads at the panel points may be computed as shown in Fig. 3-17(b). Obviously, the reactions of the girder remain unchanged whether or not a floor system is used to transmit the applied loads. However, the shears and moments at some locations are affected by the presence of the floor system.

The shear and moment diagrams for the girder in Fig. 3-17(a) are indicated by the solid lines in Figs. 3-17(c) and (d), respectively. If the uniformly distributed loads are applied directly to an identical girder without a floor system, the resulting shear and moment diagrams would be as shown by the dotted lines in the corresponding figures. Note that the shear at each panel point of the girder between floor beams is constant and is called the *panel shear*. Thus, the shear at a point just to the left of a panel point is different from that just to the right of the same panel point. Note also that the moments at the panel points of the girder are not influenced by the use of a floor system.

Example 3-8. Draw the shear and moment diagrams for the girder shown in Fig. 3-18(a).

This same girder, without floor beams but under the same loading, has been treated in Example 3-4, and the reactions of the girder in this case are identical to those given in that example. The shear and moment diagrams in Example 3-4 are indicated by dotted lines on the corresponding diagrams of this problem for the purpose of comparison.

Since only stringers *AB*, *BC*, and *CD* are subjected to applied loads, the loading, shear, and moment diagrams for these individual stringers are shown in Figs. 3-18(b), (c), and (d), respectively. Thus, the final loads acting on the girder may be represented by Fig. 3-18(e). The pairs of vertical loads at points *B*, *C*, and *D* could have been combined, but they are shown separately so that their effects can be more readily seen in the shear diagram of the girder. The distance between the two forces in each pair is considered to be infinitesimal or zero. The shear and moment diagrams of the girder are represented by the solid lines in Figs. 3-18(f) and (g), respectively. It can be seen that the dotted lines in Fig. 3-18(f) may be obtained by superimposing the individual shear diagrams in Fig. 3-18(c) onto the solid lines representing the shear diagram of the girder, and the dotted lines in Fig. 3-18(g) may be obtained by superimposing the individual moment diagrams in Fig. 3-18(d) onto the solid lines representing the moment diagram of the girder. Hence, the shears and moments along a girder subjected to applied loads directly may be obtained by superposition of the corresponding shears and moments in a similar girder supporting floor beams and the shears and moments in the individual stringers between floor beams. Such conclusions lead to some very useful applications in determining shears and moments in beams subjected to irregular loading.

Figure 3-18

Forces and Moments in Beams and Frames   Chap. 3

In engineering applications, beams may be subjected to rather irregular loading patterns. Usually such irregular loading patterns can be approximated by some simple mathematical curves without introducing significant errors. For instance, an airplane subjected to lift pressure is shown in Fig. 3-19. Each wing can be considered as a cantilever beam subjected to a loading intensity along its length as shown in Fig. 3-20(a). Since the width of the wing varies, the loading intensity q per unit length of the beam is obtained from the product of the wing width b and the lift pressure p, which is expressed in force per unit area.

Figure 3-19

Figure 3-20

Imagine that stringers and floor beams are introduced for transmitting the distributed load to the cantilever beam. Then, the distributed load along the length of the beam can be replaced by equivalent concentrated loads at the locations of the imaginary floor beams. For the sake of simplicity, the floor beams may be equally spaced, and the fictitious panel length depends only on the accuracy desired for the resulting shears and moment in the beam. For instance, the cantilever beam in Fig. 3-20(b) is divided into six equal panels, which may be considered as six imaginary stringers. The concentrated loads shown in the figure are equal in magnitude to the corresponding reactions of the imaginary stringers. The shear and moment diagrams for the given irregular loading intensity are shown dotted in Figs. 3-20(c) and (d) respectively; those for the equivalent concentrated loads are indicated by the solid lines in the corresponding diagrams.

If the shears and moments for the individual imaginary stringers can be computed, they can be superimposed on the corresponding quantities obtained from the equivalent concentrated loads to obtain the true shears and moments in the cantilever beam due to the original loading. For design purposes, however, only the shears and moments at a finite number of points on the beams are usually desired. Thus, those points on the beam may be designated as the fictitious panel points. As the number of panels increases, greater accuracy may be obtained for the approximation of the loading curve.

The loading curve may be approximated by segments of straight lines, second-degree curves, or higher-degree curves. Two points are required to define a straight line, three points for a second-degree curve, and one more point for each increase in the degree of a curve. It has been found that straight line segments or second-degree curves are sufficiently accurate for practical purposes, and further refinements by higher-degree curves are not necessary.

Consider first the case of approximation by straight line segments. Let h be the length of the equal panels selected for the purpose of computing equivalent concentrated loads. If the loading intensity q is distributed along the length of the x-axis as shown in Fig. 3-21(a), the panel at each panel point is influenced by the loading on the panels immediately adjacent to the panel point only if a straight line approximation is used. Thus, for the end point A, we need to consider only panel AB, whereas for the interior panel B, we will consider

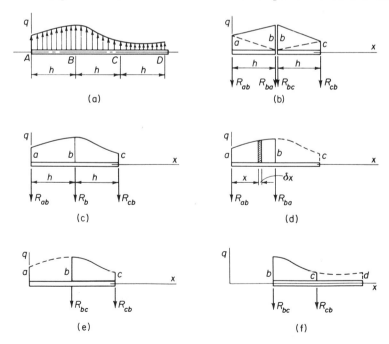

Figure 3-21

Forces and Moments in Beams and Frames   Chap. 3

both panels AB and BC as shown in Fig. 3-21(b). If the ordinates of the loading at points A, B, and C are denoted by a, b, and c respectively, the reactions of the imaginary stringers may be obtained from the trapezoidal areas in the loading diagram. Thus, from Fig. 3-21(b),

$$R_{ab} = \frac{1}{3}ah + \frac{1}{6}bh = \frac{h}{6}(2a + b) \qquad (3\text{-}11a)$$

$$R_{ba} = \frac{1}{6}ah + \frac{1}{3}bh = \frac{h}{6}(a + 2b) \qquad (3\text{-}11b)$$

Similarly,

$$R_{bc} = \frac{h}{6}(c + 2b)$$

$$R_{cb} = \frac{h}{6}(b + 2c)$$

The equivalent concentrated load at a typical interior point is equal in magnitude to the sum of the reactions from both sides of that point. Thus, for point B,

$$R_b = R_{ba} + R_{bc} = \frac{h}{6}(a + 4b + c) \qquad (3\text{-}11c)$$

If the loading curve in Fig. 3-21(a) is approximated by a second-degree curve, three ordinates are necessary to define such a curve. For the interior point B, it is logical to select the ordinates a, b, and c. Thus, the loading curve between A and C will be considered. For the end point A, however, the best we can do is to choose ordinates a, b, and c. If a, b, and c are known, we can obtain a second-degree curve to pass through these points as follows:

$$q = \frac{a}{2h^2}(x - h)(x - 2h) - \frac{b}{h^2}x(x - 2h) + \frac{c}{2h^2}x(x - h)$$

It can be readily verified that this second-degree function satisfies the requirement that $q = a$, b, and c at $x = 0$, h, and $2h$ respectively. From the conditions of equilibrium of panel AB shown in Fig. 3-21(d), the following equations are obtained:

$$\sum F_y = 0, \qquad R_{ab} + R_{ba} = \int_0^h q\, dx$$

$$\sum M_a = 0, \qquad R_{ba}h = \int_0^h qx\, dx$$

Solving these two equations simultaneously, one obtains

$$R_{ab} = \frac{h}{24}(7a + 6b - c) \qquad (3\text{-}12a)$$

$$R_{ba} = \frac{h}{24}(3a + 10b - c) \qquad (3\text{-}12b)$$

Similarly, for panel BC in Fig. 3-21(e), the following relations may be derived:

$$R_{bc} = \frac{h}{24}(3c + 10b - a)$$

$$R_{cb} = \frac{h}{24}(7c + 6b - a)$$

Thus, the equivalent concentrated load at a typical interior point is equal in magnitude to the sum of the reactions from both sides of that point. For point B,

$$R_b = R_{ba} + R_{bc} = \frac{h}{12}(a + 10b + c) \qquad (3\text{-}12\text{c})$$

It should be pointed out that the reactions for panel BC may also be obtained from the ordinates b, c, and d shown in Fig. 3-21(d) as follows:

$$R_{bc} = \frac{h}{24}(7b + 10c - d)$$

$$R_{cd} = \frac{h}{24}(3b + 10c - d)$$

However, these values are not used in computing R_b because we have selected ordinates a, b, and c for approximating the panel load at point B. On the other hand, these values are needed in the computation of the panel load at point C. If D is the terminal point, the panel load at D is equal to

$$R_{dc} = \frac{h}{24}(7d + 10c - b) \qquad (3\text{-}12\text{d})$$

Note that in Eqs. (3-12), the ordinate at a panel point has the greatest influence on the panel load at that point. For the panel load at A, for instance, the ordinate a has the largest coefficient and the ordinate c has only a minor influence in Eq. (3-12a). For the panel load at B, the influence of ordinate b in Eq. (3-12c) is obvious.

Example 3-9. Figure 3-22 shows a cantilever beam subject to a distributed loading that can be approximated by straight line segments. Determine the equivalent concentrated loads at the panel points.

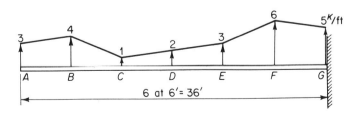

Figure 3-22

Forces and Moments in Beams and Frames   Chap. 3

Since the beam is divided into six equal panels, the equivalent concentrated loads may be computed by either Eqs. (3-11a) and (3-11b) for separate reactions from stringers to the left and to the right of a panel point or Eq. (3-11c) for the combined reactions from the stringers on both sides of the panel point. Thus,

$$R_{ab} = \tfrac{6}{6}[(2)(3) + 4] = 10; \qquad R_{ba} = \tfrac{6}{6}[(2)(4) + 3] = 11$$

$$R_{bc} = \tfrac{6}{6}[(2)(4) + 1] = 9; \qquad R_{cb} = \tfrac{6}{6}[(2)(1) + 4] = 6$$

$$R_{cd} = \tfrac{6}{6}[(2)(1) + 2] = 4; \qquad R_{dc} = \tfrac{6}{6}[(2)(2) + 1] = 5$$

$$R_{de} = \tfrac{6}{6}[(2)(2) + 3] = 7; \qquad R_{ed} = \tfrac{6}{6}[(2)(3) + 2] = 8$$

$$R_{ef} = \tfrac{6}{6}[(2)(3) + 6] = 12; \qquad R_{fe} = \tfrac{6}{6}[(2)(6) + 3] = 15$$

$$R_{fg} = \tfrac{6}{6}[(2)(6) + 5] = 17; \qquad R_{gf} = \tfrac{6}{6}[(2)(5) + 6] = 16$$

or

$$R_a = R_{ab} = 10$$

$$R_b = R_{ba} + R_{bc} = 20$$

$$R_c = R_{cb} + R_{cd} = 10$$

$$R_d = R_{dc} + R_{de} = 12$$

$$R_e = R_{ed} + R_{ef} = 20$$

$$R_f = R_{fe} + R_{fg} = 32$$

$$R_g = R_{gf} = 16$$

Example 3-10.   Figure 3-23 shows a simply supported beam subjected to a distributed loading that can be approximated by a second-degree curve. Compute the equivalent concentrated loads at the panel points.

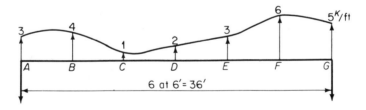

Figure 3-23

The beam is divided into six equal panels and the equivalent concentrated loads at the panel points may be computed by Eq. (3-12) as follows:

$$R_a = \tfrac{6}{24}[(7)(3) + (6)(4) - 1] = 11$$

$$R_b = \tfrac{6}{12}[3 + (10)(4) + 1] = 22$$

$$R_c = \tfrac{6}{12}[4 + (10)(1) + 2] = 8$$

$$R_d = \tfrac{6}{12}[1 + (10)(2) + 3] = 12$$

$$R_e = \tfrac{6}{12}[2 + (10)(3) + 6] = 19$$

$$R_f = \tfrac{6}{12}[3 + (10)(6) + 5] = 34$$
$$R_g = \tfrac{6}{24}[(7)(5) + (6)(6) - 3] = 17$$

3-9 NUMERICAL PROCEDURE FOR COMPUTING
SHEARS AND MOMENTS

After the equivalent concentrated loads are computed, a numerical procedure may be used for rapid and systematic calculation of shears and moments in a beam. Essentially, the procedure is based on the summation process explained in Section 3-3 and represented by Eqs. (3-5) and (3-6). In applying the process to a beam subjected to concentrated loads only, the procedure is greatly simplified since the area in the loading diagram is zero and the area in the shear diagram consists of rectangular elements that may be considered as products of the shear in a panel and the panel length. Thus, the procedure is reduced to computing the shears from one end of the beam to the other by adding or subtracting the successive shears multiplied by the panel length over which the shear acts. By considering upward loads as positive, the successive calculation of shears and moments can be carried out by adding, respectively, loads and shears from left to right, starting from a point of known shear and moment.

For example, the free end of the cantilever beam in Fig. 3-20(b) is a point of zero shear and zero moment. If the equivalent concentrated loads in the figure are known, the ordinates of the shear diagram can be obtained by adding the series of concentrated loads from left to right as indicated by the solid lines in Fig. 3-20(c). It may be noted that the *actual shear* due to the original loading varies within a panel, whereas the *panel shear* due to the equivalent concentrated loads remains constant within a panel. The true shears at the panel points may be obtained easily if the equivalent concentrated loads to the right and to the left of a panel point are computed separately. In most cases, however, the average shears are accurate enough for design purposes, particularly if the number of panels is large. The ordinates of moment diagram in Fig. 3-20(d) are obtained by the summation from left to right of the area in the shear diagram. The moments at the panel points are identical to the actual moments at the corresponding points due to the original loading.

When only the moments at two points are known, such as zero moment at the two supports of a simply supported beam, the summation process must be modified. Either the shear at one of the two points of known moments is first computed by statics, or the shear at that point may be assumed to have an arbitrary value that will be subsequently corrected. The latter approach is based on Eqs. (3-3) and (3-4) as well as Eqs. (3-5) and (3-6), and involves a translational correction for shears and a rotational correction for moments.

The numerical procedure for computing shears and moments may be summarized as follows:*

---

*See N. M. Newmark, "Numerical Procedure for Computing Deflections, Moments, and Buckling Loads," *Trans. ASCE*, 108 (1943), p. 1161.

1. Compute the equivalent concentrated loads by making a proper approximation of the loading curve, using either straight line segments or a second-degree curve. If the actual shears at the panel points are required, separate reactions from stringers to the left and to the right of a panel point should be computed. If only the panel shears are needed, equivalent concentrated loads representing combined reactions from stringers at the panel points are sufficient.

2. Starting from a point of known shear and moment, add the equivalent concentrated loads from left to right, or substract the loads from right to left, to obtain shears. Similarly, add the products or shear and the panel length from left to right, or subtract the same products from right to left, to obtain moments.

3. The procedure can be simplified by postponing the multiplication of the shears by the panel length until the end of the computations. As a matter of fact, common factors of multiplication involved in all steps may be left out until the end of the computations.

4. When only the moments at two points are known, the shear at one of these two points can be arbitrarily assumed, and the same procedure may still be used. If the resulting moment at the second point is different from the known moment at that point, the correction for moment may be made by a linear moment diagram which corresponds to a constant shear correction. Thus, the final moments may be obtained from the sum of the linear moment correction and the corresponding trial moments based on arbitrarily assumed shear at a point, and the final shears may be obtained from the constant shear correction and the corresponding trial shears.

The above procedure can be conveniently carried out in a tabulated form using the following notations: q for the intensity of distributed load at a panel point, Q for the equivalent concentrated load at a panel point, S for the panel shear, and M for the moment at a panel point. If the actual shear at a panel point is needed, it will be denoted by $\bar{S}$. For solutions involving trial shears and moments, S' is used for the trial shear in a panel, M' for the trial moment at a panel point, S'' for the shear correction, and M'' for the moment correction.

Example 3-11. For the cantilever beam subjected to a distributed loading shown in Fig. 3-24(a), compute the shears and moments at the panel points.

The equivalent concentrated loads for this beam have already been computed in Example 3-9. The computation of shears and moments can be carried out in the figure. The first line in the table is the given distributed loading. The second line represents the equivalent concentrated loads to the left and to the right of the panel points. The third line shows the average shears in the panels, which are obtained by starting with zero shear to the left of point A and by adding the equivalent concentrated loads successively from left to right. Thus,

$$S_{ab} = 0 + 10 = 10$$

$$S_{bc} = 10 + 11 + 9 = 30, \text{ etc.}$$

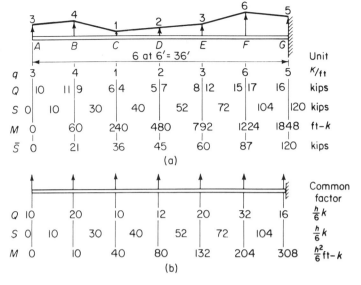

Figure 3-24

The fourth line indicates the moments at the panel points by starting with zero moment at point A and by adding the product of the shears and the panel length successively from left to right. Or,

$$M_b = 0 + (10)(6) = 60$$

$$M_c = 60 + (30)(6) = 240, \text{ etc.}$$

The last line in the figure gives the actual shears at the panel points, which are obtained in the same manner as the panel shears except that only the equivalent concentrated load to the left of a panel point under consideration is included in the summation. For instance,

$$\overline{S}_b = 10 + 11 = 21$$

$$\overline{S}_c = 21 + 9 + 6 = 36, \text{ etc.}$$

The units of the computed quantities are shown at the right-hand column of the figure.

The procedure can be simplified as shown in Fig. 3-24(b). In general, the computation of equivalent concentrated loads may involve fractions if h is not divisible by 6. It is therefore advisable to leave out the factor $h/6$ in the computation of the equivalent concentrated loads and to consider it as a common factor in the right-hand column of the figure. For this particular problem, this factor is reduced to $h/6 = \frac{6}{6} = 1$. In the computation of moments, another common factor h may be taken out as indicated by the term $h^2/6$ in the right-hand column.

Example 3-12. For the simply supported beam subjected to a distributed loading shown in Fig. 3-25(a), compute the panel shears and the moments at panel points.

The equivalent concentrated loads for this beam have been computed in Example 3-10. The computation of shears and moments can be carried out in the figure after the reaction at A is obtained. Thus, for $R_a = 52.7$ kips, a shear of 52.7

Figure 3-25

is shown to the left of point A. If we carry through the computation as shown, the resulting moment at point G should be zero. The computed value of 0.2 for the moment at point G is due to the rounding off of the decimal points, and it serves the purpose of showing how errors can be accumulated in such a procedure. Figure 3-25(b) shows the solution of the same problem by assuming arbitrarily a zero shear at the left of point A. Since the resulting moment at point G is $-316h$, a linear moment correction corresponding to the rotation of the base line in the moment diagram is applied so that the moment at point G will be zero. Then the correction for other panel points may be obtained by a simply ratio as follows:

$$M'' \text{ for point } G = +316h$$

$$M'' \text{ for point } F = (\tfrac{5}{6})(316h) = 263.3h$$

$$M'' \text{ for point } E = (\tfrac{4}{6})(316h) = 210.7h, \text{ etc.}$$

The shear correction is constant throughout corresponding to the translation of the base line in the shear diagram and is equal to the moment correction at point G divided by the span length of the beam, or

$$S'' = \frac{316h}{6h} = 52.7$$

The final panel shears and the final moments at panel points may be obtained by superposition as follows:

$$S = S' + S''$$

$$M = M' + M''$$

If M'' at G is a negative quantity instead of a positive quantity, the negative sign should be included in the summations for final shears and moments.

It should be pointed out that the arbitrarily assumed shear at point A can be any value, including zero. As a matter of fact, if a value of +50 is used, the resulting moment at point G will be much smaller and the moment correction will be smaller. From a practical point of view, the latter assumed value leads to less numerical work. Hence, it is advisable to assume an arbitrary value for shear approximately equal to the magnitude of the reaction at that point if it can be estimated intelligently.

Example 3-13. For the beam with a distributed loading shown in Fig. 3-26(a), compute the shears in the panels and the moments at the panel points.

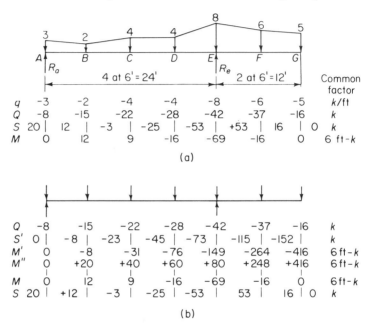

Figure 3-26

The equivalent concentrated loads at the panel points may be obtained from Eqs. (3-11), and are indicated in the second line in the figure. The reactions are found to be $R_a = 20$ kips and $R_e = 148$ kips. Then, the shears and moments may be computed as shown in the figure. It is only necessary to point out that at point E there is an upward force of 148 as well as a downward force of 42. Thus, the shear in panel EF is obtained from the shear in panel DE as follows:

$$S_{ef} = -53 - 42 + 148 = 53$$

The rest of the computation is rather routine and needs no further explanation.

However, if the reactions are not found, and the shears and moments are obtained by assuming arbitrarily a shear at the boundary, we must be very careful in making the corrections. This approach is shown in Fig. 3-26(b). Note that the shear to the left of point A is first assumed to be zero and that the reaction at point E is assumed to be zero in the computation of the shear in panel EF in the second line of the figure. These assumptions lead to the moments in the third line, which must be corrected according to the requirements that the moment at point G be zero and the moment at point E be equal to that caused by the loads in the cantilever end of the beam. Before going into the fourth line in the figure, we try to compute this moment at E. Starting from the right end of the sixth line, we make use of the known condition that the shear to the right of point G is zero and subtract the equivalent concentrated loads successively to obtain the shear in panels FG and EF. Thus,

$$S_{fg} = 0 - (-16) = 16$$

$$S_{ef} = 16 - (-37) = 53$$

Similarly, starting from the right end of the fifth line, we know that the moment at point G is zero and can therefore compute the moments at panel points F and E as follows:

$$M_f = (0 - 16)h = -16h$$

$$M_e = (-16 - 53)h = -69h$$

Note that $h = 6$ is the common factor taken out of the computation in the figure. In order to make $M_e = -69$ and $M_g = 0$, we must apply corrections $M_e'' = 80$ and $M_g'' = 416$ as shown in the fourth line in the figure. The moment corrections at other points of the beam are obtained by observing the linear relationships from point A to point E and from point E to point G. Thus, by neglecting the common factor h, we have

$$M_b'' = \frac{80}{4} = 20$$

$$M_c'' = \frac{80}{2} = 40$$

$$M_d'' = (80)(\tfrac{3}{4}) = 60$$

$$M_f'' = 80 + (416 - 80)/2 = 248$$

3-10 SIMPLE STRUCTURES IN SPACE

When a plane rigid frame or curved member is subjected to loads that do not lie in the plane of the structure, there are in general six stress resultants at a section normal to the axis of a member. Such a structure constitutes a system in space even if the structure itself lies in a plane. Although most structures in space are statically indeterminate, we shall discuss a few simple cases that can be solved by statics alone.

Consider, for example, the cantilever beam in Fig. 3-27(a), which is

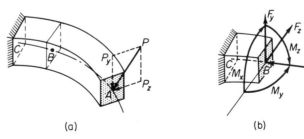

(a)   (b)

Figure 3-27

curved in the horizontal plane and is subjected to an inclined load P lying in a plane normal to the curved axis at point A. If a section is passed through any point B along the axis of the curve, the six stress resultants acting on the section are represented by internal forces F_x, F_y, and F_z, and internal moments M_x, M_y, and M_z, as shown in Fig. 3-27(b). Let the positive directions of the stress resultants be indicated by the positive directions of a right-handed coordinate system as shown when the section at B is viewed from A. These stress resultants are identified as follows:

F_x = axial force normal to the plane of the section

F_y = shear force in the vertical direction

F_z = shear force in the horizontal direction

M_x = torque about x-axis

M_y = bending moment in the horizontal plane about y-axis

M_z = bending moment in the vertical plane about z-axis

Since six equations of equilibrium can be established for a free body in space, the six stress resultants at a section can be determined from the conditions of equilibrium.

If the inclined load P is resolved into vertical and horizontal components P_y and P_z at point A, the component P_z lies in the plane of the structure and causes F_x, F_z, and M_y at a section while the component P_y is acting normal to the plane of the structure and produces F_y, M_x and M_z. Since the former case has been dealt with in the discussion of rigid frames, we shall consider only the latter case here. The total effect of the inclined load P on the girder may be obtained from the superposition of the separate effects of each component.

A curved member subjected to loads normal to the plane of the curved axis is commonly known as a *bow girder*. In general, the axis of the girder may be a smooth curve or a broken line with straight or curved segments. In order to obtain the stress resultants at any section along the member, however, the axis of the member must be described by a consistent coordinate system. Figure 3-28(a) shows the plan view of a bow girder with loads acting normal to the plane. Let s be defined as the distance along the axis of the member, starting

(a)   (b)

Figure 3-28

from the free end. Such a coordinate system is convenient and useful only if the member consists of straight segments. On the other hand, polar coordinates (r, θ) may be used to describe a curve. Even in the latter case, the complexity of the solution depends on the shape of the curve and the loading. When an infinitesimal element $\delta s = r\, \delta\theta$ is isolated from the member in Fig. 3-28(a), the equilibrium of the element is maintained by the stress resultants shown in Fig. 3-28(b), in which w is the intensity of the external load acting on the element. The positive directions for the stress resultants on each face of the element are given in the figure. Thus, the differential relationship of the stress resultants may also be established.

Example 3-14. Write a set of general expressions for the vertical shear F_y, torque M_x, and bending moment M_z at a section of a cantilever bow girder whose axis is shown by the plan view in Fig. 3-29(a). A downward load P is applied at point A of the girder.

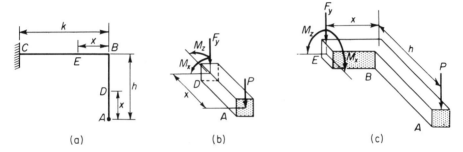

(a)   (b)   (c)

Figure 3-29

Since the axis of the girder consists of two straight segments AB and BC, we can consider the two segments separately. For a general point D in segment AB, part AD is isolated as a free body as shown in Fig. 3-29(b). Thus,

$$\sum F_y = 0, \qquad F_y = -P$$

$$\sum (M_x)_d = 0, \qquad M_x = 0$$

$$\sum (M_z)_d = 0, \qquad M_z = Px$$

Similarly, for a general point E in segment BC, part ABE is isolated as shown in Fig. 3-29(c). Then,

$$\sum F_y = 0, \qquad F_y = -P$$

$$\sum (M_x)_e = 0, \qquad M_x = -Ph$$

$$\sum (M_z)_e = 0, \qquad M_z = Px$$

Example 3-15. For the bow girder in Example 3-14, write a set of general expressions for the vertical shear F_y, torque M_x, and bending moments M_z if a downward uniformly distributed load w is applied on the full length of segment AB instead of a concentrated load P applied at point A.

For a general point D in segment AB, we have

$$\sum F_y = 0, \qquad F_y = wx$$

$$\sum (M_x)_d = 0, \qquad M_x = 0$$

$$\sum (M_z)_d = 0, \qquad M_z = wx^2/2$$

For a general point E in segment BC, we get

$$\sum F_y = 0, \qquad F_y = wh$$

$$\sum (M_x)_e = 0, \qquad M_x = -wh^2/2$$

$$\sum (M_z)_e = 0, \qquad M_z = whx$$

3-11 CIRCULAR BOW GIRDERS

When the axis of a bow girder is described by a circular arc, the problem can easily be solved by using the polar coordinates. Consider, for instance, the cantilever bow girder whose axis is shown in the plan view in Fig. 3-30(a). The axis of the girder is a circular arc of radius r, and the angle subtended between the free and fixed ends of the girder is θ_1. A point C on the curve may be located by the angle θ measured from the free end A to point C. If a downward concentrated load P is applied at point A, the stress resultants at a section passing through point C are as shown in Fig. 3-30(b). Since the distances AD and CD in Fig. 3-30(a) are given by the geometrical relations

$$AD = r \sin \theta$$
$$CD = r(1 - \cos \theta)$$

the stress resultants at section C are obtained from the conditions of equilibrium as follows:

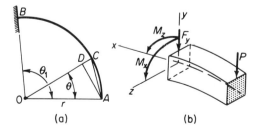

(a)   (b)   **Figure 3-30**

$$\sum F_y = 0, \qquad F_y = -P$$

$$\sum (M_x)_c = 0, \qquad M_x = -Pr(1 - \cos \theta)$$

$$\sum (M_z)_c = 0, \qquad M_z = Pr \sin \theta$$

Thus, the components of reaction at the fixed support B may be computed by letting $\theta = \theta_1$ in the above equations.

If the cantilever bow girder is loaded with a downward uniformly distributed load w along the entire arc length, the same approach may be used. Consider, for example, an infinitesimal element subtended by the central angle $\delta\alpha$ as shown in Fig. 3-31. Since the length of the arc $\delta s = r\delta\alpha$, the load acting on the element is $wr\, \delta\alpha$. Thus, the stress resultants at point C due to the downward load acting on the infinitesimal element at point E are

$$\delta F_y = -wr\, \delta\alpha$$

$$\delta M_x = -(wr\, \delta\alpha)r[1 - \cos (\theta - \alpha)] = -wr^2[1 - \cos (\theta - \alpha)]\delta\alpha$$

$$\delta M_z = (wr\, \delta\alpha)[r \sin (\theta - \alpha)] = wr^2 \sin (\theta - \alpha)\delta\alpha$$

Figure 3-31

Then, the stress resultants at point C due to the uniform load from point A to point C may be obtained by integration as follows:

$$F_y = \int_0^\theta wr\, d\alpha = -wr\alpha \Big|_0^\theta = -wr\theta \tag{3-13a}$$

$$M_x = -\int_0^\theta wr^2\left[1 - \cos (\theta - \alpha)\right] d\alpha$$

$$= -wr^2\left[\alpha + \sin (\theta - \alpha)\right]_0^\theta = -wr^2(\theta - \sin \theta) \tag{3-13b}$$

$$M_z = \int_0^\theta wr^2 \sin (\theta - \alpha)d\alpha = wr^2 \cos (\theta - \alpha)\Big|_0^\theta$$

$$= wr^2(1 - \cos \theta) \tag{3-13c}$$

A bow girder may also be simply supported at three points, as shown in Fig. 3-32(a). The uniformly distributed load w is acting downward while the vertical reactions V_0, V_1, and V_2 are assumed to act upward. For a section at any point A between supports 0 and 1, the angle θ is measured from the reference

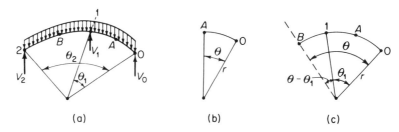

(a)   (b)   (c)

Figure 3-32

point 0 to point A as shown in the plan view in Fig. 3-32(b). Then, the stress resultants at A due to downward load w and upward reaction V_0 are as follows:

$$F_y = V_0 - wr\theta$$

$$M_x = V_0 r(1 - \cos\theta) - wr^2(\theta - \sin\theta)$$

$$M_z = -V_0 r \sin\theta + wr^2(1 - \cos\theta)$$

Similarly, for a section at any point B between supports 1 and 2, the angle θ is measured from the reference point 0 to point B as shown in the plan view in Fig. 3-32(c). Thus, the stress resultants at B due to the downward load w and the upward reactions V_0 and V_1 are

$$F_y = V_0 + V_1 - wr\theta$$

$$M_x = V_0 r(1 - \cos\theta) + V_1 r[1 - \cos(\theta - \theta_1)] - wr^2(\theta - \sin\theta)$$

$$M_z = -V_0 r \sin\theta - V_1 r \sin(\theta - \theta_1) + wr^2(1 - \cos\theta)$$

By considering the entire structure as a free body, we obtain

$$\sum F_y = 0, \qquad V_0 + V_1 + V_2 - wr\theta_2 = 0 \tag{3-14a}$$

$$\sum (M_x)_2 = 0, \qquad V_0 r(1 - \cos\theta_2) + V_1 r[1 - \cos(\theta_2 - \theta_1)]$$

$$- wr^2(\theta_2 - \sin\theta_2) = 0 \tag{3-14b}$$

$$\sum (M_z)_2 = 0, \qquad -V_0 r \sin\theta_2 - V_1 r \sin(\theta_2 - \theta_1)$$

$$+ wr^2(1 - \cos\theta_2) = 0 \tag{3-14c}$$

The last two equations may be simplified by dividing through each of them by a factor r. Hence, the vertical reactions can be computed from these equations of equilibrium.

Example 3-16. Compute the vertical reactions for the circular bow girder shown in Fig. 3-33(a) with a plan view shown in Fig. 3-33(b).

In this problem, $w = 10$ kips/ft, $r = 10$ ft, $\theta_1 = 45° = 0.7854$ radian, and $\theta_2 = 90° = 1.5708$ radians. Then, from Eqs. (3-14), we have

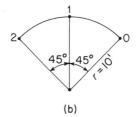

(a)   (b)

Figure 3-33

$$V_0 + V_1 + V_2 - (10)(10)(1.5708) = 0$$

$$V_0(1 - 0) + V_1(1 - 0.7071) - (10)(10)(1.5708 - 1) = 0$$

$$-V_0(1) - V_1(0.7071) + (10)(10)(1 - 0) = 0$$

or

$$1.0000V_0 + 1.0000V_1 + 1.0000V_2 = 157.08$$

$$1.0000V_0 + 0.2929V_1 = 57.08$$

$$1.0000V_0 = 0.7071V_1 = 100.00$$

The solution of these simultaneous equations gives

$$V_0 = V_2 = 26.73 \text{ kips}, \qquad V_1 = 103.62 \text{ kips}$$

PROBLEMS

3-1. Derive the differential relationships of load, shear, and moment in a beam using each of the sign conventions shown in Fig. P3-1.

(a)   (b)

Figure P3-1   **Figure P3-2**

3-2. Determine the axial force, shear, and moment at a section just to the right point D and those at a section just to the right of point E of the structure shown in Fig. P3-2.

3-3. Write a set of general expressions for the axial force, shear, and moment for a section between supports B and C in Fig. P3-3. Use support B as the point of reference for the coordinate in locating a point between B and C.

Figure P3-3

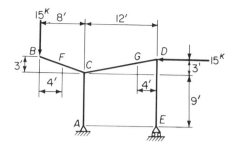

Figure P3-4

3-4. Compute the axial force, shear, and moment at points F and G in the rigid frame shown in Fig. P3-4.

3-5 to **3-18.** Draw the shear and moment diagrams for each member in each of the structures shown in Figs. P3-5 to P3-18.

Figure P3-5

Figure P3-6

Figure P3-7

Figure P3-8

Figure P3-9

Figure P3-10

Forces and Moments in Beams and Frames   Chap. 3

Figure P3-11

Figure P3-12

Figure P3-13

Figure P3-14

Figure P3-15

Figure P3-16

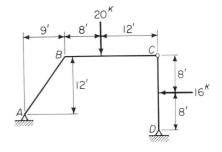

Figure P3-17

Figure P3-18

3-19 to **3-26**. Compute the panel shears and the moments at the panel points for each of the beams shown in Figs. P3-19 to P3-26.

Figure P3-19   **Figure P3-20**

Figure P3-21   **Figure P3-22**

Figure P3-23

Figure P3-24

Figure P3-25

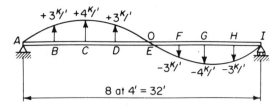

+3^{K}/' +4^{K}/' +3^{K}/'

A   B   C   D   E   O   F   G   H   I

−3^{K}/' −4^{K}/' −3^{K}/'

8 at 4' = 32'

Figure P3-26

3-27. Compute the vertical shear, torque, and bending moment at the fixed support C of the cantilever bow girder whose axis in a horizontal plane is shown in Fig. P3-27. A downward vertical load of 20 kips is applied at the free end A and a downward uniformly distributed load of 1 kip/ft is applied along the length AB of the girder.

Figure P3-27   **Figure P3-28**

3-28. Compute the vertical shear, torque, and bending moment at the fixed support C of the cantilever circular bow girder whose axis in a horizontal plane is shown in Fig. P3-28. A downward uniformly distributed load of 2 kips/ft is applied along arc AB of the girder.

3-29. Determine the vertical reactions of the balcony girder that is loaded with a uniformly distributed load of 5 kips/ft along the entire circular girder as shown in Fig. P3-29(a). The axis of the girder in a horizontal plane is shown in Fig. P3-29(b).

(a)   (b)

Figure P3-29

3-30. Compute the vertical shear, torque, and bending moment at the fixed support C of the cantilever bow girder in Problem 3-28 if a downward uniform load of 2 kips/ft is applied along arc BC instead of arc AB of the girder.

4

Bar Forces in Trusses

If straight bars are joined together at their ends by frictionless pins to form a rigid system on which loads are applied only at the joints, the resulting idealized structure is known as a *truss*. The system is said to be rigid in the sense that it undergoes no movement other than small deflections under applied loads. Since the bars in such a system are arranged in the form of triangles or polygons that are not closed by solid plates as in plate girders, this type of structure is sometimes called an *open truss*. If the bars or members of a truss are confined to the same plane, the truss is termed a *plane truss;* otherwise, it is said to be a *space truss*.

An *ideal truss* is characterized by the fact that its members are subjected to axial forces only because the smooth pins at the ends of a member cannot transmit moment and the line of action of the internal force in a member must pass through the pins at its ends. The *internal axial force* in a member of the truss is called the *bar force*.* For a *real truss,* however, the joints are somewhat restrained from rotation, and the dead weight of the members is not concentrated at the joints. As a result, bending exists in the members of a real truss and causes moments and shears in the members. Since the stresses introduced by these moments are relatively small compared with those caused by bar forces, especially if the centerlines of the members in a real truss meet at one

---

*In some textbooks, the term *stress* is used to denote the bar force, but in this book *stress* is defined strictly as the intensity of force per unit area.

point at each joint, the stresses due to bar forces are considered as *primary stresses,* whereas the stresses due to bending are termed *secondary stresses.* The latter can be superimposed on the former, and the two can be investigated as separate problems.

Trusses are used extensively in buildings, bridges, and many other important industrial constructions because they can be adapted to transmit heavy loads over relatively long spans. Since they are usually designed for specific purposes, their shapes and sizes vary greatly. In this chapter, we shall confine our discussions to the analysis of ideal plane trusses that are statically determinate and are subjected to stationary loads.

The overall criteria of statical determinacy for plane and space trusses have been given in Section 2-7. We should point out again that either of these conditions is necessary but not sufficient to ensure the statical determinacy of a truss. The final test is to check whether the truss constitutes a rigid system that cannot be collapsed under all loading conditions. The kinematic instability of a truss is not always obvious, but it can be detected immediately if the results of the computed reactions or bar forces in a system turn out to be infinite or inconsistent.

From the point of view of analysis, statically determinate trusses may be classified into three categories: simple, compound, and complex. A *simple truss* is defined as a system of bars assembled by first joining together three bars at their ends in the form of a triangle and then adding to this configuration two more bars for each additional joint. A *compound truss* is defined as a rigid system formed by interconnecting two or more simple trusses, the rigidity being provided by a sufficient number of independent components of constraint at the interconnection between the simple trusses. If the arrangement of bars in a truss fails to satisfy either the definition of a simple truss or that of a compound truss, even though the criterion for statical determinacy still holds true, the system is said to be a *complex truss.*

In this chapter we are primarily interested in the analysis of bar forces in plane trusses, although the same principles may be applied to the solution of space trusses. We shall, therefore, discuss the three major categories of statically determinate trusses in terms of plane trusses only. Figure 4-1 shows several simple trusses, each of which has been formed by starting with triangle *ABC* and then establishing the remaining joints in alphabetical order. Intersections where bars cross each other freely without connection are not considered as joints. Figure 4-2 illustrates several compound trusses, each of which

Figure 4-1

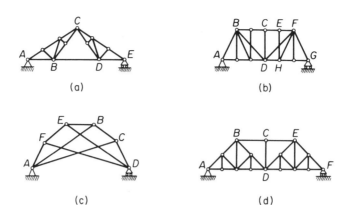

(a)

(b)

(c)

(d)

Figure 4-2

has been formed by interconnecting two simple trusses by three independent components of constraint. In Fig. 4-2(a), the portion *ABC* is formed in accordance with the definition of a simple truss, but beyond points *B* and *C* this procedure cannot be applied. However, a second simple truss *CDE* may be connected to the first one by member *BD* and hinge *C*. If the portions *ABC* and *CDE* are isolated as free bodies, there will be an axial force acting along *BD* and two components of force at hinge *C*. These three components of force are necessary and sufficient to provide rigidity for the interconnected truss, and they may be determined from the condition of equilibrium of the free bodies. In Fig. 4-2(b), two simple trusses *ABCD* and *EFGH* are interconnected by members *CE*, *DH*, and *DF*, which provide three independent components of constraint; in Fig. 4-2(c), two simple trusses *ABC* and *DEF* are interconnected by members *AF*, *BE*, and *CD*, which are the components of constraint. In Fig. 4-2(d), two simple trusses *ABCD* and *DEF* are interconnected by member *CE* and hinge *D*. However, compound trusses may also be formed by two simple trusses with less than three independent components of constraint at the interconnection if extra components of reaction are added to make up the difference. Figure 4-3 shows two of these compound trusses. In Fig. 4-3(a) the structure is formed by two simple trusses *ABC* and *CDE* that are interconnected by two components of constraint plus an extra component of reaction that replaces the third component of constraint normally needed at the interconnection of simple trusses. In Fig. 4-3(b), simple trusses *ABDC* and *EDFG* are interconnected by two components of constraint at joint *D* only, but the additional support *H* provides an extra component of reaction for each of the simple trusses. Figure 4-4 shows two complex trusses that do not fulfill the requirements of simple or compound

(a)

(b)

Figure 4-3

Bar Forces in Trusses   Chap. 4

(a)

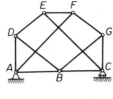

(b)

Figure 4-4

trusses. Nevertheless, they satisfy the criterion of statically determinate plane trusses.

4-2 COMMON PATTERNS OF PLANE TRUSSES

Although plane trusses of various shapes may be adopted for specific purposes, most of those used in buildings and bridges follow a few simple patterns that have been found to be economical under ordinary conditions encountered in practice. Since the primary function of a roof or bridge truss is to transmit loads between supports, the structural action of a truss is analogous to that of a beam or girder. The members that form the perimeter of a truss are called *chord members*. The top and bottom chord members in a truss serve the same purpose as the flanges of a plate girder. The interior members between chord members are known as *web members*. They have the same function as the solid web plate of the plate girder. Whenever possible, symmetrical trusses are preferred because of the simplicity of their analysis and fabrication. We shall mention briefly here the conventional names and the general characteristics of these patterns.

Roof trusses.   The top chords of roof trusses may be either pitched or flat. The ratio of rise to span length of a roof truss is called the *pitch,* which varies from 1/4 to 1/3 for ordinary pitched roof trusses. The ratio of depth to span length of flat roof trusses is usually between 1/12 and 1/8. The panel length of the trusses is determined by the spacing of the roof purlins, which are supported at the joints of top chord members. Figures 4-5(a), (b), and (c) show three common types of trusses for pitched roofs of moderate span. The Fink truss in Fig. 4-5(c) may be used for spans of greater length, but it must be modified to provide more joints at the upper chord if the roof is to be supported at relatively short intervals as shown in Fig. 4-5(d) or (e). For a relatively flat roof, the Warren truss shown in Fig. 4-5(f) may be used. However, the web system of a truss for a flat roof may also be patterned after the Pratt truss or Howe truss, shown in Figs. 4-5(a) and (b) respectively.

Bridge trusses.   Bridge trusses may be classified according to the manner in which the floor loads are transmitted to the trusses. If the floor system is connected to the bottom chord of a truss, the truss is said to be a *through truss* in the sense that the traffic passes through the truss. If the floor system is

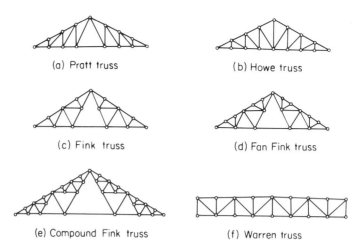

(a) Pratt truss

(b) Howe truss

(c) Fink truss

(d) Fan Fink truss

(e) Compound Fink truss

(f) Warren truss

Figure 4-5

connected to the top chord of a truss, the truss is called a *deck truss*. When the floor system is located between the top chord and the bottom chord, the truss is known as *half-through* or *pony truss*. Figure 4-6 shows various patterns of bridge trusses that are adaptable to either through trusses, deck trusses, or pony trusses.

For bridge trusses of moderate span, the top and bottom chord members are usually made parallel in order to simplify the fabricating process. For longer spans, polygonal top chords are used to reduce the dead weight of the truss. This is analogous to cutting off the cover plates of a plate girder in the region where the cover plates are no longer needed to resist bending. For

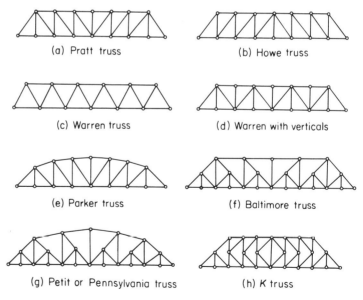

(a) Pratt truss

(b) Howe truss

(c) Warren truss

(d) Warren with verticals

(e) Parker truss

(f) Baltimore truss

(g) Petit or Pennsylvania truss

(h) *K* truss

Figure 4-6

Bar Forces in Trusses   Chap. 4

economical designs, the ratio of maximum depth to span length of a bridge truss is usually between 1/10 and 1/5, and the slope of the diagonal web members varies from 45° to 60° with a horizontal line. Figures 4-6(a), (b), (c), and (d) represent the most common types of bridge trusses of moderate span. The type shown in Fig. 4-6(e) may be used for slightly longer spans.

As the span length of a truss increases, the panel length also becomes longer if the slope of the diagonal web members is maintained at an angle of 45° to 60° with a horizontal line. The panel length of a truss is a factor of economy of the floor system, which in turn affects the dead weight of the truss. If a heavy floor system is to be avoided, trusses with subdivided panels such as those shown in Figs. 4-6(f) and (g) may be used. The short diagonals in trusses with subdivided panels are usually referred to as *subties* if they are tension members, or as *substruts* if they are compression members. The *K*-truss shown in Fig. 4-6(h) may also serve the same purpose without the introduction of subdivided panels.

Long-span trusses. For long-span structures, trusses such as those shown in Fig. 4-7 are often used. The arch truss in Fig. 4-7(a) has the advantage of gaining the rise as well as spanning over a long distance. The economy of a

(a) Arch truss

(b) Cantilever truss

(c) Suspension bridge with stiffening truss

Figure 4-7

cantilever bridge such as the one shown in Fig. 4-7(b) over a simple truss of the same span is realized largely because the moments caused by uniform loads on a cantilever truss are in general smaller and most of the dead weight of the cantilever truss is concentrated near the supports. The cantilever truss is especially applicable where falsework is impractical or undesirable during erection. In Fig. 4-7(c), the stiffening truss of the suspension bridge is used to distribute the live loads uniformly to the hangers so that the cables will not change shape when the loads move from one point to another on the bridge.

4-3 BAR FORCES IN SIMPLE TRUSSES

The basic approach to the analysis of a truss is to study the internal forces in its members, which can be accomplished by passing imaginary sections through the members of the truss for which the bar forces are required. Since the truss as a whole is in static equilibrium, any free body isolated from the truss must also be in equilibrium.

The bar forces in a truss may be obtained by variations of this basic approach. The two most common methods used for the solution of simple trusses are the *method of joints* and the *method of sections*. In the former, each joint of a truss is isolated as a free body. If there are not more than two unknown bar forces at a joint, these unknowns may be determined from the two equations of static equilibrium available for a coplanar concurrent force system. Thus, a joint that satisfies this requirement is first selected as the starting point, and the procedure is then carried out joint by joint so that the results of analysis from one joint may be used for the next adjacent joints. In the latter method, sections are passed through various members of the truss for which the bar forces are required. If there are not more than three unknown bar forces at a section, the unknowns may be determined from the three equations of static equilibrium available for a coplanar nonconcurrent force system. For both methods, there are exceptions to the rules stated above that will be discussed later.

Since a complete analysis of a truss involves the determination of bar forces in all of its members, they must be obtained in a well-organized sequence. A sign convention is adopted for the sense of direction of bar forces in a truss as follows: A bar force is considered as *positive* when it produces *tension* in a member and as *negative* when it causes *compression* in the member. Thus, in any free body cut by a section passing through members of a truss, a tensile or positive bar force is represented by an arrowhead pulling away from a joint, and a compressive or negative bar force is represented by an arrowhead pushing toward a joint. For simple trusses, whether a member is subjected to tension or compression can easily be recognized, and correct senses of direction can be assigned to the bar forces; otherwise, the bar forces may be assumed to have a sense of direction corresponding to the positive sign convention. In that case, a positive result will indicate that the assumed sense of

Bar Forces in Trusses   Chap. 4

direction is correct, and a negative result means that actual sense of direction is the reverse of the assumed direction.

In the analysis of trusses it is often convenient to work with the horizontal and vertical components of the bar forces, since the equations of equilibrium are usually obtained by the summation of forces in two mutually perpendicular directions and by the summation of moments due to these components of forces. Because the lengths of members in a truss are known quantities while the angles between any two members are seldom computed, the horizontal and vertical components of a bar force are usually related to the corresponding projections of the member instead of being expressed in trigonometric functions.

There are numerous techniques that may be used to expedite the determination of bar forces in plane trusses. Such techniques will be illustrated by appropriate examples.

4-4 APPLICATION OF METHOD OF JOINTS

The method of joints can always be applied to simple trusses because in any such truss there are only two bars meeting at the last joint formed in accordance with the definition. If external loads or reactions are also applied at this joint, they are either known or can be obtained first. Hence, the two unknown bar forces at the joint can be determined from the two equations of equilibrium at that joint. Then for the next-to-the-last joint established according to the basic definition, there are also only two unknown bar forces which can be solved readily in the same manner. Hence, the bar forces in all members of a truss can be determined by considering the joints as free bodies in the reverse order from which the joints have been established. If the joints in a truss can be established in different orders, there will be more than one order according to which the bar forces in the truss may be solved by the method of joints.

In general, the two unknown bar forces at a joint can be determined from the solution of two simultaneous equations resulting from the consideration of the joint in equilibrium. However, the numerical computation may be somewhat simplified if, by the proper choice of coordinate axes, only one unknown appears in each equation. In all numerical examples in this chapter, the bar forces are in the unit of kips and the distances are in the unit of feet.

Example 4-1. Compute the bar forces in all members of the simple truss in Fig. 4-8(a). The reactions at A and H may be computed as follows:

$$\sum M_a = 0, \qquad -80V_h + 20(60 + 40 + 20) + (50)(25) = 0, \qquad V_h = 45.6$$

$$\sum F_x = 0, \qquad H_a = (\tfrac{3}{5})(50) = 30$$

$$\sum F_y = 0, \qquad V_a = (3)(20) + (\tfrac{4}{5})(50) - 45.6 = 54.4$$

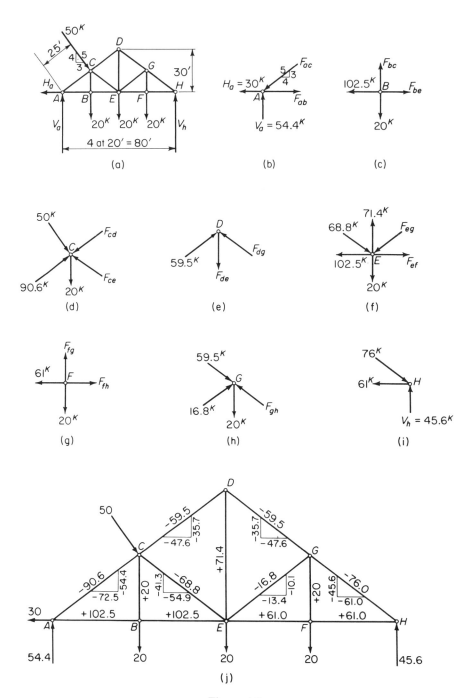

Figure 4-8

Bar Forces in Trusses   Chap. 4

Since there are only two unknown bar forces at either joint A or joint H, one of them can be chosen as the starting point. If we consider A as a free body as shown in Fig. 4-8(b), for instance, the internal forces in members AB and AC, as represented by F_{ab} and F_{ac} respectively, are the only unknowns. The senses of direction of F_{ab} and F_{ac} are arbitrarily assumed. However, it is not difficult to visualize in this case that, since the vertical component of reaction at A is directed upward, the vertical component of F_{ac} must be acting downward in order to maintain the equilibrium of the joint. The sense of direction of F_{ac}, therefore, is pushing toward the joint, and member AC is in compression. Again, because the horizontal component of reaction at A as well as the horizontal component of F_{ac} is directed toward the left, F_{ab} must be acting toward the right. Thus, the sense of direction of F_{ab} is pulling away from the joint, and member AB is in tension. The equations of equilibrium for the components of forces in horizontal and vertical directions at joint A can be written as follows:

$$\sum F_y = 0, \qquad 54.4 - (\tfrac{3}{5})F_{ac} = 0, \qquad F_{ac} = 90.6$$

$$\sum F_x = 0, \qquad F_{ab} - (\tfrac{4}{5})F_{ac} - 30 = 0, \qquad F_{ab} = 102.5$$

The positive results confirm that the assumed senses of direction for both members are correct. In order to indicate these senses of direction without referring to the free-body diagram, the magnitude of a bar force may be prefixed by a sign, such as $F_{ac} = -90.6$, indicating that the member is in compression and $F_{ab} = +102.5$, indicating that the member is in tension.

Next, proceed to joint B, at which there are only two unknown bar forces as shown in Fig. 4-8(c). Thus, from $\sum F_y = 0$, $F_{bc} = 20$; from $\sum F_x = 0$, $F_{be} = 102.5$. Similarly, for joint C shown in Fig. 4-8(d), we obtain

$$\sum F_y = 0, \qquad (\tfrac{3}{5})F_{ce} - (\tfrac{3}{5})F_{cd} + 54.4 - (\tfrac{4}{5})(50) - 20 = 0$$

or

$$F_{ce} - F_{cd} = (\tfrac{5}{3})(5.6) = 9.3$$

$$\sum F_x = 0, \qquad (\tfrac{3}{5})(50) + 72.5 - (\tfrac{4}{5})F_{cd} - (\tfrac{4}{5})F_{ce} = 0$$

or

$$F_{cd} + F_{ce} = (\tfrac{5}{4})(102.5) = 128.3$$

Solving these two equations simultaneously, we have $F_{cd} = 59.5$ and $F_{ce} = 68.8$. Since the results for F_{cd} and F_{ce} are positive, the assumed senses of direction are correct, i.e., both F_{cd} and F_{ce} are in compression.

The bar forces in the remaining members may be obtained in a similar manner by the consideration of joints D, E, F, and G as free bodies as shown in Figs. 4-8(e), (f), (g), and (h) respectively. It is sufficient to point out that at joint G, there is only one unknown bar force which requires only one equation of equilibrium for its solution, and the second equation of equilibrium can be used as a check. The free-body diagram for joint H shown in Fig. 4-8(i) is not needed for the solution of bar forces and is included for checking purposes only.

The results of analysis of the entire truss are summarized in Fig. 4-8(j) in which the bar forces are prefixed by either a positive or a negative sign that indicates whether the member is in tension or in compression. The vertical and horizontal components of the bar forces in inclined members are also shown in the figure. We should point out that the formal procedure of drawing separate free-body diagrams and writing equations of equilibrium for each case is not always necessary after the student has familiarized himself with the basic idea. Referring to joint A in Fig. 4-8(j), for instance, it is obvious that the vertical component of the bar force in member AC must be equal and opposite to the vertical reaction at A since there is no other vertical force acting at joint A. The horizontal component of the bar force in member AC can be obtained by multiplying the vertical component by a ratio representing the reciprocal of the slope of the member. Then, the bar force in AC can be determined accordingly while the bar force in member AB is equal and opposite to the algebraic sum of the horizontal reaction at A and the horizontal component of the bar force in member AC. Thus, if the horizontal and vertical components of a bar force are represented by H and V respectively,

$$V_{ac} = -54.4 \qquad H_{ac} = (-54.4)(\tfrac{4}{3}) = -72.5$$

$$F_{ac} = (-54.4)(\tfrac{5}{3}) = -90.6$$

$$F_{ab} = 72.5 + 30 = +102.5$$

It may also be of interest to note that if joint H were chosen as the starting point, it would involve less numerical work since there is no horizontal reaction at H. Furthermore, the bar force in member BC can be determined from the consideration of joint B alone even though there are three unknown bar forces meeting at that joint, but the bar forces in members AB and BE cannot be obtained without also considering other joints in the truss.

Example 4-2.   Determine the bar forces in members AB and BC of the simple truss shown in Fig. 4-9(a).

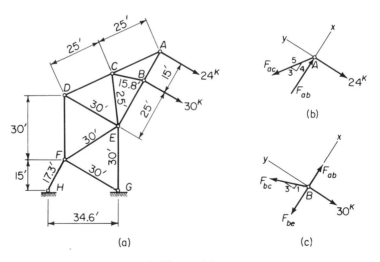

(a)

(b)

(c)

Figure 4-9

Bar Forces in Trusses   Chap. 4

In this case the bar forces can be obtained from joints A and B without computing the reactions first since there are only two unknown bar forces at joint A. Furthermore, the numerical computation may be simplified by choosing the coordinate axes for writing the equations of equilibrium in the directions shown in Fig. 4-9(b). Thus, from $\Sigma F_y = 0$, $F_{ac} = (24)(\frac{5}{3}) = 40$, and from $\Sigma F_x = 0$, $F_{ab} = (40)(\frac{4}{5}) = 32$, with senses of direction as indicated in the figure. Similarly, the same coordinate axes may be used for the solution of the bar forces meeting at joint B, as shown in Fig. 4-9(c). It can be seen that the bar force in member BC may be determined from the consideration of joint B alone since it is the only unknown bar force acting at the joint that has a component along the y-axis. Thus, for $\Sigma F_y = 0$, $F_{bc} = (30)(\sqrt{10}/3) = 31.6$ in tension. The remaining bar forces in the truss may be obtained by going through successive considerations of equilibrium of all joints in the truss.

4-5 APPLICATION OF METHOD OF SECTIONS

In the analysis of simple trusses, it is sometimes more convenient to determine the bar forces in certain members by the method of sections, which can also be used as an independent check of those bar forces obtained by the method of joints. Since the method of sections consists essentially of isolating a portion of the truss by an imaginary section passing through the members for which the bar forces are desired, the free body generally represents a coplanar non-concurrent force system in equilibrium. For some problems it may be more expedient to cut more than one section through the members of a truss, or to use the method of sections in connection with the method of joints.

In general, the three unknown bar forces at a section can be determined from the solution of three simultaneous equations resulting from the consideration of equilibrium of the free body isolated by the section. However, the numerical computation may be greatly simplified if, by the proper choice of centers of moments, only one unknown appears in each of these equations. All bar forces in the numerical examples are in the unit of kips.

Example 4-3. Determine the bar forces in members EF, EG, and CD of the truss shown in Fig. 4-10(a).

The free body in Fig. 4-10(b) is obtained by passing a section through members DF, EF, and EG. The senses of direction of the bar forces are assumed to be

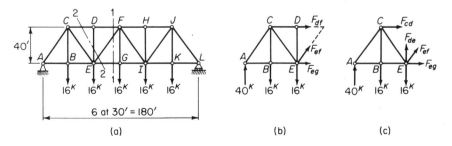

(a)   (b)   (c)

Figure 4-10

positive as indicated in the figure. Then, from the summation of all forces in the vertical direction, or $\Sigma\, F_y = 0$,

$$V_{ef} + 40 - (2)(16) = 0, \qquad V_{ef} = -8$$

Hence,

$$F_{ef} = (-8)(\tfrac{5}{4}) = -10$$

From the summation of moments of all forces about joint F, or $\Sigma\, M_f = 0$,

$$(40)(90) - (16)(60 + 30) - 40F_{eg} = 0, \qquad F_{eg} = 54$$

The bar force in member CD can be obtained from the consideration of joint D in equilibrium if the bar force in member DF is known or determined first. Thus, by summing all forces in the horizontal direction, or $\Sigma\, F_x = 0$,

$$F_{df} + 54 + (-10)(\tfrac{3}{5}) = 0, \qquad F_{df} = -48$$

This result may also be obtained by taking moments of all forces about joint E in Fig. 4-10(b), or $\Sigma\, M_e = 0$,

$$(40)(60) - (16)(30) + 40F_{df} = 0, \qquad F_{df} = -48$$

Finally,

$$F_{cd} = F_{df} = -48$$

The bar force in member CD may also be obtained directly by passing section 2-2 through the truss. The free body to the left of the section is shown in Fig. 4-10(c), in which there are four unknown bar forces. However, three of these four unknown bar forces meet at one point, and it is possible to obtain the fourth by taking moments of all forces about joint E in Fig. 4-10(c). Thus, $\Sigma\, M_e = 0$,

$$(40)(60) - (16)(30) + 40F_{cd} = 0, \qquad F_{cd} = -48$$

Example 4-4. Compute the bar forces in members BC, CD, CE, DE, and DG, of the truss shown in Fig. 4-11(a).

(b)

(a)

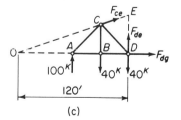

(c)

Figure 4-11

Bar Forces in Trusses   Chap. 4

We proceed by passing section 1-1 through members BD, CD, and CE, and passing section 2-2 through members CE, DE, and DG. The resulting free bodies to the left of sections 1-1 and 2-2 are shown in Figs. 4-11(b) and (c), respectively. Hence, three equations of static equilibrium may be written for each of the free-body diagrams, and the unknown bar forces can be obtained accordingly.

For the free-body diagram shown in Fig. 4-11(b), for instance, we can establish $\Sigma F_x = 0$, $\Sigma F_y = 0$, and $\Sigma M_c = 0$. It is obvious, however, that even if F_{bd} is first determined from $\Sigma M_c = 0$, both F_{cd} and F_{ce} will appear in the equations $\Sigma F_x = 0$ and $\Sigma F_y = 0$, which must be solved simultaneously. A simpler procedure may result if three independent equations of equilibrium are obtained by taking moments about three different points. Thus, $\Sigma M_c = 0$ may still be used for the solution of bar force F_{bd}, i.e.,

$$(100)(30) - 30F_{bd} = 0, \qquad F_{bd} = 100$$

Similarly, from $\Sigma M_d = 0$,

$$(100)(60) - (40)(30) + \left(\frac{1}{\sqrt{10}}F_{ce}\right)(30) + \left(\frac{3}{\sqrt{10}}F_{ce}\right)(30) = 0$$

Note that the vertical and horizontal components of the bar force F_{ce} are used in the above equation since the moment arms of these components are obvious, whereas the moment arm of the bar force itself must be computed from the geometry of the truss. From either consideration, $F_{ce} = -126$. The third equation may be established by taking moments about point O, which is the intersection of the lines of action of F_{bd} and F_{ce}. The moment arm for bar force F_{cd} then becomes $ON = 120/\sqrt{2}$. Hence, from $\Sigma M_0 = 0$,

$$(120/\sqrt{2})F_{cd} - (100)(60) + (40)(90) = 0, \qquad F_{cd} = 28.3$$

As a check, consider $\Sigma F_y - 0$,

$$100 - 40 + (1/\sqrt{10})(-126) - (1/\sqrt{2})(28.3) = 100 - 40 - 40 - 20 = 0$$

In Fig. 4-11(c), the bar forces in members DE and DG can be determined by taking moments about points O and E respectively. Thus, for $\Sigma M_0 = 0$,

$$(40)(120 + 90) - 120F_{de} - (100)(60) = 0, \qquad F_{de} = 20$$

and for $\Sigma M_e = 0$,

$$(100)(60) - (40)(30) - 40F_{bd} = 0, \qquad F_{bd} = 120$$

Example 4-5. For the truss shown in Fig. 4-12(a), determine the bar forces in members DF, DG, EF, and EH.

The reactions of the truss are first obtained as follows:

$$\Sigma F_x = 0, \qquad H_k = 20$$

$$\Sigma M_d = 0, \qquad (120)(30) + (60)(20) - (60)(40 + 20) - 40V_k = 0, \qquad V_k = 30$$

$$\Sigma F_y = 0, \qquad V_d = (3)(60) - 30 = 150$$

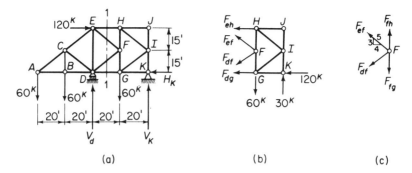

Figure 4-12

If a part of the structure is isolated by section 1-1 as shown in Fig. 4-12(b), there are four unknown bar forces in the free body. Since only three equations of equilibrium are available, the fourth equation must be furnished by an additional requirement from the consideration of joint F in equilibrium. For the free-body diagram of joint F shown in Fig. 4-12(c), it is obvious that from $\Sigma F_x = 0$, the algebraic sum of horizontal components of F_{df} and F_{ef} must be zero. Thus,

$$\tfrac{4}{5}F_{df} + \tfrac{4}{5}F_{ef} = 0, \quad \text{or} \quad F_{df} = F_{ef}$$

Then, from Fig. 4-12(b), we obtain

$$\Sigma F_y = 0, \qquad \tfrac{3}{5}(F_{ef} - F_{df}) + 30 - 60 = 0, \qquad F_{df} = -25, \qquad \text{and} \quad F_{ef} = 25$$

$$\Sigma M_g = 0, \qquad 30F_{eh} + (30)(20) = 0, \qquad F_{eh} = -20$$

$$\Sigma M_h = 0, \qquad 30F_{dg} + (120)(30) - (30)(20) = 0, \qquad F_{dg} = -100$$

It should be noted that neither F_{df} nor F_{ef} appears in the equations for $\Sigma M_g = 0$ and $\Sigma M_h = 0$, since the vertical components of these two forces pass through the moment center, and the horizontal components are equal and opposite to each other. As a check, $\Sigma F_x = 0$, or

$$F_{eh} + F_{dg} + 120 = -20 - 100 + 120 = 0$$

Example 4-6. Determine the bar force in member AC of the truss shown in Fig. 4-13(a).

The reactions can be obtained by inspection. Since there are four unknown bar forces in the free body shown in Fig. 4-13(b), it is necessary to seek an additional equation or to eliminate one unknown from the system. This is accomplished by isolating a free body as shown in Fig. 4-13(c), from which F_{ae} may be determined. Then, F_{ac} may be obtained by taking moments of all known forces about the intersection of the lines of action of F_{ad} and F_{bc}.

Referring to Fig. 4-13(c), we take moments about point G whereby F_{ce} and F_{df} produce no moments. We can also resolve F_{ae} into vertical and horizontal components so that only the vertical component need be considered. Thus, $\Sigma M_g = 0$ gives

$$\left(\frac{3}{8.54}F_{ae}\right)(60) + (20)(60) - (80)(60) = 0, \qquad F_{ae} = 170.8$$

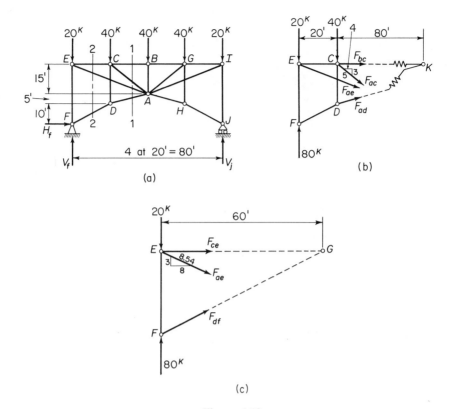

Figure 4-13

Similarly, in Fig. 4-13(b), we take moments about point K, with F_{ae} resolved into components at E and F_{ac} resolved into components at C. Then,

$$\left(\frac{3}{8.54}F_{ae}\right)(100) + (20)(100) - (80)(100) + \left(\frac{3}{5}F_{ac}\right)(80) + (40)(80) = 0$$

$$F_{ac} = -66.7$$

4-6 SPECIAL APPLICATION TO PARALLEL CHORD TRUSSES

For all types of parallel chord trusses with equal panels, the solution can be simplified by a slight modification of the method of sections if all panel loads are equal as in the case of dead loads. We may conceive the structural action of such a truss as a simple beam. Then the bar forces can be conveniently obtained from the shears and moments at various sections of the structure. This modified method is sometimes called the *method of shears and moments*.

Consider, for example, the parallel chord truss in Fig. 4-14(a). With height h and panel length p, all diagonal members have equal length d. In order to obtain the bar forces, sections are passed through various panels. For instance, section 1-1 is passed through panel CD in Fig. 4-14(a), resulting in the

(a)   (b)   (c)

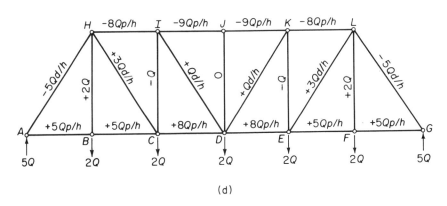

(d)

Figure 4-14

free-body diagram in Fig. 4-14(b), with the shear S and moment M at the section as indicated. The shearing resistance is provided by the vertical component of the bar force in the inclined member DI, and the resisting moment is equal to the couple produced by the bar forces in members CD and IJ. Thus, shear S is the shear in the panel CD whereas moment M may be considered as the moment about a conveniently chosen panel point such as I in this case. Thus,

$$S = 5Q - 4Q = +Q \quad \text{and} \quad M = (5Q)(2p) - (2Q)(p) = 8Qp$$

The senses of direction as well as the magnitude of the bar forces in members DI and CD can be derived from S and M as follows:

$$F_{di} = S\frac{d}{h} = \frac{Qd}{h} \quad \text{and} \quad F_{cd} = \frac{M}{h} = \frac{8Qp}{h}$$

Similarly, the bar force in a vertical member such as CI may be obtained from Fig. 4-14(c), which has been isolated by section 2-2 in Fig. 4-14(a). Hence,

$$F_{ci} = S = Q$$

Since shears and moments at various sections of the structure can easily be obtained, the bar forces can be computed rapidly by the trigonometric relations of right triangles without drawing separate free-body diagrams. As an illustration, shears and moments for the truss are tabulated in Table 4-1.

Table 4-1

Panel	Shear S	Panel point	Moment M
AB	$+5Q$	B or H	$5Qp$
BC	$+3Q$	C or I	$8Qp$
CD	$+ Q$	D or J	$9Qp$
DE	$- Q$	E or K	$8Qp$
EF	$-3Q$	E or L	$5Qp$
FG	$-5Q$		

Thus, the bar forces can be computed directly and are indicated in Fig. 4-14(d).

Another convenient way to obtain bar forces in a parallel chord truss with equal panel loads is through a slight modification of the method of joints. The bar forces are found by noting that the vertical components of web members are identical to the shears in the respective panels as we pass sections around successive joints. Such a method is called the *method of index forces*. Consider, for example, the truss in Fig. 4-14(d). The bar force in member AH is seen to have a magnitude of $(5Q)(d/h)$, in which $5Q$ is the shear in the panel and d/h is an index for converting the vertical component to the bar force in the inclined direction. A similar approach may be followed from joint to joint. The bar forces thus obtained are called *index forces*. Further details of the procedure will be omitted here.

4-7 COMPOUND TRUSSES

The method of analysis used for the solution of simple trusses may also be applied to compound trusses. Quite frequently, however, the bar forces in a compound truss cannot be solved completely by the method of joints alone. For such cases, it is necessary to break up the compound truss into component simple trusses and to obtain the components of constraint at the interconnection between simple trusses first. This can be accomplished by the method of sections. In the compound truss shown in Fig. 4-15, for example, we

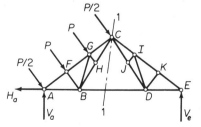

Figure 4-15

may begin the solution of the truss by considering joint A as a free body after the components of reactions are determined, and proceed to joint F after obtaining the bar forces in members AB and AF. Then the next step leads to either joint B or joint G, at which there are three unknown bar forces. If we start from joint E on the other end of the truss, similar situations prevail at joints D and I. By passing section 1-1 through the truss as shown and thus isolating the simple trusses at the constraints, the bar force in member BD may be obtained by taking moments of all forces to the left or to the right of the section about joint C. As a result, the remaining two unknown bar forces at joint B can be solved by the available equations of equilibrium, and the bar forces at joint G can be obtained accordingly.

For some special cases, such as the truss shown in Fig. 4-16, the method of sections may be avoided. If we start the solution of the truss from joint A, we will immediately arrive at joint B or F, at which there are three unknown bar forces. It may be observed, however, that the bar force in member GH can be obtained from the consideration of joint G as a free body even if there are three unknown bar forces at that joint. Furthermore, the bar force in member FH can be computed by considering joint H as a free body if the bar force in member GH is known. Nevertheless, the basic approach of breaking up a compound truss at the constraints can be applied to any general case in which the method of joints or method of sections seems to fail to yield a solution.

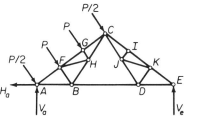

Figure 4-16

Example 4-7. The compound truss in Fig. 4-17(a) consists of two simple trusses ABC and DEF that are linked together by three components of constraint AF, EB, and CD. Determine the bar forces in members AF, EB, and CD.

By breaking up the interconnections between two simple trusses, as shown in Figs. 4-17(b) and 4-17(c), we can obtain the bar forces in members AF, EB, and CD. From Fig. 4-17(b), we have

$$\sum F_y = 0, \qquad 2P - P - P + \tfrac{4}{5}F_{cd} - \tfrac{4}{5}F_{af} = 0, \qquad \text{or} \qquad F_{af} = F_{cd}$$

$$\sum F_x = 0, \qquad F_{eb} - \tfrac{3}{5}F_{af} - \tfrac{3}{5}F_{cd} = 0, \qquad \text{or} \qquad F_{eb} = \tfrac{3}{5}(F_{af} + F_{cd})$$

$$\sum M_a = 0, \qquad (5.5d + 7.5d)P + (4d)F_{eb} - (7.5d)(\tfrac{4}{5}F_{cd}) - (2d)(\tfrac{3}{5}F_{cd}) = 0$$

or

$$7.2F_{cd} - 4F_{eb} = 13P$$

Bar Forces in Trusses   Chap. 4

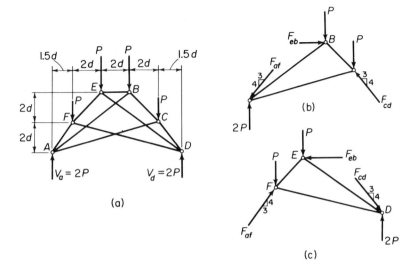

Figure 4-17

Solving these three equations simultaneously, we get

$$F_{af} = F_{cd} = 5.41P \quad \text{and} \quad F_{eb} = 6.5P$$

Then, the bar forces in all other members of the compound truss can be computed by the method of joints.

Example 4-8. Determine the bar forces in all members of the truss shown in Fig. 4-18(a).

Since the truss is symmetrical with respect to its centerline, only half of it is shown in the figure. The problem can be solved by passing a section through the constraints connecting the two halves of the truss so that the bar force in member BD can be determined first. Then, the bar forces in all members of the truss are found by the method of joints as shown in the figure. However, the problem can also be solved without first obtaining the bar force in member BD by the method of sections, if the bar forces in members GJ and GI are first determined by considering successively the equilibrium of joints J and G respectively. Then the remaining bar forces can be obtained without difficulty.

A different approach involving the principle of superposition may also be used for the solution of this problem. If members GJ and GI in the truss are replaced by a substitute member BJ as shown in Fig. 4-18(b), the bar forces in the resulting truss can be completely solved by the method of joints. Such a substitution causes no change in the bar forces in the members of the original truss except in those members bounded by the panel BIJG. This can be seen from the fact that the bar forces in members AF, AH, FH, HI, FI, and FB can be solved by the method of joints starting from joint A, and those in members CG and CJ can also be solved after the components of reaction at C are obtained. All these bar forces are not related to those in panel BIJG and will not be affected by them. On the other hand, the bar force in the substitute member BJ is, in reality, non-existent and may be construed as two equal and opposite forces temporarily placed

(a)

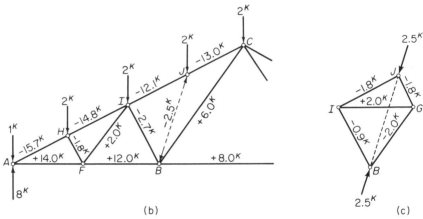

(b)   (c)

Figure 4-18

at joints B and J that will eventually be removed. Furthermore, the panel $BIJG$ shown in Fig. 4-18(c) may be considered as a separate system acted on by forces at joints B and J that are opposite to the corresponding forces representing the substitute member in Fig. 4-18(b). If Fig. 4-18(c) is superimposed on Fig. 4-18(b), the effect of the substitute member on the truss will be eliminated. The final results of superposition are identical to those shown in Fig. 4-18(a).

Example 4-9. Determine the bar forces in members BC, BF, FK, IF, FJ, IJ, JK, and BI of the symmetrical compound truss with subdivided panels in Fig. 4-19(a).

For a compound truss with subdivided panels, a section may be passed through a panel with not more than three members such as section 1-1 in Fig. 4-19(a). From the isolated free body in Fig. 4-19(b), we have

$$\sum M_k = 0, \qquad \left(\frac{5}{\sqrt{26}}F_{bc}\right)(48) + (20)(60 + 40 + 20) + (10)(60 + 20)$$

$$- (140)(80) = 0$$

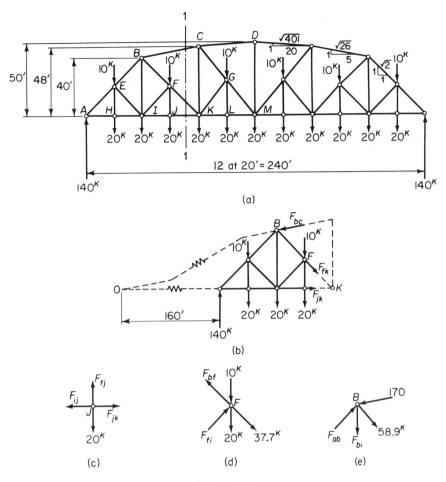

Figure 4-19

$$F_{bc} = \frac{100}{3}\sqrt{26} = 170(-)$$

$$\sum M_b = 0, \qquad 40F_{jk} + (20 + 10)(20) - (20 + 10)(20) - (140)(40) = 0$$

$$F_{jk} = 140(+)$$

$$\sum M_0 = 0, \qquad (140)(160) - (20)(180 + 200 + 220) - (10)(180 + 220)$$

$$-\left(\frac{1}{\sqrt{2}}F_{fk}\right)(240) = 0$$

$$F_{fk} = \frac{80}{3}\sqrt{2} = 37.7(+)$$

Considering joint J as a free body as shown in Fig. 4-19(c), we get

$$\sum F_x = 0, \qquad F_{ij} = F_{jk} = 140(+)$$

$$\sum F_y = 0, \qquad F_{fj} = 20(+)$$

Then, from the consideration of joint F as a free body as shown in Fig. 4-19(d), we obtain

$$\sum F_x = 0, \qquad \frac{1}{\sqrt{2}}F_{fi} - \frac{1}{\sqrt{2}}F_{bf} + \frac{37.7}{\sqrt{2}} = 0$$

$$\sum F_y = 0, \qquad \frac{1}{\sqrt{2}}F_{fi} + \frac{1}{\sqrt{2}}F_{bf} - 20 - 10 - \frac{37.7}{\sqrt{2}} = 0$$

Hence,

$$F_{fi} = 15\sqrt{2} = 21.2(-), \qquad F_{bf} = 41.7\sqrt{2} = 58.9(+)$$

Finally, by considering joint B as a free body as shown in Fig. 4-19(e), we have

$$\sum F_x = 0, \qquad \frac{1}{\sqrt{2}}F_{ab} - F_{bi} - \frac{170}{\sqrt{26}} - \frac{58.9}{\sqrt{2}} = 0$$

$$\sum F_y = 0, \qquad \frac{1}{\sqrt{2}}F_{ab} + \frac{58.9}{\sqrt{2}} - \left(\frac{5}{\sqrt{26}}\right)(170) = 0$$

Thus,

$$F_{ab} = 125\sqrt{2} = 176(-), \qquad F_{bi} = 50(+)$$

4-8 COMPLEX TRUSSES

Since a complex truss does not satisfy either the definition of a simple truss or that of a compound truss, the method of joints or the method of sections usually fails to provide a *direct* solution of this type of truss. However, the method of joints can always be used to establish the relations between bar forces at the joints of a truss. Then, the bar forces can be solved ultimately from a set of simultaneous equations. For a statically determinate complex truss, $m + r = 2j$, or the sum of the number of unknown bar forces and the number of unknown components of reaction must be equal to twice the number of joints in the truss. Since two equations of equilibrium can be written for the forces acting at a joint, the total number of equations available for the entire truss is $2j$. Thus, a total of $m + r$ unknowns in the system can be solved by an equal number of equations. If the unknown components of reaction can be computed first, the extra equations in the set of simultaneous equations can be used as a check.

Consider, for example, the complex truss shown in Fig. 4-20(a). After the reactions are computed, it is found that there are three or more unknown bar forces at each joint of the truss. Since $m = 11$, $r = 3$, and $2j = 14$ in this case,

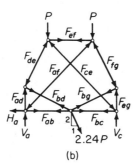

Figure 4-20

(a)   (b)

a total number of 14 equations will be available for the solution of the problem. Referring to the designation of bar forces in Fig. 4-20(b), we can write two equations for joint A as follows:

$$\sum F_x = 0, \qquad F_{ab} - 0.707F_{af} - H_a = 0$$

$$\sum F_y = 0, \qquad -F_{ad} - 0.707F_{af} + V_a = 0$$

and at joint D,

$$\sum F_x = 0, \qquad \frac{2}{2.24}F_{bd} - \frac{1}{2.24}F_{de} = 0$$

$$\sum F_y = 0, \qquad F_{ad} - \frac{2}{2.24}F_{de} - \frac{1}{2.24}F_{bd} = 0$$

Similar equations can always be written for other joints; hence, the solution of the problem is assured. From a practical point of view, however, such an approach is undesirable since it involves the solution of a large number of simultaneous equations.

Since a complex truss in general consists of polygons as well as triangles, it is especially susceptible to kinematic instability because of the orientations of certain members. This type of instability can readily be detected if a set of simultaneous equations is set up from the consideration of equilibrium of all joints. In that case, the determinant formed by the coefficients of the unknown bar forces is the controlling factor. If this determinant is not zero, there will be a unique solution to the problem and hence the structure is statically determinate. If the determinant happens to be zero, there will be infinite sets of answers that may satisfy the simultaneous equations.

4-9 SIMPLE TRUSSES IN SPACE

Although we are primarily concerned with the analysis of plane trusses in this chapter, the same methods may also be applied to statically determinate space trusses. As a matter of fact, we have approached the problems from a general point of view with the intention of extending all applications from plane to space trusses. However, although the principles for the analysis of space trusses are simple, the solution of a space truss is usually rather tedious because of the three-dimensional geometry of the structure, and the large number of members involved. We shall, therefore, confine our present discussions to simple trusses in space.

The simplest element forming a space truss consists of three bars that do not lie on one plane, as shown in Fig. 4-21, in which the bars are connected by smooth ball-and-socket joints. In general, a ball-and-socket joint provides three components of constraint in three orthogonal directions. Thus, joint A in the figure is completely constrained in space by bars AB, AC, and AD. If joints B, C, and D are the supports in the foundation, the element is a rigid truss in space. An additional joint may be introduced by adding three more bars that do not lie in one plane and by connecting them to either previously established joints or the foundation as shown in Fig. 4-22. A simple truss in space can therefore be formed by connecting the three bars defining the first element to a rigid foundation and establishing each additional joint by three more bars that do not lie in one plane.

Figure 4-21

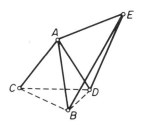

Figure 4-22

A simple truss formed in this manner is statically determinate regardless of the number of components of reaction because it can always be solved by the method of joints, starting from the last joint thus formed and proceeding from joint to joint in the reversed order of that in the process of formation. However, the statical determinacy of space trusses can also be checked by the criterion $m + r - 3j = 0$, as explained in Section 2-7 (Chapter 2). Because of the large number of members often involved in a space truss, some members of the truss may be inactive or have zero bar force under a given loading condition. The analysis of a space truss can be simplified by noting these inactive members.

The method of joints is always applicable in the analysis of simple trusses in space. However, the method can be considerably simplified for systematic treatment if the ratios of the bar force to the length of the members are used instead of the bar forces themselves. Such a simplified procedure is called the *method of tension coefficients*.* Since the senses of direction of the bar forces in space trusses in general are not obvious, all bar forces can be assumed to be

---

*See R. V. Southwell, "Primary Stress-Determination in Space Frames," *Engineering*, vol. 109 (1920), p. 165.

tension. Then, a positive answer will indicate that the assumed sense is correct and a negative result will mean that the assumed sense is opposite to that of the actual sense. Consider a simple element of a space truss consisting of three bars as shown in Fig. 4-23(a). The location of all joints can be specified by the coordinates in the x, y, and z directions. For each of the bar forces the components of force may be expressed in terms of the components of length of the member. Let $\bar{x}$, $\bar{y}$, and $\bar{z}$ be the components of length L of a member, say AB, as shown in Fig. 4-23(b), and let F_x, F_y, and F_z be the components of force F in the same member as shown in Fig. 4-23(c). Then, the components of force F may be obtained from the similar triangles as follows:

$$F_x = \frac{\bar{x}}{L}F = \frac{F}{L}\bar{x} = t\bar{x}$$

$$F_y = \frac{\bar{y}}{L}F = \frac{F}{L}\bar{y} = t\bar{y}$$

$$F_z = \frac{\bar{z}}{L}F = \frac{F}{L}\bar{z} = t\bar{z}$$

in which $L = \sqrt{\bar{x}^2 + \bar{y}^2 + \bar{z}^2}$. Then,

$$F = \sqrt{F_x^2 + F_y^2 + F_z^2} = tL$$

The ratio $t = F/L$ is called the *tension coefficient* of the member. It can be seen from Fig. 4-23(a) that, for member AB, $\bar{x} = x_b - x_a$, $\bar{y} = y_b - y_a$, and $\bar{z} = z_b - z_a$. Note that, in considering joint A, coordinates of joint A are *subtracted* from the corresponding coordinates of the joint at the far end of the member. Hence, $\bar{x}$, $\bar{y}$, and $\bar{z}$ may be positive or negative. Similar relations may be obtained for members AC and AD. Thus, the components of all bar forces meeting at joint A may be computed.

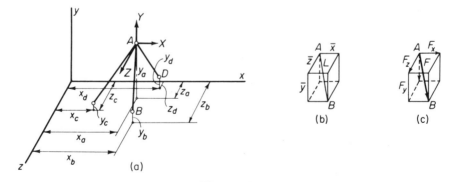

Figure 4-23

Let X, Y, and Z be external forces at joint A in the directions of x, y, and z-axes, respectively. Then, from the consideration of equilibrium of joint A, we have

$$\sum F_x = 0, \qquad (F_{ab})_x + (F_{ac})_x + (F_{ad})_x + X = 0$$

$$\sum F_y = 0, \qquad (F_{ab})_y + (F_{ac})_y + (F_{ad})_y + Y = 0$$

$$\sum F_z = 0, \qquad (F_{ab})_z + (F_{ac})_z + (F_{ad})_z + Z = 0$$

Expressed in terms of the tension coefficients, these equations become:

$$t_{ab}\bar{x}_{ab} + t_{ac}\bar{x}_{ac} + t_{ad}\bar{x}_{ad} + X = 0$$

$$t_{ab}\bar{y}_{ab} + t_{ac}\bar{y}_{ac} + t_{ad}\bar{y}_{ad} + Y = 0$$

$$t_{ab}\bar{z}_{ab} + t_{ac}\bar{z}_{ac} + t_{ad}\bar{z}_{ad} + Z = 0$$

Since $\bar{x}$, $\bar{y}$ and $\bar{z}$ for all members can be determined from the geometry of the structure, the tension coefficients can be solved from this set of simultaneous equations. Finally, the bar forces are obtained from the relations $F_{ab} = t_{ab}L_{ab}$, $F_{ac} = t_{ac}L_{ac}$, and $F_{ad} = t_{ad}L_{ad}$.

The same procedure may be used to solve the bar forces at any joint of a simple truss in space as long as the number of unknown bar forces at a joint is not greater than three. Therefore, we shall always start the solution from a joint with not more than three unknowns and proceed successively to other joints. The procedure can be efficiently carried out in a tabulated form.

Example 4-10. Compute the bar forces in all members of the space truss shown in Fig. 4-24.

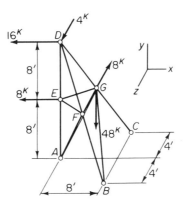

Figure 4-24

For the given structure, with the x-, y-, and z-axes directed as shown, the absolute values of the components of length of each member are obtained, and the length of the member itself is computed accordingly as shown in Table 4-2. Then, from the consideration of equilibrium of each joint, we can establish three equations of equilibrium. Starting from joint D we have

$$\sum F_x = 0, \qquad 4t_{df} + 4t_{dg} - 16 = 0$$

$$\sum F_z = 0, \qquad 2t_{df} - 2t_{dg} + 4 = 0$$

$$\sum F_y = 0, \qquad -8t_{df} - 8t_{dg} - 8t_{de} = 0$$

from which we obtain $t_{dg} = 3$, $t_{df} = 1$, and $t_{de} = -4$.

Table 4-2.

Member	$|\bar{x}|$	$|\bar{y}|$	$|\bar{z}|$	L (ft)	$t(= F/L)$	F (kips)
DE	0	8	0	8.00	-4.0	-32.0
DF	4	8	2	9.17	1.0	$+ 9.2$
DG	4	8	2	9.17	3.0	$+27.5$
EA	0	8	0	8.00	-4.0	-32.0
EF	4	0	2	4.48	1.0	$+ 4.5$
EG	4	0	2	4.48	1.0	$+ 4.5$
FA	4	8	2	9.17	-0.5	$- 4.6$
FB	4	8	2	9.17	1.5	$+13.7$
FG	0	0	4	4.00	0	0
GA	4	8	2	9.17	-3.5	-32.1
GB	4	8	6	10.77	1.0	$+10.8$
GC	4	8	2	9.17	-0.5	$- 4.6$

With the known value of t_{de}, we may proceed to solve the unknowns in the members meeting at joint E. Thus,

$$\sum F_x = 0, \qquad 4t_{ef} + 4t_{eg} - 8 = 0$$

$$\sum F_z = 0, \qquad 2t_{ef} - 2t_{eg} = 0$$

$$\sum F_y = 0, \qquad -8t_{ea} + 8t_{de} = 0$$

from which we obtain $t_{ef} = 1$, $t_{eg} = 1$, and $t_{ea} = -4$.
Similarly, from joint F we can establish

$$\sum F_x = 0, \qquad -4t_{df} - 4t_{ef} - 4t_{fa} + 4t_{fb} = 0$$

$$\sum F_z = 0, \qquad -2t_{df} - 2t_{ef} - 4t_{fg} - 2t_{fa} + 2t_{fb} = 0$$

$$\sum F_y = 0, \qquad 8t_{df} - 8t_{fa} - 8t_{fb} = 0$$

Since t_{ef} and t_{df} are known, we get $t_{fa} = -0.5$, $t_{fb} = 1.5$, and $t_{fg} = 0$.
Finally, we obtain from joint G the following equations:

$$\sum F_x = 0, \qquad -4t_{dg} - 4t_{eg} - 4t_{ga} + 4t_{gb} + 4t_{gc} = 0$$

$$\sum F_z = 0, \qquad 2t_{dg} + 2t_{eg} + 4t_{fg} + 2t_{ga} + 6t_{gb} - 2t_{gc} - 8 = 0$$

$$\sum F_y = 0, \qquad 8t_{dg} - 8t_{ga} - 8t_{gb} - 8t_{gc} - 48 = 0$$

With known values of t_{dg}, t_{eg}, and t_{fg}, the unknowns are obtained as follows: $t_{ga} = -3.5$, $t_{gb} = 1.0$, and $t_{gc} = -0.5$.

PROBLEMS

4-1 to **4-4.** Compute the bar forces in all members of the trusses shown in Figs. P4-1 to P4-4 by the method of joints.

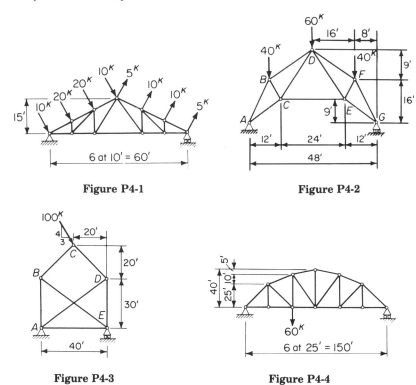

Figure P4-1

Figure P4-2

Figure P4-3

Figure P4-4

4-5 to **4-14.** Calculate the bar forces in members marked by letters a, b, and c of the trusses shown in Figs. P4-5 to P4-14 by the method of sections.

Figure P4-5

Figure P4-6

Bar Forces in Trusses   Chap. 4

Figure P4-7

Figure P4-8

Figure P4-9

Figure P4-10

Figure P4-11

Figure P4-12

Figure P4-13

Figure P4-14

4-15 to 4-18. Solve the bar forces in all members of the trusses shown in Figs. P4-15 to P4-18 by the method of shears and moments.

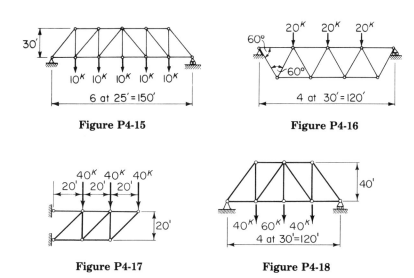

Figure P4-15

Figure P4-16

Figure P4-17

Figure P4-18

4-19 to 4-22. Calculate the bar forces in all members of the compound trusses shown in Figs. P4-19 to P4-22.

Figure P4-19

Figure P4-20

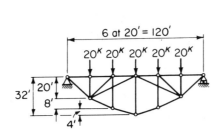

Figure P4-21

Figure P4-22

4-23 to 4-30. Calculate the bar forces in members marked by letters a, b, and c of the compound trusses shown in Figs. P4-23 to P4-30.

Figure P4-23

Figure P4-24

Figure P4-25

Figure P4-26

Figure P4-27

Figure P4-28

Figure P4-29

Figure P4-30

4-31 and **4-32.** Calculate the bar forces in all members of the complex trusses shown in Figs. P4-31 and P4-32.

Figure P4-31

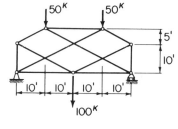

Figure P4-32

4-33 and **4-34.** Calculate the bar forces in all members of the space trusses shown in Figs. P4-33 and P4-34.

Figure P4-33

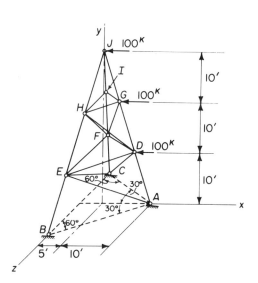

Figure P4-34

5

Cables and Arches

5-1 GEOMETRICAL PROFILES OF CABLES AND ARCHES

In many engineering structures, such as suspension bridges and transmission lines, cables are suspended between supports and subjected to vertical loads. Since a cable is flexible and cannot resist bending or compression, the internal force acting on any section of a cable can only be axial tension. When a cable of a given length is suspended between two supports, the shape of the cable is defined by the applied loads. For example, a cable uniformly loaded along the horizontal span takes the shape of a parabola, whereas a cable uniformly loaded along its length assumes the shape of a catenary. Cables loaded uniformly (or nearly so) along the horizontal span are by far the type most commonly used in structures—for example, cables supporting the roadway of a suspension bridge.

If a set of concentrated vertical loads is applied on a cable suspended between the supports, the coordinates of the points defining the geometrical profile of the cable can be determined from the equilibrium conditions of the cable at the points of loading. Since the tensile force in each segment of the cable between two applied vertical loads must have the same direction as that of the cable segment, the tensions in all cable segments can be computed by the method of joints.

On the other hand, arches are often subjected to predominantly axial compression under certain loading conditions. However, since an arch rib is rigid, it can resist shears and moments as well as axial forces. Furthermore, the shape of an arch rib does not change with applied loads, and it can be specified by the coordinates of the curve describing the centroidal axis of the arch rib.

For curved members in ordinary structures, such as arches, the radius of curvature of a member is usually so large in comparison with the depth of the member that the effect of the curvature may be neglected in locating the neutral axis of the member. Thus, the centroidal axis of the member may be considered as the neutral axis for bending. The axial force, shear, and moment at a section of a curved member can be as readily obtained as those for straight members. However, the location of a point on a curved member is specified by two coordinates instead of one. Thus, it is desirable to obtain an equation representing the curve by which the two coordinates are related. Furthermore, the slopes of the tangents at various points of the curve also can be determined from the derivative of the equation. Then, the axial force and the shear at any section can be specified in the axial and transverse directions of that particular section, respectively.

Before going into the methods of analyzing cables and arches, we shall consider the concept of pressure lines based on graphical analysis. Such an understanding will provide some insight on the choice of common geometrical profiles of cables and arches for engineering structures.

5-2 GRAPHICAL ANALYSIS OF STRUCTURES

In the analysis of simple structural systems, it is sometimes advantageous to obtain the solution of a problem by means of graphical construction. Since forces and displacements are vector quantities that are characterized by a magnitude, a vector direction, and a point of application, both the conditions of equilibrium of a structure and the geometry of its deflected shape can be represented graphically. However, a graphical solution is more than merely a convenient procedure for solving complex problems; it may lead to a basic understanding of the action of a structure under applied loads even if it is carried out in sketch form without great precision.

Consider the coplanar nonconcurrent force system as shown in Fig. 5-1(a),

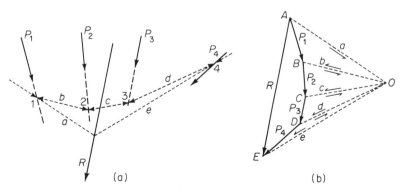

(a)

(b)

Figure 5-1

which is referred to as the *space diagram*. The corresponding force polygon is constructed in Fig. 5-1(b). We shall choose an arbitrary point O in Fig. 5-1(b) and join it with the apexes of the force polygon by dotted lines a, b, c, d, and e. The point O is called the *pole*, and the dotted lines are known as the *rays*. If arrowheads are placed next to the rays as shown, they may be regarded as vectors representing the components of the given forces. For example, the force P_1 may be resolved into components represented by vectors AO and OB, the force P_2 into components represented by vectors BO and OC, and so on. We shall now transfer these components back to the space diagram in Fig. 5-1(a). By selecting a convenient point 1 on the line of action of force P_1 in the figure, we draw two lines a and b passing through point 1 and at the same time parallel, respectively, to rays a and b in Fig. 5-1(b). The lines a and b in Fig. 5-1(a) are called *strings* and represent respectively the directions of the component vectors AO and OB of the force P_1. The string b intersects the force P_2 at point 2, through which string c is drawn to be parallel to ray c in Fig. 5-1(b). The same procedure is followed so that strings d and e can be drawn in Fig. 5-1(a). The polygon formed by the strings a, b, c, d, and e is called the *string* polygon, or *funicular* polygon. It may be concluded that if P_1, P_2, P_3, and P_4 are resolved into components as shown in Fig. 5-1(b), all components except AO and OE will eliminate each other. The combination of the remaining two components AO and OE leads to the same resultant R represented by the vector AE. The line of action of this resultant must pass through the intersection of strings a and e in Fig. 5-1(a). In other words, the system of forces P_1, P_2, P_3, and P_4 may be considered as being replaced by two forces having the same magnitude and direction as vectors AO and OE in the force polygon and acting along strings a and e of the string polygon.

If the force polygon constructed from a system of given forces is closed, i.e., the ending point coincides with the starting point, the resultant force is zero and the last ray coincides with the first ray. Consider, for example, the force system in Fig. 5-2(a), for which the force polygon is constructed in Fig. 5-2 (b). Since points E and A coincide, the ray a as represented by vector AO and the ray e as represented by vector OE also coincide. Hence, in the string polygon of Fig. 5-2(a), the strings a and e are parallel and at a perpendicular distance h apart. The resultant, therefore, is a couple, having a magnitude equal to the product of the vector AO and the distance h. On the other hand, the force system in Fig. 5-2(c) may also lead to the same force polygon shown in Fig.

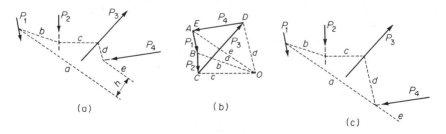

(a) (b) (c)

Figure 5-2

5-2(b), but the resulting string polygon in Fig. 5-2(c) indicates that strings a and e are colinear. In this case, not only does the resultant force vanish but the resultant couple is also equal to zero. The force system is therefore in equilibrium.

Example 5-1. Determine graphically the reactions at supports A and C of the three-hinged arch shown in Fig. 5-3(a).

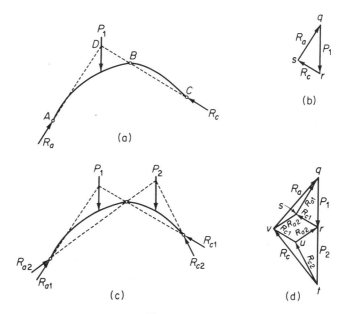

Figure 5-3

Since no external force is applied on the part of the arch rib from C to B, the rib CB, when isolated as a free body, is a two-force member in which the reaction acting at hinge C must be equal, opposite, and colinear to the force acting at hinge B. In other words, the line of action of the reaction R_c must pass through hinges C and B. If this line of action is extended until it intersects the applied force at point D, the line of action of the reaction R_c may be determined by the line joining points A and D. With the applied force plotted in a convenient scale, the reactions can be measured from the force polygon shown in Fig. 5-3(b).

If there is another force acting on rib BC as well as a force on rib AB of the arch, as shown in Fig. 5-3(c), we can first obtain the reactions resulting from each of the loads individually as if the other load were not acting. Hence, two force triangles qrs and rtu are obtained as indicated in Fig. 5-3(d), in which R_{a1} and R_{c1} are reactions at hinges A and C respectively due to P_1 alone and R_{a2} and R_{c2} are the corresponding reactions at A and C due to load P_2 alone. The resultant of the reactions at each support can be determined graphically by constructing lines vs parallel to ur and vu parallel to sr. Since $vsru$ is a parallelogram, the opposite sides are equal to each other. It is obvious, therefore, that vectors vq and tv represent the reactions R_a and R_c, respectively.

In the discussion of the construction of string polygons, we note that a system of forces such as P_1, P_2, P_3, and P_4 shown in Fig. 5-4(a) may be replaced by the two components of the resultant represented by the first and the last rays in the force polygon shown in Fig. 5-4(b). Hence, the system of forces P_1, P_2, P_3, and P_4 may be held in equilibrium by R_a and R_e, which are equal, opposite, and colinear to the respective components of the resultant. If an imaginary weightless cable or string is placed along strings a, b, c, d, and e of the string polygon, the string is in equilibrium under the action of the given forces and reactions. This concept may be generalized to include a string polygon of the shape shown in Fig. 5-4(c) as a result of the selection of the pole O' in Fig. 5-4(d). In that case, we can imagine the strings a', b', c', d', and e' of the string polygon as a bar chain capable of resisting compression that is held in equilibrium under the action of the given forces and reactions. Consider, for example, a simply supported beam as shown in Fig. 5-5(a). If a string polygon is constructed to pass through supports A and B as shown in Fig. 5-5(b), the resulting configuration may be thought of as the deflected shape of a cable or string supported at A and B under the action of loads P_1 and P_2. This configuration is identical to that of the moment diagram for the beam.

In the analysis of arches and frames, such an imaginary string or bar chain is often constructed to represent the successive resultants in their proper

Figure 5-4

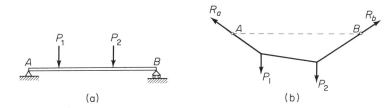

Figure 5-5

position along the length of the structure and is called a *pressure line*. For the three-hinged arch shown in Fig. 5-6(a), for instance, a string polygon representing the pressure line may be drawn through the three hinges as explained in the previous section. The moment at any point on the arch axis is equal to the force represented by the corresponding string of the pressure line multiplied by the perpendicular distance from this point to the string. The same concept may be applied to a rigid frame with three hinges, such as the one shown in Fig. 5-6(b). Thus, the moment at any point on the horizontal member of the frame is equal to the horizontal component of the corresponding string of the pressure line multiplied by the vertical ordinate between that point and the pressure line. Similarly, the moment at any point on a vertical member of the frame is equal to the vertical component of the corresponding string of the pressure line multiplied by the horizontal distance between that point and the pressure line. Thus, the pressure line itself is a moment curve, having the axis of the structure as its base line.

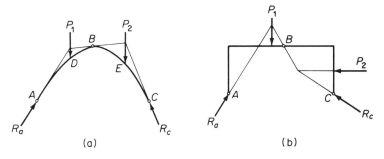

Figure 5-6

We may critically examine the efficiency of structural forms by means of the pressure line concept. A structural form is most efficient if all of its parts are subjected to approximately the same level of stress. Thus, members under direct stresses are more efficient in transmitting loads than those subjected to bending stresses so far as the utilization of the material is concerned. Unless other factors are involved in the selection of structural forms, bending should be avoided or minimized whenever possible. Consider, for example, the structural systems in Fig. 5-7 in which a load is transmitted to the foundation. Since all structures shown are statically determinate and each contains three hinges, the pressure line in each case can be constructed to pass through three given

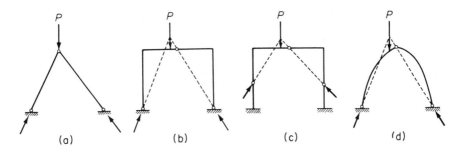

Figure 5-7

points as indicated in the figures. In Fig. 5-7(a), the load is transmitted to the supports by direct bar forces, but in Figs. 5-7(b), (c), and (d), moments exist along the length of the structure although the magnitudes of the moments vary according to the location of the pressure lines. Thus, Fig. 5-7(a) represents the most efficient system.

If there are several loads to be transmitted to the foundation, a pressure line may still be constructed through three given points. In Fig. 5-8(a), for instance, the pressure line is constructed to pass through point C on the line of action of the force P_1 as well as supports A and B, and the force polygon is shown in Fig. 5-8(b). Theoretically, a bar chain represented by the broken line $ACDB$ is the most efficient structure to transmit the forces P_1 and P_2 to the foundation. If the magnitudes of P_1 and P_2 change even slightly, however, the shape of the bar chain changes as shown in Fig. 5-8(c) corresponding to the force polygon in Fig. 5-8(d). Thus, a bar chain consisting of more than three hinges is unstable, and its shape can be uniquely determined only if the magnitudes as well as the positions of the applied loads are known.

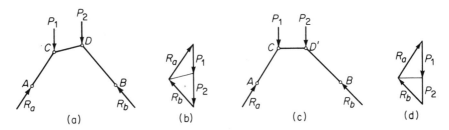

Figure 5-8

For a uniformly distributed load transmitted to the foundation through a statically determinate structure with three hinges as shown in Fig. 5-9(a), it can easily be seen that the pressure line is parabolic. If a three-hinged parabolic arch is selected, the arch rib will be subjected to direct forces only under the action of the uniform load. On the other hand, if a rigid frame as shown in Fig. 5-9(b) is used, the moments will be large at the rigid joints.

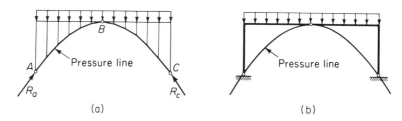

Figure 5-9

5-4 CABLES UNDER CONCENTRATED LOADS

If a set of vertical loads $P_1, P_2, \ldots, P_i, \ldots, P_n$ is applied on a cable suspended between two supports as shown in Fig. 5-10, the cable will assume the shape of a polygonal curve that depends on the magnitude and location of the loads.

Figure 5-10

Since the cable cannot transmit moment or shear, only axial tension T is present at any section. The reactions T_a and T_b at supports A and B may be resolved into vertical and horizontal components. Then, from the conditions of equilibrium, we obtain

$$\sum F_x = 0, \qquad H_a = H_b = H, \text{ a constant} \tag{5-1a}$$

$$\sum F_y = 0, \qquad V_a + V_b = \sum_{i=1}^{n} P_i \tag{5-1b}$$

$$\sum M_b = 0, \qquad V_a L - \sum_{i=1}^{n} P d_i - Hh = 0 \tag{5-1c}$$

where d_i is the horizontal distance from the load P_i to support B. Since there are four unknown components of reaction and only three equations of equilibrium, the fourth equation is supplied by the requirement that the moment at any section of the cable be zero. Thus, in a free body either to the right or to the left of a section, the sum of the moments of all forces about the section point on the cable must be zero. For the free body to the left of a section through point C, which is at a horizontal distance x from the left support A as shown in Fig. 5-10, the following equation may be obtained:

$$\sum M_c = 0, \qquad V_a x - \sum_{i=1}^{m} P_i e_i - Hy = 0 \qquad (5\text{-}1\text{d})$$

where $y = t + r$. The vertical distance t is proportional to the difference in elevation h between supports A and B according to the geometrical relation $t/x = h/L$. The vertical distance r is referred to as the *sag* of the cable at point C. If the sag at any point of the cable is known, the shape of the cable under a given set of concentrated loads P_i (for $i = 1, 2, \ldots, n$) is completely specified.

Very often, the sag of the cable under a concentrated load, say P_m, is given along with the magnitudes and lines of action of loads P_i. Consequently, the values x and y corresponding to the given sag r for P_m, as well as e_i measured from P_m (for $i = 1, 2, \ldots, m$), are known. Then, the horizontal and vertical components of reaction at supports A and B can be obtained from Eqs. (5-1) as follows:

$$H = \frac{1}{r}\left[\frac{x}{L}\sum_{i=1}^{n} P_i d_i - \sum_{i=1}^{m} P_i e_i\right] \qquad (5\text{-}2\text{a})$$

$$V_a = \frac{1}{L}\sum_{i=1}^{n} P_i d_i + \frac{Hh}{L} \qquad (5\text{-}2\text{b})$$

and

$$V_b = \sum_{i=1}^{n} P_i - \frac{1}{L}\sum_{i=1}^{n} P_i d_i - \frac{Hh}{L} \qquad (5\text{-}2\text{c})$$

In order to provide a stepwise procedure for computing the components of reaction, let us denote

$$M' = Hr = \frac{x}{L}\sum_{i=1}^{n} P_i d_i - \sum_{i=1}^{m} P_i e_i \qquad (5\text{-}3\text{a})$$

$$R_{a'} = \frac{1}{L}\sum_{i=1}^{n} P_i d_i \qquad (5\text{-}3\text{b})$$

$$R_{b'} = \sum_{i=1}^{n} P_i - \frac{1}{L}\sum_{i=1}^{n} P_i \qquad (5\text{-}3\text{c})$$

Then, Eqs. (5-2) can be simplified as follows:

$$H = \frac{M'}{r} \qquad (5\text{-}4\text{a})$$

$$V_a = R_{a'} + \frac{Hh}{L} \qquad (5\text{-}4\text{b})$$

$$V_b = R_{b'} - \frac{Hh}{L} \qquad (5\text{-}4\text{c})$$

When the supports A and B of the cable are at the same elevation, i.e., $h = 0$, then $V_a = R_{a'}$ and $V_b = R_{b'}$ while H remains unchanged from Eq. (5-2a).

The horizontal component of reaction H is sometimes referred to as the *horizontal tension*, which is constant throughout the cable. Thus, if a free-body diagram is drawn by passing a vertical section just to the left or just to the right of a concentrated load P_m, the horizontal component of the cable tension at either section must be H. Hence the tensions in all segments of the cable can be computed successively by the method of joints.

Example 5-2. Determine the component of reactions for the cable shown in Fig. 5-11, for which $r = 30$ ft and $t = 30$ ft at point C.

Figure 5-11

Since the sag of the cable at point C is given, we can obtain, in addition to the equilibrium equations, the moment at C when the cable to the left of C is considered a free body. That is,

$$\sum F_x = 0, \qquad H_a = H_b = H$$

$$\sum F_y = 0, \qquad V_a + V_b = 50$$

$$\sum M_b = 0, \qquad 120V_a - (10)(20)(1 + 2 + 3 + 4 + 5) - 45\,H = 0$$

$$\sum M_c = 0, \qquad 80V_a - (10)(20)(1 + 2 + 3) - 60\,H = 0$$

from which we find $H = 26.7$ kips, $V_a = 35$ kips and $V_b = 15$ kips.

Alternately, we can make use of Eqs. (5-3a) and (5-3b) as follows:

$$M' = (25)(80) - (10)(20)(1 + 2 + 3) = 800 \text{ ft-kips}$$

$$R_{a'} = \tfrac{1}{120}[(10)(20)(1 + 2 + 3 + 4 + 5)] = 25 \text{ kips}$$

Then, from Eqs. (5-4),

$$H = \tfrac{800}{30} = 26.7 \text{ kips}$$

$$V_a = 25 + (26.7)(45)/(120) = 35 \text{ kips}$$

$$V_b = 50 - 25 - (26.7)(45)/(120) = 15 \text{ kips}$$

It should be noted that once the vertical loads are given, the polygonal curve is uniquely determined. In other words, the ordinates at various points of the polygonal curve are interrelated in accordance with the applied loads and cannot be

           Cables and Arches   Chap. 5

arbitrarily assumed. If the sag r at one point in the cable is known, the sag at any other point may be obtained after the horizontal tension H is computed. Thus, for the cable in Fig. 5-11, $r_c = 30$ ft and $H = 26.7$ kips. Therefore,

$$r_d = \frac{M'}{H} = \frac{1}{26.7}(25)(20) = 18.75 \text{ ft}$$

$$r_e = \frac{1}{26.7}[(25)(40) - (10)(20)] = 30.0 \text{ ft}$$

$$r_f = \frac{1}{26.7}[(25)(60) - (10)(40 + 20)] = 33.75 \text{ ft}$$

5-5 CABLES WITH UNIFORM LOADS

When a cable is loaded uniformly along the horizontal span, it assumes the shape of a parabola as shown in Fig. 5-12(a). For any section at a horizontal distance x from the left support, the horizontal tension H due to uniform load w from Eq. (5-2a) is as follows:

$$Hr = \tfrac{1}{2}wLx - \tfrac{1}{2}wx^2$$

At $x = L/2$, for which the sag r is equal to f, then

$$H = \frac{wL^2}{8f} \tag{5-5}$$

Substituting this value of H into the previous equation, we obtain

$$r = \frac{4fx}{L^2}(L - x)$$

Since $y = r + t = r + hx/L$,

$$y = \frac{4fx}{L^2}(L - x) + \frac{hx}{L} \tag{5-6}$$

(a)

(b)

Figure 5-12

This is the equation of a parabola having point A as the origin and the positive coordinate axes directed as shown in Fig. 5-12(a).

The tension at any point of the cable may be obtained from the free body cut by a section through that point, as shown in Fig. 5-12(b). If the horizontal tension H is known, the tension T at any point in the cable at a horizontal distance x from the left support is given by

$$T = H \sec \theta = H \frac{ds}{dx}$$

where ds is measured along the length of the cable.

By taking the derivative of Eq. (5-6), we obtain

$$\frac{dy}{dx} = \frac{4f}{L^2}(L - 2x) + \frac{h}{L}$$

Thus,

$$\frac{ds}{dx} = \sqrt{1 + \left(\frac{dy}{dx}\right)^2} = \left[1 + \left(\frac{4f}{L} - \frac{8fx}{L^2} + \frac{h}{L}\right)^2\right]^{1/2}$$

If $n = f/L$ is defined as the sag ratio of a cable, the tension in the cable is equal to

$$T = H\left[1 + 16n^2 + \frac{64n^2x^2}{L^2} + \frac{h^2}{L^2} - \frac{64n^2x}{L} - \frac{16nxh}{L^2} + \frac{8nh}{L}\right]^{1/2} \qquad (5\text{-}7a)$$

The maximum tension occurs at one of the supports where the slope of the curve has maximum absolute value. Thus, for $x = 0$,

$$T_a = H\left[1 + 16n^2 + \frac{h^2}{L^2} + \frac{8nh}{L}\right]^{1/2} \qquad (5\text{-}7b)$$

and for $x = L$,

$$T_b = H\left[1 + 16n^2 + \frac{h^2}{L^2} - \frac{8nh}{L}\right]^{1/2} \qquad (5\text{-}7c)$$

Hence, T_a represents the maximum tension in the cable.

If the supports of a cable are at the same elevation, Eqs. (5-6) and (5-7) may be simplified by letting $h = 0$, i.e.,

$$y = \frac{4fx}{L^2}(L - x) \qquad (5\text{-}8)$$

and

$$T = H\left[1 + 16n^2 + \frac{64n^2x}{L}\left(\frac{x}{L} - 1\right)\right]^{1/2} \qquad (5\text{-}9a)$$

For $x = 0$ or $x = L$,

$$T_{\max} = H\left[1 + 16n^2\right]^{1/2} \qquad (5\text{-}9b)$$

Example 5-3. The cable shown in Fig. 5-13 is subjected to a uniform load of 1 kip/ft. The supports of the cable are at the same elevation. $L = 160$ ft, $f = 40$ ft, and $n = f/L = 0.25$. Determine the maximum tension in the cable.

Figure 5-13

From Eq. (5-5), we have

$$H = \frac{(1)(160)^2}{(8)(40)} = 80 \text{ kips}$$

and from Eq. (5-8),

$$y = \frac{(4)(0.25)x}{160}(160 - x) = x - \frac{x^2}{160}$$

The tension in the cable can be obtained from Eq. (5-9a):

$$T = (80)\left[1 + (16)(0.25)^2 + \frac{(64)(0.25)^2 x}{160}\left(\frac{x}{160} - 1\right)\right]^{1/2}$$

$$= (80)\left[2 + \frac{x}{40}\left(\frac{x}{160} - 1\right)\right]^{1/2}$$

At supports A and B, where $x = 0$ and $x = L$, respectively,

$$T_a = T_b = 80\sqrt{2} = 106.5 \text{ kips}$$

5-6 SUSPENDED GIRDERS

If a girder is suspended from a cable at uniformly spaced intervals, and hinged at the center as well as at the ends, as shown in Fig. 5-14, a simple statically determinate suspension bridge is formed. The cable tends to take the form of an equilibrium polygon for any set of applied loads. Thus, the cable takes a parabolic shape under the dead load, which is uniformly distributed along the horizontal span. The main function of the girder is to distribute the moving loads so that the cable remains essentially parabolic under the action of such loads. The girder transmits very little load to its supports and all loads are primarily carried by the hangers. It may be assumed that, with the stiffening system, the hanger loads are equal throughout the entire span.

Consider, for example, the system in Fig. 5-14(a) for which the load is concentrated at point D'. A free-body diagram of the entire system may be drawn as in Fig. 5-14(b), in which there are six unknown components of reaction. Since there are only three equations of equilibrium, we must seek additional equations from other considerations. If a vertical section is cut through

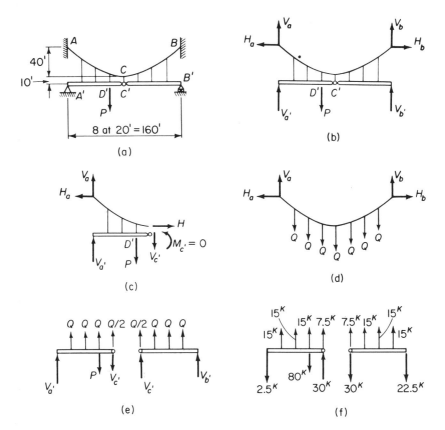

Figure 5-14

the cable and the girder arbitrarily as shown in Fig. 5-14(c), there will be a vertical component as well as the horizontal component of tension H in the cable, and there are in general shear and moment in the girder. However, if the section is passed through CC', the vertical component of the tension in the cable is zero since C is the lowest point of the cable, and the moment in the girder is zero because of the hinge at C'. Thus, the problem is greatly simplified, and one more independent equation is gained from the condition of the release. When the cable is separated from the girder as shown in Fig. 5-14(d), the vertical loads Q from the hangers can be related to the components of reaction of the cable. With the given condition of release $\Sigma M_{c'} = 0$, all components of reaction acting on the cable, i.e., V_a, V_b, and H, may be obtained by Eqs. (5-3) and (5-4). The remaining components of reaction $V_{a'}$ and $V_{b'}$ acting on the girder may then be obtained from the equations of equilibrium when the entire system is taken as a free body, or from the free-body diagrams shown in Fig. 5-14(e).

The tension at any section of the cable may be obtained from Eq. (5-9a), with maximum tension at the supports as given by Eq. (5-9b). The shear and moment at any section of the girder may be obtained from the free-body diagrams in Fig. 5-14(e) after the magnitude of the vertical loads Q has been found.

Example 5-4. The dimensions of the statically determinate suspended bridge shown in Fig. 5-14(a) are given as follows: $L = 8 @ 20$ ft $= 160$ ft, $f = 40$ ft, and $CC' = 10$ ft. A concentrated load of $P = 80$ kips is acting at point D'. Compute the reactions at all supports.

From the consideration of the entire system as a free body, as it is shown in Fig. 5-14(b),

$$\sum M_b = 0, \qquad (V_a + V_{a'})(160) - (80)(100) = 0, \qquad V_a + V_{a'} = 50 \text{ kips}$$

$$\sum F_x = 0, \qquad H_a = H_b = H$$

$$\sum F_y = 0, \qquad (V_a + V_{a'}) + (V_b + V_{b'}) = 80, \qquad V_b + V_{b'} = 30 \text{ kips}$$

From the consideration of the left half of the system as a free body, as shown in Fig. 5-14(c), $\sum M_{c'} = 0$,

$$(V_a + V_{a'})(80) - 40H - (80)(20) = 0$$

$$40H = (50)(80) - (80)(20) = 2,400, \qquad H = 60 \text{ kips}$$

From the consideration of equilibrium of the cable isolated from the girder, as shown in Fig. 5-14(d), $V_a = V_b = 7Q/2$. For $\sum M_c = 0$,

$$(7Q/2)(80) - (Q)(3 + 2 + 1)(20) = (60)(40)$$

$$160Q = 2,400, \qquad Q = 15 \text{ kips}$$

$$V_a = 3.5Q = 52.5 \text{ kips}, \qquad V_b = 52.5 \text{ kips}$$

Hence,

$$V_{a'} = 50 - V_a = 50 - 52.5 = -2.5 \text{ kips}$$
$$V_{b'} = 30 - V_b = 30 - 52.5 = -22.5 \text{ kips}$$

Finally, consider the left half of the girder as a free body as shown in Fig. 5-14(e), $\sum M_{c'} = 0$,

$$(V_{a'})(80) + (15)(3 + 2 + 1)(20) - (80)(20) = 0$$

$$V_{a'} = -2.5 \text{ kips (checked)}$$

The minus sign indicates that the sense of direction of $V_{a'}$ shown in Fig. 5-14(e) should be reversed. Similarly, $V_{b'}$ may be obtained by considering the right half of the girder as a free body. Thus, the components of reaction of the girder can be completely determined from Fig. 5-14(e). Such results with correct senses of direction are shown in Fig. 5-14(f).

Example 5-5. For the suspension bridge shown in Fig. 5-15(a), draw the shear and moment diagrams for the girder.

This structure is identical to that of the previous example except that hangers are present at points A and B also. When the entire system is considered as a free body, the equations of equilibrium obtained in the previous example still

(a)

(c)

(b)

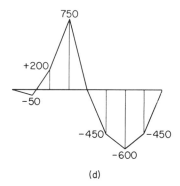

(d)

Figure 5-15

hold. Thus, $H = 60$ kips. When the cable is isolated as a free body, the hanger loads at A and B are each $Q/2$ as shown in Fig. 5-15(b). Hence, the cable may be considered as uniformly loaded with $w = 8Q/160 = Q/20$. Then, from Eq. (5-5), we get

$$H = \frac{(Q/20)(160)^2}{(8)(40)} = 4Q$$

or

$$Q = \frac{H}{4} = 15 \text{ kips}$$

Thus, the vertical reactions may be obtained in a manner similar to the previous example as follows:

$$V_a = 60 \text{ kips}, \qquad V_b = 60 \text{ kips}$$

$$V_{a'} = -10 \text{ kips}, \qquad V_{b'} = -30 \text{ kips}$$

Obviously, each cable reaction has been increased by an amount of $Q/2 = 7.5$ kips over that in the previous example while each girder reaction has been decreased by the same amount.

Since this problem can be treated as one with uniformly distributed load, the vertical reactions in the cable can also be obtained directly from the slope of the cable at each support. Note that in this case,

$$\frac{dy}{dx} = \frac{4f}{L^2}(L - 2x) = \frac{(4)(40)}{(160)^2}(160 - 2x) = 1 - \frac{2x}{160}$$

For $x = 0$, $dy/dx = 1$, and for $x = 160$ ft, $dy/dx = -1$. Hence

$$V_a = V_b = H = 60 \text{ kips}$$

The shear and moment diagrams for the girder are shown in Figs. 5-15(c) and (d) respectively. It may be observed from the shear diagram that the load $Q/2$ in each end hanger does not affect the shears in the girder. The ordinates in the shear diagram are obtained by the summation of loads from left to right of the girder, whereas the ordinates in the moment diagram are obtained by the summation of the areas in the shear diagram.

5-7 SUSPENDED TRUSSES

The roadway of a suspension bridge may be stiffened by trusses instead of girders. The main function of the stiffening truss is also to distribute moving loads so that the cable remains essentially parabolic under the action of such loads. Consequently, the loads on the equally spaced vertical hangers are assumed to be equal through the entire span.

The principle of analyzing suspended trusses is identical to that for analyzing suspended girders. A suspended truss with a release is statically determinate. Hence, the components of reaction of the cable and the truss can be obtained from the consideration of equilibrium of the isolated systems as represented by the cable and the truss.

Example 5-6. For the statically determinate suspended truss in Fig. 5-16(a), compute the bar forces in members a, b, c, d and e of the truss.

For this problem, the components of reaction of the cable and the truss are identical to those for the cable and the beam in Example 5-5. Consequently, we

(a)   (b)

Figure 5-16

can consider the free body in Fig. 5-16(b) in determining the bar forces in the left half of the truss. Using either the method of joints or the method of sections, we obtain

$$F_a = -\left(\frac{20}{25}\right)(30 + 7.5) = -30 \text{ kips } (C)$$

$$F_b = \left(\frac{32}{25}\right)(30 + 7.5) = 48 \text{ kips } (T)$$

$$F_c = 15 \text{ kips } (T)$$

$$F_d = \left(\frac{32}{25}\right)(80 - 37.5 - 15) = 35.2 \text{ kips } (T)$$

$$F_e = \left(\frac{20}{32}\right)(48 - 35.2) = 8 \text{ kips } (T)$$

5-8 COMMON TYPES OF ARCHES

Arches are structural forms that span two immovable supports and are shaped like inverted cables under uniform loads. The most common types of arches are the hingeless arch, two-hinged arch, and three-hinged arch, as shown in Figs. 5-17(a), (b), and (c) respectively. A hingeless arch is statically indeterminate to three degrees, while a two-hinged arch is statically indeterminate to one degree. A three-hinged arch is statically determinate and will therefore be treated in detail in this chapter. The arch with a tie-rod in Fig. 5-17(d) is sometimes used to resist the horizontal thrust so that one of the supports may be placed on a roller. The stiffened tied-arch in Fig. 5-17(e) consists of a stiff girder (relative to the arch rib) so that the load on the girder can be transmitted relatively evenly through the vertical hangers to the arch rib. The arch types in both Figs. 5-17(d) and (e) are statically indeterminate.

Arches can generally resist bending and shear as well as direct compression. However, if an arch rib has the shape of a second-degree parabola and is subjected to a uniform load throughout its horizontal projection, it can be shown that there is no moment acting at any section along the arch rib. For example, consider the arch rib in Fig. 5-18(a), which is assumed to resist no moment. Then, from symmetry, the vertical reactions due to a uniform load w per horizontal foot are $V_a = V_b = wL/2$; and from $\Sigma M_c = 0$ on the left half as a free body, the horizontal reactions are found to be $H_a = H_b = H = wL^2/8f$. Furthermore, because of symmetry, $V_c = 0$ and $H_c = H$ in Fig. 5-18(b). By taking moments at point D in Fig. 5-18(b), we have

$$\frac{wx^2}{2} - V_d x + H_d y = 0$$

Noting that $H_d = H = wL^2/8f$ and $V_d = wx$, we find

$$y = \frac{4f}{L^2}x^2 \tag{5-10}$$

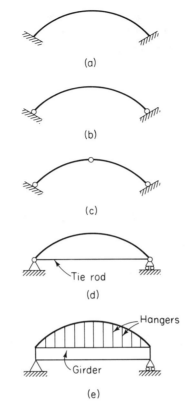

(a)

(b)

(c)

Tie rod
(d)

Hangers

Girder
(e)

Figure 5-17

$w/\text{horiz. ft}$

(a)

$w/\text{horiz. ft}$

(b)

Figure 5-18

which is the equation of a second-degree parabola with point C as the origin. This result is expected since the arch rib is essentially an inverted cable. Consequently, an arch under a uniform load throughout its horizontal projection is not subjected to bending if the arch rib has the shape of a second-degree parabola, whether the arch is hingeless, two-hinged, or three-hinged.

In general, we can choose a convenient set of coordinate axes for a second-degree parabola by using the equation

$$y = Ax^2 + Bx + C$$

in which A, B, and C are constant. For the coordinate system in Fig. 5-19(a), we have $y = 0$ at $x = 0$, and $y = 33.75$ for $x = \pm 60$. Thus, $A = \frac{3}{320}$, $B = 0$, and $C = 0$. The resulting equation is

$$y = \frac{3}{320}x^2 \quad \text{and} \quad \frac{dy}{dx} = \frac{3}{160}x$$

Thus, the slope at any point of the arch can be obtained by substituting the value of x into the first derivative of the curve.

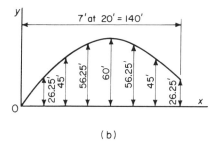

(a)   (b)

Figure 5-19

If another coordinate system is chosen as shown in Fig. 5-19(b), we can proceed in the same manner in evaluating the constants in the equation for a second-degree parabola. In this case, $y = 0$ at $x = 0$, $y = 60$ at $x = 80$, and $dy/dx = 0$ at $x = 80$. Thus, $A = -\frac{3}{320}$, $B = \frac{3}{2}$, and $C = 0$. The equation of the arch axis then becomes

$$y = -\tfrac{3}{320}x^2 + \tfrac{3}{2}x$$

Again, the slope at a point of the arch can be obtained from the first derivative of this equation.

5-9 THREE-HINGED ARCHES

Since three-hinged arches are statically determinate, they can be treated as statically determinate frames with curved members. The only complication is that the coordinates of points at which the loads are applied or at which the internal forces and moments are sought must be determined from the shape of the arch rib. Furthermore, the normal compressive force N and the tangential shear force S at a section are often required for design purpose instead of the horizontal and vertical components of forces in the directions of the coordinate axes defining the arch rib.

In order to draw the shear and moment diagrams for a curved member, however, we encounter difficulties that are not present in the case of straight members. First, the direction of the axis of the member changes along its length. Thus, the axial force and shear at any section depend on the angle between a horizontal line and the tangent to the curve at that point. Secondly, the base line for the shear and moment diagrams is a curve instead of a straight line. As a matter of convenience, shear and moment diagrams on the *horizontal projection* of the axis of the curved member are sometimes used if the external loads are all vertical. These diagrams are useful for design purposes, but their limitations should be recognized.

Example 5-7. Figure 5-20(a) shows a three-hinged arch whose axis is represented by the parabolic curve in Fig. 5-19(a). Determine the axial force, shear, and moment at points D and E of the arch, if $x_1 = 40$ ft, $y_1 = 45$ ft, $x_2 = 40$ ft, and $y_2 = 30$ ft.

If a section is passed through point D of the arch axis, the free body on the left-hand side of the section can be represented by either Fig. 5-20(b) or 5-20(c).

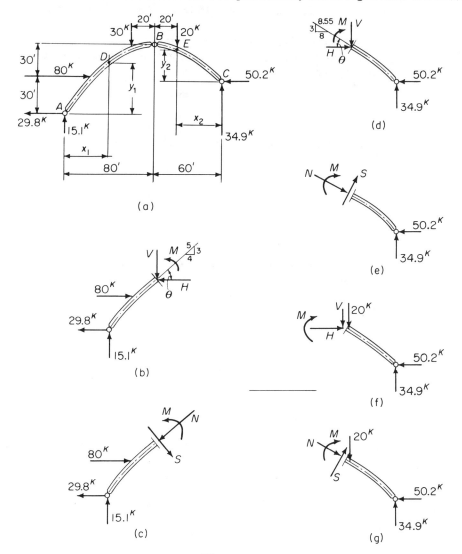

Figure 5-20

In the former case, the components of forces at the section are resolved into horizontal and vertical directions whereas in the latter, the components of forces at the section are shown in axial and transverse directions. Since the direction of the arch axis changes from point to point, it is easier to sum up all the external forces and reactions acting on the free body in horizontal and vertical directions. Thus, from Fig. 5-20(b),

$$\sum F_x = 0, \qquad H = 50.2 \text{ kips}$$

$$\sum F_y = 0, \qquad V = 15.1 \text{ kips}$$

$$\sum M_d = 0, \qquad M = 15.1x_1 + 29.8y_1 - 80(y_1 - 30) \text{ ft-kips}$$

The axial force N and the shear S in Fig. 5-20(c) can easily be obtained from the consideration of the equilibrium of the free body, or they may be expressed in the following form:

$$N = H \cos \theta + V \sin \theta$$

$$S = -H \sin \theta + V \cos \theta$$

For example, if $x_1 = 40$ ft and $y_1 = 45$ ft, $\tan \theta = \frac{3}{4}$. Then, $\sin \theta = \frac{3}{5}$ and $\cos \theta = \frac{4}{5}$. Hence,

$$N = (50.2)(\tfrac{4}{5}) + (15.1)(\tfrac{3}{5}) = 40.2 + 9.1 = 49.3 \text{ kips}$$

$$S = (15.1)(\tfrac{4}{5}) - (50.2)(\tfrac{3}{5}) = 12.1 - 30.1 = -18.0 \text{ kips}$$

$$M = (15.1)(40) + (29.8)(45) - (80)(15) = 744 \text{ ft-kips}$$

When a section is passed through point E, the right-hand side of the section may be considered as a free body. For $x_2 = 40$ and $y_2 = 30$, the section coincides with the vertical load of 20 kips. Therefore, we can only take a section either just to the right or just to the left of the vertical load. The former is shown by the free body in Fig. 5-20(d) or 5-20(e), and the latter is illustrated by the free body in Fig. 5-20(f) or 5-20(g). For either case, we obtain the following relations:

$$N = H \cos \theta + V \sin \theta$$

$$S = H \sin \theta - V \cos \theta$$

Since $\tan \theta = \frac{3}{8}$ for $x_2 = 40$ and $y_2 = 30$,

$$\sin \theta = 3/8.55 = 0.351 \quad \text{and} \quad \cos \theta = 8/8.55 = 0.936$$

From Fig. 5-20(d) for a section just to the right of point E,

$$\sum F_x = 0, \qquad H = 50.2 \text{ kips}$$

$$\sum F_y = 0, \qquad V = 34.9 \text{ kips}$$

$$\sum M_e = 0, \qquad M = 34.9x_2 - 50.2y_2 \text{ ft-kips}$$

Then from Fig. 5-20(e),

$$N = (50.2)(0.936) + (34.9)(0.351) = 47.1 + 12.2 = 59.3 \text{ kips}$$
$$S = (50.2)(0.351) - (34.9)(0.936) = 17.6 - 32.6 = -15.0 \text{ kips}$$
$$M = (34.9)(40) - (50.2)(30) = -110 \text{ ft-kips}$$

Similarly, from Fig. 5-20(f) for a section just to the left of point E,

$$\sum F_x = 0, \qquad H = 50.2 \text{ kips}$$

$$\sum F_y = 0, \qquad V = 34.9 - 20 = 14.9 \text{ kips}$$

$$\sum M_e = 0, \qquad M = 34.9x_2 - 50.2y_2 \text{ ft-kips}$$

Then from Fig. 5-20(g),

$$N = (50.2)(0.936) + (14.9)(0.351) = 47.1 + 5.2 = 52.3 \text{ kips}$$
$$S = (50.2)(0.351) - (14.9)(0.936) = 17.6 - 14.0 = 3.6 \text{ kips}$$
$$M = -110 \text{ ft-kips}$$

Note that N and S are influenced by the location of the section because of different values of V just to the left or to the right of point E, but M is unaffected since the moment arm for the vertical load at point E is zero for all practical purposes.

Example 5-8. Prove that the bending moment at any point of the three-hinged arch shown in Fig. 5-21(a) is equal to the corresponding vertical ordinate of the shaded area multiplied by a constant factor. If the arch axis is a semicircle that is represented by the equation

$$(x - r)^2 + y^2 = r^2$$

in which r is the radius of the circle, evaluate this constant factor.

Since no external load is applied on segment BC of the arch, the reaction R_c must pass through hinge B in order to maintain the equilibrium of the segment when it is isolated as a free body. When the entire arch is considered as a free body, there are three forces acting on the structure, i.e., the external load P and the reactions R_a and R_c. Thus, R_a must pass through the intersection of P and R_c. Lines AF and CF in Fig. 5-21(b) represent the lines of action of reactions R_a and R_c, respectively.

From the equation of the circle, the ordinate y of a point on the circle may be expressed as

$$y = \sqrt{r^2 - (x - r)^2} = \sqrt{2rx - x^2} \qquad \text{(a)}$$

The equation for line AF is given by

$$y = 3x \qquad \text{(b)}$$

whereas the equation for line CF is

$$y = 2r - x \qquad \text{(c)}$$

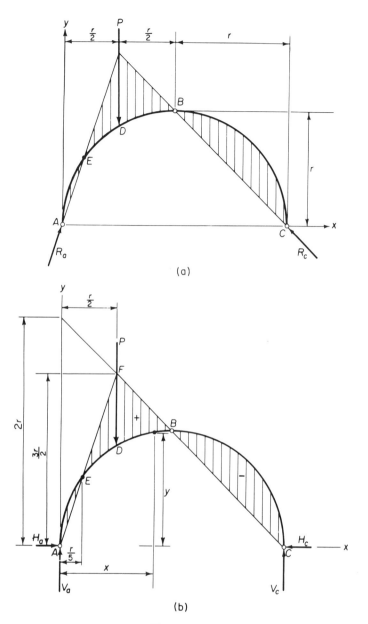

Figure 5-21

The intersection E of line AF and the circle may be obtained from the simultaneous solution of Eqs. (a) and (b). Thus, $x = r/5$.

Let t be the ordinate of the shaded area that is the vertical intercept between two curves, i.e., the difference of the ordinates of two curves. Thus,

$$t = \sqrt{2rx - x^2} - 3x \qquad \text{for } 0 \leqq x \leqq r/5$$

$$t = 3x - \sqrt{2rx - x^2} \qquad \text{for } r/5 \leq x \leq r/2$$

$$t = 2r - x - \sqrt{2rx - x^2} \qquad \text{for } r/2 \leq x \leq r$$

$$t = \sqrt{2rx - x^2} - 2r + x \qquad \text{for } r \leq x \leq 2r$$

From the conditions of equilibrium of the entire structure, we obtain the components of reactions as follows:

$$\sum F_x = 0, \qquad H_a = H_c = H$$

$$\sum F_y = 0, \qquad V_a + V_c = P$$

$$\sum M_a = 0, \qquad 2rV_c - Pr/2 = 0$$

From the condition of release at B, we obtain an additional equation by considering only segment BC of the arch

$$\sum M_b = 0, \qquad rV_c - rH = 0$$

Thus,

$$V_a = 3P/4, \qquad V_c = P/4, \quad \text{and} \quad H = P/4$$

The bending moment at any point on the arch whose ordinate is (x, y) may be obtained as follows:

for $0 \leq x \leq r/5$, $\qquad M = V_a x - Hy = -\dfrac{P}{4}(\sqrt{2rx - x^2} - 3x)$

for $r/5 \leq x \leq r/2$, $\qquad M = V_a x - Hy = \dfrac{P}{4}(3x - \sqrt{2rx - x^2})$

for $r/2 \leq x \leq r$, $\qquad M = V_a x - Hy - P\left(x - \dfrac{r}{2}\right)$

$$= \dfrac{P}{4}(2r - x - \sqrt{2rx - x^2})$$

for $r \leq x \leq 2r$, $\qquad M = V_c(2r - x) - Hy$

$$= -\dfrac{P}{4}(\sqrt{2rx - x^2} - 2r + x)$$

It may be noted that for all values of x, the bending moment at a point on the arch is equal to $P/4$ times the corresponding ordinate of the shaded area. Hence, $P/4$ is the constant factor.

It is interesting to note that the moments at various points of the arch can be measured directly from the shaded area in the figure if a proper scale is used. More important is the fact that such a conclusion is also applicable to arches of any shape with any loading as long as the lines of action between reactions and loads can be drawn. Thus, the determination of moments at various sections of an arch will be greatly simplified by this consideration.

As described earlier in this chapter, an arch rib that is under horizontal uniform loads throughout its span will be subjected predominantly to compression. For a three-hinged arch with a parabolic profile, the bending moment at any point of the arch axis is, in fact, zero.

Let us consider a three-hinged arch with a uniform load of 1 kip per horizontal foot throughout its entire span, as shown in Fig. 5-22(a).

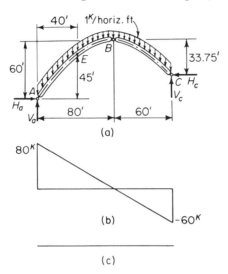

(a)

(b)

(c)   **Figure 5-22**

The reactions are found to be as follows: $H_a = 53.3$ kips, $V_a = 80$ kips, $H_c = 53.3$ kips, and $V_c = 60$ kips. Then, the horizontal component of forces acting at any section of the arch is constant, and the variation of the vertical component can be represented by the shear diagram based on the horizontal projection of the arch axis as shown in Fig. 5-22(b). Moments at various points of the arch are found to be zero. For example,

$$M_e = (80)(40) - (53.3)(45) - (1)(40)^2/2 = 0$$

Thus, the moment diagram plotted on the horizontal projection of the arch axis has zero area as shown in Fig. 5-22(c).

This example points out a very important feature of arches. While the vertical reaction from the vertical loads on an arch tends to produce a positive moment at a section, the horizontal reaction tends to reduce such a moment. Hence, the moment at any section of an arch is much smaller than the moment at the same section of a beam with equal span and subjected to the same vertical loads. For an arch span fully loaded with a uniform vertical load, the moment curve resulting from vertical forces alone has the shape of a second-degree parabola. If the arch axis is also a second-degree parabola, the negative moment at a section caused by the horizontal reaction eliminates exactly the positive moment at that section caused by the vertical forces. That is the reason for the zero moment at any point along the arch axis.

Example 5-9. Figure 5-23(a) shows a three-hinged arch, the right half of which has a uniform load of 1 kip per horizontal foot. Draw the shear and moment diagrams on the horizontal projection of the arch axis.

(a)

(b)

(c)

Figure 5-23

The reactions at A and C are first obtained as follows:

$$\sum M_c = 0, \qquad 140V_a - 26.25H_a - (1)(60)^2/2 = 0$$

$$\sum F_x = 0, \qquad H_a = H_c$$

$$\sum F_y = 0, \qquad V_a + V_c = (1)(60)$$

$$\sum M_b = 0, \qquad 80V_a = 60H_a$$

Hence, $H_a = 22.8$ kips, $V_a = 17.1$ kips, $H_c = 22.8$ kips, and $V_c = 42.9$ kips.

Since there is no external load on the segment AB, the resultant of H_a and V_a must pass through hinge B in order to maintain the equilibrium of the two-force member AB when it is separated as a free body. This requirement is indicated by the condition of release $\sum M_b = 0$, which implies that $V_a/H_a = \frac{60}{80} = \frac{3}{4}$. As a check, this same relation is obtained from the ratio of the actual components of reaction at A, or $V_a/H_a = 17.1/22.8 = \frac{3}{4}$.

Since there is no external horizontal load, the horizontal component of forces acting at any section of the arch is constant. The vertical component of these forces at the same section varies along the horizontal projection of the arch axis, and such variation is indicated by the shear diagram in Fig. 5-23(b). Hence, the axial force and transverse shear at any section normal to the arch may be obtained by resolving the horizontal and vertical components of forces at that section into axial and transverse components. Moments are computed for points on the arch axis at 20-ft intervals of the horizontal projection, and are plotted on the moment diagram with the horizontal projection on the arch axis as the base line as shown in Fig. 5-23(c). For instance,

$$M_d = (17.1)(20) - (22.8)(26.25) = -257 \text{ ft-kips}$$

$$M_e = (17.1)(40) - (22.8)(45.0) = -342 \text{ ft-kips}$$

$$M_f = (17.1)(60) - (22.8)(56.25) = -257 \text{ ft-kips}$$

$$M_b = 0$$

$$M_g = (42.9)(40) - (22.8)(30) - (1)(40)^2/2 = 232 \text{ ft-kips}$$

$$M_h = (42.9)(20) - (22.8)(18.75) - (1)(20)^2/2 = 230 \text{ ft-kips}$$

It should be pointed out that such a moment diagram does not give the true variation of moments along the arch axis; it serves only as a convenient framework for tabulating the computed moments at the desired locations.

Example 5-10.   The arch in Fig. 5-24(a) is supporting a floor system. The distributed

(a)

(b)

(c)

(d)

Figure 5-24

load on the girder is transmitted to the arch through the vertical posts. Draw the shear and moment diagrams on the horizontal projection of the arch axis.

The vertical loads transmitted to the arch rib through the vertical posts are shown in Fig. 5-24(b). Thus, the reactions at the supports are computed accordingly. The vertical shears are shown on a horizontal base in Fig. 5-24(c); the moments are plotted on the horizontal projection of the arch axis as shown in Fig. 5-24(d). These diagrams may be compared with those of Fig. 5-23 for the same arch without vertical posts for transmitting floor loads. Note that the vertical shears are affected by the introduction of the vertical posts to the system, but the moments at the panel points remain unchanged. We should point out again that the variation of moments along the arch axis cannot be correctly represented by a moment diagram based on the horizontal projection. Ordinates of the moments other than those at the panel points are not true values. The straight line segments joining the moments at panel points in Fig. 5-24(d) are introduced for the sake of simplicity. Fortunately, shears and moments at the panel points are usually the only points of interest for design purposes. Hence, from a practical point of view, the ordinates of the moment diagram between panel points are not important.

5-11 STIFFENED TIED-ARCHES

As indicated in Section 5-8, a stiffened tied-arch consists of a stiffening system, such as a girder or a truss, which has a stiffness far greater than that of the arch rib. Although stiffened tied-arches are generally statically indeterminate, it is possible to consider an idealized case that is statically determinate by introducing some simplifying assumptions. Thus, we may gain some understanding of the behavior of stiffened tied-arches in the analysis of simplified versions of suspension bridges.

Consider, for example, the tied arch with a stiffening girder as shown in Fig. 5-25(a). In attempting to analyze such a structure, we introduce the following assumptions:

1. If the applied load is uniformly distributed along the horizontal span, such as the weight of the floor system, it will be carried entirely by the arch.
2. If the applied load on the bridge is not uniform, as in the case of moving vehicles, it will be transmitted to the hangers through the stiffening girder.
3. Since the hangers are closely and uniformly spaced, the hanger loads are assumed to be uniform when the stiffness of the girder is large relative to that of the arch rib. Furthermore, if the shape of the arch rib is a second-degree parabola, it will be subjected only to direct compression under the uniform load.

Consequently, we can decompose the stiffened tied-arch in Fig. 5-25(a) into a three-hinged arch and a girder as shown in Figs. 5-25(b) and (c), respectively. On the basis of the stated assumptions and implied approximations, we can obtain the reactions and internal forces in the structure.

(a)

(b)

(c)

Figure 5-25

Suppose that the stiffened tied-arch in Fig. 5-25(a) is a second-degree parabola with a span length of $L = 240$ ft and a rise of $f = 40$ ft. The spacing between hangers is $s = L/n$ where n is number of spaces in the span, and the load Q in each hanger is therefore $Q = wL/n = ws$ where w is a uniform load along the span. Assuming that any concentrated load applied to the girder will be distributed uniformly among the hangers, we may see that

$$w = \frac{P}{L} = \frac{480}{240} = 2 \text{ k/ft}$$

or

$$Q = ws = (2)(20) = 40 \text{ kips}$$

By considering the left half of Fig. 5-25(b) as a free body, we find from $\Sigma M_c = 0$,

$$120V_{a'} = 40H + (120)(Q/2) + (5 + 4 + 3 + 2 + 1)(20)Q$$

$$H = 9Q = (9)(40) = 360 \text{ kips}$$

and from symmetry, $\Sigma\,F_y = 0$ leads to

$$V_{a'} = V_{b'} = 6Q = (6)(40) = 240 \text{ kips}$$

Note that $V_{a''} = V_{a'} - Q/2 = 220$ kips and $V_{b''} = V_{b'} - Q/2 = 220$ kips in Fig. 5-25(c), which will be transmitted directly to the supports.

It can be seen that if a uniform w instead of a concentrated load is applied to the stiffening girder, the stiffening girder in Fig. 5-25(c) will not carry the vertical load, since the downward uniform load w will be balanced by the loads Q in the uniformly spaced hangers. Then, by applying $w = 2$ k/ft directly to the arch in Fig. 5-25(b), we get from $\Sigma\,M_c = 0$ for the left half,

$$H = \frac{wL^2}{8f} = \frac{(2)(240)^2}{(8)(40)} = 360 \text{ kips}$$

Example 5-11. Draw the shear and moment diagrams for the stiffening girder in Fig. 5-25(c).

Since $Q = 40$ kips and $V_{a''} = V_{b''} = 220$ kips, we find from considering the equilibrium of the stiffening girder

$$V_a = 320 \text{ kips} \quad \text{and} \quad V_b = 160 \text{ kips}$$

Hence, the shear and moment diagrams can be obtained as in Figs. 5-26(a) and (b), respectively.

(a)

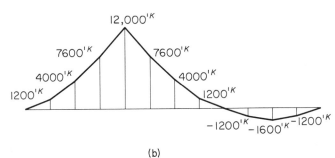

(b)

Figure 5-26

PROBLEMS

5-1 to **5-4.** Compute the ordinates of the cable at the points of concentrated loads and the maximum tension in the cable for each of the cables shown in Figs. P5-1 to P5-4.

Figure P5-1

Figure P5-2

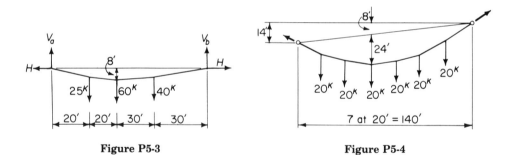

Figure P5-3   **Figure P5-4**

5-5. Determine the tension of the cable at points A, B, and C in Fig. P5-5.

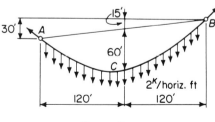

Figure P5-5

5-6 to **5-9**. Draw the shear and moment diagrams for each of the suspended girders shown in Figs P5-6 to P5-9.

Figure P5-6   **Figure P5-7**

Figure P5-8

Figure P5-9

5-10 and **5-11**. Compute the bar forces in members marked by letters a, b, and c of the stiffening trusses of the suspension bridges shown in Figs. P5-10 and P5-11.

Figure P5-10

Figure P5-11

5-12 to **5-15**. Draw the shear and moment diagrams on the horizontal projection of the arch axis for each of the three-hinged arches shown in Figs. P5-12 to P5-15.

Figure P5-12

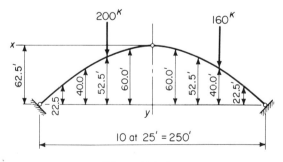

Figure P5-13

Cables and Arches   Chap. 5

Figure P5-14

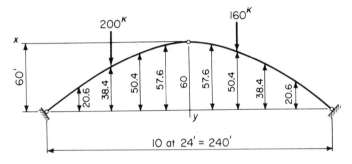

Figure P5-15

5-16. The three-hinged arch shown in Fig. P5-16(a) consists of two segments whose equations are shown in Fig. P5-16(b). Determine the axial force, shear, and moment at a section just to the right of point D and those at a section just to the right of point E of the structure.

Figure P5-16

5-17. The axis of the three-hinged arch shown in Fig. P5-17 is a semicircle. The brackets inside the arch are rigidly attached. Compute the axial force, shear, and moment at point D of the arch.

Figure P5-17

5-18 to **5-19.** The arch rib of each of the stiffened tied-arches in Fig. P5-18 and Fig. P5-19 has the shape of the a second-degree parabola. Determine the loads carried by the hangers, and draw the shear and moment diagrams for the stiffening girder in each problem.

Figure P5-18

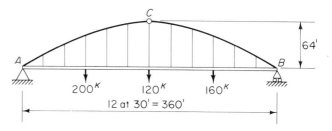

Figure P5-19

6

Displacements

6-1 ELASTIC DEFLECTIONS OF SIMPLE STRUCTURES

The displacements of a deformable system resulting from applied loads or other causes are commonly called *deflections*. In a narrower sense, the term *deflection* is used to denote linear displacement only. The applied loads on a structure generally produce internal forces and moments in various parts of the structure. The internal forces and moments at any section of the structure may be related to the stresses acting on the section, which can in turn be expressed in terms of strains by the stress-strain relation of the material. Since deflections are the outward indications of the accumulation of strains compatible with the geometry of the structure, the deflections of a structure under loads can be computed if the stress-strain relation of the material is known.

From a broader point of view, the computation of deflections is often a preliminary step in setting up the conditions for the analysis of statically indeterminate structures. For such cases, the main point of interest will no longer be the general deflections of a structure, but rather a particular deflection for which certain conditions of geometrical compatibility must be maintained. Thus, the techniques or methods of computing deflections may be classified broadly as (1) methods for computing a number of deflections simultaneously and (2) methods for computing one particular deflection.

On the other hand, according to the basic approach used in the solution of the problem, the methods of computing deflections may be classified as the *equilibrium* approach, which is based on the conditions of equilibrium of the system, and the *energy* approach, which is derived from the principle of conservation of energy. In general, the equilibrium approach can readily be applied to the computation of deflections at a number of points on the structure, and the energy approach is especially useful for the computation of one particular deflection at a time. Thus, each approach has certain advantages for specific purposes. In this chapter we shall confine our discussion to the equilibrium approach with emphasis on the geometry of structures; in Chapter 9 the energy approach will be developed for the calculation of deflections at specific points of structures.

In order to compute the general deflections of simple structures such as statically determinate beams, frames, and trusses by means of the equilibrium approach, we must study the geometry of the deflected structures by means of which the applied loads and the deflections are related. Since the deflections tolerated in engineered structures are usually very small, we are primarily interested in the elastic deflections. Hence, the angles of rotation as well as the displacements in a deflected structure are small quantities in comparison with the dimensions of the structure. For the sake of simplicity, in this chapter, we shall confine our discussion to linearly elastic materials in the computation of displacements and rotations.

In order to designate the senses of direction of displacements correctly and systematically, it is often convenient to adopt a sign convention. On the other hand, sign conventions have their limitations because they are not always adaptable to complicated structures. Therefore, it is sometimes easier to deal with the absolute values of these quantities if the geometry of the deflected structure is observed so that the senses of direction of displacements cannot be mistaken. Whenever a sign convention is adopted in connection with a method of solution in this chapter, it will be clearly defined. However, the physical meaning of the signs will also be explained by study of the geometry of structures.

6-2 MOMENT-CURVATURE RELATION

If an initially straight member is subjected to bending, the shape of the deformed neutral axis is called the *elastic curve*. Consider a small element δx, as shown in Fig. 6-1 that is isolated from a member subjected to pure bending. Since no shear exists at any section of a member in pure bending, the bending moment equals M at every section of the member. Let y be the ordinate of a point from the neutral axis of the element, being positive when the point is above the neutral axis. Assuming that sections that are plane before bending remain plane after bending, the relation between bending stress and bending moment can be established from the consideration of equilibrium of forces and moments acting on the element. The bending stress σ in a fiber at a distance y from the neutral axis is given for linearly elastic materials as follows:

$$\sigma = -\frac{My}{I} \tag{a}$$

in which M is the moment at a section and I is the moment of inertia of the cross section. The minus sign indicates compressive stress for positive y if the moment is positive. The same assumption of linear strain distribution leads to the conclusion that the initially parallel planes on the sides of an element before bending must intersect after bending as shown in Fig. 6-1. The intersection O is called the *center of curvature* and the distance ρ from the intersection O to the neutral axis is called the *radius of curvature*. For a fiber at a distance y from the neutral axis, the original length of the element δx is shortened by an amount δu_y, and the strain at that fiber is equal to $\epsilon = \delta u_y/\delta x$. As δx approaches zero as a limit,

$$\epsilon = -\frac{du_y}{dx} \tag{b}$$

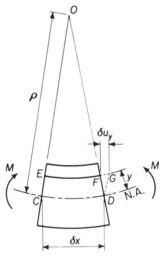

Figure 6-1

Since δx is infinitely small, OCD and FGD may be considered to be similar triangles from which

$$\frac{\delta u_y}{y} = \frac{\delta x}{\rho} \quad \text{or} \quad \frac{du_y}{dx} = \frac{y}{\rho} \tag{c}$$

From Eqs. (b) and (c), we get

$$\epsilon = -\frac{y}{\rho}$$

For elastic materials for which Hooke's law applies,

$$\sigma = \epsilon E = -\frac{Ey}{\rho} \tag{d}$$

By equating Eqs. (a) and (d), the moment-curvature relation can be expressed as follows:

$$\frac{M}{EI} = \frac{1}{\rho} \qquad (6\text{-}1)$$

This is essentially a force-deformation relation in which M is the applied force and the curvature $1/\rho$ is the resulting deformation. The quantity EI is called the *flexural rigidity* or *bending stiffness* of the member.

    If a structural member is subjected to shear and axial force as well as bending moment, additional deformation is caused. For slender members, however, the deformation due to shear or axial force is small and negligible in comparison with that due to bending. It is assumed, therefore, that Eq. (6-1) can generally be applied to members subjected to a combined action of axial force, shear, and bending. When shear forces exist at various sections of a member, the bending moment is no longer constant along the length of the member. When the moment changes from point to point in the member, the curvature changes accordingly. On the other hand, if the moment of inertia of the member varies along its length, the curvature also changes. In either case, $1/\rho$ will no longer be constant at different points of the beam, but the moment-curvature relation in Eq. (6-1) still holds at any particular point.

    The over-all shape of the elastic curve is directly related to the curvature along the length of a member. Let u and v be the horizontal and vertical displacements, respectively, of a point on the elastic curve, as shown in Fig. 6-2(a). If the member is supported at point O, a point A on the neutral axis of the undeflected beam will move to point A' on the elastic curve after bending, resulting in displacement u toward the left of the original position and displacement v in the upward direction. For ordinary engineering structures, only small deflections and small slopes are involved, and the angle θ of the slope is on the order of magnitude of a thousandth of a radian. It can be assumed, therefore, that

$$\sin \theta = \tan \theta = \theta \text{ in radian}$$

and

$$\cos \theta = 1$$

(a)   (b)   **Figure 6-2**

For an element δx shown in Fig. 6-2(b), δu is small and negligible in comparison with δv because $\delta u = \theta\,\delta v$, in which θ is a small quantity. It is necessary, therefore, to consider only the vertical displacement v. However, the horizontal displacement u can be expressed as a function of v by observing the geometrical relation in Fig. 6-2(b). For $\delta u = \delta s - \delta x$, the displacement u at any point on the elastic curve is equal to

$$u = \int_0^x (ds - dx) \tag{e}$$

Since δs may be expressed in terms of the slope of the elastic curve and approximated by expanding the expression into a binomial series, we have

$$\delta s = [(\delta x)^2 + (\delta v)^2]^{1/2} = \left[1 + \left(\frac{dv}{dx}\right)^2\right]^{1/2} \delta x$$

$$= \left[1 + \frac{1}{2}\left(\frac{dv}{dx}\right)^2 - \frac{1}{8}\left(\frac{dv}{dx}\right)^4 + \cdots\right]\delta x \tag{f}$$

By taking only the first two terms in the series, and by substituting Eq. (f) into Eq. (e), we obtain

$$u = \int_0^x \frac{1}{2}\left(\frac{dv}{dx}\right)^2 dx \tag{6-2}$$

Hence, the horizontal displacement u can be evaluated if the equation of the elastic curve for the vertical displacement v is first obtained.

The vertical displacement v of the elastic curve can readily be related to the curvature. In elementary calculus, it has been shown that if v denotes the ordinate and x the abscissa of a point on a curve, as shown in Fig. 6-3(a), the curvature is given by:

$$\frac{1}{\rho} = \frac{\dfrac{d^2v}{dx^2}}{\left[1 + \left(\dfrac{dv}{dx}\right)^2\right]^{3/2}}$$

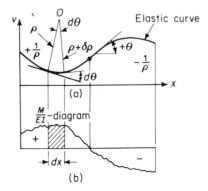

(a)

(b)

Figure 6-3

By substituting this expression into Eq. (6-1), we obtain

$$\frac{\dfrac{d^2v}{dx^2}}{\left[1 + \left(\dfrac{dv}{dx}\right)^2\right]^{3/2}} = \frac{M}{EI} \tag{6-3}$$

It may be observed that the solution of Eq. (6-3) is rather difficult to obtain. However, since the slope of the elastic curve dv/dx is small, the term $(dv/dx)^2$ is negligible in comparison with unity. Then Eq. (6-3) becomes

$$\frac{d^2v}{dx^2} = \frac{M}{EI} \tag{6-4}$$

Finally, the elastic curve of a deflected member can be obtained from the solution of the differential equation represented by Eq. (6-4).

In view of the fact that $\tan \theta = \theta$ for small angles, the slope of the elastic curve can be represented by θ or

$$\frac{dv}{dx} = \theta \tag{6-5}$$

Then, Eq. (6-4) becomes

$$\frac{d\theta}{dx} = \frac{M}{EI} \tag{6-6}$$

Since the curvature is defined by Eq. (6-4), a positive curvature corresponds to a positive moment. Equation (6-6) further indicates that a positive change in slope between two points on the elastic curve corresponds to a positive moment as shown by the part of the deflection curve that is concave upward in Fig. 6-3(a). If the ordinates of the moment diagram along the length of a member are divided by the corresponding EI of the beam at the same section, the ordinates of the resulting M/EI diagram have the same sign as the corresponding moments. Thus, the sign of the curvature at a point on the elastic curve shown in Fig. 6-3(a) must correspond to that of the same section on the M/EI diagram in Fig. 6-3(b).

6-3 DEFLECTION OF BEAMS

The equation of the elastic curve of a beam subjected to a given loading can be obtained by integrating twice the expression M/EI in Eq. (6-4) with respect to x. Carrying out the integration in two steps, the equations for slopes and deflections of a beam can be obtained from Eqs. (6-5) and (6-6). Thus,

$$\theta = \int \frac{M}{EI}\,dx + C_1 \tag{6-7}$$

$$v = \int \theta \, dx + C_2 \qquad \text{(6-8)}$$

In order to evaluate the integrals and the constants of integration in Eqs. (6-7) and (6-8), we proceed as follows:

1. From the conditions of equilibrium of forces and moments, the bending moment along the beam can be expressed as a function of x. The procedure for carrying out this step has been fully explained in Chapter 3.

2. The bending stiffness EI can be determined from the material characteristics and the dimensions of the cross section of the beam. If EI is constant throughout the entire length of the beam, it can be conveniently handled in Eqs. (6-7) and (6-8). If EI is variable, it must also be expressed as a function of x.

3. The constants of integration can be determined from the requirements that the continuity of the elastic curve be maintained and that the displacement boundary conditions of the elastic curve be satisfied. Continuity implies that no abrupt change in deflection or slope of the deflection curve is permissible. The displacement boundary conditions refer to the known conditions of deflection and slope at the supports. For example, at a hinge or roller support no deflection of the elastic curve can take place, and at a fixed support no deflection or rotation of the elastic curve can occur.

The physical meaning of the displacement boundary conditions in determining the constants of integration in Eqs. (6-7) and (6-8) can easily be explained if these equations are rearranged as follows:

$$\theta = \int \frac{M}{EI} \, dx + C_1 = \int k \, dx + C_1$$

$$v = \int \theta \, dx + C_2 = \int \left(\int k \, dx \right) dx + C_1 x + C_2$$

in which the curvature M/EI is denoted by k. Thus, the integrals in the equations for slope and deflection are defined by the curvature only and are independent of the boundary conditions. The ordinates of the points on the slope and deflection curves, of course, are influenced by the boundary conditions which are represented by the constants of integration C_1 and C_2. As an example, consider two simply supported beams, one horizontal and the other inclined, as shown in Figs. 6-4(a) and (b), respectively. If the ordinate of the M/EI diagram at every *vertical* section is the same for both beams, then the slope and deflection curves for the beam in Fig. 6-4(a) have the same shapes as the respective curves for the beam in Fig. 6-4(b). Since the boundary conditions of these beams are different, the ordinates of these diagrams in Figs. 6-4(a) and (b) are not the same. However, the ordinates of the slope curve in one case may

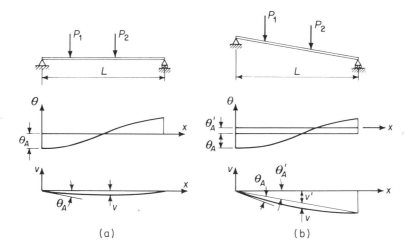

Figure 6-4

differ from those in the other case by a constant amount equivalent to the vertical translation of the x-axis, and the ordinates of the deflection curve may differ by an amount equivalent to the rotation of the x-axis. In general, if the integrals representing the shapes of the slope and deflection curves are evaluated first by assuming $C_1 = C_2 = 0$, corrections equivalent to $\theta = C_1$ and $v = C_1 x + C_2$ may be added to the corresponding integrals later.

The slope and deflection equations may also be expressed in the form of definite integrals for the interval $a < x < b$ as follows:

$$\theta_b - \theta_a = \int_a^b \frac{M}{EI}\, dx \tag{6-9}$$

$$v_b - v_a = \int_a^b \theta \, dx \tag{6-10}$$

Equation (6-9) implies that the slope at any point of a beam is equal to the slope at a previous point along the axis of the beam plus the area of the M/EI diagram between these two points. Similarly, Eq. (6-10) states that the deflection at any point of the beam is equal to the deflection at a previous point along the axis of the beam plus the area under the slope curve between these two points. Thus, the computation of slopes and deflections becomes a process of summation starting from an initial point of known slope and deflection.

We can make use of the relationships in Eqs. (6-5), (6-6), (6-9), and (6-10) in plotting the variations of slope and deflection along the length of the beam. For example, we observe that the point of maximum deflection is the point of zero slope, and that the point of maximum slope is the point of zero moment. The ordinates of the slope and deflection curves can be obtained from step-by-step summation as represented by Eqs. (6-9) and (6-10).

In view of Eqs. (6-5) and (6-6), together with Eqs. (3-1) and (3-2), it may be concluded that if the equation of the elastic curve is known, not only the slope θ of the elastic curve but also the moment M, the shear S, and the applied load q at any point of the beam may be obtained by successive differentiations as follows:

$$\theta = \frac{dv}{dx}$$

$$M = EI\frac{d\theta}{dx} = EI\frac{d^2v}{dx^2}$$

$$S = \frac{dM}{dx} = EI\frac{d^3v}{dx^3} \qquad (6\text{-}11)$$

$$q = \frac{dS}{dx} = EI\frac{d^4v}{dx^4}$$

Conversely, the equation of the elastic curve may be obtained by successive integrations from the applied load, as given by Eqs. (3-3) and (3-4), together with Eqs. (6-7) and (6-8). Denoting the curvature M/EI by k, we have

$$S = \int q \, dx + C_1$$

$$M = \int S \, dx + C_2$$

$$\theta = \int \frac{M}{EI} \, dx + C_3 = \int k \, dx + C_3 \qquad (6\text{-}12)$$

$$v = \int \theta \, dx + C_4$$

in which the constants of integration C_1, C_2, C_3, and C_4 are determined from the boundary conditions. The first two equations of Eqs. (6-12) involve only the principles of statics, and the constants C_1 and C_2 depend on the force boundary conditions of shear and moment. The last two equations of Eqs. (6-12) include the material characteristics E and the geometrical properties of section I, and the constants C_3 and C_4 depend on the displacement boundary conditions of slope and deflection.

Example 6-1.   A cantilever beam of span length L and of constant bending stiffness EI is subjected to a moment M_0 at the free end as shown in Fig. 6-5. Determine the equation of the elastic curve.

Since the moment along the length of the beam is constant, or $M = M_0$, we obtain from Eqs. (6-7) and (6-8).

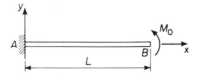

Figure 6-5

$$\theta = \frac{M_0 x}{EI} + C_1 \qquad\qquad\qquad (a)$$

$$v = \frac{M_0 x^2}{EI} + C_1 x + C_2 \qquad\qquad (b)$$

The displacement boundary conditions of this beam are as follows:

$$\theta = 0 \text{ at } x = 0 \quad \text{and} \quad v = 0 \text{ at } x = 0$$

Hence, the equation of the elastic curve is

$$v = \frac{M_0 x^2}{2EI} \qquad\qquad\qquad (c)$$

The last equation indicates that the elastic curve is parabolic whereas, in reality, it should be a circular arc, since the moment M_0 is constant along the length of the beam, and consequently the radius of curvature is also constant. This inconsistency is the result of the use of the expression for curvature in Eq. (6-4) instead of that in Eq. (6-3).

We can now compare the order of magnitude of the displacements u and v for this particular problem. The maximum displacements occur at the free end B of the beam where $x = L$. Thus, from Eq. (c),

$$v_b = \frac{M_0 L^2}{2EI}$$

For Eq. (6-2), we obtain first $dv/dx = M_0 x/EI$. Then,

$$u_b = \int_0^L \frac{1}{2}\left(\frac{M_0 x}{EI}\right)^2 dx = \frac{M_0^2 x^3}{6(EI)^2}\bigg|_0^L = \frac{M_0^2 L^3}{6E^2 I^2}$$

The ratio of u_b to v_b can be expressed as follows:

$$\frac{u_b}{v_b} = \frac{M_0 L}{3EI}$$

For ordinary engineering problems, $L/3EI$ is a very small quantity, and hence u_b is negligible in comparison with v_b.

Example 6-2. A simply supported beam of span length L and constant bending stiffness EI is subjected to a uniformly varying load as shown in Fig. 6-6(a). Plot the ordinates of shear, moment, slope, and deflection along the length of the beam.

If the reactions from the applied load are first obtained as shown in Fig. 6-6(a), the force boundary conditions can be expressed as $S = w_0 L/6$ at $x = 0$ and $M = 0$ at $x = 0$. Thus, by starting from $q = -w_0 x/L$,

$$S = \int q\, dx + C_1 = -\frac{w_0 x^2}{2L} + \frac{w_0 L}{6}$$

$$M = \int S\, dx + C_2 = -\frac{w_0 x^3}{6L} + \frac{w_0 L x}{6} + 0$$

$$k = \frac{M}{EI} = \frac{w_0}{6EIL}(-x^3 + L^2 x)$$

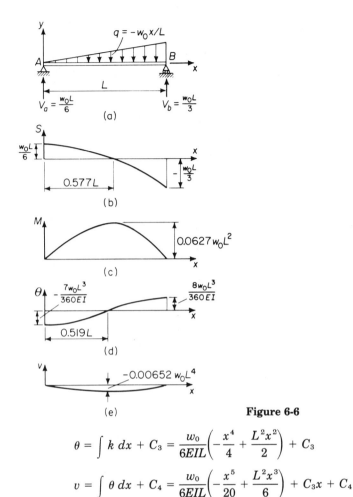

Figure 6-6

$$\theta = \int k \, dx + C_3 = \frac{w_0}{6EIL}\left(-\frac{x^4}{4} + \frac{L^2 x^2}{2}\right) + C_3$$

$$v = \int \theta \, dx + C_4 = \frac{w_0}{6EIL}\left(-\frac{x^5}{20} + \frac{L^2 x^3}{6}\right) + C_3 x + C_4$$

The displacement boundary conditions are $v = 0$ at $x = 0$ and $x = L$. Then,

$$C_4 = 0 \quad \text{and} \quad C_3 = -\frac{7w_0 L^3}{360EI}$$

Hence,

$$\theta = \frac{w_0}{360EIL}(-15x^4 + 30L^2 x^2 - 7L^4)$$

$$v = \frac{w_0}{360EIL}(-3x^5 + 10L^2 x^3 - 7L^4 x)$$

The maximum moment occurs at the point where $S = 0$, from which $x = 0.577L$ and $M_{\max} = 0.0627w_0 L^2$. Similarly, the maximum deflection occurs at the point where $\theta = 0$, from which $x = 0.519L$ and $v_{\max} = -0.00652w_0 L^4$. The equations for shear, moment, slope, and deflection are plotted in Figs. 6-6(b), (c), (d), and (e), respectively.

In Section 3-4, the integrations of singular functions were introduced primarily for the purpose of providing complete generality to the concept of obtaining shears and moments from the given loading functions by direct integration. We pointed out that, for practical purposes, such a method offers little advantage over other methods. In the computation of deflections, however, this general concept not only brings unity to the procedure of successive integrations but also simplifies the solution of certain types of problems.

When the applied load on a beam is not a continuous function along its length, the conditions of compatibility at each point of discontinuity must be considered in the solution of slope and deflection of the beam by direct integration if the integrations of singularity functions are not introduced. Thus, for each discontinuity, there appear two additional constants of integration in the slope and deflection of the beam which may be evaluated from the conditions of compatibility. For problems with several discontinuities, the solution leads to a large number of simultaneous equations involving constants of integration as unknowns. This situation can be avoided by the introduction of singularity functions.

In the case of beams with variable bending stiffness, such as beams with cut-off cover plates, discontinuities also exist in the curvature diagrams. Such situations can also be treated by the use of singularity functions. One of the most useful applications of the singularity functions is the computation of deflection of beams with releases. Without the benefit of singularity functions, the deflection at each part of the beam between releases or supports must be computed separately. By introducing the concept of singularity functions in the curvature diagram, it can be treated in the same way as for beams without releases.

There are other advantages in the use of singularity functions, especially in the computation of deflections of beams that are statically indeterminate. In that case, the redundant reactions can be treated as singularity functions of forces.

Example 6-3. A simply supported beam of span length L and constant bending stiffness EI is subjected to a concentrated load P as shown in Fig. 6-7(a). Find the equation of the elastic curve.

The problem will be worked out in two ways. First, moment equations are written separately for segment AC and CB of the beam; secondly, the notations for singularity functions are used. The coordinate system shown in Fig. 6-7(b) will be adopted for both cases.

The equations for moment in segments AC and CB of the beam can be obtained by statics, and the integrations of these equations are carried out as follows:

For segment AC,

$$M = \frac{Pb}{L}x$$

(a)

(b)

Figure 6-7

$$\theta = \frac{Pbx^2}{2EIL} + C_1$$

$$v = \frac{Pbx^3}{6EIL} + C_1x + C_2$$

For segment CB,

$$M = \frac{Pb}{L}x - P(x - a)$$

$$\theta = \frac{P}{EI}\left[\frac{bx^2}{2L} - \frac{x^2}{2} + ax\right] + C_3$$

$$v = \frac{P}{EI}\left[\frac{bx^3}{6L} - \frac{x^3}{6} + \frac{ax^2}{2}\right] + C_3x + C_4$$

There are four constants of integration in the two sets of equations for slope and deflection. From the displacement boundary conditions, we have $v = 0$ at $x = 0$ and at $x = L$, from which we obtain

$$C_2 = 0$$

$$0 = \frac{PL^2}{6EI}(b - L + 3a) + C_3L + C_4 = \frac{PaL^2}{3EI} + C_3L + C_4$$

Two other conditions are sought from the continuity of the elastic curve. That is, at $x = a$ the slope and deflection are unique whether they are obtained from segment AC or segment CB. Thus, at point C

$$\theta_c = \frac{Pba^2}{2EIL} + C_1 = \frac{Pa^2}{2EI}\left(\frac{b}{L} + 1\right) + C_3$$

$$v_c = \frac{Pba^3}{6EIL} + C_1a + C_2 = \frac{Pa^3}{6EI}\left(\frac{b}{L} + 2\right) + C_3a + C_4$$

Solving these four equations simultaneously, we get

$$C_1 = -\frac{Pb}{6EIL}(L^2 - b^2) \qquad C_2 = 0$$

$$C_3 = -\frac{Pa}{6EIL}(2L^2 + a^2), \qquad C_4 = \frac{Pa^3}{6EI}$$

Finally, we obtain for $0 \leqq x \leqq a$,

$$v = \frac{Pb}{6EIL}[x^3 - (L^2 - b^2)x]$$

and for $a \leqq x \leqq L$,

$$v = \frac{Pb}{6EIL}\left[x^3 - \frac{L}{b}(x - a)^3 - (L^2 - b^2)x\right]$$

Using the notations for singularity functions in Section 3-4, we have in this case a loading function

$$q = -P\langle x - a\rangle^{-1}$$

Integrating twice, we get

$$S = -P\langle x - a\rangle^0 + C_1$$

$$M = -P\langle x - a\rangle^1 + C_1 x + C_2$$

From the static boundary conditions $M = 0$ at $x = 0$ and at $x = L$, we obtain $C_2 = 0$ and $C_1 = P(L - a)/L = Pb/L$. Thus,

$$S = \frac{Pb}{L} - P\langle x - a\rangle^0$$

$$M = \frac{Pbx}{L} - P\langle x - a\rangle^1$$

These are essentially identical to the equations for shear and moment obtained by statics.

In order to compute the slope and deflection, we integrate the equation for curvature. Thus,

$$k = \frac{M}{EI} = \frac{P}{EI}\left[\frac{bx}{L} - \langle x - a\rangle^1\right]$$

$$\theta = \frac{P}{2EI}\left[\frac{bx^2}{L} - \langle x - a\rangle^2\right] + C_3$$

$$v = \frac{P}{6EI}\left[\frac{bx^3}{L} - \langle x - a\rangle^3\right] + C_3 x + C_4$$

The geometrical boundary conditions are $v = 0$ at $x = 0$ and at $x = L$. Then, we get

$$C_4 = 0, \qquad C_3 = -\frac{Pb}{6EIL}(L^2 - b^2)$$

Hence,

$$v = \frac{Pb}{6EIL}\left[x^3 - \frac{L}{b}\langle x - a\rangle^3 - (L^2 - b^2)x\right]$$

Note that the second term on the right-hand side of the equation has a bracket notation because it is zero when $x < a$ and is equal to $(L/b)(x - a)^3$ when $x > a$.

Example 6-4. Derive the equation of the elastic curve for the compound beam shown in Fig. 6-8(a).

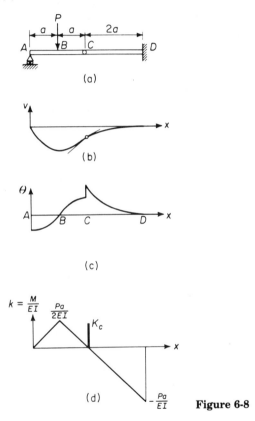

Figure 6-8

Since a hinge is present at point C, it is usually necessary to break up the compound beam into parts AC and CD because there is a kink or an abrupt change of slope in the deflection curve at point C. Exaggerating the deflection curve in Fig. 6-8(b), the tangent to the curve at the left of hinge C is seen to be different from that at the right of hinge C. Therefore, a sudden jump or step exists at point C of the curve showing the variation of slope in Fig. 6-8(c). At the corresponding point of the curvature curve or M/EI diagram in Fig. 6-8(d), an abrupt angle change or "concentrated curvature" should be introduced if the compound beam is to be treated as a single unit. Thus, by integrating the curvature curve, the abrupt angle change at point C becomes a jump or step at the corresponding point in the slope curve; and by integrating the slope curve, this step becomes a kink in the deflection curve. Hence, the compatibility conditions at the hinge will be automatically satisfied if a proper angle change is introduced at the corresponding point in the curvature curve.

Fortunately, this angle change need not be known in advance in order to solve the problem. As long as the beam is statically determinate, there will be an additional component of reaction at the support when a hinge is introduced in the beam. This additional component of reaction provides an extra boundary condition which may be used to evaluate the unknown angle change at C in the curvature curve. Since the equation of moment is given by

$$M = \frac{Px}{2} - P\langle x - a \rangle^1$$

We may introduce an arbitrary angle change K_c at point C of the curvature curve so that

$$\frac{M}{EI} = \frac{Px}{2EI} - \frac{P}{EI}\langle x - a \rangle^1 + K_c\langle x - 2a \rangle^{-1}$$

Then, by successive integrations, we have

$$\theta = \frac{Px^2}{4EI} - \frac{P}{2EI}\langle x - a \rangle^2 + K_c\langle x - 2a \rangle^0 + C_1$$

$$v = \frac{Px^3}{12EI} - \frac{P}{6EI}\langle x - a \rangle^3 + K_c\langle x - 2a \rangle^1 + C_1 x + C_2$$

From the boundary condition $v = 0$ at $x = 0$, we have $C_2 = 0$. From the other two boundary conditions $v = 0$ and $\theta = 0$ at $x = 4a$, we obtain the following equations respectively:

$$0 = \frac{P(4a)^3}{12EI} - \frac{P}{6EI}(3a)^3 + K_c(2a) + C_1(4a)$$

$$0 = \frac{P(4a)^2}{4EI} - \frac{P}{2EI}(3a)^2 + K_c + C_1$$

From the solution of these two equations, we get

$$K_c = \frac{17Pa^2}{12EI} \quad \text{and} \quad C_1 = -\frac{11Pa^2}{12EI}$$

Hence, the elastic curve of the beam is given by

$$v = \frac{Px}{12EI}(x^2 - 11a^2) - \frac{P}{6EI}\langle x - a \rangle^3 + \frac{17Pa^2}{12EI}\langle x - 2a \rangle^1$$

6-5 MOMENT AREA METHOD

Another approach used in computing slopes and deflections along the length of a beam is to provide a semigraphic interpretation relating slopes and deflections *directly* to the M/EI diagram. First, we shall introduce the theorems relating the M/EI diagram and the shape of the elastic curve that are independent of the boundary conditions. Next, we shall apply the theorems to the computation of slope and deflection of beams with various boundary conditions.

According to Eq. (6-9), the change in slope between two points on the elastic curve, commonly known as the *angle change*, can be represented by the area of the M/EI diagram between these two points. However, in Eq. (6-10), the change in deflection is not expressed explicitly in terms of the area of the M/EI diagram. Therefore, we seek an indirect approach in which the displacement of a point on the elastic curve from the tangent to the elastic curve at a second point is obtained. Since such a displacement represents the deviation of the curve from a tangent, measured vertically in this case, it is called the *tangential deviation*. Referring to Fig. 6-9(a), $\Delta\theta_{ba}$ is the angle change from point A to point B, and t_{ba} is the tangential deviation of point B from a tangent at point A. It should be noted that the order of the subscripts in $\Delta\theta_{ba}$ and t_{ba} is important since a reverse of the order will result in $\Delta\theta_{ab}$ and t_{ab}, as shown in Fig. 6-9(b).

(a) (b) **Figure 6-9**

The procedure of computing the angle change and the tangential deviation from the area of the M/EI diagram is commonly embodied in the moment-area theorems. From Eq. (6-9), we have

$$\Delta\theta_{ba} = \theta_b - \theta_a = \int_a^b \frac{M}{EI}\, dx$$

This is known as the *first moment-area theorem*, which states that the angle change from point A to point B on the elastic curve is equal to the area of that portion of the M/EI diagram bounded by the ordinates through A and B. Similarly,

$$\Delta\theta_{ab} = \theta_a - \theta_b = -\Delta\theta_{ba}$$

Furthermore, according to the first theorem, the infinitesimal angle $\delta\theta$ between tangents at points C and D in Fig. 6-10 is equal to the shaded portion of the

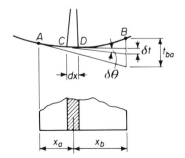

Figure 6-10

M/EI diagram. Since the slopes along the elastic curve are very small, the vertical distance δt may be approximated by the arc length, which is equal to the angle change $\delta\theta$ multiplied by the horizontal distance x_b. Thus, by using point B as the origin and the positive direction of x_b as shown,

$$t_{ba} = \int_b^a x_b d\theta = \int_b^a x_b \frac{M}{EI} dx_b = \bar{x}_b \int_b^a \frac{M}{EI} dx_b = \bar{x}_b \int_a^b \frac{M}{EI} dx$$

or, by using point A as the origin and the positive direction of x_a as shown,

$$t_{ab} = \int_a^b x_a d\theta = \int_b^a x_a \frac{M}{EI} dx_a = \bar{x}_a \int_a^b \frac{M}{EI} dx_a = \bar{x}_a \int_a^b \frac{M}{EI} dx$$

in which $\bar{x}_b$ and $\bar{x}_a$ represent the distances from the centroid of the area of the M/EI diagram to points B and A, respectively, and the integral represents the area of the M/EI diagram between points A and B. Thus, the *second moment-area theorem* can be stated as follows: The tangential deviation from a point B to the tangent at another point A is equal to the moment of the area of the M/EI diagram bounded by the ordinates through A and B about an axis through point B. Since $\bar{x}_a$ or $\bar{x}_b$ is always positive, the sign of the tangential deviation depends only on the sign of the M/EI diagram. For a positive moment, the tangential deviation is positive and the point on the elastic curve is *above* the tangent; for a negative moment, the tangential deviation is negative and the point on the elastic curve is *below* the tangent as shown in Fig. 6-11.

Let us now consider the significance of the boundary conditions in the application of the moment-area theorems. In general, neither the slope nor the deflection at a point on the beam is given directly by these theorems. The geometry of the deflected beam must therefore be taken into consideration in applying these theorems to the solution of a problem. In the case of a cantilever beam as shown in Fig. 6-12, the slope θ_a and the deflection v_a at the fixed end A are known to be zero. Thus, the slope θ_c and the deflection v_c at any point C of the beam under any loading may be given as follows:

$$\theta_c = \Delta\theta_{ca} = \int_a^c \frac{M}{EI} dx \qquad (6\text{-}13a)$$

$$v_c = t_{ca} = \bar{x}_c \int_a^c \frac{M}{EI} dx \qquad (6\text{-}13b)$$

(a)   (b)

Figure 6-11

$\frac{M}{EI}$ – diagram

Figure 6-12

Displacements   Chap. 6

Figure 6-13

In the case of a simply supported beam as shown in Fig. 6-13, if a tangent is drawn at point A, the slope θ_c and the deflection v_c at any point C can be obtained from the geometry of the deflected beam as follows:

$$\theta_c = \theta_a + \Delta\theta_{ca} = -\frac{t_{ba}}{L} + \Delta\theta_{ca}$$

$$v_c = -t_{ba}\frac{x}{L} + t_{ca}$$

Note that the sign in front of t_{ba} is negative because t_{ba} is positive for a positive moment whereas θ_a and $\theta_a x$ should be negative for a positive moment. The quantities $\Delta\theta_{ca}$, t_{ca}, and t_{ba} can be computed directly from the moment-area theorems, i.e.,

$$\Delta\theta_{ca} = \int_a^c \frac{M}{EI}\,dx$$

$$t_{ca} = \bar{x}_c \int_a^c \frac{M}{EI}\,dx$$

$$t_{ba} = \bar{x}_b \int_a^b \frac{M}{EI}\,dx$$

in which $\bar{x}_c$ and $\bar{x}_b$ are the distances from points C and B to the centroids of the moment areas bounded by points A and C and by A and B respectively. Then,

$$\theta_c = -\frac{\bar{x}_b}{L}\int_a^b \frac{M}{EI}\,dx + \int_a^c \frac{M}{EI}\,dx \qquad (6\text{-}14a)$$

$$v_c = -\frac{x}{L}\bar{x}_b\int_a^b \frac{M}{EI}\,dx + \bar{x}_c\int_a^c \frac{M}{EI}\,dx \qquad (6\text{-}14b)$$

It can readily be seen that the computation of angle change and tangential deviation is a matter of following a set of formulas whereas the application of these theorems to compute slope and deflection depends on the ability to sketch the correct shape of the elastic curve. This is always possible if the moment diagram for a given beam is known. When the moment diagram consists of simple geometrical elements such as triangles, rectangles, and second-degree parabolas, the solution by the moment-area method is rather simple, otherwise, the computation of areas and centroids of areas becomes quite tedious. It is sometimes possible to simplify the computation of these quantities by replacing the actual moment diagram with several separate moment diagrams, each of which consists of simple geometrical elements only and all of which are superimposed to obtain the actual moment diagram. For convenient reference, the geometrical properties of triangles and second-degree parabolas are summarized in Fig. 6-14.

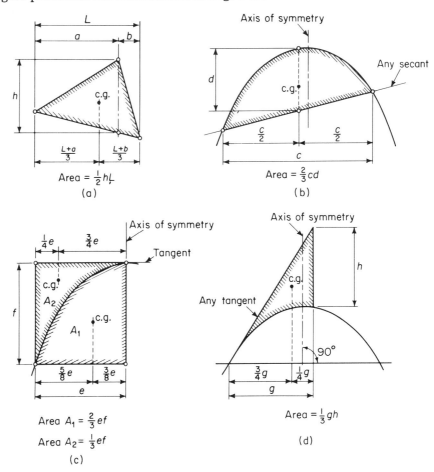

Figure 6-14

Example 6-5. Compute the deflection at point D of the beam shown in Fig. 6-15(a). $E = 30 \times 10^3$ ksi and $I = 100$ in.^{4}

First construct the moment diagram and sketch the elastic curve for the beam. Then, a tangent is drawn at point B and the following relation is established:

$$v_d = t_{db} + \theta_{ba} L_2$$

Since t_{db} is negative, corresponding to a negative moment, and θ_{ba} is positive for

Displacements   Chap. 6

(a)

(b)

Figure 6-15

a positive slope, v_d will be negative indicating a downward deflection if t_{db} is numerically greater than $\theta_{ba} L_2$. The computation can be carried out by first plotting the moment diagram as shown in Fig. 6-15(b). Then,

$$t_{ab} = \frac{1}{2}\left(\frac{350}{EI}\right)(10)(6.67) + \frac{1}{2}\left(\frac{350}{EI}\right)(5.4)(11.8) - \frac{1}{2}\left(\frac{300}{EI}\right)(4.6)(18.5)$$

$$= \frac{10,000}{EI} \text{ ft}^3\text{-k}$$

$$\theta_{ba} = \frac{t_{ab}}{L} = \frac{10,000}{20EI} = \frac{500}{EI} \text{ ft}^2\text{-k}$$

$$t_{db} = \frac{1}{2}\left(\frac{-300}{EI}\right)(6)(4) = -\frac{3,600}{EI} \text{ ft}^3\text{-k}$$

$$v_d = -\frac{3,600}{EI} + \left(\frac{500}{EI}\right)(6) = -\frac{600}{EI} \text{ ft}^3\text{-k}$$

$$= -\frac{(600)(1,728)}{(30,000)(100)} = -0.34 \text{ in.}$$

The computation of t_{ab} can be simplified if we consider the moment diagram between points a and b in Fig. 6-15(b) as the superposition of a positive triangle $ac'b'$ and a negative triangle abb', thus avoiding the necessity of locating point e. The ordinate $c'c''$ represents the moment at point C of the beam when the moment at point B of the beam is zero, i.e., when there is no load acting at point D of the beam. Thus,

$$c'c'' = (100)(20)/4 = 500$$

The areas and centroidal distances of these triangles then can be obtained directly from Fig. 6-14. Hence,

$$t_{ab} = \frac{1}{2}\left(\frac{500}{EI}\right)(20)(10) - \frac{1}{2}\left(\frac{300}{EI}\right)(20)(13.3) = \frac{10,000}{EI} \text{ ft}^3\text{-k}$$

The advantage of the method of superposition is even greater when the moment diagram consists of parabolas instead of triangles.

Example 6-6. Compute the deflection at point B of the compound beam shown in Fig. 6-8(a) by the moment-area method.

The construction of the M/EI diagram for such a compound beam with a hinge has been explained in Example 6-4. From the M/EI diagram in Fig. 6-8(d), we note that K_c may be treated as a concentrated area lying on a vertical line. Hence, the centroid of the area to point A is equal to $2a$. Thus, starting from a point A with known tangential deviation of point A from a tangent at point D, we have

$$t_{ad} = \frac{1}{2}\left(-\frac{Pa}{EI}\right)(2a)\left(\frac{4a}{3} + 2a\right) + \frac{1}{2}\left(\frac{Pa}{2EI}\right)(2a)(a) + K_c(2a) = 0$$

from which $K_c = 17Pa^2/12EI$. Then,

$$t_{bd} = \frac{1}{2}\left(-\frac{Pa}{EI}\right)(2a)\left(\frac{4a}{3} + a\right) + \frac{1}{2}\left(\frac{Pa}{2EI}\right)(a)\left(\frac{a}{3}\right) + \frac{17Pa^2}{12EI}(a)$$

$$= -\frac{5Pa^3}{6EI}$$

Hence, the deflection at point B is equal to

$$v_b = t_{bd} = -\frac{5Pa^3}{6EI}$$

6-6 ELASTIC WEIGHT METHOD

In the derivation of the equation of the elastic curve for a deflected beam, we observe the similarity between the procedure of obtaining deflection from curvature and that of obtaining moment from applied load, provided that comparable boundary conditions also exist in the determination of the constants of integration. A comparison of the two procedures may be made by noting Eqs. (3-3) and (3-4) for shear and moment, and Eqs. (6-7) and (6-8) for slope and deflection. The significance of the force boundary conditions in determining the constants of integration in Eqs. (3-3) and (3-4) has been discussed in Section 3-3. The physical meaning of the displacement boundary conditions in determining the constants of integration in Eqs. (6-7) and (6-8) has been explained in Section 6-3. Thus, we can make a complete analogy of the two procedures by noting the duality of these two sets of equations.

The concept of conjugate beams is introduced for the purpose of carrying out the solution of one set of equations by referring to the solution of the other set as an analogy. Since the shear and moment at a point of a beam subject to a given loading may be computed from statics, by analogy the slope and deflection at a point of the actual beam may be thought of as the shear and moment at the corresponding point of a fictitious beam having the curvature curve or M/EI diagram as the applied load. This fictitious beam must have force boundary conditions identical to the displacement boundary conditions of the actual beam, and is therefore called a *conjugate beam*. Such a method of computing deflections is known as the *elastic weight method* or *conjugate beam method* since the M/EI diagram is used as the applied load (elastic weight) on the conjugate beam. In many respects, the applications of this method are similar to those of the moment-area method. However, the concept of conjugate beams permits further applications in computing beam deflections by numerical methods and in computing truss deflections, which will be discussed later in this chapter.

The analogy between the roles of curvature, slope, and deflection in the actual beam and their counterparts in the conjugate beam may be given as follows:

Actual beam	Conjugate beam
curvature $k = M/EI$	load q
slope θ	shear S
deflection v	moment M

Imagine that the conjugate beam has the same span as that of the actual beam and has force boundary conditions identical to the displacement boundary conditions of the actual beam. Then, the equivalence of boundary conditions may be given for a few basic cases as follows:

Actual beam	Conjugate beam
simple support ($\theta \neq 0$, $v = 0$)	simple support ($S \neq 0$, $M = 0$)
fixed end ($\theta = 0$, $v = 0$)	free end ($S = 0$, $M = 0$)
free end ($\theta \neq 0$, $v \neq 0$)	fixed end ($S \neq 0$, $M \neq 0$)
interior hinge ($\theta \neq 0$, $v \neq 0$)	interior support ($S \neq 0$, $M \neq 0$)
interior support ($\theta \neq 0$, $v = 0$)	interior hinge ($S \neq 0$, $M = 0$)

Hence, *for a simply supported beam, the supporting conditions of the conjugate beam are identical to those of the actual beam* as shown in Fig. 6-16(a). For a cantilever beam, the end conditions of the conjugate beam will be the reverse of those of the actual beam as shown in Fig. 6-16(b). Other examples of statically determinate structures are given in Figs. 6-16(c), (d), and (e).

If the M/EI diagram of the actual beam is applied as a load to the conjugate beam, it can be demonstrated that the shear at any point of the conjugate beam is the slope at the corresponding point in the actual beam, and that the moment at any point of the conjugate beam is the deflection at the corresponding point in the actual beam. Consider, for instance, the special cases of cantilever beam and simply supported beam for which the slope and deflection at

Actual beam   Conjugate beam

(a)

(b)

(c)

(d)

(e)

Figure 6-16

any point have been formulated in terms of the M/EI diagram in Section 6-5. In order to avoid confusion, the quantities relating to the conjugate beam are given in primed notations and those for the actual beam are shown in unprimed notations. Referring to the conjugate beam in Fig. 6-17, we obtain from statics the shear and the moment at point C as follows:

$$S'_c = \int_a^c \frac{M}{EI}\,dx \tag{6-15a}$$

$$M'_c = \bar{x}_c \int_a^c \frac{M}{EI}\,dx \tag{6-15b}$$

For the conjugate beam in Fig. 6-18, we obtain by taking moments about B,

$$R'_a = \frac{\bar{x}_b}{L} \int_a^b \frac{M}{EI}\,dx$$

Hence,

$$S'_c = -\frac{\bar{x}_b}{L} \int_a^b \frac{M}{EI}\,dx + \int_a^c \frac{M}{EI}\,dx \tag{6-16a}$$

$$M'_c = -\frac{x}{L}\bar{x}_b \int_a^b \frac{M}{EI}\,dx + \bar{x}_c \int_a^c \frac{M}{EI}\,dx \tag{6-16b}$$

in which $\bar{x}_c$ and $\bar{x}_b$ are the distances from points C and B to the centroids of the moment area bounded by points A and C and by A and B, respectively. A comparison of Eqs. (6-13) and (6-14) with Eqs. (6-15) and (6-16) will establish the fact that the elastic weight method leads to the same results as the moment area method for these two cases.

(a) Actual beam   (a) Actual beam

(b) M/EI-diagram   (b) M/EI-diagram

(c) Conjugate beam   (c) Conjugate beam

Figure 6-17   **Figure 6-18**

Example 6-7. For the beam shown in Fig. 6-19(a), compute the deflection at point E by the elastic weight method. $E = 30,000$ ksi and $I = 800$ in.[4]

The actual beam can be broken up into separate units at points C and D, whereby the moment diagram can be obtained as shown in Fig. 6-19(b). The conjugate beam is shown in Fig. 6-19(c). Because of the symmetry of the structure and loading, each reaction of the conjugate beam is equal to one-half of the applied elastic loads as follows:

$$EIR'_c = -\tfrac{1}{2}(-120)(12) - \tfrac{1}{2}(-60)(6) - \tfrac{1}{2}(120)(12)$$

$$R'_c = \frac{180}{EI} \text{ ft}^2\text{-k}$$

(a) Actual beam

(b) Moment diagram

(c) Conjugate beam   **Figure 6-19**

Hence, the deflection of the actual beam at E is the same as the moment of the conjugate beam at E, or

$$EIM'_e = \tfrac{1}{2}(-120)(12)(8 + 12) + \tfrac{1}{2}(-60)(6)(4 + 6 + 12)$$

$$+ (180)(12) + \tfrac{1}{2}(120)(12)(4) = -12{,}940 \text{ ft}^3\text{-k}$$

or

$$v_e = -\frac{12{,}940}{EI} \text{ ft}^3\text{-k} = -\frac{(12{,}940)(1{,}728)}{(30{,}000)(800)} = -0.93 \text{ in.}$$

6-7 NUMERICAL METHOD FOR COMPUTING BEAM DEFLECTIONS

When the curvature curve or M/EI diagram of a beam consists of irregular shapes, the deflection of the beam can be obtained most conveniently by a numerical procedure commonly known as *Newmark's method*.* The application of this method to compute shear and moment in a beam has been explained in Section 3-8, and by analogy, it can be used to compute slope and deflection in a beam as well. The relations between curvature, slope and deflection of the beam are derived from the relations between load, shear, and moment of a conjugate beam. Thus, the ordinate k of the curvature curve of the actual beam can be obtained first by dividing the ordinates of the moment diagrams by the corresponding values of bending stiffness EI. Then the equivalent concentrated curvatures or angle changes at regularly spaced "panel points" can be obtained from the ordinates of the curvature curve or M/EI diagram. Let the equivalent concentrated curvatures at a panel point be denoted by K. Then, the K values at various panel points may be computed as reactions of stringers having the M/EI diagram as applied loads by Eqs. (3-11) and (3-12). These equivalent concentrated curvatures may then be applied as loads at the panel points of the conjugate beam. Finally, the slope in a panel and the deflection at a panel point of the actual beam may be obtained by the same procedure for computing shear in a panel and moment at a panel point of the actual beam.

Consider, for example, the simple beam shown in Fig. 6-20(a), the span of which is divided into four equal panels. The introduction of the panel points has the effect of replacing the elastic curve of the beam by a bar chain represented by the dotted lines insofar as computation of slopes and deflections are concerned. In the elastic curve of the beam, the change of curvature is gradual while in the bar chain the changes of curvature are concentrated at points B, C, and D as represented by the angle changes K_b, K_c, and K_d in Fig. 6-20(b). The slopes of the bar chain are constant within a panel and do not represent the true slopes of the elastic curve, but the deflections at the joints of the bar chain are identical to those at the panel points of the beam. If the true slopes at the panel points of the elastic curve are desired, the equivalent concentrated curvatures

*See N. M. Newmark, "Numerical Procedure for Computing Deflections, Moments, and Buckling Loads," *Trans. ASCE*, 108, (1943), p. 1161.

214

Displacements   Chap. 6

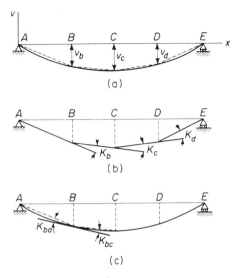

(a)

(b)

(c)

Figure 6-20

to the left and right of each panel point can be computed separately. Then, the slope of the tangent to the elastic curve at a panel point may be obtained by adding the suitable part of concentrated angle change to the corresponding panel slope as shown in Fig. 6-20(c).

By adopting the sign convention of curvature, slope, and deflection as in Eqs. (6-5) and (6-6), the successive calculation of slopes and deflections can be carried out by adding, respectively, curvatures and slopes from left to right, or by subtracting from right to left, starting from a point of known slope and deflection. In the case of a cantilever beam, for example, the fixed end is a point of zero slope and zero deflection. The computation of slope and deflection may begin from that point. When only the deflections at two points are known, such as the conditions of no deflections at the supports of a simple beam, the slope at one of the supports may be arbitrarily assumed. After the deflections at the panel points are computed, a check is made on the deflection at the second support. If the computed deflection at that point is different from the known boundary condition, a correction equivalent to the rotation of the x-axis may be applied to the trial deflections based on the arbitrarily assumed slope at the first support. The slopes at the panel points can be corrected by an adjustment corresponding to the translation of the x-axis. For solutions given in tabulated form, the following notations are adopted: k for the curvature at a panel point, K for the equivalent concentrated curvature at a panel point, θ for the panel slope, and v for the deflection at a panel point. If the actual or true slope at a panel point is needed, it will be denoted by $\bar{\theta}$. For solutions involving trial slopes and deflections, θ' is used for the trial slope in a panel, v' for the trial deflection at a panel point, θ'' for the slope correction, and v'' for the deflection correction.

The numerical computation of slopes and deflections can also be conveniently carried out in a tabulated form. As a matter of fact, if the shears and moments in the same beam are also computed by numerical integration, the two sets of computations can be tabulated together. The units of all quantities can be taken out to the last column of the tabulation as common factors. However, great care must be taken so that correct units will accompany the final results. It should be noted that the unit for curvature is 1/length, the unit for concentrated curvature and for slope is radian or a dimensionless quantity, and the unit for deflection is length.

Example 6-8. A cantilever beam with variable moment of inertia as shown in Fig. 6-21 is subjected to a concentrated load of 20 kips at the free end. For $I_0 = 3{,}000$ in.^{4} and $E = 30 \times 10^3$ ksi, find the deflections of the beam at intervals of $1/6$ the span length by numerical integration.

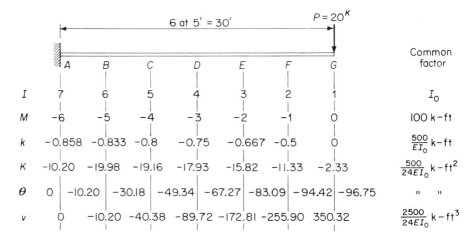

Figure 6-21

The moment of inertia of this beam varies continuously from I_0 at the free end to $7I_0$ at the fixed end, with intermediate values given at intervals of $h = L/6$. Since the ordinates of moments can readily be obtained, the ordinates of curvature k are computed by dividing the ordinates of moments by the corresponding values of EI. The equivalent concentrated curvatures K are computed by Eqs. (3-12) because the variation of curvature can best be approximated in this way. Since the slope and the deflection at the fixed end are known to be zero, the numerical integration can be carried out in a straightforward manner, starting from the left to the right both for slopes and for deflections. The common factor for deflections can be simplified at the final stage as follows:

$$\frac{(2{,}500)(12)^3 \text{ k-in.}^3}{(24)(30{,}000)(3{,}000) \text{ k-in.}^2} = 0.002 \text{ in.}$$

Example 6-9. A simply supported beam with variable moment of inertia as shown in Fig. 6-22 is subjected to a uniformly distributed load. Compute the deflections of the beam at intervals of $1/6$ of the span length.

The ordinates of the moment diagram for a uniformly loaded simple beam are first computed and tabulated in the figure. Dividing these ordinates by the

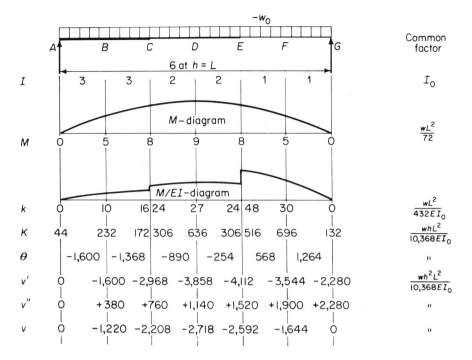

Figure 6-22

corresponding EI, we obtain the k values. At point C of the beam, for instance, the moment ordinate is $(8)(wL^2/72)$. In dividing this ordinate by EI, we have different values of k to the left and to the right of point C respectively as follows:

$$\frac{(8)(wL^2/72)}{3EI_0} = (16)\left(\frac{wL^2}{432EI_0}\right)$$

$$\frac{(8)(wL^2/72)}{2EI_0} = (24)\left(\frac{wL^2}{432EI_0}\right)$$

The equivalent concentrated curvatures K are computed from Eqs. (3-12). At point B, for instance,

$$K_b = \frac{h}{12}[0 + (10)(10) + 16]\frac{wL^2}{432EI_0}$$

$$= \left(\frac{116}{12}\right)\frac{wL^2h}{432EI_0} = (232)\frac{wL^2h}{10,368EI_0}$$

Because of the discontinuity of the M/EI diagram at point C, we should compute separately the values of K for panel BC and CD. Thus,

$$K_{cb} = \frac{h}{24}[(7)(16) + (6)(10) - 0]\frac{wL^2}{432EI_0} = (172)\frac{wL^2h}{10,368EI_0}$$

$$K_{cd} = \frac{h}{24}[(7)(24) + (6)(27) - 24]\frac{wL^2}{432EI_0} = (306)\frac{wL^2h}{10,368EI_0}$$

It should be pointed out that the expressions for R_{ab} and R_{ba} in Eqs. (3-12) are applicable even if the ordinate c in the equations is fictitious. For example, the M/EI curve for beam segment AC may be projected beyond point C in the computation of K_{cb}, and the same result will be obtained. The next step is to assume an arbitrary value for θ' at the left support A where the deflection is known to be zero. As far as the deflections are concerned, it makes no difference whether a value of θ' is assumed to the left of point A since the equivalent concentrated curvature $K = 44$ at point A does not enter into the deflection computation. Finally, a linear correction is applied to the trial deflections v' so that the deflection at the right support G becomes zero.

6-8 GEOMETRY OF DEFLECTED RIGID FRAMES

The methods of computing beam deflections can readily be applied to the computation of deflections of rigid frames if the general shapes of the deflected structures are known. The deflected shape of the individual straight members in a rigid frame is prescribed by the M/EI diagram along the length of the member. Furthermore, the angle at a rigid joint before deformation must remain the same after deformation. Thus, if the members meeting at a rigid joint are bent into curves, the tangents to the curves at the joint must hold the same relative position to each other as the members did before deformation. With these guiding principles, the shapes of deflected rigid frames can be easily sketched as illustrated by the following examples.

Figure 6-23 shows a rigid frame with a vertical load acting on member AB. Since bending occurs only in member AB, member BC remains straight after deformation. Since the horizontal displacement of a point in member AB is small in comparison with its vertical displacement, joint B is assumed to remain in the same position. If the slope of member AB at point B is θ_b, it will also cause a rotation of θ_b in member BC because $\angle A'BC'$ must equal $\angle ABC$. Since the angle θ_b is very small, the vertical displacement of a point in member BC is small and negligible in comparison with its horizontal displacement. Thus, point B is assumed to be undeflected in horizontal and vertical directions, and the horizontal displacement at C is equal to the rotation θ_b multiplied by the length BC.

A similar case is shown in Fig. 6-24, in which member AB will also rotate as a result of the applied load on the horizontal member BC because the angle at joint B must remain 90 degrees when the horizontal member BC is subjected to bending. Since joint A is hinged, no deflection is permitted at that point, and point B will be displaced horizontally to allow rotation in member AB. Again, the vertical displacement of point B is small and negligible in comparison with its horizontal displacement so that point B' is considered to be at the same elevation as point B. For a similar reason, length $B'C'$ is taken to be equal to BC, and the horizontal displacement of point C is equal to that of point B. Finally, the horizontal displacement at any point on member CD is equal to the horizontal displacement at point C plus the horizontal displacement due to the rotation of member CD. For example, at point D, $u_d = u_c + u_d'$.

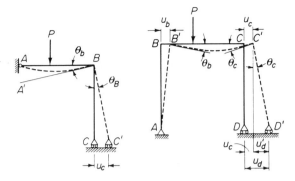

Figure 6-23   **Figure 6-24**

Consider another case, as shown in Fig. 6-25, in which a horizontal force is applied at point C. Since member BC as well as member AB is subjected to bending in this case, the horizontal displacement of a point on member BC can be considered as the superposition of a displacement if end B were fixed and a displacement due to the rotation of member BC. Thus, at point C, $u_c = u_c' + u_c''$.

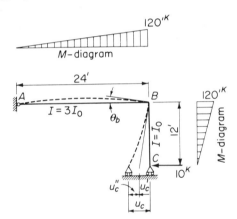

Figure 6-25

In some cases, the shape of the deflected structure is not obvious but it can always be sketched from the moment diagram. For the frame in Fig. 6-26, for example, the applied loads shown in Fig. 6-26(a) cause moments as shown in Fig. 6-26(b). Hence, the points of inflection can be located from the points of zero moment, and the curvatures of the individual elements follow the signs of the moment diagram as shown in Fig. 6-26(c). Without actually carrying out the computation, however, it is possible to sketch a deflected shape as shown in either Fig. 6-26(d) or Fig. 6-26(e). Hence, these sketches represent only qualitatively the deflected shape of the structure.

Now that we have sketched the deflected shape of a rigid frame, the influence of the deflection of individual members on that of the others with respect to a fixed reference point can be used to compute first the deflections of the individual members without the influence of the other members, and then the actual deflection is computed on the basis of superposition.

(a)

(b)

(c)

(d)

(e)

Figure 6-26

Example 6-10. Find the horizontal displacement of the point C of the frame shown in Fig. 6-25 due to a horizontal force of 10 kips acting at point C. E and I_0 are constant.

The moment diagram and the shape of the deflected frame have been plotted in the figure as previously explained. Hence, θ_b can be obtained from member AB by the method of elastic weights as follows:

$$\theta_b = \frac{1}{2}\left(\frac{-120}{3EI_0}\right)(24)\left(\frac{2}{3}\right) = -\frac{320}{EI_0}\ \text{ft}^2\text{-k}$$

The horizontal deflection of point C is caused partly by the rotation of member BC and partly by the bending of member BC. Thus, that portion due to rotation is equal to

$$u_c' = (12)\left(-\frac{320}{EI_0}\right) = -\frac{3{,}840}{EI_0}\ \text{ft}^3\text{-k}$$

The horizontal deflection due to bending also can be obtained by the moment area method as follows:

$$u_c'' = \frac{1}{2}\left(\frac{-120}{EI_0}\right)(12)\left(\frac{2}{3}\right)(12) = -\frac{5,760}{EI}\ \text{ft}^3\text{-k}$$

The final deflection is therefore equal to

$$u_c = u_c' + u_c'' = -\frac{9,600}{EI_0}\ \text{ft}^3\text{-k}$$

Note that θ_b is negative because the slope of the tangent at point B of deflected member AB is negative. This in turn causes the tangent at point B of the deflected member BC to be negative if we view the member BC from the "inside" of the structure. Thus, the negative signs for all deflections mean that point C moves inward or to the left of the original position.

Example 6-11. Compute the horizontal deflection of the point D of the rigid frame in Fig. 6-26(a). E and I_0 are constant.

The shape of the deflected frame is sketched from the moment diagram as in the previous example. However, for complicated loadings it is difficult to estimate the magnitudes of the deflections as shown in the figure and to conclude whether point D moves inward or outward. However, we still can obtain the correct result if a consistent displacement diagram is used. Considering only the *absolute values* of the displacements, we obtain from Fig. 6-26(c) the horizontal displacement at point D as follows:

$$u_d = u_d'' - u_d' + u_b = u_d'' - u_d' + u_b'' - u'_b \tag{a}$$

Or, from Fig. 6-26(d), we get

$$u_d = u_b + u_d' - u_d'' = u_b' - u_b'' + u_d' - u_d'' \tag{b}$$

Note that the sign for u_d in Eq. (a) will be opposite to that in Eq. (b) if the same *absolute values* of u_b', u_d', u_b'', and u_d'' are used in both equations. A positive result of u_d indicates that the corresponding deflected shape is correct, and a negative result of u_d means that the assumed direction of displacement should be reversed.

In carrying out the numerical computation of this problem, we may observe that the moment diagram for member BC of the frame may be considered as the superposition of a positive moment diagram on a negative moment diagram, both of which are based on the dotted line. Since we are interested in $u_b' + u_d'$ instead of each of these quantities, and since the vertical legs AB and CD are of the same length, it can be seen that

$$u_b' + u_d' = (8)(\theta_b + \theta_c)$$

Thus, we need not even compute θ_b or θ_c but instead use the sum of θ_b and θ_c, which is nothing but the area of the M/EI diagram between B and C, or

$$\theta_b + \theta_c = \frac{1}{2}\left(\frac{150}{2EI_0}\right)(8) + \frac{1}{2}\left(\frac{-80-40}{2EI_0}\right)(8) = \frac{60}{EI_0}$$

and

$$u_b' + u_d' = (8)\left(\frac{60}{EI_0}\right) = \frac{480}{EI_0}$$

Similarly, by the moment area method,

$$u_b'' = \frac{1}{2}\left(\frac{-80}{EI_0}\right)(8)\left(\frac{16}{3}\right) = -\frac{5,120}{3EI_0}$$

$$u_d'' = \frac{1}{2}\left(\frac{-40}{EI_0}\right)(4)\left(4 + \frac{8}{3}\right) = -\frac{1,600}{3EI_0}$$

Finally, from Eq. (b) corresponding to Fig. 6-26(d), we get

$$u_d = \frac{480}{EI_0} - \frac{5,120}{3EI_0} - \frac{1,600}{3EI_0} = -\frac{1,760}{EI_0} \text{ ft}^3\text{-k}$$

The negative sign indicates that the point D moves inward or to the left of the original position.

It may appear that Fig. 6-26(c) is the correct deflected shape since point D moves to the left as shown in that figure. However, if we compute θ_b and θ_c separately using the method of elastic weights, we find that

$$\theta_b = -\frac{25}{3EI_0} \qquad \theta_c = \frac{205}{3EI_0}$$

In other words, while the algebraic sum of θ_b and θ_c indeed equals $60/EI_0$, the negative sign of θ_b indicates that the deflected shape of the frame should be as shown in Fig. 6-26(e). Then, by using the *absolute values* of the displacements, we find that

$$u_d = u_d'' - (u_d' - u_b) = u_d'' - u_d' + u_b$$

or

$$u_d = u_d'' - u_d' + u_b' + u_b'' \qquad\qquad (c)$$

Hence

$$u_d = \frac{1,600}{3EI_0} - (8)\left(\frac{205}{3EI_0}\right) + (8)\left(\frac{25}{3EI_0}\right) + \frac{5,120}{EI_0} = \frac{1,760}{EI_0} \text{ ft}^3\text{-k}$$

The positive result indicates that the assumed direction of leftward movement of point D in Fig. 6-26(e) is correct.

6-9 GENERAL PROCEDURE FOR COMPUTING DEFLECTIONS IN RIGID FRAMES

Although it is desirable to visualize the geometry of deflected structures and to exercise judgment to obtain a qualitative picture of the deflections, a systematic approach will simplify the computation, especially if the loading is complicated. We shall, therefore, develop a general procedure for computing deflections in statically determinate rigid frames over a single span.

Consider first a cantilever frame as shown in Fig. 6-27(a). Since there are only three components of constraint at support A, the frame is statically determinate. Let it be required to determine the displacement of a point on the frame with respect to its original position. We can choose any pair of mutually perpen-

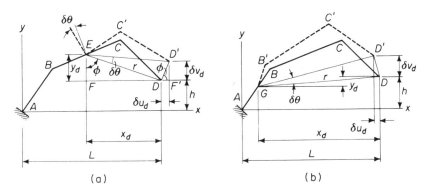

Figure 6-27

dicular axes as the reference system, and it is just as convenient to use the horizontal and vertical axes as shown in Fig. 6-27(a). Then, the displacement of a point can be determined if we can compute the components of displacement in the x and y directions. At point D, for instance, the displacement can be represented by components u_d and v_d, which are defined as positive in the positive directions of the x and y axes, respectively.

Imagine that an infinitesimally small angle change $\delta\theta$ is applied at point E of the frame while the other part of the frame is being held rigid as shown in Fig. 6-27(a). If the angle change is rotated in a counter clockwise direction, a positive curvature is introduced at that point as evidenced by the shape of BEC'. As a result of this, point D undergoes a displacement of DD' which can be resolved into components δu_d and δv_d in the x and y directions, respectively. Let the distance DE be denoted by r and the angle between DE and a vertical reference line passing through point E be φ. Then, the displacement DD' may be represented by the arc length $r\,\delta\theta$. By using the ordinary assumptions of small displacement and small angle change, it can be demonstrated that $\triangle DEF$ and $\triangle DD'F'$ are similar triangles. If the horizontal and vertical distances between points D and E are denoted by x_d and y_d, respectively, the sides of similar triangles are proportional as follows:

$$\frac{\delta u_d}{r\,\delta\theta} = \frac{y_d}{r} \quad \text{and} \quad \frac{\delta y_d}{r\,\delta\theta} = \frac{x_d}{r}$$

or

$$\delta u_d = y_d\delta\theta \quad \text{and} \quad \delta v_d = x_d\delta\theta$$

For a positive angle change $\delta\theta$ at E, both δu_d and δv_d are positive when point E is above and to the left of point D as shown in Fig. 6-27(a). Thus, the distances x_d and y_d are considered to be positive when they are directed inward and upward, respectively. If a similar $\delta\theta$ is applied at point G, which is below point D as shown in Fig. 6-27(b), δu_d then becomes negative. For a negative angle change, there is a reversal of sign for all displacement components but the positive directions of x_d and y_d remain unchanged.

Sec. 6-9 General Procedure for Computing Deflections in Rigid Frames **223**

When a rigid frame is subjected to external loads, the angle change at any point on the frame is caused by the bending moment M at a section passing through that point, and can be expressed as $\delta\theta = (M/EI)\delta s$, in which δs denotes the length of an element along the axis of the frame. Hence, the components of deflection at point D due to external loads can be obtained as follows:

$$u_d = \int_s y_d \, d\theta = \int_s y_d \frac{M \, ds}{EI} \tag{6-17a}$$

$$v_d = \int_s x_d \, d\theta = \int_s x_d \frac{M \, ds}{EI} \tag{6-17b}$$

Note that the bending moment M due to external loads varies along the axis of the frame. An example of such variation is shown by the M/EI diagram plotted along the axis of the frame in Fig. 6-28. The integrals in Eqs. (6-17a) and (6-17b) represent the products of the area of the M/EI diagram and the corresponding distances from point D in the x and y directions. These distances are measured from point D, in horizontal and vertical directions, respectively, to the projection of the centroid of the M/EI diagram on the axis of the frame, such as $\bar{x}_{d1}$ and $\bar{y}_{d1}$, $\bar{x}_{d2}$ and $\bar{y}_{d2}$, and $\bar{x}_{d3}$ and $\bar{y}_{d3}$ for areas A_1, A_2, and A_3, respectively, in Fig. 6-28. Note that the distance $\bar{y}_{d1}$ is negative in this case. Thus, the components of deflection at point D can be expressed as the summation of the moments of the M/EI diagram about point D.

Figure 6-28

Next we shall consider another type of statically determinate frame that is hinged at one support and simply supported on the other, as shown in Fig. 6-29(a). We are primarily interested in the displacement of the roller at point D. The roller does not necessarily rest on a horizontal surface, but the x-axis can always be oriented in the direction of the displacement. Let R be the distance between point D and the fixed reference point A, and L and h be its projections on x- and y-axes, respectively. Imagine that an infinitesimally small angle change $\delta\theta$ is applied at point E causing a positive curvature at that point. The frame will have a deformed shape as shown dotted in the figure, and the displacement at point D will be $\delta u_d'$. If the portion of the frame from A to E were held fixed in position while the angle change $\delta\theta$ is applied at point E, the portion of the frame from E to D would deform as shown in Fig. 6-29(b), causing a vertical displacement δv_d as well as a horizontal displacement δu_d. When the entire deformed structure is being rotated about point A so that it will be restored to the position represented by the dotted line in Fig. 6-29(a),

Displacements   Chap. 6

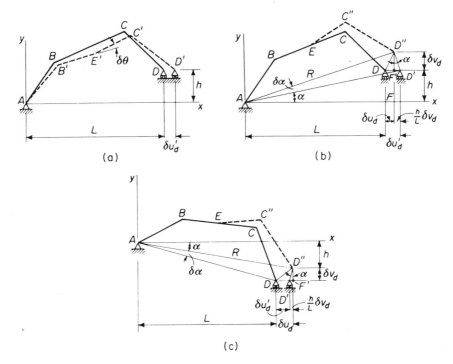

Figure 6-29

point D'' will move to point D'. Thus, the horizontal displacement $\delta u'_d$ is the sum of δu_d and $\delta u''_d$. Again, by using the ordinary assumptions of small displacement and small angle change, it can be shown that $\triangle ADF$ and $\triangle D'F'D''$ are similar triangles. Thus,

$$\frac{\delta u''_d}{\delta v_d} = \frac{h}{L} \quad \text{or} \quad \delta u''_d = \delta v_d \frac{h}{L}$$

Hence,

$$\delta u'_d = \delta u_d + \delta v_d \frac{h}{L}$$

or, by integration,

$$u'_d = u_d + v_d \frac{h}{L} \tag{6-17c}$$

in which u_d and v_d are defined by Eqs. (6-17a) and (6-17b).

If the right support D is at a lower elevation in comparison with the left support A as shown in Fig. 6-29(c), then u'_d will be smaller than u_d since the rotation about point A tends to decrease the horizontal displacement. However, Eq. (6-17c) will still be valid if h is considered as positive when it is above the x-axis and negative when it is below the x-axis. When both supports are at the same elevation, $h = 0$ and $u'_d = u_d$.

Example 6-12. Compute the horizontal and vertical components of displacement at point D of the frame shown in Fig. 6-30(a). E and I are constant along the entire length of the frame.

(a)

(b)

Figure 6-30

After computing the ordinates of the moment diagram as shown in Fig. 6-30(b), the calculation can be carried out in a tabulated form in Table 6-1.

Table 6-1

No.	$A = \int \dfrac{M}{EI}\, ds$ (ft²-k)	x_d (ft)	y_d (ft)	$A x_d$ (ft³-k)	$A y_d$ (ft³-k)
1	$\dfrac{1,333}{EI}$	15	20	$\dfrac{20,000}{EI}$	$\dfrac{26,600}{EI}$
2	$\dfrac{3,180}{EI}$	30	10	$\dfrac{95,400}{EI}$	$\dfrac{31,800}{EI}$
3	$\dfrac{4,250}{EI}$	27.5	12.5	$\dfrac{117,000}{EI}$	$\dfrac{53,100}{EI}$
				$v_d = \dfrac{232,400}{EI}$	$u_d = \dfrac{111,560}{EI}$

Example 6-13. Compute the horizontal displacement of point E in the rigid frame shown in Fig. 6-31(a). E and I_0 are constant.

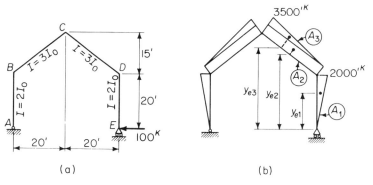

(a)

(b)

Figure 6-31

The computation can also be carried out in tabulated form. As a matter of fact, the constant EI_0 can be omitted from the computation until the last step, as shown in Table 6-2, in which $EI_0 = 1$. Because of the symmetry of Fig. 6-31(b), only half of the frame need be considered.

Table 6-2

No.	$A = \int \dfrac{M}{EI} ds$	y_e	Ay_e
1	10,000	13.33	133,300
2	16,667	27.5	458,000
3	6,250	30.0	187,500
			778,800

Hence,

$$u'_e = (2)(778,800)/EI_0 = 1,557,600/EI_0$$

6-10 DEFLECTION OF ARCHES

The general procedure for computing deflections in rigid frames can also be extended to the computation of deflection of arches. For the arch shown in Fig. 6-32, for example, Eq. (6-17c) in Section 6-9 is entirely valid since there have been no restrictions on whether the frame should consist of broken lines or a smooth curve. In evaluating the integrals in Eqs. (6-17a) and (6-17b), however, we encounter difficulties inherent in curved members. Usually, additional assumptions must be made in order to solve such problems.

Figure 6-32

In order that the integrals in Eqs. (6-17a) and (6-17b) be integrable mathematically, we must express the terms y and ds in terms of x. Very fortunately, many arches encountered in practice are parabolic and have a variable moment of inertia along the axis with a minimum value at the crown. Thus, the ordinate y can be expressed as a polynomial of x, and the moment of inertia I at any section can be assumed, without serious error, to be as follows:

$$I = I_c \sec \beta = I_c \frac{ds}{dx}$$

in which I_c is the moment of inertia at the crown and β is the angle between a tangent at a point on the arch axis and a horizontal line. Thus, the horizontal displacement for point B in Fig. 6-32 becomes

$$u_b' = \int_s y_b \frac{M\,dx\,(I/I_c)}{EI} + \frac{h}{L}\int_s x_b \frac{M\,dx\,(I/I_c)}{EI}$$

$$= \frac{1}{EI_c}\left[\int_0^L y_b M\,dx + \frac{h}{L}\int_0^L x_b M\,dx\right] \qquad (6\text{-}18)$$

When y_b and x_b are expressed in terms of x, the integrals in Eq. (6-18) can be evaluated analytically.

Example 6-14. The parabolic arch shown in Fig. 6-33 is subjected to a concentrated load P. The equation of the arch axis, with point A as origin, is

$$y = \frac{4f}{L^2}(Lx - x^2)$$

Compute the horizontal displacement at point B.

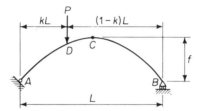

Figure 6-33

Since the moment at any section of the arch axis is

$$M = (1 - k)x \qquad \text{for} \quad 0 < x < kL$$

and

$$M = k(L - x) \qquad \text{for} \quad kL < x < L$$

the horizontal displacement at point B, according to Eq. (6-18), is equal to

$$u_b' = \frac{1}{EI_c}\int_0^L yM\,dx$$

$$= \frac{4f}{L^2 EI_c}\left[\int_0^{kL}(Lx - x^2)(1 - k)x\,dx + \int_{kL}^L (Lx - x^2)k(L - x)\,dx\right]$$

$$= \frac{fkL^2}{3EI_c}(1 - 2k^2 + k^3)$$

6-11 GEOMETRY OF DEFLECTED TRUSSES

When the members of a truss change in length owing to external causes, the joints in the truss undergo displacements consistent with the deformation of individual members. Since a change in length in one or more sides of a triangle

Displacements   Chap. 6

will cause changes in its interior angles, the displacements of the joints in a truss are related to the angle changes of the deflected structure. Thus, the angle changes and deflections at the joints of a truss must be compatible with the deformation of individual members.

If the change in length of the truss members is caused by external loads, the axial deformation in each member is given by $e = FL/AE$, in which F is the bar force in the member under consideration, L is the length of the member, A is the cross-sectional area of the member, and E is the modulus of elasticity of the material. If the change in length is caused by temperature changes, the axial deformation in each member can be obtained by the inclusion of such changes. The change in length may be deliberately made in fabrication so that the truss is cambered. Cambering is a process of changing the lengths of the members of a truss slightly so that under a specified loading condition, usually referred to as the *camber loading*, the truss will have the theoretical dimensions after the falsework is removed. The most common way of achieving such a result is to shorten the tension members by the amount they would lengthen under the specified loading and lengthen the compression members by the amount they would shorten under the same loading.

The displacements of joints of a truss can be obtained directly from the axial deformation of members. However, there are certain similarities between the deflection of a beam and that of a truss. If the chord members of the truss between supports form a straight line as shown in Fig. 6-34, the angle changes at the joints of these chord members are analogous to the concentrated angle changes at various panel points of a girder supporting floor beams. Whereas the deflected shape of a beam is represented by a smooth curve, the deflected shape of a truss consists of a series of broken lines. In Section 6-2 it was demonstrated that in the case of a beam, the horizontal displacement of a point on the neutral axis is small and negligible in comparison with its vertical displacement. Insofar as the horizontal displacement of a joint caused by the changes in slope of the horizontal chord members in the truss is concerned, the same assumption still holds true. However, horizontal displacements of joints may also be caused by axial deformations of these chord members, which cannot be neglected in comparison with the vertical displacements of the joints. In the case of a truss in which the chord members between supports form a polygonal curve as shown in Fig. 6-35, the displacements of joints in both vertical and horizontal directions are influenced by the axial deformations of the inclined chord members as well as the angle changes at the joints. Hence, the horizontal displacements as well as vertical displacements of the joints of a truss are often required.

Figure 6-34

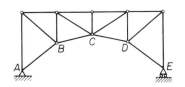

Figure 6-35

Before we can apply the elastic weight method to compute the deflections at the joints of a truss, we must first compute the angle changes at the joints as a result of the change in length of members of the truss. Since a triangle is the basic element of a truss, we shall consider first the angle changes in a triangle caused by a change in length of its sides.

Let the vertex angles of a triangle ABC be A, B, and C, and the corresponding opposite sides be a, b, and c. Let e_a, e_b, and e_c be the axial deformations of sides a, b, and c, respectively, and ΔA, ΔB, and ΔC be the changes in the vertex angles A, B, and C, respectively, with positive sign indicating an increase and negative sign indicating a decrease in each case. Since the sum of the interior angles of a triangle must be the same before and after deformation, it is necessary that the *algebraic* sum of the angle changes in all interior angles be zero, or

$$\Delta A + \Delta B + \Delta C = 0$$

Now consider the case of a triangle ABC in which only the length of side a is *increased* by an amount e_a, as shown in Fig. 6-36(a). As a result, angles A and B are changed by the amount of ΔA_a and ΔB_b, respectively. Note that ΔA_a is positive and ΔB_b is negative in this case. Because of the assumption of small deflections and small angle changes, the arcs CC' and DC' with points A and B, respectively, as centers can be represented by straight lines perpendicular to AC and BD, respectively. From the enlarged figure of triangle $CC'D$ shown in Fig. 6-36(b), it is obvious that

$$\angle CC'D = \angle ACB = \angle C$$

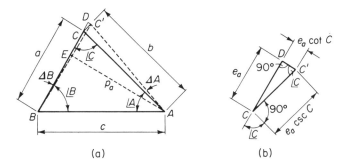

(a)   (b)

Figure 6-36

Hence,

$$CC' = e_a \csc C \quad \text{and} \quad DC' = e_a \cot C$$

If a perpendicular line p_a is drawn from vertex A to the opposite side a in Fig. 6-36(a), it can be seen that

$$a = BC = BE + EC = p_a(\cot B + \cot C)$$

or

$$p_a = \frac{a}{(\cot B + \cot C)}$$

Furthermore, triangles ACF and $CC'D$ are similar. Since the sides of these triangles are proportional, $CC'/b = e_a/p_a$. The angle changes due to the change in length e_a of side a only can therefore be expressed as follows:

$$\Delta A_a = \frac{CC'}{b} = \frac{e_a}{p_a} = \frac{e_a}{a}(\cot B + \cot C)$$

$$\Delta B_a = -\frac{DC'}{a} = -\frac{e_a}{a}\cot C$$

$$\Delta C_a = -(\Delta A_a + \Delta B_a) = -\frac{e_a}{a}\cot B$$

Similarly, if the angle changes in the triangle due to the change in length e_b of side b only are denoted by ΔA_b, ΔB_b, and ΔC_b, and those due to the change in length e_c of side c only are denoted by ΔA_c, ΔB_c, and ΔC_c, the following relations can be obtained:

$$\Delta A_b = -\frac{e_b}{b}\cot C, \qquad\qquad \Delta A_c = -\frac{e_c}{c}\cot B$$

$$\Delta B_b = \frac{e_b}{b}(\cot A + \cot C), \qquad \Delta B_c = -\frac{e_c}{c}\cot A$$

$$\Delta C_b = -\frac{e_b}{b}\cot A \qquad\qquad \Delta C_c = \frac{e_c}{c}(\cot A + \cot B)$$

Thus, the total angle changes due to the change in length in all sides of a triangle equal the sums of individual changes, respectively, i.e.,

$$\Delta A = \frac{e_a}{a}(\cot B + \cot C) - \frac{e_b}{b}\cot C - \frac{e_c}{c}\cot B$$

$$\Delta B = -\frac{e_a}{a}\cot C + \frac{e_b}{b}(\cot A + \cot C) - \frac{e_c}{c}\cot A \qquad (6\text{-}19)$$

$$\Delta C = -\frac{e_a}{a}\cot B - \frac{e_b}{b}\cot A + \frac{e_c}{c}(\cot A + \cot B)$$

These relations can also be expressed in another form by noting that the strain is defined as the deformation per unit length. Thus, by denoting the strains in sides a, b, and c by $\epsilon_a = e_a/a$, $\epsilon_b = e_b/b$, and $\epsilon_c = e_c/c$, respectively, we obtain:

$$\Delta A = (\epsilon_a - \epsilon_c)\cot B + (\epsilon_a - \epsilon_b)\cot C$$

$$\Delta B = (\epsilon_b - \epsilon_a)\cot C + (\epsilon_b - \epsilon_c)\cot A \qquad (6\text{-}20)$$

$$\Delta C = (\epsilon_c - \epsilon_b)\cot A + (\epsilon_c - \epsilon_a)\cot B$$

We can now proceed to compute the angle changes in a deflected truss. Consider, for instance, the deflection of the bottom chord of the truss shown in Fig. 6-37(a), which is symmetrical with respect to the center line. As the truss deflects downward, θ_b and θ_c increase. Thus, $\Delta\theta_b$ and $\Delta\theta_c$ in Fig. 6-37(b) are positive. This is equivalent to the sign convention of having positive angle change corresponding to positive moment in beams. From Fig. 6-37(a), it is obvious that an increase in angle θ must be accompanied by a decrease in the sum of interior angles of triangles for a particular joint. Thus,

$$\Delta\theta_b = -(\Delta\beta_1 + \Delta\beta_2)$$

$$\Delta\theta_c = -2(\Delta\gamma_1 + \Delta\gamma_2)$$

$$\Delta\theta_d = \Delta\theta_b$$

 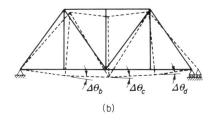

(a)   (b)

Figure 6-37

For a cantilever truss, a similar procedure can be applied. In Fig. 6-38(a), for example, angles θ_a and θ_b will decrease if the truss deflects downward. Thus, $\Delta\theta_a$ and $\Delta\theta_b$ in Fig. 6-38(b) are negative. The angle changes $\Delta\theta_a$ and $\Delta\theta_b$ can be obtained as follows:

$$\Delta\theta_a = -\Delta\alpha$$

$$\Delta\theta_b = (\Delta\beta_1 + \Delta\beta_2 + \Delta\beta_3)$$

(a)   (b)   **Figure 6-38**

6-13 ELASTIC WEIGHT METHOD FOR COMPUTING TRUSS DEFLECTIONS

In sections 6-6 and 6-7, we pointed out that the relation between angle change and deflection in a beam is analogous to the relation between load and moment of a beam of the same span, provided that the displacement boundary conditions of the former correspond with the force boundary conditions of the latter. Since the angle changes at the joints of a truss have the same characteristics as the concentrated angle changes in a girder supporting floor beams, it is obvious that the elastic weight method may be applied to compute the vertical displacements of the joints in a truss if other requirements of the conjugate beam concept are satisfied. Furthermore, the numerical computation may be tabulated in a manner similar to the numerical procedure of computing beam deflections if a large number of joints is involved in the computation. Since the chord members between supports may be considered as a bar chain, the elastic weight method of computing truss deflection is also known as the *bar chain method.*

In the computation of deflections of a straight horizontal bar chain in a truss, the angle changes at the joints may be used as elastic loads on a conjugate beam. For the simply supported truss shown in Fig. 6-37(a), for example, the angle changes at the joints of the bottom chord are related to the tangential deviations at point E as shown in Fig. 6-39(a). Thus, for small angles, we have

$$\theta_a = \frac{t_{ea}}{L} = \frac{t_{eb} + t_{ec} + t_{ed}}{L}$$

Figure 6-39

Then, the vertical displacements at the joints are equal to

$$v_b = \theta_a h$$

$$v_c = \theta_a 2h - \Delta\theta_b h$$

$$v_d = \theta_a 3h - \Delta\theta_b 2h - \Delta\theta_c h$$

For a sign convention having upward displacement as positive, θ_a as well as v_b, v_c, and v_d should result in a negative sign. If we take a conjugate beam of the same span length and with upward elastic loads acting as shown in Fig. 6-39(b), the reaction at A of the conjugate beam is equal to θ_a, and the moments at points B, C, and D are equal to the deflections at joints B, C, and D of the truss, respectively. Note that the upward elastic loads correspond to positive angle changes and that the angle changes at points A and E need not be known since they would only influence the reactions but not the moments at points B, C, and D of the conjugate beam. For the cantilever truss shown in Fig. 6-38(a), the angle changes at the joints of the bottom chord may also be related to the tangential deviations as shown in Fig. 6-40(a). Thus, for small angles, we get

$$v_c = t_{ca} + t_{cb} = \Delta\theta_a 2h + \Delta\theta_b h$$

$$v_b = \Delta\theta_a h$$

Again, the displacements v_b and v_c should result in a negative sign if upward displacement is defined as positive. The elastic loads on the conjugate beam in Fig. 6-40(b) are downward in this case because the angle changes are negative. Note that the force boundary conditions of the conjugate beam are made to correspond to the displacement boundary conditions of the truss. Thus, the moments at points B and C of the conjugate beam are equal to the deflections at joints B and C of the truss, respectively.

(a)

(b)

Figure 6-40

The horizontal displacement of a joint in a horizontal bar chain is equal to the accumulation of axial deformations of the chord members from the point of reference to that joint. For the truss shown in Fig. 6-39(a), for example, point A is the point of reference. Let δ_{ab}, δ_{bc}, δ_{cd}, and δ_{de} be the axial deformations of members AB, BC, CD, and DE, respectively. Then, the horizontal displacements of joints B, C, D, and E are respectively equal to

$$u_b = \delta_{ab}$$

$$u_c = \delta_{ab} + \delta_{bc}$$

$$u_d = \delta_{ab} + \delta_{bc} + \delta_{cd}$$

$$u_e = \delta_{ab} + \delta_{bc} + \delta_{cd} + \delta_{de}$$

Example 6-15. For the truss shown in Fig. 6-41(a), determine the vertical deflections at joints L_1 and L_2. The truss is symmetrical and the axial deformations in the members are noted in the figure.

(a)

(b)

Figure 6-41

At joint L_1 the changes of angles $L_0 L_1 U_1$ and $L_2 L_1 U_1$ are needed for the computation of θ_{L_1}, and at joint L_2, only the changes of angles $L_1 L_2 U_1$ and $U_1 L_2 U_2$ are computed because of the symmetry of the truss. The calculation of these angle changes by Eq. (6-19) is carried out in Table 6-3. The last row for each joint in the table represents the algebraic sum of the changes of the interior angles at the joint. For joint L_2, the sum is multiplied by two because only half of the interior angles has been considered in the computation. The factor of 12 that is multiplied by the change of interior angles results from the conversion of the lengths of members from feet to inches. This factor need not be carried in the computation if adequate provision is made for its inclusion or cancellation later.

The conjugate beam for computing deflections is shown in Fig. 6-41(b). Note that applied loads are taken as upward because the sign of $\Delta\theta$ should be opposite to that of the sum of changes of interior angles. Since the moments at points L_1 and L_2 of the conjugate beams are negative, the deflections at joints L_1 and L_2 of

Table 6-3

Joint	Angle	Member	e(in.)	12 × Change of interior angles
		$L_0 U_1$	-0.3	$-\dfrac{0.3}{50}\left(\dfrac{3}{4}+\dfrac{4}{3}\right) = -0.105$
	$L_0 L_1 U_1$	$U_1 L_1$	$+0.1$	$-\dfrac{0.1}{40}\left(\dfrac{4}{3}\right) = -0.0033$
		$L_0 L_1$	$+0.2$	$-\dfrac{0.1}{30}\left(\dfrac{3}{4}\right) = -0.005$
L_1		$U_1 L_2$	$+0.3$	$\dfrac{0.3}{50}\left(\dfrac{3}{4}+\dfrac{4}{3}\right) = +0.105$
	$U_1 L_1 L_2$	$U_1 L_1$	$+0.1$	$-\dfrac{0.1}{40}\left(\dfrac{4}{3}\right) = -0.0033$
		$L_1 L_2$	$+0.2$	$-\dfrac{0.1}{30}\left(\dfrac{3}{4}\right) = -0.005$
	Sum			-0.0166
		$U_1 L_1$	$+0.1$	$\dfrac{0.1}{40}\left(\dfrac{4}{3}\right) = +0.0033$
	$L_1 L_2 U_1$	$U_1 L_2$	$+0.3$	$-\dfrac{0.3}{50}\left(\dfrac{4}{3}\right) = -0.008$
		$L_1 L_2$	$+0.2$	0
L_2		$U_1 U_2$	-0.2	$-\dfrac{0.2}{50}\left(\dfrac{3}{4}\right) = -0.005$
	$U_1 L_2 U_2$	$U_2 L_2$	0	0
		$U_1 L_2$	$+0.3$	$-\dfrac{0.3}{50}\left(\dfrac{3}{4}\right) = -0.0045$
	Sum			$(2)(-0.0142)$

the truss are negative or downward. Hence,

$$\Delta\theta_{L_1} = +\frac{0.0166}{12} \quad \text{and} \quad \Delta\theta_{L_2} = (2)\left(+\frac{0.142}{12}\right) = +\frac{0.0284}{12}$$

Then,

$$v_{L_1} = -\left(\frac{0.0308}{12}\right)(30)(12) = -0.924 \text{ in.}$$

$$v_{L_2} = -\left(\frac{0.0308}{12}\right)(60)(12) + \left(\frac{0.0166}{12}\right)(30)(12) = -1.35 \text{ in.}$$

Example 6-16. For the truss shown in Fig. 6-42(a), compute the vertical deflections at joints L_1 and L_2. $E = 30 \times 10^3$ ksi.

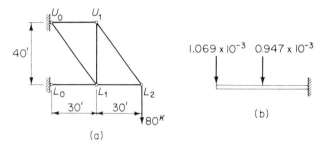

(a)

(b)

Figure 6-42

The bar forces in the truss members are first analyzed and the elastic strains in various members are computed as shown in Table 6-4. The computation of the angle changes has been carried out in Table 6-5. In Table 6-5 angle A represents the particular interior angle for which the change is computed, and the change ΔA is multiplied by a factor of 10^3 in the last column of the table.

Table 6-4

Member	Bar force F (kips)	Area A (in.^{2})	Strain $= e/L = F/AE$
$L_0 L_1$	-120	8	-0.500×10^{-3}
$L_1 L_2$	$- 60$	8	-0.250×10^{-3}
$U_0 U_1$	$+ 60$	8	$+0.250 \times 10^{-3}$
$U_0 L_1$	$+100$	10	$+0.333 \times 10^{-3}$
$U_1 L_2$	$+100$	10	$+0.333 \times 10^{-3}$
$U_1 L_1$	$- 80$	6	-0.444×10^{-3}

The elastic load on the conjugate beam for this problem is shown in Fig. 6-42(b). Then, the vertical deflections may be computed by taking moments at points L_1 and L_2 of the conjugate beam.

$$v_{L_1} = (-1.069 \times 10^{-3})(30)(12) = -0.385 \text{ in.}$$

$$v_{L_2} = (-1.069 \times 10^{-3})(60)(12) + (-0.947 \times 10^{-3})(30)(12)$$

$$= -0.770 - 0.341 = -1.111 \text{ in.}$$

Table 6-5

Joint	Angle A	$10^3 \times (\epsilon_a - \epsilon_c) \cot B$	$10^3 \times (\epsilon_a - \epsilon_b) \cot C$	$10^3 \times \Delta A$
L_0	$U_0 L_0 L_1$	$(0.333 - 0)(\tfrac{4}{3}) = \quad 0.444$	$(0.333 + 0.5)(\tfrac{3}{4}) = \quad 0.625$	$+1.069$
L_1	$L_0 L_1 U_0$	$(0 + 0.5)(0) = \quad 0$	$(0 - 0.333)(\tfrac{4}{3}) = -0.444$	-0.444
	$U_0 L_1 U_1$	$(0.250 - 0.333)(\tfrac{3}{4}) = -0.063$	$(0.25 + 0.444)(0) = \quad 0$	-0.063
	$U_1 L_1 L_2$	$(0.333 + 0.444)(\tfrac{4}{3}) = \quad 1.016$	$(0.333 + 0.25)(\tfrac{3}{4}) = \quad 0.438$	$+1.454$
	Sum			$+0.947$

6-14 DEFLECTION OF CABLES

When a cable is subjected to external loads, it elongates under the action of the tension; temperature variations also cause a change in length. The result is vertical deflection or change in the cable sag since the span length between supports of the cable remains constant. We shall confine our discussion to uniformly loaded cables.

Length of cables. The total length s of a cable can be obtained by integrating the length of element ds over the entire length as follows:

$$s = \int_0^s ds = \int_0^L \left[1 + \left(\frac{dy}{dx}\right)^2\right]^{1/2} dx \tag{6-21}$$

Although it is theoretically possible to carry out the integration for the general case of a uniformly loaded cable represented by Eq. (3-16), the result is rather cumbersome. Therefore, we shall derive first an expression for a special case for which the supports are at the same elevation. Let us choose the coordinate axes as shown in Fig. 6-43. Then, the equation of a parabola can be written as

$$y = \frac{4fx^2}{L^2} \tag{a}$$

Figure 6-43

Since $dy/dx = 8fx/L^2$, we have

$$s = 2\int_0^{L/2} \left[1 + \frac{64f^2 x^2}{L^4}\right]^{1/2} dx$$

Expanding the quantity under the integral sign into an infinite series by means of the binomial theorem, we obtain

Sec. 6-14   Deflection of Cables   237

$$s = 2 \int_0^{L/2} \left[1 + \frac{1}{2}\left(\frac{64f^2x^2}{L^4} \right) - \frac{1}{8}\left(\frac{64f^2x^2}{L^4} \right)^2 + \cdots \right] dx$$

$$= L\left(1 + \frac{8f^2}{3L^2} - \frac{32f^4}{5L^4} + \cdots \right)$$

Taking only the first three terms and letting the sag ratio $n = f/L$,

$$s = L\left(1 + \frac{8n^2}{3} - \frac{32n^4}{5} \right) \tag{6-22}$$

When the supports of the cable are not at the same elevation, as shown in Fig. 6-44, the equation of the cable is given by

$$y = \frac{4f}{L^2}(Lx - x^2) + \frac{hx}{L} \tag{b}$$

Figure 6-44

Thus, the integral in Eq. (6-21) becomes rather complicated. However, the approximate length of the cable can be obtained from Eq. (6-22). Let L' be the length of the inclined chord between supports and f' be the sag at midspan normal to the inclined chord. If the angle of inclination is denoted by θ, it can be seen that $L' = L \sec \theta$, and $f' = f \cos \theta$. Hence,

$$n' = \frac{f'}{L'} = \frac{f}{L}\cos^2 \theta$$

and

$$s = L'\left(1 + \frac{8n'^2}{3} - \frac{32n'^4}{5} + \cdots \right)$$

$$= L \sec \theta \left(1 + \frac{8f^2}{3L^2}\cos^4 \theta - \frac{32f^4}{5L^4}\cos^8 \theta + \cdots \right) \tag{6-23}$$

Elongation of cables.   The elongation of a cable subjected to uniform load can be obtained by integrating the elongation of an element ds along the entire length. Thus

$$\Delta s = \int_0^s \frac{T\,ds}{AE} = \frac{1}{AE}\int_0^s T\,ds = \frac{1}{AE}\int_0^s H\frac{ds}{dx}\,ds$$

$$= \frac{H}{AE}\int_0^L \left(\frac{ds}{dx} \right)^2 dx = \frac{H}{AE}\int_0^L \left[1 + \left(\frac{dy}{dx} \right)^2 \right] dx \tag{6-24}$$

Displacements   Chap. 6

Again, for the cable represented by Eq. (a), we have

$$\Delta s = \frac{2H}{AE} \int_0^{L/2} \left[1 + \frac{64f^2x^2}{L^4} \right] dx$$

$$= \frac{HL}{AE} \left(1 + \frac{16}{3}n^2 \right)$$

(6-25)

If the supports of the cable are not at the same elevation, the term dy/dx in Eq. (6-24) may be obtained from Eq. (b) as follows:

$$\frac{dy}{dx} = \frac{4f}{L} - \frac{8fx}{L^2} + \frac{h}{L}$$

(c)

Hence,

$$\Delta s = \frac{H}{AE} \int_0^L \left[1 + \left(4n - \frac{8nx}{L} + \frac{h}{L} \right)^2 \right] dx$$

$$= \frac{HL}{AE} \left(1 + \frac{h^2}{L^2} + \frac{16}{3}n^2 \right)$$

(6-26)

Change of cable sag. From Eq. (6-22), we can write

$$s = L \left[1 + \frac{8f^2}{3L^2} - \frac{32f^4}{5L^4} \right]$$

If we differentiate s with respect to f, we obtain the following:

$$\frac{\partial s}{\partial f} = \frac{16}{3} \frac{f}{L} - \frac{128f^3}{5L^3}$$

$$= \frac{16}{3}n - \frac{128}{5}n^3$$

Physically, $\partial s/\partial f$ represents the rate of change of s with respect to f while the span length L is maintained constant. If $\partial s/\partial f$ is expressed in the form of $\Delta s/\Delta f$, in which Δs and Δf are small finite quantities, we have the following relation:

$$\Delta f = \frac{\Delta s}{\frac{16}{3}n - \frac{128}{5}n^3}$$

(6-27)

Example 6-17. The cable shown in Fig. 6-45 is subjected to a uniform load of 1 kip/horizontal ft. The supports of the cable are at the same elevation.

1^K/horizontal ft   **Figure 6-45**

$L = 1,600$ ft, $f = 80$ ft, and $n = f/L = 0.05$. $E = 30 \times 10^3$ ksi and $A = 80$ in.^{2} Determine the length of the cable and the elongation of the cable caused by the load.

$$s = 1,600[1 + \tfrac{8}{3}(0.05)^2 - \tfrac{32}{5}(0.05)^4] = 1,706.7 \text{ ft}$$

$$H = \frac{(1)(1,600)^2}{(8)(80)} = 4,000 \text{ kips}$$

$$\Delta s = \frac{(4,000)(1,600)}{(80)(30,000)}\left[1 + \frac{16}{3}(0.05)^2\right] = 2.70 \text{ ft}$$

If the shape of the cable is to remain parabolic under the load, the initial length of the cable before loading should be reduced by the amount of 2.70 ft, or the initial length is $1,706.7 - 2.7 = 1,704$ ft.

Example 6-18. For the previous example, determine the change in the cable sag under load. Also, compute the change of the sag for a temperature rise of 100 degrees F. The coefficient of linear expansion is $6.5 \times 10^{-6}/°\text{F}$.

For the external load, $\Delta s = 2.70$ ft,

$$\Delta f = \frac{2.70}{(\tfrac{16}{3})(0.05) - (\tfrac{128}{5})(0.05)^3} = \frac{2.70}{0.2635} = 10.1 \text{ ft}$$

For temperature rise,

$$\Delta s = (100)(6.5)(10^{-6})(1,706.7) = 1.047 \text{ ft}$$

$$\Delta f = \frac{1.047}{0.2635} = 3.98 \text{ ft}$$

PROBLEMS

6-1. Derive the differential relationship between moment M and deflection v for a beam using the sign convention in Fig. P6-1.

Figure P6-1

6-2 to 6-6. The beams shown in Figs. P6-2 to P6-6 have constant modulus of elasticity E and moment of inertia I. Derive the equations for slope and deflection for each beam by successive integrations. Also calculate the deflection at point C of each beam by the moment-area method.

Figure P6-2

Figure P6-3

$E = 30 \times 10^3$ ksi
$I = 250$ in.^{4}

Figure P6-4

$E = 30 \times 10^3$ ksi
$I = 200$ in.^{4}

Figure P6-5

Figure P6-6

6-7 and **6-8.** Calculate the slope and deflection at points A and C of the beams shown in Figs. P6-7 and P6-8 by the conjugate beam method. The modulus of elasticity E and the moment of inertia I of the beams are constant.

Figure P6-7

Figure P6-8

6-9 to **6-17.** Calculate the deflections at the panel points of the beams shown in Figs. P6-9 through P6-17 by Newmark's method. The modulus of elasticity $E = 30 \times 10^3$ ksi.

(Use $h = 6'$)

Figure P6-9

(Use $h = \frac{L}{4}$)

Figure P6-10

Figure P6-11

Figure P6-12

Figure P6-13

Figure P6-14

Figure P6-15

Figure P6-16

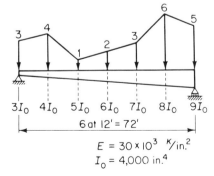

Figure P6-17

Displacements   Chap. 6

6-18 and **6-19.** Calculate the horizontal and vertical displacements of joint D of the frames shown in Figs. P6-18 and P6-19.

Figure P6-18   **Figure P6-19**

6-20 to **6-22.** Calculate the horizontal displacement of joint E for the frames shown in Figs. P6-20 through P6-22.

Figure P6-20   **Figure P6-21**

Figure P6-22

6-23. The parabolic arch shown in Fig. P6-23 has a variable moment of inertia $I = I_c \sec \beta$ in which I_c is the moment of inertia at the crown and β is the angle between a tangent at a point on the arch axis and a horizontal line. Compute the horizontal displacement of point B for $k = 0.2, 0.4, 0.6,$ and 0.8.

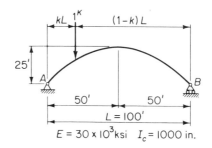

kL 1^K $(1-k)L$

$25'$

A B

$50'$ $50'$

$L = 100'$

$E = 30 \times 10^3$ ksi $I_c = 1000$ in.

Figure P6-23

6-24 to **6-28.** Find the vertical deflections of the joints at the lower chords of the trusses shown in Figs. P6-24 through P6-28 by the elastic weight method.

$26'$ $52'$ $26'$

D $-0.2''$ E

$15'$ $-0.3''$ $+0.3''$ $+0.3''$ $-0.3''$

$+0.2''$ $+0.2''$ C

A $30°$ B $30°$

$52'$ $52'$

Figure P6-24

$20'$ $40'$ $40'$ $20'$

E $-0.4''$ F $-0.4''$ G

$20'$ $-0.3''$ $+0.3''$ $-0.3''$ $+0.3''$ $-0.3''$ $+0.2''$

A $+0.4''$ $+0.4''$ $-0.3''$ D

B C

$40'$ $40'$ $40'$

Figure P6-25

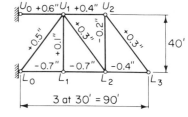

U_0 $+0.6''$ U_1 $+0.4''$ U_2

$+0.5''$ $+0.1''$ $+0.3''$ $-0.2''$ $+0.3''$

$40'$

$-0.7''$ $-0.7''$ $-0.4''$

L_0 L_1 L_2 L_3

3 at $30' = 90'$

Figure P6-26

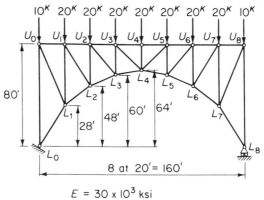

10^K 20^K 20^K 20^K 20^K 20^K 20^K 20^K 10^K

U_0 U_1 U_2 U_3 U_4 U_5 U_6 U_7 U_8

L_3 L_4 L_5

L_2 L_6

$80'$

L_1 $60'$ $64'$ L_7

$28'$ $48'$

L_0 L_8

8 at $20' = 160'$

$E = 30 \times 10^3$ ksi

$A = 10$ in.^{2} for all members

Figure P6-27

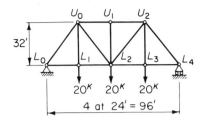

Figure P6-28

6-29. The side span of a suspension bridge cable as shown in Fig. P6-29 has a span of 600 ft and a sag of 30 ft. The load on the cable may be considered as 1 kip/horizontal ft. The area of the cable is 60 in.², and the modulus of elasticity of the material is 30,000 ksi. Compute the length of the cable under load. If the cable is to remain parabolic under load, what should be the initial length of the cable before the load is applied?

$E = 30 \times 10^3$ ksi
$A = 5$ in.² for all members

Figure P6-29

6-30. Work Problem 6-29 if the sag f is 60 ft in Fig. P6-29 instead of 30 ft while all other dimensions remain the same.

7

Moment Distribution and Approximate Analysis

7-1 BASIC CONCEPTS

In previous chapters, it has been shown that the reactions and internal forces of a statically determinate structure can be obtained from the equilibrium of the structure, and that the displacements of such a structure can be determined from the force-deformation relations of the material and the conditions of geometrical compatibility of displacements. For statically indeterminate structures, these steps of analysis are usually intermingled. If the stress-strain relation of the material is linearly elastic, the equations representing the force-deformation relations of a structure are also linear functions of unknown reactions or internal forces. Thus, a statically indeterminate structure which obeys Hooke's law is often called a *linear structural system*, and the determination of the reactions and internal forces in such a system by solving the equations resulting from the conditions just described is sometimes referred to as an *elastic analysis*. The elastic analysis of structural systems with emphasis on the methods most suitable for computer applications will be discussed in Chapters 10 through 14.

In this chapter, we shall consider the moment distribution method, which is unique among the traditional methods of elastic analysis for its wide acceptance by structural engineers for more than three decades prior to the advent of electronic computers. The moment distribution method provides not only a simple numerical procedure in the analysis of statically indeterminate beams and frames which are linearly elastic, but the method also offers valuable insights to the behavior of such structures in the process of solution. The method can yield a set of results (i.e., redundant components of reaction and internal forces) as accurately as desired through successive convergence; on the other hand, a reasonably good approximate solution may be obtained even with a smaller number of cycles of operation. Because of its well deserved popularity, numerous extensions and modifications of the moment distribution method for special applications may be found in the technical literature. However, we shall emphasize only the basic concepts of the moment distribution method and its application as an aid to approximate analysis.

The analysis of a statically indeterminate structure will be greatly simplified if the conditions of geometrical compatibility are satisfied only approximately while the conditions of equilibrium are maintained. Such an approach is referred to as an *approximate analysis*. The approximate analysis of a linear structural system can be accomplished through the recognition of the approximate deflected shape of the structure under loads, whereby assumptions may be introduced to facilitate the computation of redundant components of reactions and internal forces. Successive approximations of the redundancies may also be obtained by using the moment distribution method.

No one who is inexperienced in structural analysis and design can be expected to make accurate assumptions in reducing a redundant system to a statically determinate one for approximate analysis. The assumptions introduced for different types of statically indeterminate structures are usually based on previous experience in the analysis of similar structures for which the accuracy of results has been tested against the results obtained by rigorous elastic analysis. In this regard, the moment distribution method is extremely useful for developing intuitive perception and insight of structural behavior and for keeping the mathematical solution in proper perspective.

An approximate analysis of statically indeterminate structures may serve as a planning tool for making preliminary decisions on structural form, proportion of members, material, and cost. It offers a simple but reasonably reliable way for assessing the effectiveness of a structural form and for estimating the approximate sizes of its members. The results of an approximate analysis often provide sufficient information for making a preliminary cost estimate. Above all, an approximate analysis encourages the development of a better appreciation of the behavior of structures, and can serve as a qualitative evaluation of elaborate computations often encountered through the use of more complex methods of elastic analysis.

7-2 SINGLE-SPAN BEAMS WITH DIFFERENT SUPPORT CONDITIONS

In order to determine the approximate locations of points of inflection in statically indeterminate structures, we often attempt to sketch the deflected shape of unknown cases on the basis of our knowledge from known cases. With hindsight, the estimate is always better. It is therefore useful to examine some typical cases from which inference can be made. Since the determination of internal forces in single-span beams is not influenced by the existence of other members, as in the case of continuous beams or frames, the results obtained for single-span beams are more amenable to generalization. In sketching the deflected shape of a bending member, we often exaggerate the lateral deflection relative to its axial dimension for emphasis, as indicated by the figures in this chapter.

The moment-curvature relation of a bending member has been given by Eq. (6-1) in Chapter 6 as

$$\frac{M}{EI} = \frac{1}{\rho}$$

where M is the applied moment and $1/\rho$ is the resulting curvature. Note also that ρ is the radius of curvature and EI is the bending stiffness of the member. Thus, zero moments occur at points of zero curvature; and since points of inflection of a bending member are points of zero curvature, they must also be points of zero moment. Members with constant EI are referred to as *prismatic members*, and for such members, maximum moments occur at points of maximum curvature. The curvature of a beam is in turn related to the deflection v along the x-axis with positive direction from left to right for Eq. (6-4) as

$$\frac{d^2v}{dx^2} = \frac{M}{EI}$$

where v is defined as positive for an upward displacement and negative for a downward displacement. Hence, the deflection of a single-span beam can be obtained by successive integration as described in Section 6-3.

Consider, for example, a prismatic beam with constant EI which supports a uniform load w throughout its span. Three different support conditions are shown in Fig. 7-1. For the simply supported beam in Fig. 7-1(a), which is statically determinate, its deflected shape will be as indicated. The maximum positive moment corresponds to the maximum convex curvature at the center of the beam, while zero moments occur at the ends where the beam can rotate freely. For the propped cantilever in Fig. 7-1(b), which is statically indeterminate to one degree, the fixed end is prevented from rotation and thus a negative moment corresponding to the concave curvature occurs at that end. Consequently, a point of inflection is found to exist at a distance of $0.25L$ from the fixed end and the point of maximum deflection is found to be $0.578L$ from the same end, where L is the span length. For the beam fixed at both ends in Fig. 7-1(c), which is statically indeterminate to two degrees, both ends are prevented from rotation and negative moments corresponding to the concave curvature occur at both ends. The maximum deflection corresponding to the maximum convex curvature occurs at the center of the beam. Hence, two points of inflection are known to exist at a distance of $0.211L$ from each end of the beam of span L. The location(s) of the point(s) of inflection in each case can be determined from the elastic analysis of the structure according to the principles discussed in Chapter 6. However, if their locations are estimated approximately without conducting an elastic analysis, the solution of each problem can be reduced to that of satisfying the equilibrium of the structure with the points of inflection acting as hinges.

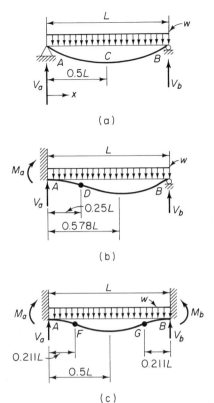

(a)

(b)

(c)

Figure 7-1

Specifically, the deflections of the prismatic beams with a uniform load in Fig. 7-1 have been obtained by successive integrations by noting the force and displacement boundary conditions. Let x be the distance from the left support; then for the given support conditions, the results are as those summarized in Table 7-1. Note that the deflections of these beams become progressively smaller as the restraint at the ends is increased. This knowledge may help us

Table 7-1 DEFLECTION OF BEAMS UNDER UNIFORM LOAD

Types of supports	Deflection at any point x from the left support	Maximum deflection downward
(a) simply supported	$v = -\dfrac{wL^4}{24EI}\left[\left(\dfrac{x}{L}\right)^2 - 2\left(\dfrac{x}{L}\right)^3 + \left(\dfrac{x}{L}\right)\right]$	$\dfrac{5wL^4}{384EI} = 0.013021\dfrac{wL^4}{EI}$ at $x = L/2$
(b) propped cantilever	$v = -\dfrac{wL^4}{48EI}\left[2\left(\dfrac{x}{L}\right)^4 - 5\left(\dfrac{x}{L}\right)^3 + 3\left(\dfrac{x}{L}\right)^2\right]$	$0.005416\dfrac{wL^4}{EI}$ at $x = 0.578L$
(c) fixed ends	$v = -\dfrac{wL^4}{24EI}\left[\left(\dfrac{x}{L}\right)^4 - 2\left(\dfrac{x}{L}\right)^3 + \left(\dfrac{x}{L}\right)^2\right]$	$\dfrac{wL^4}{384EI} = 0.002604\dfrac{wL^4}{EI}$ at $x = L/2$

in sketching the relative magnitudes of the deflected shapes of these beams. When the points of inflection are located approximately, we can determine the components of reaction and internal forces accordingly.

Example 7-1. Find the reactions and moments for the propped cantilever in Fig. 7-1(b) if the point of inflection is assumed to be $0.25L$ from the left support A.

The propped cantilever can be replaced by two separate free-body diagrams isolated at the point of inflection (i.e., the point of zero moment) as shown in Fig. 7-2(a). From the conditions of equilibrium, we obtain

$$V_d = V_b = \left(\frac{w}{2}\right)(0.75L) = \frac{3wL}{8}$$

$$M_h = \frac{w}{8}(0.75L)^2 = \frac{9wL^2}{128}$$

$$V_a = \frac{3wL}{8} + w(0.25L) = \frac{5wL}{8}$$

$$M_a = -\left(\frac{3wL}{8}\right)(0.25L) - \frac{1}{2}w(0.25L)^2 = -\frac{1}{8}wL^2$$

(a)

(b)

(d)

(c)

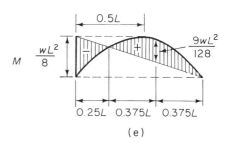

(e)

Figure 7-2

Moment Distribution and Approximate Analysis   Chap. 7

The shear and moment diagrams of the structure are shown in Figs. 7-2(b) and (c), respectively. Note that the shear and moment diagrams may also be obtained by the superposition of the shear and moment diagrams of a simple beam with uniform load and the corresponding diagrams of the simple beam due to the end moment at end A, as indicated in Figs. 7-2(d) and (e), respectively, in which the positive and negative values cancel each other in the overlapping area.

Example 7-2. Find the reactions and moments for the fixed end beam supporting a uniform load in Fig. 7-1(c) if the points of inflection are assumed to be $0.211L$ from each end.

The fixed-end beam can be replaced by three separate free-body diagrams isolated by the points of inflection (i.e., points of zero moment) as shown in Fig. 7-3(a). Because of symmetry of the beam and the loading,

$$V_f = V_g, \qquad V_a = V_b, \qquad M_a = M_b$$

Then, from the conditions of equilibrium, we obtain

$$V_f = \frac{w}{2}(0.578L) = 0.289wL$$

$$M_c = \frac{w}{8}(0.289L)^2 = 0.0418wL^2$$

(a)

(b)

(d)

(c)

(e)

Figure 7-3

$$V_a = \frac{wL}{2}$$

$$M_a = -(0.289wL)(0.211L) - \frac{w}{2}(0.211L)^2 = -0.0832wL^2$$

The exact values of M_c and M_a are $wL^2/24$ and $-wL^2/12$, respectively. The shear and moment diagrams of the structure are shown in Figs. 7-3(b) and (c), respectively. Again, these shear and moment diagrams may also be obtained from the superposition of the shear and moment diagrams of a simple beam with uniform load and the corresponding diagrams of the simple beam due to a moment at each end, as indicated in Figs. 7-3(d) and (e), respectively.

7-3 FIXED-END MOMENTS

The moments at the ends of a single-span beam fixed at both ends are referred to as the *fixed-end moments*. In a broader sense, the moment at the fixed-end of a propped cantilever (with one end fixed and the other end simply supported) is also a fixed-end moment; however, the use of the term fixed-end moment for this case should be clearly qualified wherever necessary. Since the propped cantilever and the fixed-end beam are statically indeterminate to one and two degrees, respectively, each fixed-end moment represents a redundance in the beam. Once we determine the redundant forces or moments in a statically indeterminate beam, other components of reaction and internal forces (or moments) may be obtained by the principles of statics.

In Section 7-2, we have considered the simple cases of a propped cantilever and a fixed-end beam subject to a uniform load throughout the span. Fixed-end moments, as well as other components of reactions and internal forces (or moments) due to other types of loading on a propped cantilever or a fixed-end beam, can also be determined from elastic analysis. Furthermore, the points of inflection of the deflected beam can be located by finding the points of zero moment in each case. Let M^F denote the moment at one of the fixed ends of the fixed-end beam, using M_a^F and M_b^F to distinguish the fixed-end moments at ends A and B, respectively. Let M_a^f denote the moment at the fixed end A of the propped cantilever when the moment at end B is zero. Each beam is assumed to have a length L and a constant value of EI. For a variety of loading conditions, the moment diagrams of these beams that have been obtained by elastic analysis are summarized in Tables 7-2 and 7-3 for the fixed-end beam and the propped cantilever, respectively. Note that in each case, the point(s) of inflection of the beam are located at the point(s) of zero moment.

Example 7-3. If $a = L/3$ and $b = 2L/3$ for case (c) in Table 7-2, find the fixed-end moments at ends A and B.

By substituting the values of a and b into the equations in Table 7-2, we obtain

$$M_a^F = -\frac{4}{27}PL$$

Table 7-2 FIXED-END MOMENTS IN BEAMS FIXED AT BOTH ENDS

Loading Condition	Moments and Reactions
(a)	$M_a^F = M_b^F = -\dfrac{wL^2}{12}$ $M_c = +\dfrac{wL^2}{24}$ at $x = \dfrac{L}{2}$ $x_a = x_b = 0.211L$ $V_a = V_b = \dfrac{wL}{2}$
(b)	$M_a^F = M_b^F = -\dfrac{PL}{8}$ $M_c = +\dfrac{PL}{8}$ at $x = \dfrac{L}{2}$ $x_a = x_b = 0.25L$ $V_a = V_b = \dfrac{P}{2}$
(c)	$M_a^F = \dfrac{Pab^2}{L^2}$; $M_b^F = -\dfrac{Pa^2b}{L^2}$ $M_j = +\dfrac{2Pa^2b^2}{L^3}$ at $x = a$ $x_a = \dfrac{aL}{L+2a}$; $x_b = \dfrac{bL}{L+2b}$ $V_a = \dfrac{Pb^2}{L^3}(3a+b)$; $V_b = \dfrac{Pa^2}{L^3}(a+3b)$
(d)	$M_a^F = -\dfrac{wL^2}{30}$; $M_b^F = -\dfrac{wL^2}{20}$ $M_k = +0.0214wL^2$ at $x = 0.548L$ $x_a = 0.237L$; $x_b = 0.192L$ $V_a = \dfrac{3wL}{20}$; $V_b = \dfrac{7wL}{20}$

$$M_b^F = -\frac{2}{27}PL$$

$$M = 0, \quad \text{at } x_a = \frac{L}{5} \text{ and at } x_b = \frac{2L}{7}$$

$$M_j = \frac{8}{81}PL$$

Example 7-4. If $a = L/3$ and $b = 2L/3$ for case (c) in Table 7-3, find the fixed-end moment at A. Also consider the case if $a = 2L/3$ and $b = L/3$.

Table 7-3 FIXED-END MOMENTS IN PROPPED CANTILEVER BEAMS

Loading Condition	Moments and Reactions
(a)	$M_a^f = -\dfrac{wL^2}{8}$ $M_c = +\dfrac{9wL^2}{28}$ at $x = 0.625L$ $x_a = L/4 = 0.25L$ $V_a = \dfrac{5wL}{8}$; $V_b = \dfrac{3wL}{8}$
(b)	$M_a^f = -\dfrac{3PL}{16}$ $M_c = +\dfrac{5PL}{32}$ at $x = L/2$ $x_a = \dfrac{3L}{11} = 0.273L$ $V_a = \dfrac{11P}{16}$; $V_b = \dfrac{5P}{16}$
(c)	$M_a^f = -\dfrac{Pab}{2L^2}(L + b)$ $M_j = +\dfrac{Pa^2b}{2L^3}(2L + b)$ at $x = a$ $x_a = \dfrac{aL(L + b)}{a(2L + b) + L(L + b)}$ $V_a = \dfrac{Pb}{2L^3}(3L^2 - b^2)$; $V_b = \dfrac{Pa^2}{2L^3}(3L - a)$
(d)	$M_a^f = -\dfrac{wL^2}{15}$ $M_k = +0.0298wL^2$ at $x = 0.553L$ $x_a = 0.225L$ $V_a = \dfrac{2wL}{5}$; $V_b = \dfrac{wL}{10}$

By substituting the values of $a = L/3$ and $b = 2L/3$ into the equations in Table 7-3, we get

$$M_a^f = -\frac{5}{27}PL$$

$$M = 0, \qquad \text{at } x_a = \frac{5}{23}L = 0.217L$$

$$M_j = \frac{8}{81}PL$$

On the other hand, if $a = 2L/3$ and $b = L/3$, we find

$$M_a^f = -\frac{4}{27}PL$$

$$M = 0, \qquad \text{at } x_a = \frac{4}{13}L = 0.308L$$

$$M_j = \frac{14}{81}PL$$

7-4 JOINT ROTATION AND ROTATIONAL STIFFNESS

A statically indeterminate continuous beam or frame consists of more than one member. All continuous members entering a joint in the structure must have the same translation and rotation at the joint. Thus, the deflected shape of a two-span continuous beam is expected to have a continuity of slope and deflection at the intermediate support, while that of two simply supported single-span beams placed side by side will exhibit a discontinuity reflecting the behavior of individual beams, as indicated in Figs. 7-4(a) and 7-4(b), respectively.

(a)

(b)

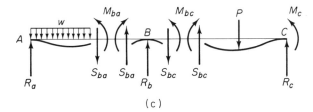

(c)

Figure 7-4

In the case of a two-span continuous beam in Fig. 7-4(a), joint B may be isolated from the adjoining members by a section just to the left and another one just to the right of the joint as shown in Fig. 7-4(c). Using the designer's sign convention defined in Section 3-2, the positive directions for moments and shears at the ends of members AB and BC are also shown in Fig. 7-4(c). In general, the tangent at joint B of the elastic curve representing the deflected shape of the continuous beam is not horizontal, and the rotation of the tangent at the joint is referred to as *joint rotation*. However, all moments acting at a joint resulting from adjacent members must be in equilibrium. Thus, in Fig. 7-4(c), the moments M_{ba} and M_{bc} at joint B are equal and opposite to the corresponding moments acting at end B of members AB and BC, respectively; and in considering the equilibrium of the moments acting at joint B, we note that $M_{ba} = M_{bc}$.

The resistance of a joint to rotation is the sum of the rotational resistances of all members entering a joint. For the continuous beam in Fig. 7-4(a), for example, only two members enter joint B at the intermediate support, and the resistance of that joint is the sum of the rotational resistances of members AB and BC entering joint B. The rotational resistance of a member at a joint is measured by the *rotational stiffness* of the member at the joint, which is defined as the moment at that joint causing a unit rotation (in radian) at the end under consideration, given the force and displacement boundary conditions at the other end of the member. The rotational stiffness of member AB at joint B is denoted by K_{ba} and that of member BC at joint B is denoted by K_{bc}. Thus, the total rotational stiffness of joint B with two entering members AB and BC is given by

$$K_b = K_{ba} + K_{bc} \qquad (7\text{-}1)$$

Since the rotational stiffness at a joint of a member is affected by the boundary conditions at the far end, the two most common cases for the far end of a member with constant EI are shown in Figs. 7-5(a) and 7-6(a). In each case, joint B is rotated by an amount θ_{ba} such that a moment M is caused by the rotation, and joint A is the far end which is either hinged or fixed. The rotation θ_{ba} at joint B of member AB may be related to the moment M by means of the moment area method or the elastic weight method discussed in Chapter 6.

(a)

(b)   **Figure 7-5**

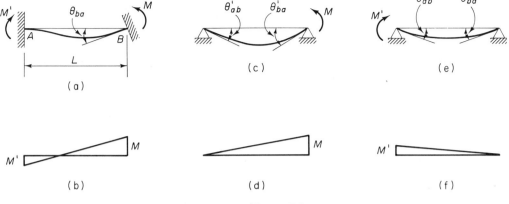

Figure 7-6

For the case in Fig. 7-5(a) where the far end A is hinged, the moment diagram resulting from a positive moment M at end B is shown in Fig. 7-5(b). According to the elastic weight method, the rotation θ_{ba} is equal to the reaction at the B if the M/EI diagram is applied as load to the beam. Thus,

$$\theta_{ba} = \left(\frac{2}{3}\right)\left(\frac{1}{2}\right)\left(\frac{ML}{EI}\right) = \frac{ML}{3EI}$$

For the case in Fig. 7-6(a) where the far end A is fixed, the fixed-end moment M' at end A caused by a positive moment M at end B is unknown. The moment M' is assumed to be in the positive direction, even though from the deflected shape of the beam, M' is expected to have a negative value as indicated in the moment diagram in Fig. 7-6(b). If the fixed-end A is temporarily released of the rotational constraint, as shown in Fig. 7-6(c), the resulting rotations at ends A and B can be computed by noting the moment diagram of the released beam in Fig. 7-6(d). Using the elastic weight method, the rotations at A and B are found to be

$$\theta'_{ab} = \frac{ML}{6EI}$$

and

$$\theta'_{ba} = \frac{ML}{3EI}$$

If a moment M' is applied to end B of the released beam, as shown in Fig. 7-6(e), the resulting rotations at ends A and B may be obtained by noting the moment diagram in Fig. 7-6(f). Again, using the elastic weight method, the rotations at A and B are found to be

$$\theta''_{ab} = \frac{M'L}{3EI}$$

and

$$\theta''_{ba} = \frac{M'L}{6EI}$$

Since the rotation at end A of the original beam must be zero, it is necessary that $\theta'_{ab} + \theta''_{ab} = 0$. Thus,

$$\frac{ML}{6EI} + \frac{M'L}{3EI} = 0$$

from which we obtain

$$M' = -\frac{M}{2}$$

Furthermore, $\theta_{ba} = \theta'_{ba} + \theta''_{ba}$ from which we find

$$\theta_{ba} = \frac{ML}{3EI} + \frac{M'L}{6EI} = \frac{ML}{3EI} - \frac{ML}{12EI} = \frac{ML}{4EI}$$

Since the rotational stiffness at joint B of member AB is defined as the moment which causes a unit rotation $\theta_{ba} = 1$ at B, we can obtain the value of rotational stiffness for each case. Thus, $K_{ba} = M$ when $\theta_{ba} = 1$, i.e., $K_{ba} = M/\theta_{ba}$ for the cases in Figs. 7-5(a) and 7-6(a). For member AB with a hinged end at A

$$M = \frac{3EI}{L}\theta_{ba}$$

or

$$K_{ba} = \frac{3EI}{L} \tag{7-2}$$

Similarly, for member BA with a fixed end at A

$$M = \frac{4EI}{L}\theta_{ba}$$

or

$$K_{ba} = \frac{4EI}{L} \tag{7-3}$$

It can be seen that the rotational stiffness of a member at a joint is dependent only on L and EI of the member subjected to the given boundary condition at the far end.

The ratio between the moment at the joint under consideration to the moment transmitted to the far end of the member is called the *carry-over factor*. Thus, for the beam with its far end hinged in Fig. 7-5(a), the carry-over factor from end B to end A is zero. That is,

$$C_{ba} = \frac{0}{M} = 0 \tag{7-4}$$

For the beam with its far end fixed in Fig. 7-6(a), the carry-over factor from end B to end A is given by

$$C_{ba} = \frac{M'}{M} = \frac{-M/2}{M} = -\frac{1}{2} \tag{7-5}$$

When two or more members enter into a joint, the moment applied at the joint will be distributed to the members in proportion to their rotational stiffnesses. The ratio of the rotational stiffness exerted at a joint by a particular member to the total rotational stiffness of the joint exerted by all members entering into that joint is called the *distribution factor*. Thus, for joint B, which is entered into by members AB and BC, as in Fig. 7-4(a), the distribution factors for AB and BC at joint B are

$$D_{ba} = \frac{K_{ba}}{K_{ba} + K_{bc}} = \frac{K_{ba}}{K_b} \tag{7-6a}$$

$$D_{bc} = \frac{K_{bc}}{K_{ba} + K_{bc}} = \frac{K_{bc}}{K_b} \tag{7-6b}$$

Example 7-5. For the continuous beam in Fig. 7-4(a), for which $L_2 = 1.25L_1$, find the distribution factors D_{ba} and D_{bc} at support B, assuming that EI is constant throughout.

From Fig. 7-4(a), it can be seen that $K_{ba} = 3EI/L_1$ and $K_{bc} = 4EI/L_2$. Hence, we obtain

$$D_{ba} = \frac{3/L_1}{3/L_1 + 4/L_2} = \frac{3L_2}{4L_1 + 3L_2} = 0.484$$

$$D_{bc} = \frac{4/L_2}{3/L_1 + 4/L_2} = \frac{4L_1}{4L_1 + 3L_2} = 0.516$$

Note that only the *relative* values of EI and L in two adjacent spans are needed in order to compute the distribution factors.

7-5 MOMENT DISTRIBUTION IN CONTINUOUS BEAMS

The moment distribution method, proposed by Hardy Cross in the early 1930's, is sometimes referred to as the Cross Method.* The method is based on the concept of continuity of slope and deflection at the joints of continuous beams and frames. If the fixed-end moments of individual spans of a continuous beam or frame are known, they will be distributed to adjacent spans in order to satisfy the conditions of continuity (i.e., geometrical compatibility). Consequently, the moment distribution method provides valuable insights to the deflected shapes of structures, especially in the case of continuous beams, for which the geometry is relatively simple.

*See H. Cross, "Analysis of Continuous Frames by Distributing Fixed-End Moments," *Transaction, ASCE*, 96, 1932, pp. 1–156.

Continuous beams are characterized by two or more horizontal spans with an intermediate support between two adjoining spans. Thus, only two members enter into an intermediate support which allows the members to rotate at the joint, while the member at an end span may or may not rotate at the end support as dictated by its boundary conditions. The continuity of slope and deflection of a continuous beam must be maintained at the joints as well as in the spans.

Let us imagine that the interior supports for all spans of a continuous beam are temporarily fixed, i.e. prevented from rotation by some external constraint, while the exterior supports of the end spans may be either simply supported or fixed as dictated by the boundary conditions. When the fixed end of each span is released by removing the external constraint, the fixed end moments at a joint caused by the loads acting on two adjacent members entering this joint are generally unequal, thus creating an *unbalanced moment*. This unbalanced moment should be distributed between the two adjacent members entering this joint according to their relative rotational stiffnesses such that the resulting moment at this joint will be balanced. However, the moments thus distributed among the members entering a joint may produce an unbalanced moment at the far ends of each of these members because of carry-over effects. The unbalanced moments at the far ends must in turn be distributed according to the relative rotational stiffnesses of the members entering each of those joints at the far ends. This cycle of operation will be repeated until no unbalanced moment exists at any joint in the continuous beam.

The procedure for moment distribution in continuous beams can be summarized as follows:

1. Determine the rotational stiffnesses at each end of all spans in a continuous beam according to Eq. (7-3) generally, and according to Eq. (7-2) for an end span with a hinged exterior support.

2. Assess the carry-over factors for the members meeting at each joint according to the condition at the far end of the members as represented by Eq. (7-5) or Eq. (7-4).

3. Determine the distribution factors (DF) at each joint on the basis of the relative rotational stiffnesses of the members at that joint according to Eqs. (7-6).

4. Compute the fixed end moments (FEM) for all spans of the continuous beam. The fixed end moments for common types of loading are given in Tables 7-2 and 7-3.

5. Compute the unbalanced moment at each joint resulting from the difference in fixed end moments at the joint. Distribute this unbalanced moment at each joint in proportion to the relative rotational stiffnesses of the members entering the joint. The unbalanced moments thus distributed are referred to as distributed moments (DM).

6. The distributed moments at a joint will be carried over to the far ends of adjacent members on the basis of the carry-over factors corresponding to

the conditions at the far ends. The resulting moments at the far ends are referred to as carry-over moments (COM).

7. This cycle of distribution and carry-over of the unbalanced moments at various joints will be repeated until virtually no unbalanced moment exists at any joint in the continuous beam. The number of cycles to be carried out depends on the accuracy desired, usually within 1% error for the final moments.

8. The algebriac sum of the fixed-end moments, the distributed moments and carry-over moments for members meeting at each joint which have been obtained in all cycles of operation yields the final end moments (EM) of the members.

9. The constant shear (CS) in each span due to the end moments alone can be computed by noting the relation $CS = (M_r - M_l)/L$, where M_r and M_l are, respectively, the right and the left end moments of a span whose length is L.

Before discussing further the fine points of the moment distribution method, we shall illustrate the application of the procedure with several examples.

Example 7-6. Find the shear and moment diagrams for the continuous beam with constant EI in Fig. 7-7(a), using the moment distribution procedure for determining the moments at the supports.

The rotational stiffnesses of members AB and BC at joint B of the continuous beam with constant EI are

$$K_{ba} = \frac{3EI}{48} = \frac{EI}{16}, \qquad K_{bc} = \frac{4EI}{80} = \frac{EI}{20}$$

Hence, the distribution factors for members AB and BC at joint B are found to be

$$D_{ba} = \frac{EI/16}{EI/16 + EI/20} = \frac{5}{9} = 0.556$$

$$D_{bc} = \frac{EI/20}{EI/16 + EI/20} = \frac{4}{9} = 0.444$$

Since joint A is simply supported, it does not resist rotation and hence it has zero moment. On the other hand, joint C is completely fixed and will resist fully the moment caused by the applied loads. The distribution factors (DF) are shown on the first line in Fig. 7-7(b).

The fixed-end moments of each span are computed according to the formulas and sign conventions presented in Tables 7-2 and 7-3. Thus, for span AB, which is simply supported at end A, the fixed-end moment for end B is given by

$$M_B^f = -\frac{5}{27}PL = -\frac{5}{27}(50)(48) = -444.4 \text{ ft-k (clockwise)}$$

The fixed-end moments at ends B and C of span BC are

(a)

1. DF		0.556	0.444	
2. FEM	0	−444.4	−600.0	−600.0
3. DM		−86.5	+69.1	
4. COM				−34.6
5. DM				0
6. EM		−530.9	−530.9	−634.6
7. CS	−11.1		−1.3	

(b)

(c)

(d)

(e)

Figure 7-7

Moment Distribution and Approximate Analysis   Chap. 7

$$M_B^F = -\frac{1}{8}PL = -\frac{1}{8}(60)(80) = -600 \text{ ft-k (counter-clockwise)}$$

$$M_C^F = -600 \text{ ft-k (clockwise)}$$

The fixed-end moments (FEM) are listed on the second line in Fig. 7-7(b).

The fixed-end moments in members AB and BC thus obtained are predicated on the assumption that support B of the continuous beam is constrained in a fixed position without rotation. Hence, the corresponding moments exerted by members AB and BC at joint B are unequal as indicated in Fig. 7-7(c). Note that the positive and negative directions of moments in the beams are based on the designer's sign convention. The directions of the corresponding moments at joint B are equal and opposite to those at the ends of the members entering joint B. The difference in the fixed-end moments in members AB and BC results in an unbalanced moment at joint B of the magnitude

$$600 - 444.4 = 155.6 \text{ ft-k (clockwise)}$$

This clockwise moment is resisted by the external constraint at joint B, which provides an equal and opposite resisting moment, i.e. a counter-clockwise moment $M = 155.6$ ft-k at joint B as shown in Fig. 7-7(c). When the constraint at joint B is relaxed, the joint will be free to rotate. Thus, this unbalanced moment will be transmitted to the members entering joint B, to be distributed between members AB and BC according to their relative rotational stiffnesses as follows:

$$(155.6)(0.556) = 86.5 \text{ ft-k (resulting in a negative moment for span } AB)$$

$$(155.6)(0.444) = 69.1 \text{ ft-k (resulting in a positive moment for span } BC)$$

The results of these distributed moments (DM) are shown in the third line in Fig. 7-7(b). However, the signs of the distributed moments at a joint can be more readily determined by the requirement that the resulting end moments on both sides of the joint must be equal in each cycle of operation. Thus, for member AB which has a fixed-end moment of -444.4 ft-k at B, a distributed moment of -86.5 ft-k will result in $-444.4 - 86.5 = -530.9$ ft-k, whereas for member BC which has a fixed-end moment of -600 ft-k at B, a distributed moment of $+69.1$ ft-k will lead to $-600 + 69.1 = -530.9$ ft-k.

The distributed moment at end B of member AB will not be carried over to end A since A is simply supported and the carry-over factor from B to A is zero. However, the distributed moment at end B of member BC will be carried to end C with a carry-over factor of $-\frac{1}{2}$. Thus,

$$(69.1)\left(-\frac{1}{2}\right) = -34.6 \text{ ft-k}$$

This carry-over moment (COM) is recorded in the fourth line of Fig. 7-7(b). Since this carry-over moment will be resisted by fixed end C, there is no distributed moment at C as indicated in the fifth line in Fig. 7-7(b). The final end moments (EM) in each span are obtained by summing algebraically the fixed-end moments, distributed moments and carry-over moments in the previous steps, and the results of the final moment are shown in the sixth line of Fig. 7-7(b).

The constant shear (CS) in each span due to end moments is also found and recorded in the 7th line of Fig. 7-7(b). Thus, for the continuous beam in Fig. 7-7(a), a constant shear of $-530.9/48 = -11.1^k$ is produced in span AB by the moment at B, while a constant shear of $(-634.6 + 530.9)/80 = -1.3^k$ is produced in span BC by the moments at B and C.

In constructing the shear and moment diagrams for continuous beams, it is convenient to superimpose the effects of the moments at supports caused by continuity to those quantities if each span were simply supported. Note that the simple beam reactions for span AB are given by

$$V_a = \frac{(50)(16)}{48} = 16.7^k, \qquad V_b = \frac{(50)(32)}{48} = 33.3^k$$

and those for span BC are

$$V_b = V_c = \frac{(60)(80)}{4} = 30^k$$

When the shears due to end moments are superimposed on the simple beam shears for each span, we obtain the end shears for that span. Thus, the end shears in span AB are

$$S_a = 16.7 - 11.1 = 5.6^k, \qquad S_b = -33.3 - 11.1 = -44.4^k$$

and the end shears in span BC are

$$S_b = 30 - 1.3 = 28.7^k, \qquad S_c = -30 - 1.3 = -31.3^k$$

The results of end shears are indicated by the shaded areas in Fig. 7-7(d). The moments in spans AB and BC caused by continuity and the moments of simple beams AB and BC are also combined as shown in Fig. 7-7(e). It can be seen that the maximum positive moments in spans AB and BC are obtained, respectively, as follows:

$$\frac{(50)(32)(16)}{48} - \frac{(2)(530.9)}{3} = 533.3 - 353.9 = 179.4 \text{ ft-k}$$

$$\frac{(60)(80)}{4} - \frac{530.9 + 634.6}{2} = 1200 - 592.8 = 607.2 \text{ ft-k}$$

Of course, these shear and moment diagrams can be redrawn in the more conventional forms using a horizontal base line for the entire continuous beam. However, the approach used in this example simplifies the calculation of the ordinates for the diagrams.

Example 7-7. Find the shear and moment diagrams for the continuous beam with values of I specified in Fig. 7-8(a), using the moment distribution method for finding the moments at the supports.

Because of symmetry of the beam and the loading, the computation is simplified. Thus,

$$K_{ba} = K_{cd} = \frac{3EI_0}{48} = \frac{EI_0}{16}$$

$$K_{bc} = K_{cb} = \frac{4E(2I_0)}{80} = \frac{EI_0}{10}$$

(a)

DF		0.385	0.615		0.615	0.385	
FEM DM	0	−444.4 −59.9	−600.0 +95.7	−600.0 +95.7	−444.4 59.9	0
COM DM		−18.4	−47.8 +29.4	−47.8 +29.4	−18.4	
COM DM		−5.7	−14.7 +9.0	−14.7 +9.0	−5.7	
COM DM		−1.7	−4.5 +2.8	−4.5 +2.8	−1.7	
COM DM		−0.5	−1.4 +0.9	−1.4 +0.9	−0.5	
EM	0	−530.6	−530.6	−530.6	−530.6	0
CS		−11.0		0		+11.0	

(b)

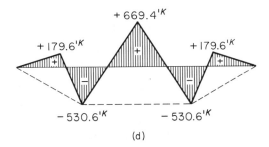

(c)

+ 669.4'ᴷ

+ 179.6'ᴷ   + 179.6'ᴷ

− 530.6'ᴷ   − 530.6'ᴷ

(d)

Figure 7-8

Then,

$$D_{ba} = D_{cd} = \frac{5}{13} = 0.385, \qquad D_{bc} = D_{cb} = \frac{8}{13} = 0.615$$

The fixed-end moments for the spans are identical to those obtained in Example 7-6.

The moment distribution procedure for this problem is shown in Fig. 7-8(b) which is self-explanatory. It suffices to mention that the unbalanced moments are carried over until they become negligibly small (here, less than one). Consequently, it takes five cycles of operation to converge to the desired accuracy.

The shear and moment diagrams are shown in Figs. 7-8(c) and 7-8(d), respectively. Note that simple beam reactions for span AB are given by

$$V_a = \frac{(50)(16)}{48} = 16.7^k, \qquad V_b = \frac{(50)(32)}{48} = 33.3^k$$

and those for span BC are

$$V_b = V_c = \frac{(60)(80)}{4} = 30^k$$

Hence, the end shears in span AB are obtained as

$$S_a = 16.7 - 11.0 = 5.7^k, \qquad S_b = -33.3 - 11.0 = -44.3^k$$

and the end shears in span BC are not affected by the continuity. Similarly, the maximum positive moments in spans AB and BC are, respectively,

$$M = \frac{(50)(32)(16)}{48} - \left(\frac{2}{3}\right)(530.6) = 179.6 \text{ ft-k}$$

$$M = \frac{(60)(80)}{4} - 530.6 = 669.4 \text{ ft-k}$$

Example 7-8. The continuous beam in Fig. 7-9(a) has $I = I_0$ for span AB, $I = 2I_0$ for span BC and $I = 0.8I_0$ for the cantilever CD. Using moment distribution procedure, find the moments at the supports of this continuous beam.

Let us consider span AB as being simply supported at A and fixed at B but span BC as being fixed at both BC before the moment distribution procedure is applied. Then, the distribution factors of support B for members AB and BC are:

$$D_{ba} = \frac{3EI_0/48}{3EI_0/48 + (4E)(2I_0)/80} = \frac{5}{13} = 0.385$$

$$D_{bc} = \frac{(4E)(2I_0)/80}{3EI_0/48 + (4E)(2I_0)/80} = \frac{8}{13} = 0.615$$

The distribution factors at support C for members BC and CD are 1.0 and 0, respectively, since span CD is a cantilever which has no rotational stiffness at C. The fixed-end moments for each span should also be computed on the basis of the same support conditions used in deriving the relative rotational stiffnesses and distribution factors. Then, the moment distribution procedure can be carried out as shown in Fig. 7-9(b). It may be noted that the final end moment at support C

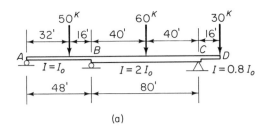

(a)

DF		0.385	0.615		1.000	0	
FEM		−444.4	−600.0		−600.0	−480.0	
DM		−59.9	+95.7		−120.0		
COM			−60.0		−47.9		
DM		−23.1	+36.9		+47.9		
COM			−23.9		−18.5		
DM		−9.2	+14.7		+18.5		
COM			−9.3		−7.4		
DM		−3.4	+5.9		+7.4		
COM			−3.7		−3.0		
DM		−1.4	+2.3		+3.0		
COM			−1.5		−1.2		
DM		−0.6	+0.9		+1.2		
EM		−542.0	−542.0		−480.0	−480.0	
CS		−11.3		+0.8		0	

(b)

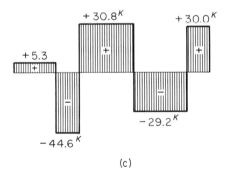

+30.8^K

+30.0^K

+5.3

−44.6^K

−29.2^K

(c)

+689.0$^{'K}$

+172.0$^{'K}$

−542.0$^{'K}$

−480$^{'K}$

(d)

Figure 7-9

is the same as the moment caused by the load at the cantilever end since the unbalanced moment at C is distributed only to member BC at each stage. The resulting shear and moment diagrams in Figs. 7-9(c) and (d), respectively, are self-explanatory.

7-6 JOINT TRANSLATION IN CONTINUOUS BEAMS

The joints of continuous beams are generally supported at the same level and therefore are prevented from translation. However, if any one of the supports moves vertically, as in the case of foundation settlement, the translation of such joint must then be considered in the determination of moments at the supports.

Let us consider first a fixed support that undergoes translation without rotation. Specifically, the fixed support B of a member AB with constant EI may be subjected to a lateral translation Δ_{ba} while the support A at the far end may be either hinged or fixed as shown in Figs. 7-10 and 7-11, respectively. If the moment at the fixed end B induced by the translation Δ_{ba} is denoted by M, then the relation between the translation Δ_{ba} and the moment M in each case may be obtained by the moment-area method discussed in Section 6-5. For member AB in Fig. 7-10(a), the moment diagram corresponding to Δ_{ba} is shown in Fig. 7-10(b). Note that t_{ab} is the tangential deviation of A from a tangent at B and is equal to Δ_{ba}. Then, according to the second moment-area theorem,

$$\Delta_{ba} = t_{ab} = \left(\frac{1}{2}\right)\left(\frac{ML}{EI}\right)\left(\frac{2L}{3}\right) = \frac{ML^2}{3EI}$$

or

$$M = \frac{3EI\,\Delta_{ba}}{L^2} \qquad (7\text{-}7)$$

Similarly for member AB in Fig. 7-11(a), the moment diagram can be constructed by observing the antisymmetry of the deflection curve; hence,

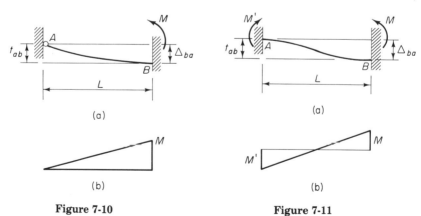

(a) (a)

(b) (b)

Figure 7-10   **Figure 7-11**

$M' = -M$ as shown in Fig. 7-11(b). Then, according to the second moment-area theorem,

$$\Delta_{ba} = t_{ab} = \left(\frac{1}{2}\right)\left(\frac{ML}{2EI}\right)\left(\frac{5L}{6}\right) + \left(\frac{1}{2}\right)\left(-\frac{ML}{2EI}\right)\left(\frac{L}{6}\right) = \frac{ML^2}{6EI}$$

or

$$M = \frac{6EI\Delta_{ba}}{L^2} \qquad (7\text{-}8)$$

For a continuous beam with lateral translation at one of its supports, the joint will undergo rotation as well as translation. Thus, the moments at the supports of the continuous beam may be determined by taking into consideration the joint rotation after the fixed end moments caused by joint translation have been determined by Eq. (7-7) or (7-8) for each of the spans affected by the joint translation. This can be accomplished by the use of the moment distribution procedure which allows for joint rotation when the unbalanced moments at the joints are distributed in each cycle of operation.

Example 7-9. The support B of the continuous beam in Fig. 7-12(a) has a vertical settlement of 0.9 inch. The beam has a constant $E = 30,000$ k/in.^{2} and $I = 19,200$ in.^{4} throughout the entire length. Determine the moments at supports B and C using the moment distribution method.

Since the settlement at support B is 0.9 inch, we have $\Delta_{ba} = \Delta_{bc} = 0.9/12 = 0.075$ ft. For $EI = (30)(19.2)(10^6)$ k-in.$^2 = (4)(10^6)$ k-ft^2, the fixed end moments in

(a)

DF		0.556	0.444		0.444	0.556	
FEM	0	+390.6	+281.3		−281.3	0	0
DM		−60.8	+48.5		+124.9	−156.4	
COM			−62.5		−24.3		
DM		−34.7	+27.8		+10.8	−13.5	
COM			−5.4		−13.9		
DM		−3.0	+2.4		+6.2	−7.7	
COM			−3.1		−1.2		
DM		−1.7	+1.4		+0.5	−0.7	
COM			−0.3		−0.7		
DM		−0.2	+0.1		+0.3	−0.4	
EM	0	+290.2	+290.2		−178.7	−178.7	0
CS		+6.0		−5.9		−3.7	

(b)

Figure 7-12

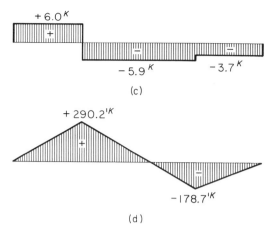

(c)

(d)

Figure 7.12 (*cont.*)

spans AB and BC can be obtained from Eqs. (7-7) and (7-8). For span AB, which is simply supported at end A,

$$M_{ba}^f = \frac{3EI\Delta_{ba}}{L_1^2} = \frac{(3)(4)(10^6)(0.075)}{(48)^2} = 390.6 \text{ ft-k}$$

For span BC, which is fixed at end C before relaxation,

$$M_{bc}^F = -M_{cb}^F = \frac{6EI\Delta_{bc}}{L_2^2} = \frac{(6)(4)(10^6)(0.075)}{(80)^2} = 281.3 \text{ ft-k}$$

The moment distribution procedure for the problem is carried out in Fig. 7-12(b) which is self-explanatory. The final shear and moment diagrams are shown in Figs. 7-12(c) and (d), respectively.

7-7 FURTHER REMARKS ON THE MOMENT DISTRIBUTION METHOD

With the advent of electronic computers, the moment distribution method has been replaced by matrix methods for the elastic analysis of complex structural systems. Nevertheless, the moment distribution method remains an important tool for making approximate analysis if complex rigid frames are broken up into simplified systems such as groups of continuous beams on each floor. In this sense, the moment distribution method can be used to provide a qualitative evaluation of the analysis of complex structures by offering a convenient check on the order of magnitude of results generated by computer programs for structural analysis.

Consequently, we have emphasized only the basic concepts of the moment distribution method without introducing many embellishments that are available. To facilitate applications to analysis of continuous beams, the fixed-end moments due to joint rotation and translation are summarized in Table 7-4, in

Table 7-4 FIXED-END MOMENTS DUE TO JOINT ROTATION AND TRANSLATION

Joint Rotation	Joint Translation
(a) $M = \dfrac{3EI}{L}\,\theta_{ba}$	(c) $M = \dfrac{3EI}{L^2}\,\Delta_{ba}$
(b) $M = \dfrac{4EI}{L}\,\theta_{ba}$	(d) $M = \dfrac{6EI}{L^2}\,\Delta_{ba}$

addition to the fixed-end moments due to vertical loads which have already been assembled to Tables 7-2 and 7-3.

In another sense, the moment distribution method is an approximate method if the procedure of successive convergence is carried out in a limited number of cycles. For example, for the continuous beam with constant EI throughout in Fig. 7-13(a), the moment distribution procedure has been performed in Fig. 7-13(b). If we stop the carry-over operation after any cycle of distributing the unbalanced moment at joint B or C, the resulting moment at the end of each cycle will be as follows:

Cycle 1:	$-444.4 - 86.5 = -530.9$ ft-k
Cycle 2:	$-530.9 - 19.2 = -550.1$ ft-k
Cycle 3:	$-550.1 - 3.7 = -553.8$ ft-k
Cycle 4:	$-553.8 - 0.8 = -554.6$ ft-k

Thus, an approximate value of the moment at joint B or C can be obtained by stopping the carry-over operation at the end of any cycle. However, since the moment distribution procedure is so easy to apply and to carry out the solution to the end, little will be gained in stopping the operation at an intermediate stage. The shear and moment diagrams based on the final end moments from moment distribution are shown in Figs. 7-13(c) and (d), respectively.

(a)

DF		0.556	0.444		0.444	0.556	
FEM	0	−444.4	−600.0		−600.0	−444.4	0
DM		−86.5	+69.1		+69.1	−86.5	
COM			−34.6		−34.6		
DM		−19.2	+13.4		+13.4	−19.2	
COM			−6.7		−6.7		
DM		−3.7	+3.0		+3.0	−3.7	
COM			−1.5		−1.5		
DM		−0.8	+0.7		+0.7	−0.8	
EM	0	−554.6	−554.6		−554.6	−554.6	0
CS		−11.6		0		+11.6	

(b)

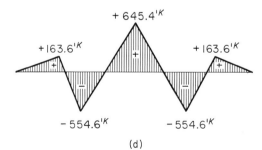

+ 5.1^K + 30.0^K + 44.9^K

− 44.9^K − 30.0^K − 5.1^K

(c)

+645.4$'^K$

+163.6$'^K$ +163.6$'^K$

−554.6$'^K$ −554.6$'^K$

(d)

Figure 7-13

The approximate analysis of a continuous beam is based on the assumption that its deflected shape can generally be sketched such that the location of points of inflection can be estimated with a fair degree of accuracy. Since each point of inflection corresponds to a point of zero moment, it may be thought of as being a hinge for the purpose of calculating reactions and internal forces. For reason of continuity, in a continuous beam there always exist enough points of inflection or hinges to reduce the beam to a statically determinate structure. The critical step is to estimate accurately the location of points of zero moment without going through the elastic analysis.

We shall begin the task of sketching the deflected shape of a continuous beam by reviewing the deflected shapes of single span beams. As shown in Fig. 7-1, the point of inflection from the left support A of the propped cantilever is greater than that for the fixed-end beam. Furthermore, a point of zero moment also occurs at the right end B of the propped cantilever, which is simply supported or hinged. Thus, both points of zero moment in the propped cantilever are to the right of those in the fixed-end beam. Generally points of inflection in a single span beam tend to move closer toward the end which has smaller rotational stiffness, and as a limiting case, the right support B of the propped cantilever coincides with the right hinge for the beam.

Using the knowledge about the location of the hinges in single span beams as a guide, we shall attempt to judge the locations of the points of inflection in continuous beams. However, even for simple cases, such as the two-span continuous beam with constant EI shown in Fig. 7-14(a), the task of estimating the lengths x_1, x_2, and x_3 is not easy because the rotation of joint B is affected by the loads in both spans AB and AC. The problem becomes simpler if one span is loaded at a time as indicated in Figs. 7-14(b) and (c). In the latter situations, the rotation of joint B is caused by the loads in the loaded span, and the deflected shape in the unloaded span is simply adjusted to this rotation according to the conditions of its end support. In a loaded span, there may exist one or two hinges, as in span AB of Fig. 7-14(b) and span BC of Fig. 7-14(c); in an unloaded span, there may be one hinge or no hinge at all, as in span BC of Fig. 7-14(b) and span AB of Fig. 7-14(c). In examining Fig. 7-14(b), we conclude that joint B offers less rotational stiffness than a fixed end to member AB. Hence, the hinge in member AB is expected to be closer to joint B than that for the case of a propped cantilever fixed at end B, since the hinge tends to move closer toward the end which has smaller rotational stiffness. Similarly, in examining Fig. 7-14(c), we note that joint B offers less rotational stiffness than a fixed end to member BC. Hence both hinges in member BC are expected to be closer to joint B than those for the case where both ends B and C are fixed. Using these guidelines, the locations of the hinges are estimated approximately as indicated by the distances in Figs. 7-14(b) and (c). Then, the reactions and internal forces for these cases can be determined by the principles of statics. Finally, the reactions and internal forces for the case in Fig. 7-14(a) can be obtained by superposition.

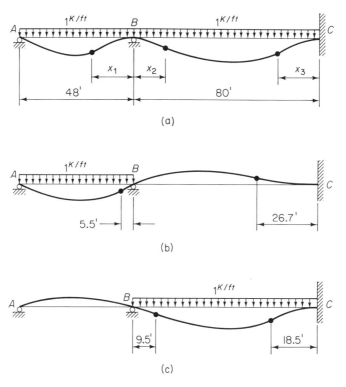

Figure 7-14

The rough deflected shape of a continuous beam can be sketched irrespective of the number of spans; however, the determination of the approximate locations of points of inflection becomes increasingly difficult as the number of spans increases. To get some better feel for the locations of points of inflection, it is necessary to consider the loading in one span at a time. Thus, the amount of work required multiplies rapidly as the number of spans increases.

The general procedure for approximate analysis of continuous beams may be summarized as follows:

1. Consider one at a time the loading at each span of a continuous beam.
2. Sketch the deflected shape of the beam under each loading and estimate the location of the points of inflection in all spans for each case.
3. Compute the reactions, shears and bending moments on the basis of the principles of statics once the points of zero moment are identified and located.
4. The final results corresponding to the loading in all spans are obtained by superposition.

The simplicity and versatility of the moment distribution procedure for continuous beams have enabled us to eliminate the unnecessary guess work

Moment Distribution and Approximate Analysis   Chap. 7

required in the approximate analysis while allowing us to develop insights about the orders of magnitude of certain design quantities through successive approximations. Thus, such a procedure is preferred as an aid to approximate analysis so long as the concept of continuity of slope and deflection of continuous beams is fully understood.

Example 7-10. Find the shear and moment diagrams as well as the points of inflection of the deflected shape for the continuous beam in Fig. 7-15(a), using the moment distribution procedure.

(a)

DF		0.556	0.444	
FEM		−288.0	−533.3	−533.3
DM		−136.4	+108.9	
COM				−54.5
DM				0
EM		−424.4	−424.4	−587.8
CS	−8.8		−2.0	

(b)

(c)

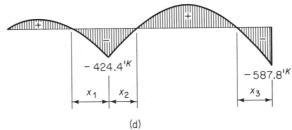

(d)

Figure 7-15

This continuous beam, which is identical to that in Fig. 7-14(a), is analyzed by the moment distribution procedure, with results indicated in Fig. 7-15(b). The shear and moment diagrams are found to be as shown in Figs. 7-15(c) and (d), respectively. If the locations of points of inflection in Figs. 7-14(b) and (c) are located correctly, the resulting shear and moment diagrams for the continuous beam in Fig. 7-14(a) obtained by the superposition of the results of approximate analysis should be close to the corresponding diagrams obtained by the moment distribution procedure. However, the moment distribution procedure is seen to be far more direct without having to resort to guess work.

Furthermore, if the locations of the points of inflection of the continuous beam with loading in both spans are required, the distances x_1, x_2, and x_3 representing these locations in Fig. 7-14(a) can also be computed. Let us consider span AB of the continuous beam only and assume that G is the point of zero moment in span AB as shown in Fig. 7-16(a). Then, considering the free body to the right of G and taking moments about G, we have

$$-424.4 + 32.8x_1 - (1)\frac{x_1^2}{2} = 0$$

from which $x_1 = 17.6$ ft or 48 ft from end B. Note that $x_1 = 48$ ft refers to the hinge (or simple support) at end A. Similarly, consider span BC only and assume H as a point of zero moment in span BC as shown in Fig. 7-16(b). Then, considering the free body to the left of H and taking moment about H, we have

$$-424.4 + 38x_2 - (1)\frac{x_2^2}{2} = 0$$

from which $x_2 = 13.6$ ft or 62.4 ft from end B. On the other hand, by considering the free body to the right of I and taking moment about I, we get

$$-587.8 + 42x_3 - (1)\frac{x_3^2}{2} = 0$$

from which $x_3 = 17.6$ ft or 66.4 ft from end C. Note that $x_2 = 13.6$ ft from B is identical to $x_3 = 66.4$ ft from C, while $x_3 = 17.6$ ft from C is identical to 62.4 ft from B since the total span length of BC is 80 ft.

(a)   (b)

Figure 7-16

Example 7-11. Find the points of inflection of the continuous beam with constant EI throughout as shown in Fig. 7-17(a).

This continuous beam is identical to that in Fig. 7-13(a), for which the shear and moment diagrams have already been obtained. Because of symmetry of the beam and the loading, we need to consider only half of the beam.

Figure 7-17

Let us consider span AB only and assume G as the point of zero moment as shown in Fig. 7-17(b). Then, considering the free body to the right of G and taking moments about G, we have

$$-554.6 + 44.9x_1 = 0$$

from which $x_1 = 12.4$ ft from end B. Similarly, consider span BC only and assume H as the point of zero moment as shown in Fig. 7-17(c). Then, considering the free body to the left of H and taking moment about H, we get

$$-554.6 + 30x_2 = 0$$

from which $x_2 = 18.5$ ft from end B.

Note that the determination of the locations of points of inflection of continuous beams under concentrated loads is simpler than that for beams under uniform loads.

7-9 RIGID FRAMES

The principles of moment distribution can also be applied to the determination of reactions and internal forces in statically indeterminate rigid frames. However, we shall consider only the approximate method for analyzing such structures and estimating the locations of points of inflection which correspond to points of zero moment in various members.

The deflected shapes of structures may be sketched directly from the given constraints and applied loads. However, we can first roughly sketch the moment diagram as an intermediate step, having gained insights from the moment diagrams of similar structures. Then, the shape of the deflected structure can be sketched in accordance with the moment diagram by noting that a positive moment produces a concave curvature and a negative moment produces a convex curvature. The sketching of the deflected shape of a rigid frame is useful not only for the purpose of estimating forces and moments but also for the computation of deflections by various methods based on the geometry of the structure.

In sketching the deflected shapes of rigid frames, it should be noted that the free-body diagram of a rigid joint must be in equilibrium. Hence, the members meeting at a joint must deform in a manner commensurate with this requirement. If sections are passed through these members at infinitesimally small distances from the joint, certain conclusions may be drawn regarding the moment-curvature relation. In Figs. 7-18(a) and (b), for example, the moments from either side of the joint must be equal and opposite to each other in order to maintain the equilibrium. Figure 7-18(c) represents an impossible case since the joint will not be in equilibrium. On the other hand, Fig. 7-18(d) is quite possible since $M_{ab} = M_{ac} + M_{ad}$ according to the direction of the moments indicated in the figure.

(a)　　　　　　(b)　　　　　　(c)　　　　　　(d)　　　　**Figure 7-18**

Since the axial deformations in members of a rigid frame are small in comparison with the bending deformations, the former is negligible in sketching the deflected shape of a frame. Generally, a rigid frame under vertical loads is subjected to horizontal joint translations as well joint rotations, unless it is prevented from translation by external constraints or if it is a symmetrical portal frame with symmetrical loading. The horizontal or lateral translation of a rigid frame under vertical loads is referred to as *sidesway*.

The deflected shapes of several rigid frames are sketched in Fig. 7-19. The rigid frame in Fig. 7-19(a) is prevented from joint translation and thus only the joint rotations are indicated in the deflected shape. The portal frame in Fig. 7-19(b) is symmetrical and is subjected to a symmetrical loading; hence no joint translation is exhibited in the deflected shape. The same cannot be said for the gable frame in Fig. 7-19(c), even though it is symmetrical and is subjected to a symmetrical loading only. The portal frame in Fig. 7-19(d) is also symmetrical but is subjected to an unsymmetrical loading, thus producing a sidesway. The points of inflection in the deflected shapes are indicated by small circles.

We can summarize our understanding of the behavior of deflected rigid frames by noting these observations:

1. The lengths of the members of rigid frames are assumed to be unchanged

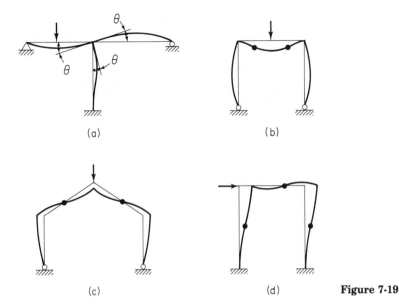

(a)

(b)

(c)

(d)

Figure 7-19

since axial deformations are small compared with lateral deflections due to bending.

2. Each joint of the deflected frame must maintain the original angles formed by the members entering the joint before loading. All angles in the deflected frame are measured by the tangents to the deflected members entering the joints.

3. For an unloaded member, there is at most a single point of inflection in its length.

For relatively simple rigid frames as those shown in Fig. 7-19, it is possible to estimate the approximate locations of the points of inflection and to perform an approximate analysis. Although the moment distribution procedure can also be applied to the elastic analysis of such frames, some modifications are necessary because of possible sidesway. In view of the complexity that may be encountered, we shall not pursue further a general approach to the approximate analysis of all rigid frames; instead we shall selectively discuss the approximate analysis of only certain types of frames for which we can predict with some degree of confidence in its accuracy on the basis of past experience when the results of such approximate analysis have been compared favorably with those obtained by more exact methods of elastic analysis.

7-10 APPROXIMATE ANALYSIS OF PORTAL FRAMES AND BENTS

Portals are primarily used to transmit horizontal forces applied at the top of the frames to their bases, such as in the case of the end portals of a bridge. Portals may be rigid frames with a horizontal top girder connected to two vertical legs hinged or fixed supports, or may be bents in which the horizontal top panel is a pin-connected truss but the two vertical legs are capable of resisting bending as well as shear and axial force.

Consider, for example, the portal frame in Fig. 7-20(a) for which both legs have the same bending stiffness and are hinged at their bases. If the bending stiffness of the top girder is of the same order of magnitude as those of the vertical legs, the deflected shape of the portal frame will have a point of inflection E at the center of the top girder as shown in Fig. 7-20(b). Since this frame is statically indeterminate to one degree, the assumption of a point of inflection is sufficient to make the structure statically determinate. From the equilibrium of the entire frame, we obtain

$$\sum M_a = 0, \qquad V_d = \frac{Pr}{q}$$

$$\sum F_y = 0, \qquad V_a = V_d = \frac{Pr}{q}$$

By considering the left half of the frame in Fig. 7-20(c) and noting that $M_e = 0$, we get

$$\sum M_e = 0, \qquad H_a = \frac{(V_a)(q/2)}{r} = \frac{P}{2}$$

Considering the right half of the frame, we can check

$$\sum M_e = 0, \qquad H_d = \frac{P}{2}$$

Hence, the horizontal force P is resisted equally by the horizontal reactions H_a and H_d.

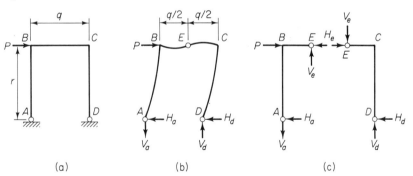

(a)   (b)   (c)

Figure 7-20

For the portal frame in Fig. 7-21(a), the bending stiffness of the top girder is of the same order of magnitude as those of the vertical legs, and both legs have the same bending stiffness and are fixed at their bases. Since this frame is statically indeterminate to three degrees, the assumption of three points of inflection as shown in Fig. 7-21(b) is sufficient to make the structure statically

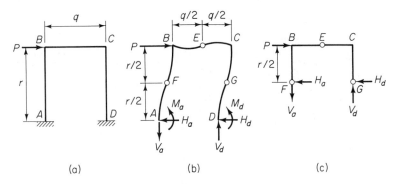

Figure 7-21

determinate. The point of inflection of the top girder can be assumed to be located at its center E while the points of inflection of the legs are assumed to be located at their mid-heights F and G. By assuming $M_f = 0$ and $M_g = 0$, we conclude that the horizontal and vertical reactions at F and G are as shown in Fig. 7-21(c) which shows the frame above points F and G as a free body. Noting also that $M_e = 0$, we can proceed as in the previous case to find

$$V_a = V_d = \frac{Pr}{2q}$$

$$H_a = H_d = \frac{P}{2}$$

Finally, by considering the legs below points F and G as free bodies, we get

$$M_a = M_d = \frac{Pr}{4}$$

Thus, the horizontal force P is again resisted equally by the horizontal reactions H_a and H_d.

Very often, the top girder of a portal frame may be very stiff in comparison with the vertical legs, or when the girder is replaced by a truss panel with or without stiffened knee braces such as the bent shown in Fig. 7-22(a). In that case, the following assumptions may be made in order to reduce a statically indeterminate portal to a statically determinate structure amenable to approximate analysis:

1. The horizontal reactions at the base of the portal frame are assumed to be equal, each being $P/2$, where P is the horizontal force applied at the top of the portal.
2. For a portal frame with vertical legs fixed at the base, a point of inflection occurs at the mid-height of each leg between the base and the stiff top girder.
3. For a bent consisting of a truss panel with or without knee braces, a point

Sec. 7-10   Approximate Analysis of Portal Frames and Bents   **281**

Figure 7-22

of inflection occurs at the mid-point of each leg between the lower side of the truss panel or knee brace and the base of the leg.

The first assumption is more general than the assumption of a point of inflection of the top girder in a portal frame since it will cover the cases when the top girder of the frame is very stiff or when a bent consists of a truss panel. This and the second assumption are sufficient for the approximate analysis of all portal frames for which the vertical legs are fixed at the base. The third assumption is a modification of the second assumption for application to bents with a top truss panel and possibly stiffened by knee braces.

Example 7-12.   The bent in Fig. 7-22(a) consists of two vertical legs AB and CD which are fixed at their bases. The top truss panel with knee braces is assumed to act as a pin-connected truss, for which the members are subjected to axial forces only. The points of inflection of the vertical legs are assumed to be at a distance $r/2$ from the bases where the horizontal reactions are $H_a = H_d = P/2$. Determine other components of reactions at supports A and D and the bar forces in the truss panel.

Considering first the bent above points J and K as a free body as shown in Fig. 7-22(b), we have

$$\sum M_j = 0, \qquad V_d = \frac{P(5r/6)}{q} = \frac{15P}{16}$$

$$\sum F_y = 0, \qquad V_a = \frac{15P}{16}$$

Considering the legs below points J and K as free bodies, we get

$$M_a = M_d = \frac{Pr}{4}$$

The bar forces in the members of the truss panel can be obtained by first considering leg AB as a free body in Fig. 7-22(c). Thus,

$$\sum M_b = 0, \qquad \left(\frac{4}{5}F_{eh}\right)\left(\frac{r}{3}\right) + \frac{Pr}{4} - \left(\frac{P}{2}\right)\left(\frac{4r}{3}\right) = 0$$

$$F_{eh} = \frac{25P}{16} \text{ (tension)}$$

$$\sum F_y = 0, \qquad \left(\frac{3}{5}\right)\left(\frac{25P}{16}\right) - \frac{15P}{16} - \frac{3}{5}F_{bh} = 0$$

$$F_{bh} = 0$$

$$\sum F_x = 0, \qquad P + \left(\frac{4}{5}\right)\left(\frac{25P}{16}\right) - \frac{P}{2} - F_{bg} = 0$$

$$F_{bg} = \frac{7P}{4} \text{ (compression)}$$

Similarly, by considering leg CD as a free body in Fig. 7-22(c),

$$\sum M_c = 0, \qquad F_{fi} = \frac{25P}{16} \text{ (compression)}$$

$$\sum F_y = 0, \qquad F_{ci} = 0$$

$$\sum F_x = 0, \qquad F_{cg} = \frac{3P}{4} \text{ (tension)}$$

By considering also joints G, H and I of the truss in equilibrium, it is not difficult to find that $F_{gh} = 25P/16$ (tension), $F_{gi} = 25P/16$ (compression) and $F_{hi} = 0$.

7-11 APPROXIMATE ANALYSIS
OF RECTANGULAR BUILDING FRAMES

A rectangular building frame may consist of a number of stories in the vertical direction and a number of bays in both horizontal directions. The vertical loads from roof or floors are carried by horizontal girders which transmit them to columns. The horizontal forces from wind are transmitted from walls to the building frame. Thus, at any given plane passing through a line of columns, we see a rectangular rigid frame consisting of girders and columns which is designed to resist both vertical and horizontal loads. Two examples of rigid rectangular building frames under vertical loads are shown in Fig. 7-23. These same building frames under lateral loads are shown in Fig. 7-24. In both cases, the deflections have been exaggerated to emphasize the response of the building frames to applied loads.

A rigid building frame is highly statically indeterminate, because the girders are rigidly connected to the columns so that all members can resist bending moment, shear, and axial force. If all columns of a rigid building frame

(a)   (b)

Figure 7-23

(a)   (b)

Figure 7-24

are fixed at the base and there are n girders in the frame, such a frame is statically indeterminate to $3n$ degrees. It is therefore necessary to remove $3n$ redundances to make the frame statically determinate. In Fig. 7-23(a), for example, there are six girders and the frame is statically indeterminate to 18 degrees, while in Fig. 7-23(b), there are 12 girders and the frame is statically indeterminate to 36 degrees. Because of the high degree of redundancy of rigid building frames, an approximate analysis is very useful in providing insights to the behavior of such structures as well as finding the approximate values of moments, shears and axial forces in various members of the frame.

In an approximate analysis of a rigid building frame, it is often convenient to consider separately the vertical loads and horizontal loads, since the assumptions necessary to deal with the two cases are different. In the case of a rigid building frame subjected to vertical loads only, the girders at each floor can be treated as continuous beams while the columns are assumed to resist the resulting unbalanced end moments from the girders, if any, at the joints. Then, each continuous beam may be analyzed by the moment distribution method or by making further approximate assumptions regarding the locations of points of inflection in the continuous beam.

As shown in Figs. 7-23(a) and (b), the girders are assumed to be partially fixed at the supports due to the constraints of the columns; hence, points of inflection corresponding to points of zero moments in the girders are so indicated. The unbalanced end moments from the girders at each floor level in turn produce moments in columns, and such moments cause the columns to deflect, with resulting points of inflection in the columns as depicted in the figures. The degrees of fixity of the column bases at the first floor (ground level) also influence the locations of inflection in the first floor columns.

For rigid building frames subjected to horizontal loads, it is important to differentiate low-rise buildings from high-rise buildings, since the deflected shapes of the two types of buildings are quite different. For low-rise buildings, for which the height is smaller than its least horizontal dimension, the deflected shape is characterized by shear deflection as shown in Fig. 7-24(a), and the points of inflection in girders and columns can be visualized as shown in that figure. For high-rise buildings, for which the height is several times greater than its least horizontal dimension, the deflected shape is dominated by overall bending deflection, as shown in Fig. 7-24(b), even though the frame also undergoes shear deflection which produces points of inflection in columns and girders. Since the division of buildings into these two extremes is arbitrary, the deflected shape of a frame can generally be expected to be a combination of both. The approximate analyses of these types of buildings are somewhat different since different assumptions will be introduced. Consequently, they will be treated separately.

7-12 RECTANGULAR FRAMES SUBJECTED TO VERTICAL LOADS

For rectangular building frames subjected to uniform vertical loads, an approximate analysis based on assumed locations of points of inflection in the girders may be used. The assumptions for such an analysis are as follows:

1. The girders at each floor are assumed to act as continuous beams supporting a uniform load. The points of inflection of each continuous beam are assumed to be located approximately at one tenth of the span length from both ends of each girder.
2. The axial deformation of a girder is negligibly small in comparison with the lateral deflection. The axial force in each girder is also negligible.
3. The unbalanced end moment from the girders at each joint is to be distributed to the columns above and below a floor by assuming that the points of inflection of all columns are located at the mid-height of the columns. The unbalanced end moment for an interior column is usually small if the adjacent spans to the column are approximately equal. In that case, only the end moment for an exterior column need be considered.

The first assumption makes it possible to consider the girders at each floor as statically determinate simple beams with span lengths equal to 0.8 of the original lengths of the girders. The choice of the one-tenth points as the approximate locations of the points of inflection is based on the estimate of partial fixity of supports at the joints. The value of $0.1L$ lies between the value of $0.211L$ for a fixed end beam of length L supporting a uniform load and the value of zero for a simply supported beam of length L.

The second assumption of negligible axial deformation implies that, if two hinges are placed at the points of inflection of each girder, the rigid building frame will become statically determinate, because it is not necessary to provide the third release to allow for horizontal movement at one of the hinge locations in the girder. Because of such approximations, the axial force in each girder is usually neglected in the analysis.

The third assumption simplifies the distribution of the unbalanced girder moments which would otherwise be based on the relative rotational stiffnesses of the members meeting at the joint (i.e., columns above and below the joint). The roof will be treated as a special case in that the unbalanced girder moments will be resisted by the columns below the roof only. If the columns at the first floor (ground level) are hinged instead of fixed, the points of inflection of the first floor columns should be located at the bases of the columns. The additional assumption to neglect the transfer of moment from the girders to the interior columns is justified if the difference in end moments from the girders supporting uniform floor loads is small, as when the adjacent girders of approximately equal length are symmetrically loaded.

Let a typical joint of a rectangular building frame, consisting of m levels and n columns, be denoted by (i, j) where i refers to the floor level starting from ground level $(i = 1)$ to roof $(i = m)$, and j refers to the column line starting from left $(j = 1)$ to right $(j = n)$. Whenever possible, we shall avoid the use of double subscripts i and j in denoting forces and moments in girders and columns in order to simplify the presentation. However, it is worth emphasizing that the girders on the ith floor are supported by columns on the $(i - 1)$th floor; thus, forces and moments in columns on the ith floor are transmitted downward from the $(i + 1)$th floor. Then, the forces and moments in the building frame subjected to vertical loads can be obtained by using an approximate analysis procedure as follows:

1. *Girder moments.* Referring to Fig. 7-25, for the girder on a typical floor i between column lines j and $j + 1$, the span length is denoted by L_j. The distance between the points of inflection of the girder with partial fixity at both ends is denoted by $L_s = L_j - (2)(0.1L_j) = 0.8L_j$. Thus, the portion of the girder between the assumed points of inflection of the girder acts as a simple beam of span L_s. For a uniform load w on each girder, the

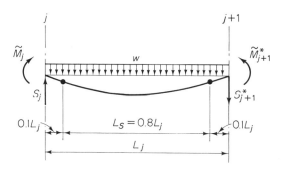

Figure 7-25

maximum positive moment at the center of a girder of span length L is given by

$$M = \frac{1}{8} wL_s^2 = 0.08\ wL_j^2 \qquad (7\text{-}9)$$

The maximum negative moment at each end of the girder is $\widetilde{M}_j = \widetilde{M}_{j+1}^* = \widetilde{M}$, or

$$\widetilde{M} = -\frac{w}{2}(0.1L_j)^2 - \frac{w}{2}(0.8L_j)(0.1L_j) = -0.045wL_j^2 \qquad (7\text{-}10)$$

The moments for the girders supporting the roof and those for the girders supporting the first floor are obtained by using Eqs. (7-9) and (7-10), respectively, for the appropriate spans. Note that the designer's sign convention for shear and moment defined in Section 3-2 has been adopted in the analysis of this building frame. That is, the positive directions of shear and moment for a horizontal member are shown in Fig. 7-25, even though the actual end moments for a girder of partial fixities at supports are in fact negative. The same sign convention is used for a column when the right-hand side of the vertical member is considered as the bottom of that member.

2. *Girder shears.* The girder shears can easily be obtained on the basis of the assumed symmetrical locations of the points of inflection for each girder with uniform loading. For such a girder shown in Fig. 7-25, the shears at the left and the right ends of span L_j are, respectively,

$$S_j = \frac{wL_j}{2} \qquad S_{j+1}^* = -\frac{wL_j}{2} \qquad (7\text{-}11)$$

3. *Column axial forces.* Column axial forces can be obtained from the shears at the ends of the girders, beginning from the roof down to first floor (ground level). At a typical joint (i, j) in Fig. 7-26, the axial force F_{i-1} in the column below the ith floor is given by

$$F_{i-1} = F_i + S_j^* - S_j \qquad (7\text{-}12)$$

where F_i is the axial force in the column, S_j^* is equal and opposite to the

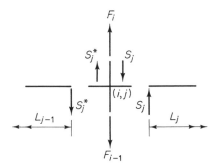

Figure 7-26

shear at the right end of the span L_{j-1}, and S_j is equal and opposite to the shear at the left end of the span L_j. Both F_{i-1} and F_i are defined as positive for tension and negative for compression.

4. *Column moments.* The column moments are computed by considering the free-body diagrams of the joints at the roof and floor levels. The unbalanced girder moments at the interior and exterior columns are to be distributed between the columns above and below the floor, assuming that the points of inflection of all columns are located at the mid-height of the column. Referring to a typical joint (i, j) on the ith floor in Fig. 7-27, M_i^* and M_i are column moments above and below the ith floor, respectively, while $\widetilde{M}_{j-1}$ and $\widetilde{M}_j$ are girder moments to the left and to the right of column line j. Summing the moments at joint (i, j) algebraically, we get

$$M_i^* - M_i + \widetilde{M}_j - \widetilde{M}_j^* = 0$$

For a girder between column lines $j - 1$ and j subjected to uniform vertical load, $\widetilde{M}_j^* = \widetilde{M}_{j-1}$. Hence,

$$M_i^* - M_i + \widetilde{M}_j - \widetilde{M}_{j-1} = 0$$

For the roof, $M_i^* = 0$ and $i = m$,

$$M_m = -\widetilde{M}_{j-1} + \widetilde{M}_j \tag{7-13}$$

For a typical floor,

$$M_i = M_i^* - \widetilde{M}_{j-1} + \widetilde{M}_j \tag{7-14}$$

At the exterior column line $j = 1$, it is seen that $\widetilde{M}_{j-1}$ in Eqs. (7-13) and (7-14) equals zero. Note that the designer's sign convention is also adopted for Fig. 7-27.

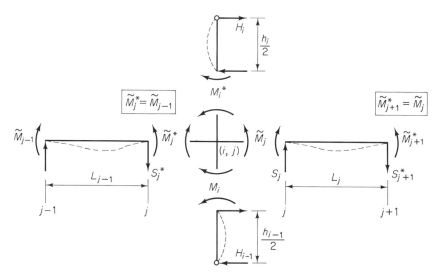

Figure 7-27

Moment Distribution and Approximate Analysis   Chap. 7

Starting from the roof ($i = m$), the column moments M_m for column lines $j = 1, 2, \ldots, n$ can be obtained consecutively from the unbalanced moments in the girders by means of Eq. (7-13). This moment M_m at the top of the column on the $(m - 1)$th floor will be transmitted to its base through the point of inflection at the mid-height $h_{m-1}/2$, with $M_{m-1}^* = -M_m$ according to the relationships shown in Fig. 7-28. Similarly, the moment M_{i+1} at the top of the column at the ith floor will transmitted to its base through the point of inflection at the mid-height $h_i/2$, with $M_i^* = -M_{i+1}$ as shown in Fig. 7-28. Hence, the column moments can be obtained from the roof down to the first floor (ground level) by means of Eq. (7-14). The fact that the sign of the moment at the top of a column on any floor is opposite to that of the moment at its base is to be expected, since it is compatible with the deflected shapes of the frames under vertical loads.

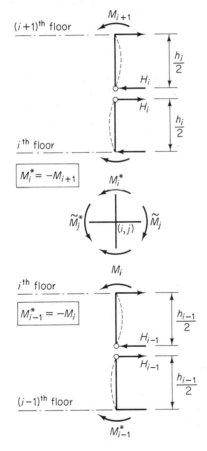

Figure 7-28

5. *Column shears.* The points of inflection in columns are assumed to be located at the mid-height of the columns, with the possible exception when the columns on the first floor are hinged at the base. In the latter

case, the moments in the first floor columns will vary linearly from the known values of moments at the top of the columns to a value of zero at the base. Generally, at a column line j, the column shear H_i at the midheight of a column at floor level i, as shown in Fig. 7-28, can be obtained by noting the relationship between the column shear and the column moment. Thus, for the positive direction of column shear as indicated in the figure.

$$H_i = \frac{M_{i+1}}{h_i/2} = \frac{2M_{i+1}}{h_i} \tag{7-15}$$

where h_i is the height of the column at floor level i, M_{i+1} is the moment at the top of the column, and $M_i^* = -M_{i+1}$ is the moment at the base of the column.

6. *Girder axial forces.* Axial forces in girders are assumed to be negligible, even though the unbalanced column shears above and below a floor will be resisted by girders at the floor.

Example 7-13. For the building frame in Fig. 7-29(a), the uniform vertical loads on the second floor girders are 0.5 k/ft and those on the roof girders are 0.25 k/ft. Find the moment diagrams in the girders and columns for the building frame, using an approximate analysis based on the assumptions introduced above.

The floor levels for the building frame are numbered $i = 1$, 2, and 3 for the first floor (ground level), second floor and roof, and the column lines are numbered $j = 1$, 2, 3, and 4 from left to right. Before carrying out the computation, it is instructive to view the free-body diagrams of the members and joints of the building frame in Fig. 7-29(f). Note that the shears and moments in this figure are shown with arrows representing their actual directions as can be observed intuitively and vertified by computation results. The axial forces have been excluded from the free-body diagrams in order to reduce the complexity of the figure.

The computation of girder moments due to vertical loads is straightforward, beginning with Eqs. (7-9) and (7-10). The resulting moment diagram for the girders is shown in Fig. 7-29(b). The procedure for computing girder shears and column axial forces is also simple. For example, the shears S_j at the left ends of the roof girders and second floor girders between column lines j and $j + 1$ are obtained by Eq. (7-11) as follows:

	Span 1–2	Span 2–3	Span 3–4
Roof	2.5^k	3.75^k	3.0^k
2nd floor	5.0^k	7.50^k	6.0^k

Hence, the column axial forces supporting the roof and the second floors are obtained from Eq. (7-12) as follows:

	$j = 1$	$j = 2$	$j = 3$	$j = 4$
2nd floor column	-2.5^k	-6.25^k	-6.75^k	-3.0^k
1st floor column	-7.5^k	-18.75^k	-20.25^k	-9.0^k

$0.25^{K/ft}$

14'

16'

(3,1)   (3,2)   (3,3)   (3,4)

$0.5^{K/ft}$

(2,1)   (2,2)   (2,3)   (2,4)

(1,1)   (1,2)   (1,3)   (1,4)

20'   30'   24'

(a)

$+8.0^{'K}$ $+18.0^{'K}$ $+11.5^{'K}$

$-4.5^{'K}$ $-4.5^{'K}$ $-10.1^{'K}$ $-10.1^{'K}$ $-6.5^{'K}$ $-6.5^{'K}$

$+16.0^{'K}$ $+36.0^{'K}$ $+23.0^{'K}$

$-9.0^{'K}$ $-9.0^{'K}$ $-20.2^{'K}$ $-20.2^{'K}$ $-13.0^{'K}$ $-13.0^{'K}$

(b)

$-4.5^{'K}$ $-5.6^{'K}$ $+3.6^{'K}$ $+6.5^{'K}$

$+4.5^{'K}$ $+5.6^{'K}$ $-3.6^{'K}$ $-6.5^{'K}$

$-4.5^{'K}$ $-5.6^{'K}$ $+3.6^{'K}$ $+6.5^{'K}$

$+4.5^{'K}$ $+5.6^{'K}$ $-3.6^{'K}$ $-6.5^{'K}$

(c)

Figure 7-29

(d)

(e)

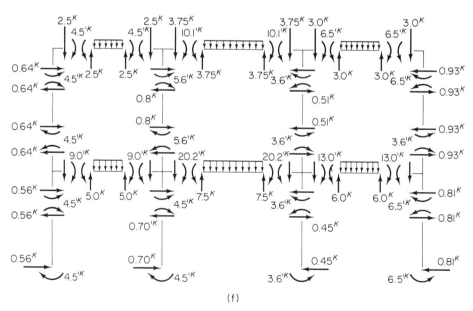

(f)

Figure 7-29 (cont.)

The computation of column moments is carried out by considering the equilibrium of moments at the joints. This procedure can be illustrated by considering the joints at both the roof level and the second floor using Eqs. (7-13) and (7-14). For the roof $(i = 3)$, we have $M_3 = -\widetilde{M}_{j-1} + \widetilde{M}_j$, i.e.,

$$\text{at } j = 1, \qquad M_3 = -M_2^* = -4.5 \text{ ft-k}$$

$$\text{at } j = 2, \qquad M_3 = -M_2^* = +4.5 - 10.1 = -5.6 \text{ ft-k}$$

$$\text{at } j = 3, \qquad M_3 = -M_2^* = +10.1 - 6.5 = +3.6 \text{ ft-k}$$

$$\text{at } j = 4, \qquad M_3 = -M_2^* = +6.5 \text{ ft-k}$$

For the second floor $(i = 2)$, we note $M_2 = M_2^* - \widetilde{M}_{j-1} + \widetilde{M}_j$, i.e.,

$$\text{at } j = 1, \qquad M_2 = -M_1^* = +4.5 - 9.0 = -4.5 \text{ ft-k}$$

$$\text{at } j = 2, \qquad M_2 = -M_1^* = +5.6 + 9.0 - 20.2 = -5.6 \text{ ft-k}$$

$$\text{at } j = 3, \qquad M_2 = -M_1^* = +3.6 + 20.2 - 13.0 = +3.6 \text{ ft-k}$$

$$\text{at } j = 4, \qquad M_2 = -M_1^* = -6.5 + 13.0 = +6.5 \text{ ft-k}$$

The resulting moment diagram for the columns is shown in Fig. 7-29(c). Furthermore, the column shears can be obtained from the corresponding column moments at floor levels 2 and 1, using Eq. (7-15):

$$\text{at } j = 1, \qquad H_2 = -0.64 \text{ kips}, \qquad H_1 = -0.56 \text{ kips}$$

$$\text{at } j = 2, \qquad H_2 = -0.80 \text{ kips}, \qquad H_1 = -0.70 \text{ kips}$$

$$\text{at } j = 3, \qquad H_2 = +0.51 \text{ kips}, \qquad H_1 = +0.45 \text{ kips}$$

$$\text{at } j = 4, \qquad H_2 = +0.93 \text{ kips}, \qquad H_1 = +0.81 \text{ kips}$$

The resulting shear diagrams for girders and columns are also shown in Figs. 7-29(d) and (e), respectively.

It may be noted that the computation may be carried out informally from the conditions of equilibrium of the free-body diagrams of the members and joints of the building frame in Fig. 7-29(f). In that case, the axial forces not shown in the figure should also be included in the computation.

7-13 PORTAL METHOD

For low-rise buildings, shear deflection is dominant in building frames subjected to horizontal loads. Thus, the approximate analysis for this type of building frame is based on certain assumptions on the distribution of horizontal shears in columns in addition to assuming the approximate locations of points of inflection in its members to reduce the degree of statical indeterminacy of the structure. Such an approach is referred to as the *portal method* since each bay of each floor in a rectangular building frame is essentially treated as a portal frame in making the assumptions on the distribution of horizontal shears in columns. Thus, the assumptions for the portal method can be stated as follows:

1. A point of inflection is located at the mid-height of each column above the second floor. A point of inflection is also located at the mid-height of each

column at the first floor if the base of the column is fixed, but is located at the bottom of a column if the base of the column is hinged.

2. The total horizontal shear at the mid-height of all columns at any floor level will be distributed among these columns so that each of the two exterior columns will carry half as much horizontal shear as each interior column of the frame.

3. A point of inflection is located at the center of each girder.

These assumptions will enable us to make an approximate analysis of a rigid building frame on the basis of the principles of statics alone.

Let the rectangular building frame under consideration consist of m levels and n column lines. The joints are denoted by the set of (i, j) values where i denotes the floor level starting from ground level $(i = 1)$ to roof $(i = m)$, and j denotes the column line starting from left $(j = 1)$ to right $(j = n)$. The portal method can be most conveniently carried out by finding the internal forces and moments in the following order.

1. *Column shears.* Pass a horizontal section at the mid-height of the columns at each floor, and consider the column shear at that section. Let the horizontal shear for each interior column be denoted by H_i and that for each exterior column be noted by $H_i/2$ for a horizontal section at the mid-height of columns at the ith floor, as shown in Fig. 7-30. Then the total horizontal shear at this level resulting from the horizontal loads P_{i+1}, $P_{i+2}, \ldots, P_m$ will be resisted by the sum of column shears, i.e.,

$$P_{i+1} + P_{i+2} + \cdots + P_m = \left(\frac{H_i}{2}\right)_1 + (H_i)_2 + \cdots + (H_i)_{n-1} + \left(\frac{H_i}{2}\right)_n$$

$$= (n - 1)H_i$$

or

$$H_i = \frac{P_{i+1} + P_{i+2} + \cdots + P_m}{n - 1} \qquad (7\text{-}16)$$

2. *Column moments.* The moment at the end of each column equals the shear at that column multiplied by half of the height of the corresponding

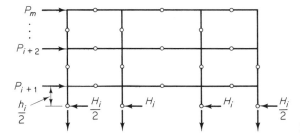

Figure 7-30

column. Thus, referring to Fig. 7-28, for each interior column ($j = 2$ to $j = n - 1$), the moment at the base of the column on the ith floor is given by

$$M_i^* = -(H_i)\left(\frac{h_i}{2}\right) = -\frac{H_i h_i}{2} \qquad (7\text{-}17)$$

and the moment at the top of the column is $M_{i+1} = -M_i^*$. Similarly, for each exterior column ($j = 1$ and $j = n$), the moment is at the base of the column on the ith floor

$$M_i^* = -\left(\frac{H_i}{2}\right)\left(\frac{h_i}{2}\right) = -\frac{H_i h_i}{4} \qquad (7\text{-}18)$$

and the corresponding moment at the top of this column is also $M_{i+1} = M_i^*$.

3. *Girder moments.* Girder moments at each joint are seen to be related to the column moments at the joint at any floor by considering the equilibrium of the free-body diagram of each joint. For a typical joint (i, j) at the ith floor and column line j in Fig. 7-31, the girder moments $\widetilde{M}_{j-1}$ and $\widetilde{M}_j$ are related to the column moments M_i^* and M_i as follows:

$$\widetilde{M}_j = M_i - M_i^* - \widetilde{M}_j^*$$

For a building frame subjected to lateral load only, the moments at the ends of a girder on a typical floor i can be related to each other by noting the assumption of a point of inflection at the mid-span as shown in Fig. 7-31. For example, in the span between column lines 1 and 2, it is necessary that $\widetilde{M}_2^* = -\widetilde{M}_1$ in order to satisfy the condition of equilibrium; more generally, in the span between column lines j and $j + 1$, we get $\widetilde{M}_{j+1}^* =$

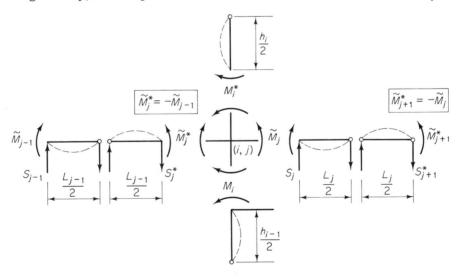

Figure 7-31

$-\widetilde{M}_j$. Noting that $\widetilde{M}_j^* = -\widetilde{M}_{j+1}$, then for a typical floor

$$\widetilde{M}_j = M_i - M_i^* - \widetilde{M}_{j-1} \qquad (7\text{-}19)$$

For the roof, $M_i^* = 0$ and $i = m$,

$$\widetilde{M}_j = M_m - \widetilde{M}_{j-1} \qquad (7\text{-}20)$$

Since the column moments are known, the girder moments can be computed beginning from the roof down to ground level ($i = m, \ldots, 2, 1$) and from left to right ($j = 1, 2, \ldots, n$) of the building frame.

4. *Girder Shears.* The shears at the ends of each girder on the ith floor can be computed from the free-body diagram in Fig. 7-31. Since a point of inflection is assumed to exist at the mid-span of L_j, the girder shear S_j at column line j can be obtained by summing the moments resulting from the left half about the point of inflection and setting it equal to 0. Hence, at the left end of the span.

$$S_j = \frac{-\widetilde{M}_j}{L_j/2} = -\frac{2\widetilde{M}_j}{L_j} \qquad (7\text{-}21)$$

5. *Column Axial Forces.* The axial forces in a column at the $(i - 1)$th floor may be obtained by summing the axial force F_i from the column at the ith floor above and the girder shears applied to the column from the girders on floor i as shown in Fig. 7-26. Thus,

$$F_{i-1} = F_i + S_j^* - S_j \qquad (7\text{-}22)$$

which is identical to Eq. (7-12) for computing column axial forces produced by vertical loads. Starting with column line $j = 1$ and working down from the roof ($i = m$), the axial forces in all columns can be computed.

6. *Girder Axial Forces.* The axial forces in the girders are assumed to be negligible.

Example 7-14. Using the portal method, find the moment diagrams in the girders and columns for the rigid frame in Fig. 7-32(a).

The moment diagrams are obtained according to the recommended computation procedure, and the results are given in Figs. 7-32(b) and (c). It is sufficient to note that the horizontal shears at the mid-height of interior columns at the second floor and the first floor are found from Eq. (7-16) to be, respectively,

$$H_2 = \frac{15}{4 - 1} = 5 \text{ kips}$$

$$H_1 = \frac{15 + 30}{4 - 1} = 15 \text{ kips}$$

Hence, the column end moments can be found from the corresponding column shears according to Eqs. (7-18) and (7-17), corresponding to exterior and interior

(a)

(b)

(c)

Figure 7-32

columns, respectively. For example, at the base of the column on the second floor $(i = 2)$,

$$\text{for } j = 1, \qquad M_2^* = -\left(\frac{5}{2}\right)(7) = -17.5 \text{ ft-k}$$

$$\text{for } j = 2, \qquad M_2^* = -(5)(7) = -35 \text{ ft-k}$$

Then, at the top of this column

$$\text{for } j = 1, \qquad M_3 = -M_2^* = 17.5 \text{ ft-k}$$

$$\text{for } j = 2, \qquad M_3 = -M_2^* = 35 \text{ ft-k}$$

The girder end moments on each floor are computed from the column end moments by Eqs. (7-19) and (7-20), starting from the column line $j = 1$. For example, at the roof level ($i = 3$), using Eq. (7-20),

$$\text{for } j = 1, \qquad \widetilde{M}_1 = 17.5 \text{ ft-k}$$

$$\text{for } j = 2, \qquad \widetilde{M}_2 = 35 - 17.5 = 17.5 \text{ ft-k}$$

and at the second floor ($i = 2$), using Eq. (7-19),

$$\text{for } j = 1, \qquad \widetilde{M}_1 = 60 + 17.5 = 77.5 \text{ ft-k}$$

$$\text{for } j = 2, \qquad \widetilde{M}_2 = 120 + 35 - 77.5 = 77.5 \text{ ft-k}$$

The constant girder shears due to the end moments for various spans are computed according to Eq. (7-21). Thus, at the roof level, the shears at the left end of the span are found to be

$$\text{span 1-2,} \qquad S_1 = -\frac{(2)(17.5)}{20} = -1.75 \text{ kips}$$

$$\text{span 2-3,} \qquad S_2 = -\frac{(2)(17.5)}{30} = -1.17 \text{ kips}$$

$$\text{span 3-4,} \qquad S_3 = -\frac{(2)(17.5)}{24} = -1.46 \text{ kips}$$

and those at the second floor are

$$\text{span 1-2,} \qquad S_1 = -\frac{(2)(77.5)}{20} = -7.75 \text{ kips}$$

$$\text{span 2-3,} \qquad S_2 = -\frac{(2)(77.5)}{30} = -5.17 \text{ kips}$$

$$\text{span 3-4,} \qquad S_3 = -\frac{(2)(77.5)}{24} = -6.46 \text{ kips}$$

The column axial forces can be computed from the girder shears according to Eq. (7-22). Thus, for the second floor columns,

$$\text{at } j = 1, \qquad F_2 = +1.75 \text{ kips}$$

$$\text{at } j = 2, \qquad F_2 = -1.75 + 1.17 = -0.58 \text{ kips}$$

$$\text{at } j = 3, \qquad F_2 = -1.17 + 1.46 = +0.29 \text{ kips}$$

$$\text{at } j = 4, \qquad F_2 = -1.46 \text{ kips}$$

and for the first floor columns,

$$\text{at } j = 1, \qquad F_1 = +1.75 + 7.75 = +9.50 \text{ kips}$$

$$\text{at } j = 2, \qquad F_1 = -0.58 - 7.75 + 5.17 = -3.16 \text{ kips}$$

$$\text{at } j = 3, \qquad F_1 = +0.29 - 5.17 + 6.20 = +1.32 \text{ kips}$$

$$\text{at } j = 4, \qquad F_1 = -1.46 - 6.20 = -7.66 \text{ kips}$$

7-14 CANTILEVER METHOD

For high-rise buildings subjected to horizontal loads, the approximate analysis also assumes approximate locations of points of inflection in the members of the building frames, but it requires additional assumptions concerning the distribution of axial forces in columns when the frame as a whole bends as a cantilever beam. Hence, such an approximate method is referred to as the cantilever method. The assumptions introduced in the cantilever method can be stated as follows:

1. The axial force in each column supporting any floor in a building frame is proportional to the horizontal distance of that column from the centroid of the areas of all columns at that level. To simplify the analysis further, it is often assumed that areas of all columns at any level are equal.
2. A point of inflection is located at the center of each girder, and a point of inflection is located at the mid-height of each column.
3. If the columns are not fixed at the base (first floor) of the building, then the locations of the points of inflection in the columns at the first floor should be modified according to the conditions at the base.

These assumptions will enable us to make an approximate analysis of a rigid rectangular building frame without considering the actual bending stiffness and areas of the members.

The cantilever method can be most conveniently carried out by finding the internal forces and moments in the following order:

1. *Column Axial Forces.* Find the centroid of all column areas at any level of the frame. If the areas of all columns at any level are equal, then the same centroid is applicable to all column areas for all levels. At any floor level i, let the cross-sectional area of each column be denoted by A. For a rectangular frame with n column lines and $(n - 1)$ bays, the centroidal distance x of all columns from the exterior column line $j = 1$ may be obtained as follows:

$$x = \frac{1}{nA} \sum_{j=1}^{n-1} L_j A \qquad (7\text{-}23)$$

where L_j is the span length of the jth bay between column line j and $j + 1$. Then the axial forces in the columns are obtained in proportion to their distances from the centroid.

2. *Girder Shears.* The shears for a girder at any floor can be obtained by the column axial forces at the corresponding level. Referring to a typical joint (i, j) in Fig. 7-26, the constant shear in span L_j in floor level i is given by

$$S_j = F_i - F_{i-1} + S_j^*$$

Since $S_j^* = S_{j-1}$ in span L_{j-1}, as shown in Fig. 7-31, it follows that along column line j,

$$S_j = F_i - F_{i-1} + S_{j-1} \tag{7-24}$$

Then the computation can begin from the exterior column line $j = 1$.

3. *Girder Moments.* Referring to Fig. 7-31, the end moments for a girder at any floor equals the shear in that girder multiplied by half of the length of that girder, since the moment at the center of each girder is zero. The moment at end j of the girder between column lines j and $j + 1$ is given by

$$\widetilde{M}_j = -(S_j)(L_j/2) = -\frac{S_j L_j}{2} \tag{7-25}$$

while the moment at end $j + 1$ is $\widetilde{M}_{j+1}^* = -\widetilde{M}_j$.

4. *Column Moments.* The end moments of columns are determined by beginning at the top of each column and working down toward its base. For a typical joint (i, j) in Fig. 7-28, the moment at the top of the column on the ith floor at column line j is given by

$$M_i = -\widetilde{M}_j + \widetilde{M}_j + M_i^*$$

Noting that $M_j^* = -\widetilde{M}_{j-1}$ in Fig. 7-31, we get

$$M_i = \widetilde{M}_{j-1} + M_j + M_i^* \tag{7-26}$$

For the column at the $(m - 1)$th floor supporting the roof level $i = m$, we have $M_i^* = 0$. Thus,

$$M_m = \widetilde{M}_{j-1} + \widetilde{M}_j \tag{7-27}$$

Note also that $M_{m-1}^* = -M_m$ as implied in Fig. 7-28.

5. *Column Shears.* The column shears are obtained from the column end moments by noting their relationship in Fig. 7-28. Thus, the column shear H_i at the mid-height of the column at the ith floor is given by

$$H_i = \frac{M_{i+1}}{h_i/2} = \frac{2M_{i+1}}{h_i} \tag{7-28}$$

Note again that M_{i+1} is the moment at the top of the column and $M_i^* = -M_{i+1}$ is the moment at the base of the column.

6. *Girder Axial Forces.* Axial forces in the girders are assumed to be negligible.

Example 7-15. Using the cantilever method, find the internal forces and moments in the rigid frame shown in Fig. 7-33.

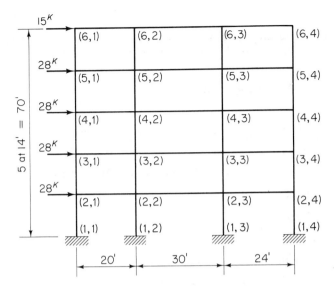

Figure 7-33

Since all four columns in the building frame at any floor level i are assumed to have the cross-sectional area A, the centroid of these columns from the column line $j = 1$ is given by Eq. (7-23).

$$x = \frac{(20A + 50A + 74A)}{4A} = 36 \text{ ft}$$

Let F_{ij} denote the column axial force in a column j at a floor level i. Then, for a typical section at the mid-height of the columns at floor level i, as shown in Fig. 7-34, the axial forces in the columns are seen to be proportional to their respective distances from the centroid. If the building frame acts as a cantilever under the given lateral loads, the columns at $j = 1$, and $j = 2$ are expected to be in tension and the columns at $j = 3$ and $j = 4$ in compression. The axial forces in columns $j = 1$ through $j = 4$ can be expressed in terms of an unknown constant factor F by letting $F_{i1} = F$. Then

$$F_{i2} = \frac{16}{36} F, \qquad F_{i3} = -\frac{14}{36} F, \qquad F_{i4} = -\frac{38}{36} F$$

Figure 7-34

Sec. 7-14   Cantilever Method

Let M_{i1} be the moment due to the lateral forces about a point at the mid-height of column $j = 1$ at floor i. Then, from the equilibrium of all forces at that point, we get

$$M_{i1} = -20F_2 - 50F_3 - 74F_4$$

or

$$M_{i1} = -(20)\left(\frac{16}{36}F\right) - (50)\left(-\frac{14}{36}F\right) - (74)\left(-\frac{38}{36}F\right) = \frac{266}{3}F$$

Thus, for $i = 5, 4, 3, 2, 1$, we can first compute the moment M_{i1} as follows:

$$M_{5,1} = (15)(7) = 105$$

$$M_{4,1} = (15)(21) + (28)(7) = 511$$

$$M_{3,1} = (15)(35 + 28)(21 + 7) = 1309$$

$$M_{2,1} = (15)(49) + (28)(35 + 21 + 7) = 2499$$

$$M_{1,1} = (15)(63) + (28)(49 + 35 + 21 + 7) = 4081$$

Since $M_{i1} = (266/3)F$, we have $F/3 = M_{i1}/266$. Consequently, the column axial forces can be obtained as shown in Table 7-5.

Table 7-5 COLUMN AXIAL FORCES (KIPS)

i	M_{i1}	$F/3$	F_{i1}	F_{i2}	F_{i3}	F_{i4}
5	105	0.3947	1.18	0.53	−0.46	−1.25
4	511	1.9211	5.76	2.56	−2.34	−6.08
3	1309	4.9211	14.76	6.56	−5.74	−15.58
2	2499	9.3947	28.18	12.53	−10.96	−29.75
1	4081	15.3421	46.03	20.46	−17.90	− 48.59

Using Eqs. (7-24), we can find the constant girder shears for each floor from the roof down. That is, at the roof level ($i = 6$), the shears S_j at the left end of each girder by noting that Eq. (7-24) becomes $S_j = -F_{5,j} + S_{j-1}$ since $F_{6,j} = 0$. Then,

$$\text{for } j = 1, \quad S_1 = -1.18$$

$$\text{for } j = 2, \quad S_2 = -0.53 - 1.18 = -1.71$$

$$\text{for } j = 3, \quad S_3 = +0.46 - 1.71 = -1.25$$

The girder shears for the remaining floors are similarly computed with results given in Table 7-6. Using Eq. (7-25), we can compute girder end moments at various spans for all floors. Thus, at the roof level ($i = 6$),

for $j = 1$, $\quad \widetilde{M}_1 = -(-1.18)(20/2) = 11.8$; $\quad$ for $j = 2$, $\quad \widetilde{M}_2^* = -11.8$

for $j = 2$, $\quad \widetilde{M}_2 = -(-1.71)(30/2) = 25.7$; $\quad$ for $j = 3$, $\quad \widetilde{M}_3^* = -25.7$

for $j = 3$, $\quad \widetilde{M}_3 = -(-1.25)(24/2) = 15.0$; $\quad$ for $j = 4$, $\quad \widetilde{M}_4^* = -15.0$

The girder end moments for the remaining floors are also given in Table 7-6.

Table 7-6 GIRDER SHEARS AND MOMENTS

ith Floor	Constant shear S_j (kips)			End moment $\widetilde{M}_j$ (ft-k)		
	Span 1–2	Span 2–3	Span 3–4	Joint 1	Joint 2	Joint 3
6	−1.18	−1.71	−1.25	11.8	25.7	15.0
5	−4.58	−6.61	−4.83	45.8	99.2	58.0
4	−9.00	−13.00	−9.50	90.0	195.0	114.0
3	−13.42	−19.39	−14.17	134.2	290.8	170.0
2	−17.85	−25.78	−18.84	178.5	386.7	226.1

We can also compute column end moments using Eqs. (7-26) and 7-27). Thus, for the roof level $m = 6$, the moments at top of the columns at the 5th floor can be computed by Eq. (7-27) as follows:

$$\text{for } j = 1, \qquad M_6 = -M_5^* = 11.8$$

$$\text{for } j = 2, \qquad M_6 = -M_5^* = 11.8 + 25.7 = 37.5$$

$$\text{for } j = 3, \qquad M_6 = -M_5^* = 25.7 + 15.0 = 40.7$$

$$\text{for } j = 4, \qquad M_6 = -M_5^* = 15.0$$

The moments at top of the columns on other floors may be computed by Eq. (7-26), and the results are given in Table 7-7.

Table 7-7 COLUMN END MOMENTS (FT-K)

Top of column at ith floor	Column 1	Column 2	Column 3	Column 4
5	11.8	37.5	40.7	15.0
4	34.0	107.5	116.5	43.0
3	56.0	177.5	192.5	71.0
2	78.2	247.5	268.3	99.0
1	100.3	317.7	344.5	127.0

The column shears are computed according to Eq. (7-28). For example, at $i = 5$, we get

$$\text{for } j = 1, \qquad H_5 = \frac{(2)(11.8)}{14} = 1.69$$

$$\text{for } j = 2, \qquad H_5 = \frac{(2)(37.5)}{14} = 5.36$$

$$\text{for } j = 3, \qquad H_5 = \frac{(2)(40.7)}{14} = 5.18$$

$$\text{for } j = 4, \qquad H_5 = \frac{(2)(15.0)}{14} = 2.14$$

The column shears at other floors can be computed in a similar manner and the results are given in Table 7-8. It is interesting to note that in Table 7-8, the last column indicates the sum of the horizontal shears for all columns at each level i. The value of each sum corresponds to the total horizontal loads acting on the frame above the horizontal section.

Table 7-8 COLUMN SHEARS (KIPS)

ith Floor	Column 1	Column 2	Column 3	Column 4	Sum
5	1.69	5.36	5.81	2.14	15
4	4.86	15.36	16.64	6.14	43
3	8.00	25.36	27.50	10.14	71
2	11.17	35.36	28.33	14.14	99
1	14.33	45.39	49.21	18.16	127

7-15 APPLICATIONS OF APPROXIMATE ANALYSIS

It cannot be overemphasized that the ultimate objective of structural analysis is to determine the necessary information concerning the critical forces and moments in various members for the design of a structure. When properly executed, an approximate analysis can provide such information in the design of relatively simple structures, or serve as an order-of-magnitude check on the results based on more exact methods of analysis, particularly if the latter is processed by an electronic computer. In either case, it is advisable to take advantage of the latitude for making reasonable assumptions based on judgement in an approximate analysis.

In the analysis of a three-span continuous beam, for example, we do not necessarily use a specified set of points of inflection in estimating all values of shears and moment in the beam. For the three-span continuous beam subjected to uniform load in Fig. 7-35(a), the positive and negative shears at the supports of each span are often conservatively estimated to allow for less than ideal conditions for the supports and the loading, with results shown in Fig. 7-35(b). Similarly, the positive and negative moments for all spans are also conservatively estimated for the same reason, with results given in Fig. 7-35(c). In both cases (for shears and moments) the maximum positive and negative values in various spans are often assessed on the basis of different loading conditions in spans and different degrees of fixity at supports; thus, the shear and moment diagrams represent the envelopes of the results of imposing a set of critical conditions.

The reasons for invoking our judgement for making proper estimates of the maximum shears and moments in the approximate analysis can easily be justified. In the case of support conditions, the exterior support of a continuous beam is never entirely free to move as a simple support, particularly if it is

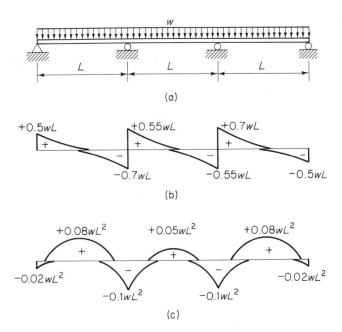

w

L L L

(a)

$+0.5wL$ $+0.55wL$ $+0.7wL$

$+$ $+$ $+$

$-$ $-$ $-$

$-0.7wL$ $-0.55wL$ $-0.5wL$

(b)

$+0.08wL^2$ $+0.05wL^2$ $+0.08wL^2$

$+$ $+$ $+$

$-0.02wL^2$ $-0.02wL^2$

$-$ $-$

$-0.1wL^2$ $-0.1wL^2$

(c)

Figure 7-35

connected to the column of a building frame. Consequently, it is only prudent to assume partial fixity for the exterior end support. Furthermore, the maximum shear and moment in a span may be influenced by the loads or the absence of loads in other spans of a continuous beam. While it is possible to determine how the spans should be loaded in order to produce each maximum effect, a subject which will be treated in the next chapter on influence lines, the use of appropriate estimates in an approximate analysis is intended to capture roughly various effects.

Furthermore, structures are often analyzed for various loading conditions, and the total effects of these loadings on the structures are then obtained by superposition. For example, a rectangular building frame may be first analyzed for vertical dead and live loads and then for lateral loads due to wind. The combination of the results of both sets of analyses will provide the necessary information concerning the critical axial forces, shears and moments in the members of the building frame for the design of this structure. It should be pointed out, however, that the critical conditions due to vertical loads and those due to lateral loads rarely occur simultaneously. Consequently, we need to exercise careful judgement concerning the probability of such occurrences in making proper estimates in combining the results of separate analyses.

We may exploit the simplicity and flexibility of the approximate methods of structural analysis to the greatest extent possible only if we maintain a design perspective and exercise careful judgement on the validity of simplifying assumptions.

PROBLEMS

7-1 to **7-10.** Find the shear and moment diagrams for each of the continuous beams in Figs. P7-1 to P7-10, using the moment distribution method for finding the moments at the supports.

Figure P7-1

Figure P7-2

Figure P7-3

Figure P7-4

Figure P7-5

Figure P7-6

Figure P7-7

Figure P7-8

Figure P7-9

Figure P7-10

7-11 to 7-20. Determine the points of inflection from the moment diagrams for each of the continuous beams in Figs. P7-1 to P7-10. Also sketch the deflected shape of each beam.

7-21 and 7-22. Find the moments at the supports of the continuous beams in Figs. P7-21 and P7-22, respectively, using the moment distribution method.

Figure P7-21

Figure P7-22

7-23. For the continuous beam in Fig. P7-21, find the moments at the supports if, in addition to the applied loads, support C has a settlement of 0.6 inch. $E = 30,000$ k/in.^{2} and $I = 18,000$ in^4.

7-24. For the continuous beam in Fig. P7-22, find the moments at the supports if, in addition to the applied loads, support B has a settlement of 1.2 inches. $E = 30,000$ k/in.^{2} and $I = 28,800$ in^4.

7-25 and **7-26.** Find (a) girder moments, (b) girder shears, (c) column axial forces, (d) column moments, and (e) column shears in each of the building frames subjected to a vertical load of 1 kip/ft on the roof and 2 kip/ft on each floor in Figs. P7-25 and P7-26.

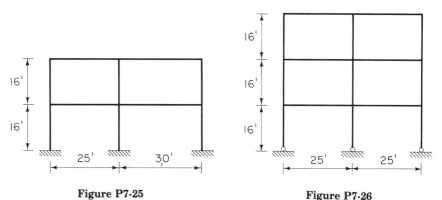

Figure P7-25   Figure P7-26

7-27 and **7-28.** Find (a) column shears, (b) column moments, (c) girder moments, (d) girder shears, and (e) column axial forces in each of the building frames subjected to lateral loads in Fig. P7-27 and P7-28, using the portal method.

Figure P7-27

Figure P7-28

7-29 and **7-30.** Find (a) column axial forces, (b) girder shears, (c) girder moments, (d) column moments, and (e) column shears in each of the building frames subjected to lateral loads in Fig. P7-29 and P7-30, using the cantilever method.

Figure P7-29

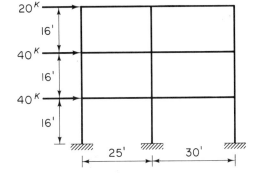

Figure P7-30

8

Influence Lines

When a moving load changes its position on a structure, it causes varying effects in the structure. There is always one position at which it will produce the most severe effect on a certain specified quantity of significance in the structure, such as the reaction at a support, the shear or moment at a section of a beam, or the bar force in a truss member. Sometimes it is possible to determine such a position by inspection, but in other cases it may be necessary to resort to trial-and-error procedure. In general, the variations of significant effects in a structure caused by a moving unit load can be expressed as functions of the position of the load. The graphical representations of such variations are called the *influence lines* or *influence diagrams*. Hence, the influence line for a specific effect (such as a reaction, shear, or moment at a specific point) may be defined as a curve, the ordinates of which show the variation of that effect caused by a unit load moving across the structure. The ordinate at any point represents the value of the effect when the unit load is acting at the corresponding point on the structure.

Let us consider as examples a few simple cases of influence lines for beams. Figure 8-1(a) shows a simple beam for which the influence line for the left reaction is required. If a unit load is placed at a distance x from the right support B, the left reaction $R_a = x/L$. Since a linear relation exists between R_a and x, R_a increases linearly as the unit load moves across the beam from support B to support A. Figure 8-1(b) is a plot of the variation of the left

(a)

(b)

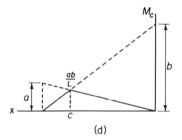

(c)

(d)   Figure 8-1

reaction where the ordinate at B is zero and the ordinate at A is unity, and the inclined line is the influence line for the left reaction. Similarly, the influence lines for shear and for bending moment at point C of a simple beam can be constructed on the same basis. In the case of the influence line for shear, the shear force at point C may be computed at follows:

$$\text{for } 0 < x < b, \qquad S_c = R_a = \frac{x}{L}$$

$$\text{for } b < x < L, \qquad S_c = R_a - 1 = -R_b = -\frac{L - x}{L}$$

Note that when $x = b$, these two equations do not yield the same value for S_c. Thus, the influence line for shear at point C of the beam is represented by Fig. 8-1(c). The abrupt change of ordinate at point C indicates that the shear at point C passes suddenly from positive to negative as the load moves from a point just to the right of point C to a point just to the left of point C. In the case

Sec. 8-1   Definitions   311 of the influence line for moment, the moment at point C is given by:

$$\text{for } 0 \le x \le b, \qquad M_c = R_a a = \frac{ax}{L}$$

$$\text{for } b \le x \le L, \qquad M_c = R_a a - 1(x - b) = R_b b = \frac{b(L - x)}{L}$$

Hence, the influence line for moment at point C can be plotted as shown in Fig. 8-1(d).

The unit for the ordinate of an influence line is that of the effect divided by the unit of force. For example, the unit for the ordinate of influence lines for reactions or shears is force divided by force or dimensionless. This simply means that the unit of the ordinate at any point is in pounds per pound (or kips per kip) of load applied at that point on the structure. Similarly, the unit for the ordinate of influence lines for moments is length-force divided by force or just length. This is interpreted to mean that the ordinate at any point is expressed in foot-pounds per pound of load applied at that point of the structure. The same results may be achieved if the moving load on the structure is assumed to be dimensionless. Thus, the ordinate at any point of an influence line may be considered as the *influence coefficient* for that effect by which the load applied at that point on the structure is multiplied in order to obtain the true magnitude of the effect.

When the live load on the structure consists of a single concentrated load P, the magnitude of an effect due to this load equals the product of the load P and the ordinate of the influence line for that effect at the point of application of the load. In order to obtain the maximum value for the effect, the load P should be placed at the point for which the ordinate of the influence diagram is maximum. Thus, for the beam shown in Fig. 8-1(a), the maximum left reaction resulting from a concentrated load P is $R_a = P(1) = P$ when the load P is placed at support A. Similarly, the maximum positive shear at point C will be $S_c = Pb/L$ when the load P is placed just to the right of point C, and the maximum moment at point C will be $M_c = Pab/L$ when the load P is placed at point C of the beam. Note that reaction R_a and shear S_c have the same unit as P, which is a force, while moment M_c has the unit of force multiplied by a length. Thus, the units of these quantities obtained from the influence lines are consistent with those obtained from direct computation.

Since the influence lines shown in Fig. 8-1 are linear functions of the distance x, the construction of influence lines can be simplified by noting the geometry of these lines. In the case of reaction R_a, we can imagine that a unit load is first placed at point A and then at point B. When the load is in the former position, R_a has a magnitude of unity, when it is in the latter position, R_a is zero. After obtaining these control points in the influence diagram, we may draw a straight line between these two points as shown in Fig. 8-1(b). In the influence diagram in Fig. 8-1(c), the dotted lines indicate that the influence line for shear S_c can be obtained from the influence lines for R_a and $-R_b$ as represented by the inclined lines above and below the horizontal base line, respectively. Then, the vertical line in the influence diagram for S_c can be located easily by the relations of similar triangles. Similarly, in the influence diagram in Fig. 8-1(d), the ordinate at the control point C can be obtained from the intersection of the inclined lines if ordinates a and b are plotted at the end points in the diagram as indicated. Thus, from the relations of similar triangles, the ordinate point C is seen to be ab/L.

For statically determinate structures, the influence lines consist of straight line segments only since the effects are always related linearly to the distance x. Thus, the construction of influence lines becomes a matter of determining the ordinates of a few control points in a diagram and then connecting the proper points by straight lines.

Example 8-1.   Construct the influence lines for the reaction at support B and the shear just to the right of support B of the beam shown in Fig. 8-2(a).

The ordinates of the control points of the influence lines can be computed by placing a unit load at points A, B, and C successively. Thus, for a unit load at A, we obtain from $\Sigma M_c = 0$,

$$16R_b = (1)(20), \qquad R_b = \tfrac{20}{16} = 1.25$$

The shear at the point just to the right of support B is obtained from the equilibrium of the free body cut by a section just to the right of B. Thus, for a unit load at A,

$$S_{br} = -1 + R_b = -1 + 1.25 = 0.25$$

For a unit load at B, it is obvious that $R_b = 1$. However, in the determination of S_{br}, the unit load must be placed slightly to the right or left of B. In that case, R_b remains practically the same but S_{br} will have a magnitude equal to 1 or 0. When the unit load is placed at point C, we have $R_b = 0$ and $S_{br} = 0$. Thus the influence lines for R_b and S_{br} can be constructed as shown in Fig. 8-2(b) and (c), respectively. Note that the influence line in Fig. 8-2(c) can also be obtained from the influence line for R_b by subtracting the dotted portion in Fig. 8-2(c), which has an ordinate of unity for the overhang of the beam.

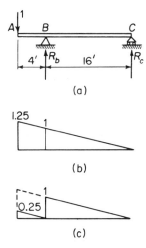

(a)

(b)

(c)

Figure 8-2

Influence lines may also be constructed on the basis of the *principle of virtual displacements* which states that for a system in stable equilibrium, the total amount of work done by the forces in the system must be zero for an arbitrary displacement. The arbitrary displacement may be imaginary, i.e., *virtual*, as long as it is geometrically compatible with the constraints of the system. Thus, in constructing an influence line, we first remove that constraint of the structure for which the effect is desired and replace it by a corresponding force. If the resulting released system is given a virtual displacement, it can be demonstrated that the shape of the displaced system resulting from the removal of the constraint is the influence line for that constraint.

Consider, for example, the influence line for reaction R_a of the simple beam in Fig. 8-3(a). If we remove the vertical constraint at A and replace it by reaction R_a, the resulting system can be lifted from A. This system is then given a small virtual rotation $\delta\varphi$ about point B. For small angles of $\delta\varphi$, the movement of point A along a circular arc can be approximated by the vertical distance δs as shown in Fig. 8-3(b). If the equilibrium of the nonrigid system is to be maintained, the virtual work δW done by all forces acting on the system must be zero. Thus,

$$\delta W = R_a \, \delta s - Py = 0$$

Note that the sign of the virtual work is positive if the displacement is in the same direction of the force and is negative if the displacement is opposite to the

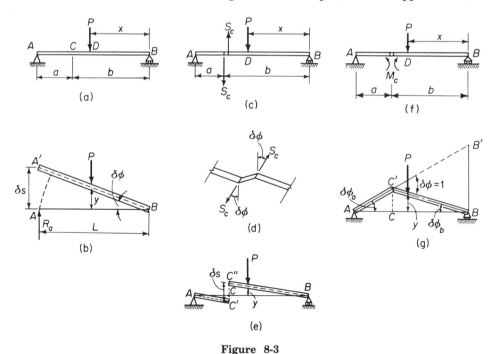

Figure 8-3

direction of the force. For a moving unit load $P = 1$ and for a unit displacement $\delta s = 1$, we have $y = R_a$. This means that the ordinate at point D of the displaced system is equal to the reaction at A due to a unit load at D. Hence, the deflected shape of the nonrigid system in Fig. 8-3(b) is the influence line for reaction R_a.

In order to obtain the influence line for shear at point C of the beam in Fig. 8-3(a), we remove the shearing constraint at point C and replace it by a pair of shear forces S_c. This may be thought of as introducing an infinitesimal element at point C so that no shear can be transmitted through the element as shown in Fig. 8-3(c). Note that the shear forces S_c on the left and right faces of the element are both positive with reference to segments AC and BC of the beam respectively. If the element is given a small displacement, causing an angular distortion $\delta\varphi$ in the element as shown in Fig. 8-3(d), it will produce rotations in beam segments AC' and BC''. Since AC' and BC'' must have the same angle of rotation $\delta\varphi$ as a result of the same angular distortion on both faces of the element, AC' and BC'' are parallel as shown in Fig. 8-3(e). For an infinitesimal element, the linear displacement $\delta s = C'C''$ may be considered as a vertical line. Thus, the virtual work done by all forces acting on the nonrigid system is

$$\delta W = S_c(CC' + CC'') - Py = S_c\,\delta s - Py = 0$$

For $P = 1$ and $\delta s = 1$, we obtain $y = S_c$. This implies that the ordinate at point D of the displaced system is equal to the shear at C due to a unit load at D. Hence, the deflected shape of the nonrigid system in Fig. 8-3(e) is the influence line for shear at point C of the beam. The ordinates of the influence line at C' and C'' may be obtained from the relations of similar triangles. Thus,

$$\frac{CC'}{C'C''} = \frac{a}{L} \quad \text{and} \quad \frac{CC''}{C'C''} = \frac{b}{L}$$

For $\delta s = C'C'' = 1$, we get

$$CC' = \frac{a}{L} \quad \text{and} \quad CC'' = \frac{b}{L}$$

In constructing the influence line for moment at point C of the beam, we remove the bending constraint for moment at C by introducing a hinge at that point, and replace the constraint by a moment M_c on each side of the hinge as shown in Fig. 8-3(f). Note that the moment M_c on each side of the hinge is positive with reference to the corresponding segment of the beam. If a small rotation $\delta\varphi$ is applied at hinge C, the system will displace as shown in Fig. 8-3(g). Then, the virtual work done by all forces acting on the nonrigid system is

$$\delta W = M_c(\delta\varphi_a + \delta\varphi_b) - Py = M_c\,\delta\varphi - Py = 0$$

For $P = 1$ and $\delta\varphi = 1$, we have $y = M_c$. Thus, the ordinate at point D of the displaced system is equal to the moment at C due to a unit load at D. The deflected shape of the nonrigid system in Fig. 8-3(g) is, therefore, the influence line for moment at point C of the beam. The ordinate of the influence line at C

can be obtained from the relations of similar triangles. For small angles of $\delta\varphi$, the vertical distance BB' can be approximated by the arc length $b\,\delta\varphi$. Hence,

$$\frac{CC'}{BB'} = \frac{a}{L} \quad \text{or} \quad CC' = \frac{ab\,\delta\varphi}{L}$$

For $\delta\varphi = 1$, we get $CC' = ab/L$.

We have demonstrated that the principle of virtual displacements may be used to construct influence lines. It is obvious that, for statically determinate structures, the influence lines consist only of straight line segments because such structures are considered as rigid except at the point where a constraint is removed, and the deflected shape of the resulting nonrigid system obtained by the method of virtual displacements is defined by straight line segments. Once the shape of an influence line is known, the ordinates may readily be determined from the geometrical relations.

Example 8-2. Construct the influence lines by the method of virtual displacements for the following effects in the beam shown in Fig. 8-4(a): (a) reaction at support A, (b) shear at point E, and (c) moment at point F.

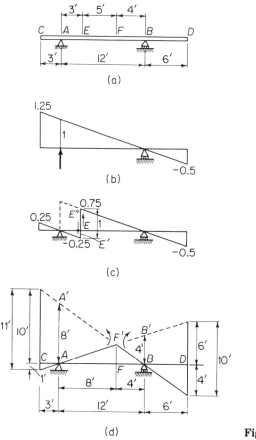

Figure 8-4

Influence Lines   Chap. 8

In constructing the influence line for reaction R_a, we remove the vertical constraint at A and introduce a unit vertical displacement at point A of the nonrigid system as shown in Fig. 8-4(b). The ordinates at points C and D are then obtained from the relations of similar triangles.

For the influence line for shear S_e, we remove the shearing constraint at E and introduce a unit vertical displacement at point E as shown in Fig. 8-4(c). Then, from the geometrical relations, we have

$$EE' = (1)(9)/12 = 0.75$$

$$EE'' = (1)(3)/12 = 0.25$$

The ordinates at points C and D are also obtained from the relations of similar triangles.

For the influence line for moment M_f, we remove the bending constraint at F and introduce a unit rotation at point F as shown in Fig. 8-4(d). Thus, $AA' = (1)(8) = 8$ and $BB' = (1)(4) = 4$. The ordinate FF' may be obtained from either the triangle ABB' or ABA'. Thus,

$$FF' = (8)(4)/12 = \tfrac{8}{3}$$

The ordinates at points C and D are found to be -1 and -4 respectively.

8-3 APPLICATION OF INFLUENCE LINES

In the previous sections, two distinctly different approaches have been presented for the construction of influence lines. Each approach is based on a different concept but each is important and has wide applications. The study of the variations of effects on a structure caused by a moving unit load is a preliminary step for the determination of the position of live loads that will produce maximum effects on the structure.

When a series of live loads moves on a structure, the maximum effects may in general be obtained from the influence lines for those effects. If the live load consists of a series of concentrated loads, the combined effect of these concentrated loads can be obtained by the principle of superposition. Consider, for instance, the beam shown in Fig. 8-5(a), on which a series of three concentrated loads P_1, P_2, and P_3, is acting. Since P_2 and P_3 are maintained at fixed

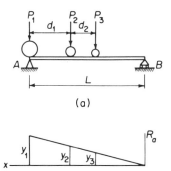

(a)

(b)

Figure 8-5

distances from P_1, the locations of P_2 and P_3 are known once the location of P_1 is assigned. Let y_1, y_2, and y_3 be the ordinates of the influence line for the left reaction R_a of the beam under the loads P_1, P_2, and P_3, respectively, as shown in Fig. 8-5(b). Then, by the principle of superposition, the total left reaction R_a due to loads P_1, P_2, and P_3 is equal to

$$R_a = P_1 y_1 + P_2 y_2 + P_3 y_3$$

In general, the effect may be the shear or moment at a point as well as the left reaction. If there are n concentrated loads P_1, P_2, ... , P_n on the beam, and if y_1, y_2, ... , y_n represent, respectively, the ordinates of the influence line for the effect involved, the effect is equal to the summation of the products of each load and influence ordinate under that load, or the total effect E is equal to

$$E = \sum_{i=1}^{i=n} P_i y_i$$

Although it is easy to compute the magnitude of a function due to a series of concentrated loads once the locations of these loads are determined, it is in general impossible to determine by inspection where those concentrated loads should be placed in order to produce a maximum value of a particular effect. In the simple case shown in Fig. 8-5, if $P_1 > P_2 > P_3$, it can be seen that the maximum value on the left reaction R_a is realized when the load P_1 is placed at point A. If the loads move toward the right, the ordinates y_1, y_2, and y_3 will be reduced and the reaction R_a will be smaller. On the other hand, if the loads move toward the left so that P_1 will be off the beam, the reaction R_a will still be smaller since P_2 and P_3 are smaller than P_1. For more complicated cases, the procedure of determining the maximum effects on the structure is essentially one of trial and error.

When the live load on the beam consists of a uniformly distributed load as shown in Fig. 8-6(a), its influence on a particular effect can also be obtained by superposition. For the left reaction R_a of the beam, for example, the load acting on an infinitesimal length δx of the beam is $w\delta x$. This load will cause a left reaction of $yw\delta x$, where y is the ordinate of the influence line for the left reaction as shown in Fig. 8-6(b). Thus, the total left reaction R_a due to the

(a)

(b)   **Figure 8-6**

uniformly distributed load between D and E is

$$R_a = \int_d^e yw \, dx = w \int_d^e y \, dx = wA_{de}$$

in which A_{de} represents the area of the influence diagram bounded by the vertical lines passing through points D and E. It should be noted again that the effect on the beam under consideration may be the shear or moment at a point of the beam instead of the reaction at the left support. In general, it may be stated that the magnitude of the effect caused by a uniformly distributed load is equal to the product of the intensity of the load w and the area A_{ij} of the influence diagram bounded by the limits of the load between points i and j on the beam, or the total effect E is equal to

$$E = wA_{ij}$$

In dealing with a moving uniform load that is assumed to be longer than the span length of the beam, it is easy to determine by inspection what portion of the beam should be loaded in order to produce the particular maximum effect. In the case of the example for the left reaction shown in Fig. 8-6(a), the magnitude of the left reaction R_a is a maximum when the entire span is loaded, i.e., when the entire area of the influence diagram in Fig. 8-6(b) is included in the computation of the left reaction. On the other hand, for the maximum positive shear at point C of the beam shown in Fig. 8-7(a), only the portion CB of the beam should be loaded since the influence diagram for shear at point C in Fig. 8-7(b) indicates that the area between points C and B is positive and the area between points A and C is negative.

Figure 8-7

If a moving uniform load is accompanied by a single roving concentrated load which may be placed at any point so as to produce the maximum effect under consideration, the maximum effect can also be determined from the influence lines by inspection. For example, the maximum moment at point C of the beam shown in Fig. 8-7(c) is realized when the roving concentrated load is placed at C since the influence ordinate for moment at C in Fig. 8-7(d) is maximum at that point.

It may be concluded that the position of either a single concentrated load or a uniformly distributed load that will produce a certain maximum effect on a structure can be determined by inspection. When the live load consists of a series of concentrated loads, the position of the loading for producing a maximum effect can be located by trial and error. For statically determinate structures, however, criteria for maximum effects due to a series of concentrated loads can be established with the aid of influence lines.

Numerically, the direct computation of maximum reactions, shears, and moments in structures subjected to a series of concentrated loads is usually rather tedious. In order to avoid the burden of numerical calculations, the moments of a series of concentrated loads spaced at fixed distances relative to each other are taken about certain given points and are tabulated in a systematic manner. Such an arrangement is generally known as the *moment table* for the given series of concentrated loads. It is based on the idea that the moment of a force system about a point may be replaced by an equivalent moment of the same magnitude and sense of direction. Consider, for example, a system of parallel forces $P_1, P_2, \ldots, P_n$ as shown in Fig. 8-8. The moment of these forces about point A is equal to

$$M_a = P_1 d_1 + P_2 d_2 + \ldots + P_n d_n$$

Similarly, the moment of these forces about point B is

$$M_b = P_1(d_1 + r) + P_2(d_2 + r) + \ldots + P_n(d_n + r)$$
$$= P_1 d_1 + P_2 d_2 + \ldots + P_n d_n + (P_1 + P_2 + \ldots + P_n)r$$
$$= M_a + Gr$$

in which G is the sum of the forces $P_1, P_2, \ldots, P_n$. Thus, the moment of the forces about point B is equal to the moment of the same forces about point A plus a couple Gr. If the forces $P_1, P_2, \ldots, P_n$ are given and the distances $d_1, d_2, \ldots, d_n$ are fixed, we can compute the moment M_a. When the distance r is given, the computation of M_b consists of adding a couple Gr to M_a only.

Figure 8-8

As an example, the wheel loads for two cranes operating in tandem together with other pertinent data are shown in Table 8-1. Under the heading for spacings in the table, the spacings between wheel loads are summed up accumulatively from left to right in the first line, and from right to left in the second line. Similarly, under the heading for loads, the wheel loads are summed up accumulatively from left to right in the first line, and from right to left in the second line. Under the heading of moments, the heavy zigzag line represents

Table 8-1

$$10^K \quad 10^K \quad 10^K \quad 10^K \qquad 15^K \quad 15^K \quad 15^K \quad 15^K$$

Wheels: ① ② ③ ④ ⑤ ⑥ ⑦ ⑧

Spacings: 5′ | 5′ | 5′ | 10′ | 5′ | 5′ | 5′

Spacings (ft)	0	5	10	15	25	30	35	40	L to R
	40	35	30	25	15	10	5	0	R to L
Loads (kips)	10	20	30	40	55	70	85	100	L to R
	100	90	80	70	60	45	30	15	R to L

Moments (ft-k) Due to loads 8 to — / Moments (ft-k) Due to loads 1 to —

2	2250	50	100	150	250	300	350	400	1
3	2200	1800	150	250	450	550	650	750	2
4	2100	1750	1400	300	600	750	900	1050	3
5	1950	1650	1350	1050	700	900	1100	1300	4
6	1575	1350	1125	900	450	975	1250	1525	5
7	1125	975	825	675	375	225	1325	1675	6
8	600	525	450	375	225	150	75	1750	7

the division for the sum of moments about a point due to a group of loads to the left of the point and for those due to a group of loads to the right of the point. The numbers above the heavy zigzag line are the sums of moments about various points under consideration due to the loads to the left of the respective points as indicated by the entry on the right edge of the table. Thus, the sum of the moments at wheel 8 due to loads from wheels 1 through 5 is

$$(10)(40 + 35 + 30 + 25) + (15)(15) = 1{,}525 \text{ ft-kips}$$

This moment may be found under wheel 8 by entering the table from the right edge on the line for moment due to wheel loads 1 through 5, i.e., the fifth line under the heading for moments. On the other hand, the numbers below the heavy zigzag line are the sums of the moments about various points under consideration due to the loads to the right of the respective points as indicated by the entry on the left edge of the table. Hence, the sum of the moments at wheel 2 due to loads from wheels 8 through 3 is

$$(15)(35 + 30 + 25 + 20) + (10)(10 + 5) = 1{,}800 \text{ ft-kips}$$

This moment is found under wheel 2 by entering the table from the left edge on the line for moment due to wheel loads 8 through 3, i.e., the second line under the heading for moments.

Example 8-3. The cranes in Table 8-1 are placed on a single beam of 40-ft span. With the position of the wheels located as shown in Fig. 8-9(a), determine (a) the reaction at support A, (b) the shear at a section between wheels 4 and 5, and (c) the moment under wheel 4. If some of the wheels pass out of the span as shown in Fig. 8-9(b), determine (a) the reaction at support A and (b) the reaction at support B.

Figure 8-9

Consider first the position of the wheels located as shown in Fig. 8-9(a). In computing the reaction at support A, the sum of the moments about support B due to the wheel loads on the span may be obtained with the aid of Table 8-1. Thus,

$$M_b = 975 + (70)(4) = 1{,}255 \text{ ft-kips}$$

in which 975 is the sum of the moments of the wheel loads on the span about wheel 6, 70 is the sum of the wheel loads on the beam, and 4 is the distance between wheel 6 and support B. Hence, the reaction at support A may be computed as

$$R_a = \frac{1{,}255}{40} = 31.8 \text{ kips}$$

The shear at a section between wheels 4 and 5 is equal to the reaction at support A minus the sum of wheels 1 through 4, or

$$S_{4\text{-}5} = 31.8 - 40 = -8.2 \text{ kips}$$

The moment at the point of the beam under wheel 4 is

$$M_4 = (31.8)(15 + 6) - 300 = 368 \text{ ft-kips}$$

for which 15 is the sum of the spacings and 300 is the sum of the moments about wheel 4 due to wheels 1 through 3.

When some of the wheels move off the span of the beam as shown in Fig. 8-9(b), the same procedure can still be applied except that the moments caused by the loads out of the span must be subtracted from the sum of the moments due to all wheel loads. Thus, the sum of the moments of the wheel loads on the span about support B can be computed as follows:

$$M_b = (1{,}750 - 750) + (100 - 20)(8) = 1{,}640 \text{ ft-kips}$$

in which 1,750 is the sum of the moments of all wheel loads about wheel 8, 750 is the sum of the moments of wheel loads 1 and 2 about wheel 8, 100 is the sum of all wheel loads, 20 is the sum of wheel loads 1 and 2, and 8 is the distance between wheel 8 and support B. Then,

$$R_a = \frac{1{,}640}{40} = 41.0 \text{ kips}$$

After R_a is obtained, R_b can be computed directly without resorting to the moment table. However, for the sake of illustration, we shall compute R_b independently of R_a. Thus, with the aid of the moment table, the sum of the moments of the wheel loads on the span about support A is

$$M_a = 1,400 + (100 - 20)(2) = 1,560 \text{ ft-kips}$$

in which 1,400 is the sum of the moments about wheel 3 due to wheels 8 through 4, 100 is the sum of all wheel loads, 20 is the sum of wheel loads 1 and 2, and 2 is the distance from wheel 3 to support A. Finally,

$$R_b = \frac{1,560}{40} = 39.0 \text{ kips}$$

8-4 COMPOUND BEAMS

The procedure for constructing influence lines for various effects on simple beams can easily be applied to compound beams. A unit load may be placed at a number of points along the beam where an abrupt change of the effect is expected. Since the efforts on a statically determinate beam caused by a moving unit load are found to be linear functions of the distance along the beam, the influence line between two computed ordinates can always be represented by a straight line.

Consider, for example, the construction of influence lines for reactions of the beam shown in Fig. 8-10(a). When the unit load is placed at A, the reaction $R_a = 1$ while the reactions at B and C are zero. If the unit load is placed at point D, the reaction at A is zero while the reactions at B and C are, respectively,

$$R_b = \frac{L_2 + h_2}{L_2} = 1 + \frac{h_2}{L_2} \quad \text{and} \quad R_c = -\frac{h_2}{L_2}$$

in which the positive result for R_b indicates an upward reaction at B and the negative sign for R_c indicates a downward reaction at C. As long as the unit load is placed outside of the beam segment AD, it will have no effect on reaction A but will continue to affect reactions B and C. Hence, the influence line for reaction at A is represented by the straight line in Fig. 8-10(b). The influence lines for reactions at B and C can be constructed by placing the unit load at points B, C, and E of the beam successively, and they are plotted in Figs. 8-10(c) and (d) respectively.

Next consider the construction of influence lines for shears at sections F and G of the same beam as shown in Fig. 8-11(a). When a unit load is placed between points A and D, the shear at F is equal to $R_a - 1$. In view of the influence line for reaction at A in Fig. 8-10(b), $S_f = 0$ at A and $S_f = -1$ at D. When the unit load is placed between D and F, the shear at F equals $S_f = -1$. As long as the unit load is placed outside of the beam segment AF, the shear at F is zero. Thus, the influence line for shear at section F is indicated in Fig. 8-11(b). The shear at section G can be obtained easily from the consideration

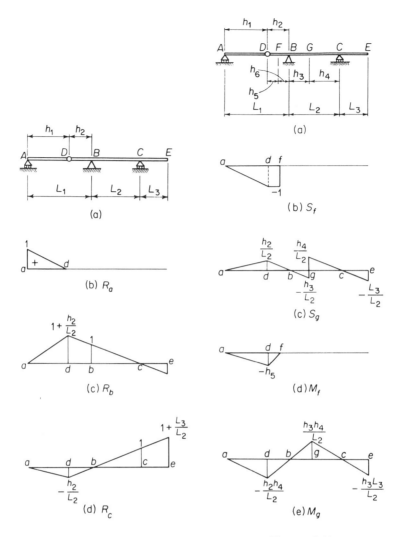

Figure 8-10

Figure 8-11

of segment GE of the beam as a free body. When the unit load is placed anywhere between points A and G, the shear at G is equal to $-R_c$. Thus, $S_g = +h_2/L_2$ for the unit load at D and $S_g = -h_3/L_2$ for the load just to the left of G. When the unit load is placed between points G and E, the shear at G is equal to $-R_c + 1$. Thus, for the unit load just to the right of G,

$$S_g = -\frac{h_3}{L_2} + 1 = +\frac{h_4}{L_2}$$

and for the unit load at E,

$$S_g = -\left(1 + \frac{L_3}{L_2}\right) + 1 = -\frac{L_3}{L_2}$$

Influence Lines   Chap. 8

The influence line for shear at section G can be plotted as shown in Fig. 8-11(c). It may be noted that the influence line for shear at a section just to the left of reaction B has the same shape as that for the shear at section F when the distance h_6 approaches zero as a limit. On the other hand, the influence line for shear just to the right of reaction B has the same shape as that for shear at section F as the distance h_3 approaches zero as a limit. Thus, the influence lines for the shears to the left and to the right of support B are entirely different.

The influence lines for moments at F and G of the same beam may be obtained in a similar manner. For a unit load at A, the moment at F is zero, and for the unit load at D, the moment at F is $-(1)(h_5) = -h_5$. The moment at F will again be zero when the unit load is placed at F or outside of the beam segment AF. Thus, the influence line for moment at F is indicated by Fig. 8-11(d). The moment at G can also be obtained easily from the consideration of segment GE of the beam as a free body. Thus, when the unit load is placed anywhere to the left of G or at G, the moment at G is equal to $R_c h_4$, or

$$M_g = 0 \qquad \text{for unit load at } A$$

$$M_g = -\frac{h_2 h_4}{L_2} \qquad \text{for unit load at } D$$

$$M_g = 0 \qquad \text{for unit load at } B$$

$$M_g = \frac{h_3 L_4}{L_2} \qquad \text{for unit load at } G$$

When the unit load is placed at a point to the right of G or at G, the moment at G is equal to $R_c h_4$ minus the product of the load and its distance from G. Hence, with the unit load at E,

$$M_g = \left(1 + \frac{L_3}{L_2}\right)h_4 - (1)(L_3 + h_4) = \frac{L_3 h_4}{L_2} - L_3$$

$$= -\left(1 + \frac{h_4}{L_2}\right)L_3 = -\frac{h_3 L_3}{L_2}$$

The influence lines shown in Figs. 8-10 and 8-11 may also be obtained by the principle of virtual displacements. Consider, for example, the influence line for reaction R_b. If the vertical constraint at B of the beam is removed and replaced by an upward force R_a, the deflected shape of the released system due to a unit virtual displacement at B will be as shown in Fig. 8-12(a). For the influence line for shear S_g, the shearing constraint at point G is removed and replaced by a pair of shear forces S_g. Then, the deflected shape of the released system resulting from a unit virtual displacement at G will be as shown in Fig. 8-12(b). For the influence line for moment M_g, the bending constraint is removed and replaced by a pair of moments M_g. Thus, the deflected shape of the released system resulting from a unit virtual rotation at G will be as shown in Fig. 8-12(c). If the ordinates of the deflected shapes in Fig. 8-12 are computed

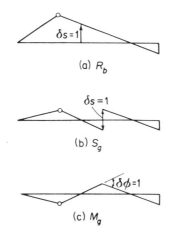

(a) R_b

(b) S_g

(c) M_g

Figure 8-12

from the relations of similar triangles, the results are identical to those for the corresponding influence lines obtained by the concept of a moving unit load.

Example 8-4. For the compound beam shown in Fig. 8-13(a), construct the influence line for (a) reaction at D, (b) shear at a section to the left of B, and (c) moment at E.

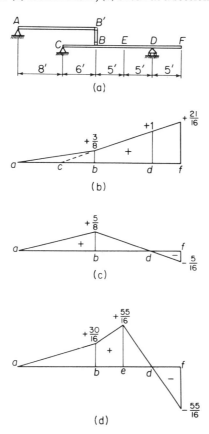

Figure 8-13

By placing a unit load at points A, B, E, and F successively, the specified effects on the beam can be computed as explained in this section. Hence, the required influence lines are constructed as shown in Figs. 8-13(b), (c), and (d), respectively.

8-5 GIRDERS SUPPORTING FLOOR BEAMS

In Section 3-7 we discussed the computation of reactions, shears, and moments for girders supporting floor beams under stationary loads. We pointed out that the introduction of floor beams on a girder has no effect on the reactions. Furthermore, the shear within each panel of a girder supporting floor beams is constant, and the moments at panel points of a girder supporting floor beams are identical to the moments at the corresponding points of a girder that supports applied loads directly. When a moving load is applied to a girder supporting floor beams, it can be seen that the influence line for reaction at a support remains the same as that for a girder without floor beams. The influence line for shear will be constructed for shear in a panel rather than at a section since the shear is constant within a panel. Although the influence line for moment at a panel point is not affected by the floor beams, the influence line for moment at a section within a panel will be slightly different. We shall, therefore, discuss the modifications necessary for the construction of influence lines for shear and moment in girders supporting floor beams.

Shears. The construction of an influence line for shear in panel CD of a girder supporting floor beams is shown in Fig. 8-14(a). The ordinates of the influence diagram can be obtained by placing the unit load at various panel points successively. As the unit load moves on a stringer from one panel point to another, the influence line between the panel points will vary linearly in the panel because the reactions of the stringer, which are in turn transmitted as loads on the girder through the floor beams, also vary linearly in the panel. As long as the unit load is in a position to the right of panel point D, the shear in panel CD equals the reaction R_a. If the unit load moves to the left of panel point C, the shear in panel CD is negative and numerically equal to reaction R_g. When the unit load is placed in panel CD, the shear in panel CD equals the reaction R_a minus the panel load at C, which is numerically equal to the stringer reaction at C. Since the reaction $R_a = (x' + 3h)/L$ and the panel load at C is x'/h, the shear in panel CD is

$$S_{cd} = \frac{x' + 3h}{L} - \frac{x'}{h} = \frac{x' + 3h - 6x'}{6h} = \frac{1}{2} - \frac{5x'}{6h}$$

which is a linear function of x'. Thus, the influence line for shear in panel CD of the girder takes the shape as shown in Fig. 8-14(b). The influence lines for shears in other panels may be constructed in a similar manner. For example, the influence line for shear in panel DE is shown in Fig. 8-14(c), and the influence line for shear in end panel AB is shown in Fig. 8-14(d).

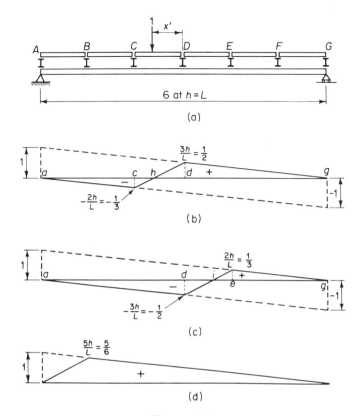

Figure 8-14

For a uniform load moving across the span of the girder, the maximum positive shear in a panel will occur when the uniform load extends over the portion of the span for which the influence ordinates are positive. For the shear in panel CD, this length is denoted by hg in Fig. 8-14(b); for the shear in panel DE, it is denoted by ig in Fig. 8-14(c). It may be noted that in the influence diagram for shear in panel CD, the positive area is greater than the negative area. Hence, the positive maximum shear is numerically greater than the negative maximum shear, and the absolute maximum shear in the panel CD is obtained when the uniform load is placed over the portion of span indicated by hg in Fig. 8-14(b). On the other hand, the negative maximum shear for panel DE is numerically greater than the positive shear for the panel. Then, the maximum shear in panel DE will be realized when the uniform load occupies the portion of span indicated by ai in Fig. 8-14(c). The points h and i in Figs. 8-14(b) and (c), respectively, are called *neutral points*, which can be located by the geometrical relation of similar triangles. It may be further observed that for girders with floor beam spacings symmetrical with respect to a centerline at the midspan, the influence diagram for shear in a panel of the girder is antisymmetrical to that in the corresponding panel on the other side of the centerline. For example, the influence line for shear in panel CD of the girder shown in Fig. 8-14(a) is antisymmetrical to that in panel DE, as is evidenced from the influence diagrams in Figs. 8-14(b) and (c). Hence, it is only necessary to construct influence lines for shear in panels on half of the span if the maximum shear in every panel of the girder is required.

Moments. The influence line for moment at a panel point of a girder supporting floor beams has the same shape as the corresponding influence line for a girder without floor beams. For example, the influence line for moment at panel point C of the girder shown in Fig. 8-15(a) is given in Fig. 8-15(b). If the influence line for moment at some section of the girder other than the panel points is desired, it can be constructed by placing a moving unit load on the span. Consider, for example, the moment at point J of the girder shown in Fig. 8-15(a). For any position of the unit load to the right of panel point D, the moment at J equals $R_a a$, and for any position of the unit load to the left of panel point C, the moment at J equals $R_g b$. When the unit load is placed in panel CD, the moment at J is equal to $R_a a$ minus the moment at J due to the panel load

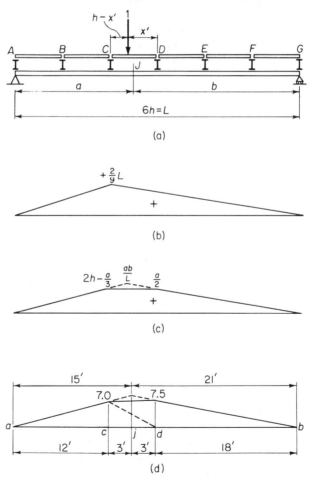

Figure 8-15

at C caused by the reaction of the stringer CD. Thus,

$$M_j = \frac{x' + 3h}{L}a - \frac{x'}{h}(a - 2h)$$

For a given point J, the length a is constant and the moment M_j is a linear function of x'. At point D, $x' = 0$, we have

$$M_j = \frac{3h}{6h}a = \frac{a}{2}$$

At point C, $x' = h$, we get

$$M_j = \frac{4h}{6h}a - (a - 2h) = 2h - \frac{a}{3}$$

Hence, the influence line between panel points C and D is represented by a straight line joining these two ordinates as shown in Fig. 8-15(c).

Example 8-5. If the beam shown in Fig. 8-15(a) has a span length of 36 ft and point J is located 15 ft from support A, determine the maximum moment at point J due to a uniform load of 2 kips/ft and a roving concentrated load of 20 kips.

In this case, $a = 15$ ft, $b = 21$ ft, $L = 36$ ft, and $h = \frac{36}{6} = 6$ ft. For the influence line for M_j shown in Fig. 8-15(d), we have $ab/L = 8.75$. Then, the ordinates at points C and D of the beam are obtained as follows:

$$y_c = (8.75)(\tfrac{12}{15}) = 7.0$$

$$y_d = (8.75)(\tfrac{18}{21}) = 7.5$$

This can be checked by direct substitution into the previously given formulas for M_j. Then,

$$y_c = 2h - \frac{a}{3} = (2)(6) - \frac{15}{3} = 7.0$$

$$y_d = \frac{a}{2} = \frac{15}{2} = 7.5$$

The uniform load will be placed over the entire span length while the roving concentrated load should be placed at point D where the ordinate of the influence line is maximum. Thus, the maximum moment due to the given loading is equal to

$$M_j = (2)(\tfrac{1}{2})[(12)(7) + (6)(7) + (6)(7.5) + (7.5)(18)] + (20)(7.5)$$

$$= 306 + 150 = 456 \text{ kips}$$

8-6 THREE-HINGED ARCHES

In the case of curved members, the influence lines for normal force, shear, and moment at a section are influenced by the horizontal reaction H. It is usually necessary to obtain first the influence line for the horizontal thrust H in the analysis of an arch rib.

Consider the three-hinged arch shown in Fig. 8-16(a). Let a moving concentrated load P be applied directly to the arch rib as indicated. By considering the entire structure as a free body, we obtain

$$\sum F_x = 0, \qquad H_a = H_c = H$$

$$\sum M_c = 0, \qquad V_a = \frac{Px}{L} + \frac{Hh}{L}$$

$$\sum M_a = 0, \qquad V_c = \frac{P(L-x)}{L} - \frac{Hh}{L}$$

By considering the left half of the structure as a free body and by taking moments about hinge B, i.e., $\sum M_b = 0$,

$$V_a a - H(r + t) = 0$$

Using the relation of similar triangles $t = ah/L$ in Fig. 8-16(a), we get

$$\left(\frac{Px}{L} + \frac{Hh}{L}\right)a - H\left(r + \frac{ah}{L}\right) = \frac{Pxa}{L} - Hr = 0$$

or

$$H = \frac{Pxa}{Lr}$$

Now imagine a fictitious beam having the same span length L and the same vertical loading as the three-hinged arch. Then, the vertical reactions of such a beam as shown in Fig. 8-16(b) are

$$R_a = \frac{Px}{L} \quad \text{and} \quad R_c = \frac{P(L-x)}{L}$$

The moment at point B of the beam is $M'_b = R_a a$. Then, the components of reactions of the three-hinged arch can be expressed in terms of the reactions of the fictitious simple beam as follows:

$$H = \frac{R_a a}{r} = \frac{M'_b}{r}$$

$$V_a = R_a + \frac{Hh}{L} = R_a + H \tan \alpha$$

$$V_c = R_c - \frac{Hh}{L} = R_c - H \tan \alpha$$

Thus, the influence line for the horizontal thrust H of the three-hinged arch is proportional to the moment at point B of the fictitious beam. The ordinates of the influence line for H can therefore be obtained from those for M'_b by dividing by the factor of proportionality r, and such an influence line is shown in Fig. 8-16(c). The influence lines for vertical reactions V_a and V_c can be obtained by

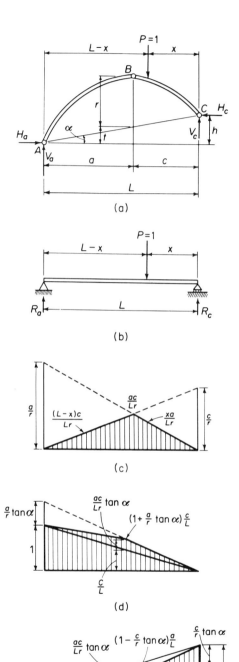

Figure 8-16

superimposing the influence diagram representing $H \tan \alpha$ onto the corresponding influence diagrams for the vertical reactions of the fictitious beam. The results of the superposition are shown in Figs. 8-16(d) and (e), respectively.

The normal force, shear, and moment at a section passing through point D of the arch rib as shown in Fig. 8-17(a) also can be expressed in terms of the reactions of the fictitious beam. Thus, for the unit load placed at a point to the right of point D,

$$N_d = V_a \sin \theta + H \cos \theta$$

$$= (R_a + H \tan \alpha) \sin \theta + H \cos \theta$$

$$= R_a \sin \theta + H \frac{(\cos \theta \cos \alpha + \sin \theta \sin \alpha)}{\cos \alpha}$$

(a)

(b)

(c)

(d)

Figure 8-17

$$= R_a \sin \theta + H\frac{\cos (\theta - \alpha)}{\cos \alpha}$$

$$S_d = V_a \cos \theta - H \sin \theta$$

$$= (R_a + H \tan \alpha) \cos \theta - H \sin \theta$$

$$= R_a \cos \theta - H\frac{(\sin \theta \cos \alpha - \sin \alpha \cos \theta)}{\cos \alpha}$$

$$= R_a \cos \theta - H\frac{\sin (\theta - \alpha)}{\cos \alpha}$$

Similarly, for the unit load placed at a point to the left of point D,

$$N_d = (R_a - 1) \sin \theta + H\frac{\cos (\theta - \alpha)}{\cos \alpha}$$

$$S_d = (R_a - 1) \cos \theta - H\frac{\sin (\theta - \alpha)}{\cos \alpha}$$

When the unit load is placed to the right of point D, the moment at point D is equal to

$$M_d = V_a d - H(r_d + t_d) = \left(R_a + \frac{Hh}{L}\right)d - H\left(r_d + \frac{dh}{L}\right) = R_a d - Hr_d$$

When the unit load is placed to the left of point D, M_d can be computed accordingly. For a given location of D, the angle θ can be computed from the shape of the arch rib. Hence, the influence lines for N_d, S_d, and M_d can be obtained by the principle of superposition as shown in Figs. 8-17(b), (c), and (d), respectively. It is necessary only to point out that the ordinates of the influence lines may also be plotted along a horizontal base if so desired.

Example 8-6. The parabolic rib of the three-hinged arch in Fig. 8-18(a) can be represented by the equation

$$y = \left(\tfrac{3}{320}\right)x^2$$

with coordinate axes directed as shown. Draw the influence lines for the normal force, shear, and moment at point D of the arch.

Since $\tan \alpha = h/L = 26.25/140 = 0.1874$, we get $\sin \alpha = 0.185$ and $\cos \alpha = 0.983$. At point D, the angle θ can be obtained by

$$\tan \theta = \left.\frac{dy}{dx}\right|_{x=40} = \left.\frac{3x}{160}\right|_{x=40} = \frac{3}{4}$$

from which $\sin \theta = \tfrac{3}{5} = 0.6$ and $\cos \theta = \tfrac{4}{5} - 0.8$. Hence,

$$\frac{\cos (\theta - \alpha)}{\cos \alpha} = \frac{(0.8)(0.983) + (0.6)(0.185)}{0.983} = 0.91$$

$$\frac{\sin (\theta - \alpha)}{\cos \alpha} = \frac{(0.6)(0.983) - (0.185)(0.8)}{0.983} = 0.45$$

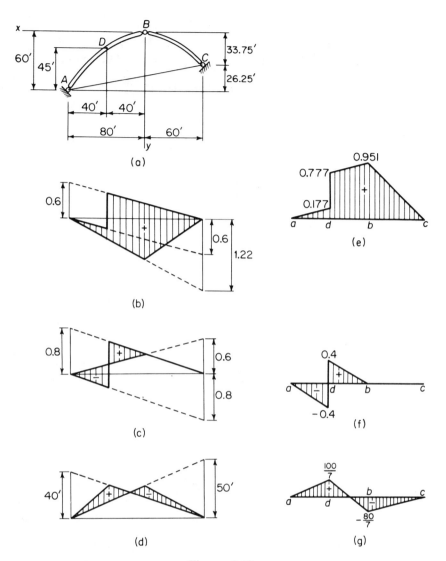

Figure 8-18

Since $c = 60$ ft, $d = 40$ ft, $r = 60 - (26.25)(\frac{80}{140}) = 45$ ft, and $r_d = 45 - 7.5 = 37.5$ ft,

$$\frac{c}{r}\frac{\cos{(\theta - \alpha)}}{\cos{\alpha}} = \left(\frac{60}{45}\right)(0.91) = 1.22$$

$$\frac{c}{r}\frac{\sin{(\theta - \alpha)}}{\cos{\alpha}} = \left(\frac{60}{45}\right)(0.45) = 0.6$$

$$\frac{c}{r}r_d = \left(\frac{60}{45}\right)(37.5) = 50$$

Thus, the influence lines for N_d, S_d, and M_d can be plotted as shown in Figs.

8-18(b), (c), and (d), respectively. However, these influence lines can also be plotted along a horizontal base as shown in Figs. 8-18(e), (f), and (g), the ordinates of which have been obtained by considering the relation of similar triangles in Figs. 8-18(b), (c), and (d), respectively.

In Fig. 8-18(e), the ordinates to the left and right of d are, respectively, equal to

$$y_{dl} = (\tfrac{40}{140})(1.22 - 0.6) = 0.177$$

$$y_{dr} = (\tfrac{40}{140})(1.22) + (\tfrac{100}{140})(0.6) = 0.777$$

Similarly,

$$y_b = (\tfrac{80}{140})(1.22) + (\tfrac{60}{140})(0.6) = 0.951$$

In Fig. 8-18(f), we have

$$y_{dl} = (\tfrac{40}{140})(-0.8) + (\tfrac{40}{140})(-0.6) = -0.4$$

$$y_{dr} = (\tfrac{100}{140})(0.8) + (\tfrac{40}{140})(-0.6) = 0.4$$

In Fig. 8-18(g), we get

$$y_d = (\tfrac{100}{140})(40) + (\tfrac{40}{140})(-50) = \tfrac{100}{7}$$

$$y_b = (\tfrac{80}{140})(-50) + (\tfrac{60}{140})(40) = -\tfrac{80}{7}$$

In the case of three-hinged arches supporting floor beams, the same procedure for the construction of influence lines may be applied with only slight modifications similar to those explained in Section 8-5 for girders supporting floor beams.

8-7 SIMPLE TRUSSES

In constructing the influence line for the bar force in a member of a simple truss, it is necessary to determine first the most convenient approach for computing the bar force. For example, a bar force may be conveniently obtained by considering a certain part of the truss as a free body and by taking moments about a certain point, or it may be more conveniently computed from the shear force at a certain section of the truss. Thus, the effect of a moving unit load on the bar force can be directly related to that on the moment at a given point or the shear at a given section of the truss. The ordinates of the influence line for the bar force may then be obtained by proportion from that for moment or shear as the case may be.

The effects of moving loads on a truss can be determined from the influence lines for the bar forces in the truss. For a moving uniform load or a combination of moving uniform load and roving concentrated load, the procedure of computing the bar forces in a truss from the influence diagrams for those members is straightforward and identical to that for computing the effects on beams discussed in Section 8-3. For a series of moving concentrated loads, criteria for maximum bar forces can also be developed but will not be included here.

Example 8-7. Draw the influence lines for the bar forces in members U_1L_1, U_1L_2, U_1U_2 and L_2L_3 of the truss shown in Fig. 8-19(a).

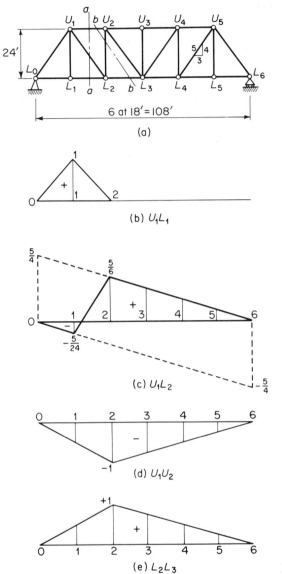

(a)

(b) U_1L_1

(c) U_1L_2

(d) U_1U_2

(e) L_2L_3

Figure 8-19

For member U_1L_1, the bar force can be directly determined from the consideration of equilibrium of joint L_1. When the unit load is placed at L_1, the bar force is equal to 1 in tension. When the unit load is placed at any other joint, the bar force is zero. Thus, the influence line for the bar force in U_1L_1 is shown in Fig. 8-19(b). For member U_1L_2, the bar force can be conveniently computed by multiplying the shear in panel L_1L_2 by a factor of $\frac{5}{4}$. Thus, at joint L_1, the ordinate of the influence line is $(-\frac{1}{6})(\frac{5}{4}) = -\frac{5}{24}$, and at joint L_2, the ordinate is $(\frac{4}{6})(\frac{5}{4}) = \frac{5}{6}$.

Since a positive shear at section a-a passing through panel L_1L_2 will cause tension in member U_1L_2, the sign of the influence coefficients for the bar force in U_1L_2 follows that of the shear in panel L_1L_2. The influence line for the bar force in U_1L_2 is shown in Fig. 8-19(c).

The bar force in member U_1U_2 can be obtained by considering the left of section b-b as a free body and by taking moments about joint L_2. Similarly, the bar force in member L_2L_3 is obtained by taking moments about joint U_2 of the free body. Although the unit load is placed at the bottom chord only, the unit load will cause the same moment about joint U_2 as about joint L_2. Thus, the ordinates of the influence line for the bar force in U_1U_2 are numerically equal to those for the bar force in L_2L_3. For instance, at joint L_2, the ordinates for both influence lines are numerically equal to the ordinate of the moment about joint L_2 divided by the height of the truss. Hence, at L_2, the ordinate is equal to

$$\frac{(2 \times 18)(4 \times 18)}{6 \times 18} \frac{1}{24} = 1$$

However, the signs of the ordinates of these influence lines are opposite to each other because member U_1U_2 is in compression and member L_2L_3 is in tension as a result of the consideration of equilibrium of the free body. The influence lines for the bar forces in U_1U_2 and L_2L_3 are shown in Figs. 8-19(d) and (e), respectively.

Example 8-8. Draw the influence line for the bar force in member DI of the truss shown in Fig. 8-20(a).

The bar force in member DI is obtained by first considering joint I as a free body and then the portion of the truss to the left of section a-a as a free body as shown in Figs. 8-20(b) and (c). It is possible therefore to relate this bar force to shear in panel CD and the moment about joint C. Let the subscripts x and y denote the components of bar forces in horizontal and vertical directions, respectively, and assume that the bar forces are directed away from the joints. Then, from the sum of the horizontal forces in Fig. 8-20(b), we have

$$(F_{di})_x = -(F_{im})_x \quad \text{or} \quad \tfrac{4}{5}F_{di} = -0.707F_{im}$$

Hence, $F_{im} = -1.135F_{di}$. Furthermore, from the conditions of equilibrium of the free body in Fig. 8-20(c), we get

$$\sum M_c = 0, \qquad (F_{lm})_x(30) + M_c = 0 \tag{a}$$

$$\sum F_y = 0, \qquad (F_{lm})_y + (F_{im})_y - (F_{di})_y + S_{cd} = 0 \tag{b}$$

in which M_c is the moment of all *external* forces about joint C and S_{cd} is the vertical shear in panel CD due to the *external* forces, the sign convention for M_c and S_{cd} being the same as that for moment and shear in beams. Note that, in taking moments about joint C, the bar forces in members DI and IM do not enter into the equation because they can be resolved into components at joint I such that the vertical components will pass through the moment center C and the horizontal components are equal and opposite, thus cancelling each other. Hence, from Eq. (a),

$$(F_{lm})_x = -\frac{M_c}{30}$$

(a)

(b) (c)

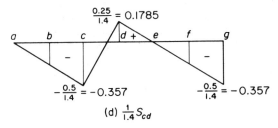

$$\frac{0.25}{1.4} = 0.1785$$

$$-\frac{0.5}{1.4} = -0.357 \qquad -\frac{0.5}{1.4} = -0.357$$

(d) $\frac{1}{1.4} S_{cd}$

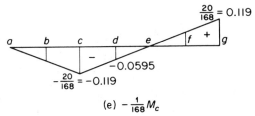

$$\frac{20}{168} = 0.119$$

$$-0.0595$$

$$-\frac{20}{168} = -0.119$$

(e) $-\frac{1}{168} M_c$

$$+0.119$$

$$-0.238$$

$$-0.476$$

(f) F_{di}

Figure 8-20

or

$$(F_{lm})_y = -\left(\frac{M_c}{30}\right)\left(\frac{5}{20}\right) = -\frac{M_c}{120}$$

and from Eq. (b),

$$-\frac{M_c}{120} + 0.707(F_{im}) - \frac{3}{5}(F_{di}) + S_{cd} = 0$$

Noting $F_{im} = -1.135F_{di}$, we obtain

$$1.4(F_{di}) = S_{cd} - \frac{M_c}{120} \qquad (c)$$

or

$$F_{di} = \frac{1}{1.4}S_{cd} - \frac{1}{168}M_c \qquad (d)$$

Thus, the influence line for F_{di} can be obtained from the influence lines for S_{cd} and M_c. The construction of the influence line for bar force in member DI is illustrated step by step in Figs. 8-20(d), (e), and (f).

Example 8-9. Determine the maximum bar forces in members U_2U_3, L_2L_3, and L_2U_3 of the truss shown in Fig. 8-21(a) due to a moving uniform load of 2 kips per foot.

Since the maximum bar force in a member of a truss subjected to a moving uniform load can be obtained from the area of the influence diagram for the bar force, the first step is to construct the influence lines for the required bar forces. By considering the portion of the truss to the left of section a-a in Fig. 8-21(a) as a free body, the bar forces in members U_2U_3 and L_2L_3 can be obtained by taking moments about joints L_2 and U_3, respectively, as follows:

$$F_{U_2U_3} = -\frac{M_{L_2}}{d} \qquad \text{and} \qquad F_{L_2L_3} = +\frac{M_{U_3}}{d}$$

in which $F_{U_2U_3}$ and $F_{L_2L_3}$ are the respective bar forces in members U_2U_3 and L_2L_3, M_{L_2} and M_{L_3} are the moments about L_2 and U_3, respectively, in the free body, and d is the depth of the truss. Since the unit load is applied to the floor system and transmitted to the joints at the bottom chord of the truss, the influence line for moment about joint L_2 of the truss is identical to that for moment at the corresponding point of a beam having the same span length as the truss. The influence line for the bar force in member U_2U_3 is therefore obtained by proportion from that for moment at L_2. The result, indicated in Fig. 8-21(b), has a maximum ordinate at L_2 equal to

$$-\frac{1}{25}\frac{(50)(125)}{175} = -\frac{10}{7}$$

In order to produce maximum moment at joint U_3, the unit load should be placed in a position U_3' beneath joint U_3, as shown in Fig. 8-21(a). However, such a load is eventually transmitted through the floor system to joints L_2 and L_3 at the bottom chord of the truss. Hence, the influence line for moment at joint U_3 is identical to that for moment at point U_3' of a girder having the same span length

(b) Bar force in U_2U_3

(c) Bar force in L_2L_3

(d) Bar force in L_2U_3

Figure 8-21

as the truss and supporting floor beams at the same panel points as the truss. The influence line for the bar force in $L_2 L_3$ is indicated by the solid lines in Fig. 8-21(c). The influence ordinate of the point of intersection of the dotted lines in the figure is equal to

$$+\frac{1}{25}\frac{(62.5)(112.5)}{175} = \frac{11.25}{7}$$

Then, the influence ordinates at L_2 and L_3 are, respectively, equal to

$$\left(\frac{11.25}{7}\right)\left(\frac{50}{62.5}\right) = \frac{9}{7} \quad \text{and} \quad \left(\frac{11.25}{7}\right)\left(\frac{100}{112.5}\right) = \frac{10}{7}$$

The bar force in member L_2U_3 can be computed from the shear at section a-a as follows:

$$F_{L_2U_3} = -\frac{2.24}{2}S_{23} = -1.12S_{23}$$

in which $F_{L_2U_3}$ is the bar force in the member and S_{23} is the shear in panel L_2L_3. Then, at L_2 and L_3 the ordinates of the influence line for the bar force in L_2U_3 are, respectively, equal to $(-1.12)(-\frac{2}{7}) = +0.32$ and $(-1.12)(\frac{4}{7}) = -0.64$, and such an influence line is plotted in Fig. 8-21(d). The neutral point in the influence diagram is located by the relation of similar triangles.

The maximum bar forces in various members are obtained from the area of the influence diagrams for the respective members multiplied by the moving uniform load. With dimensionless coefficients for the ordinates, the product of the area of the diagram (in units of length) and the uniform load (in force per unit length) gives the bar force in the unit of force. Thus, for members U_2U_3, with the entire span loaded, the maximum bar force is

$$F_{U_2U_3} = (2)(\tfrac{1}{2})(-\tfrac{10}{7})(175) = -250 \text{ kips}$$

and for member L_2L_3, also with the entire span loaded, the maximum bar force is

$$F_{L_2L_3} = (2)\left(\frac{1}{2}\right)\left[\left(\frac{9}{7}\right)(50) + \left(\frac{10}{7}\right)(100) + \left(\frac{9+10}{7}\right)(25)\right] = +274 \text{ kips}$$

For member L_2U_3, however, the maximum compression is obtained when the portion of span representing the negative area of the influence diagram is loaded, and

$$F_{L_2U_3} = -(2)(\tfrac{1}{2})(0.64)(100 + 16.7) = -74.8 \text{ kips}$$

Similarly, the maximum tension is obtained when the positive area of the influence diagram is loaded. Then

$$F_{L_2U_3} = (2)(\tfrac{1}{2})(0.32)(50 + 8.3) = +18.7 \text{ kips}$$

It should be noted that when the truss is subjected to live load only, the bar force in member L_2U_3 may be in tension or in compression, depending on the location of the moving load. Under dead load, the member is subjected to compression only. Thus, the total bar force in the member due to the combination of dead load and live load may be a tension if the tension caused by the live load is greater than the compression caused by the dead load. The variation of the sense of direction of the bar force in a member as a result of the variation of the positions of the live load on a truss is known as the *reversal of bar force*.

8-8 INFLUENCE LINES FOR CONTINUOUS BEAMS

When a constraint is removed from a structure, the resulting system is said to be the released system of the original structure. For statically determinate structures, it has been shown in Section 8-2 by the principle of virtual displacements that the deflected shape of the released system represents the shape of the influence line for that constraint in the original structure. Then, the ordinates of the influence line can readily be computed from the geometry of the deflected shape of the released system. For statically indeterminate structures the same concept may be applied to obtain the shape of an influence line although the computation of the ordinates of such an influence line is much more tedious because of the geometry of the deflected shape of the released system. Thus, *if any constraint is removed from a statically indeterminate structure and the corresponding released effect is allowed to act through a unit virtual displacement, the resulting deflected shape is an influence line for the effect.** The general shape of an influence line is called a *qualitative influence line,* which is often useful in determining where to place live loads to produce a maximum effect in a statically indeterminate structure.

Consider, for example, a continuous beam with two spans as shown in Fig. 8-22(a). The structure is statically indeterminate to one degree. If a constraint is removed from the structure, the resulting system will be statically determinate. In order to obtain the displacements of the released system, we must consider the load-deformation characteristics of the material of the structure. However, the general deflected shape of the released system may be sketched without actually computing the ordinates. If we remove the vertical constraint at support A and replace it by a vertical upward force at A, the deflected shape of the released system will be as shown in Fig. 8-22(b), which is also the qualitative influence for the reaction at A of the original structure. Similar influence lines have been drawn for reaction R_b, shear S_d, positive moment M_d, and negative moment M_b in Figs. 8-22(c) to (f), respectively. If a uniform live load is applied to the beam, we can determine by inspection of the influence lines what part of the beam should be loaded in order to produce certain maximum effects. If a roving concentrated load is included in the live load, its critical positions for various effects on the structure also may be located by inspection of the influence lines.

It can be seen that generally the influence lines for statically indeterminate structures consist of curves rather than straight line segments and that the ordinates of these influence lines can be obtained if the displacements of the corresponding released systems can be computed. Hence, the displacement computation of statically determinate structures is an important preliminary step in determining the ordinates of influence lines for statically indeterminate structures.

From the foregoing discussion, it is clear that the applications of influence lines will exceed by far the examples given for statically determinate structures in this chapter. On the other hand, criteria for maximum effects caused by a series of concentrated loads have only limited use for statically determinate structures. Our main emphasis, therefore, is placed on the concept and construction of influence lines rather than their applications to determine maximum effects of live loads except for the simplest cases.

*This is known as *Müller-Breslau's principle,* which will be discussed further in Section 8-9.

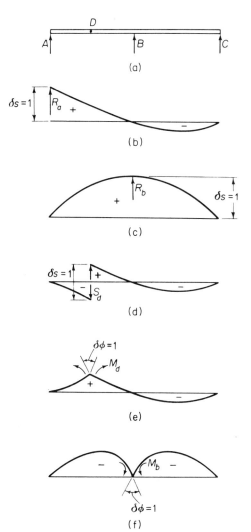

(a)

(b)

(c)

(d)

(e)

(f)

Figure 8-22

Example 8-10. A uniform live load w and a roving concentrated load P are to be placed on the continuous beam shown in Fig. 8-22(a). Determine where to place these loads in order to produce maximum effects in (a) reaction R_a, (b) reaction R_b, (c) positive shear S_d, and (d) positive moment M_d.

The positions of live loads that will produce maximum effects may be determined by inspection of the influence lines shown in Fig. 8-22. For maximum reaction R_a, the uniform load should be placed in span AB, with the roving concentrated load acting at point A. For maximum reaction R_b, both spans AB and AC should be loaded with the uniform load while the roving concentrated load should be placed at point B. For maximum positive shear S_d, only the portion DB of the beam should be loaded with the uniform load while the roving concentrated load should be placed just to the right of point D. For maximum positive moment M_d, the uniform load should be placed in span AB, with the roving concentrated load acting at point D.

In the discussion of the general concept of influence lines in Section 8-2, we pointed out that an influence line for any constraint such as a reaction, shear, or moment at a point in a structure may be obtained from the deflected shape of the released system in which the constraint has been removed. We also introduced in Section 8-8 (without proof) Müller-Breslau's principle, which states that if any constraint is removed from a statically indeterminate structure and the corresponding released effect is allowed to act through a unit virtual displacement, the resulting deflected shape is an influence line for that effect. We shall now attempt to determine quantitatively the ordinates of such influence lines.

Müller-Breslau's principle is based on the Maxwell-Betti Theorem of reciprocal displacements which will be discussed later in Section 10-3 (Chapter 10). It may be stated here (without proof) as follows: In a linear elastic structure, the displacement of point A in the a direction due to a load acting at a point B in the b direction is equal to the displacement of point B in the given b direction due to a load of the same magnitude acting at point A in the a direction. This is known as *Maxwell's theorem of reciprocal displacements.** The theorem is very general since the term *displacement* may refer to rotation or linear displacement and the term *load* means either moment or force.

Let f_{ab} denote the displacement at point A in the a direction due to a unit force at point B in the b direction, and f_{ba} will be similarly defined. Then, according to Maxwell's theorem of reciprocal displacements,

$$f_{ab} = f_{ba}$$

Similarly, let k_{ab} denote the force at point A in the a direction due to a unit displacement at point B in the b direction, and k_{ba} will be similarly defined. Then,

$$k_{ab} = k_{ba}$$

It should be noted that the forces and displacements just discussed may include moments and rotations. If a linear elastic element is subjected to pure bending, for example, the rotation φ is related to the moment M as follows:

$$\varphi = \tilde{f}M \qquad \text{or} \qquad M = \tilde{k}\varphi$$

where $\tilde{f} = \varphi/M$ is the rotation caused by a unit moment and $\tilde{k} = M/\varphi$ is the moment required to produce a unit rotation. Let $\tilde{f}_{ab}$ denote the rotation at point A in the a direction due to a unit moment at B in the b direction, and $\tilde{f}_{ba}$ will be similarly defined. Also, let $\tilde{k}_{ab}$ denote the moment at point A in the a direction, due to a unit rotation at point B in the b direction, and $\tilde{k}_{ba}$ will be similarly defined. Then

$$\tilde{f}_{ab} = \tilde{f}_{ba}$$

$$\tilde{k}_{ab} = \tilde{k}_{ba}$$

*Maxwell's theorem is a special case of Maxwell-Betti Theorem.

Consider, for instance, the continuous beam in Fig. 8-23(a), for which the influence line for the reaction at support B is desired. We remove the support at B so that the released system will be as shown in Fig. 8-23(b). In the released system, the deflection at point B due to a moving unit load $P = 1$ is denoted by δ_b'. We may also remove the external load $P = 1$ and place a unit load at point B of the released structure, causing a deflection δ_{bb} at point B as shown in Fig. 8-23(c). Thus, the reaction at support B is equal to the force required to restore point B of the beam to its undeflected position. Hence,

$$R_b = -\frac{\delta_b'}{\delta_{bb}}$$

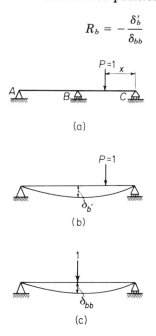

(a)

(b)

(c)   **Figure 8-23**

Note that δ_{bb} is a constant quantity since the geometrical and material properties of the beam are known, whereas δ_b' depends on the location of the moving load $P = 1$. Thus, the influence line for the reaction at support B is proportional to the influence line for deflection at point B of the released structure, the factor of proportionality being δ_{bb}. According to Maxwell's theorem of reciprocal displacements, the influence line for deflection at point B of the released structure is identical to the deflection curve of the beam with a load $P = 1$ acting at B. Hence, the ordinates of this deflection curve divided by δ_{bb} give the corresponding ordinates of the influence line for the reaction at B.

The same principle may be used for other types of constraint such as moments, shears, and bar forces in any structure provided that the material is linearly elastic. It is extremely useful in the construction of influence lines for statically indeterminate structures.

Example 8-11. Construct the influence lines for reactions R_b and R_a of a two-span continuous beam having equal spans L and constant bending stiffness EI as shown in Fig. 8-24(a).

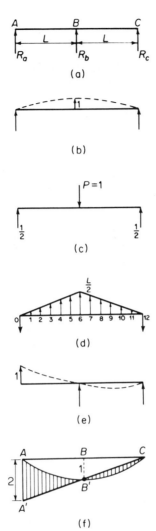

(a)

(b)

(c)

(d)

(e)

(f)

Figure 8-24

In order to obtain the influence line for reaction R_b, we remove the vertical constraint at support B and allow point B to act through a unit displacement in the direction of R_b. Then, according to Müller-Breslau's principle, the deflected shape of the released system as shown by the dotted line in Fig. 8-24(b) is the influence line for R_b.

The ordinates of the influence line can be obtained from the relation $R_b = \delta_b' / \delta_{bb}$. Since δ_b' represents the deflection at point B caused by a moving unit load at various points of the beam in Fig. 8-24(c), they are identical to the deflections at various points of the beam due to a unit load at point B. We can compute the deflections at various points of the beam due to a unit load at point B by the conjugate beam method. For the sake of convenience, let us select six points for each span, and because of symmetry, we need to consider only half of the structure. Then, from the moment diagram in Fig. 8-24(d), we obtain the vertical deflections as follows:

$$EIv_1 = \left(\frac{L^2}{4}\right)\left(\frac{L}{6}\right) - \left(\frac{1}{2}\right)\left(\frac{L}{12}\right)\left(\frac{L}{6}\right)^2\left(\frac{1}{3}\right) = \frac{107}{2,592}L^3$$

$$EIv_2 = \left(\frac{L^2}{4}\right)\left(\frac{L}{3}\right) - \left(\frac{1}{2}\right)\left(\frac{L}{6}\right)\left(\frac{L}{3}\right)^2\left(\frac{1}{3}\right) = \frac{13}{162}L^3$$

$$EIv_3 = \left(\frac{L^2}{4}\right)\left(\frac{L}{2}\right) - \left(\frac{1}{2}\right)\left(\frac{L}{4}\right)\left(\frac{L}{2}\right)^2\left(\frac{1}{3}\right) = \frac{11}{96}L^3$$

$$EIv_4 = \left(\frac{L^2}{4}\right)\left(\frac{2L}{3}\right) - \left(\frac{1}{2}\right)\left(\frac{L}{3}\right)\left(\frac{2L}{3}\right)^2\left(\frac{1}{3}\right) = \frac{23}{162}L^3$$

$$EIv_5 = \left(\frac{L^2}{4}\right)\left(\frac{5L}{6}\right) - \left(\frac{1}{2}\right)\left(\frac{5L}{12}\right)\left(\frac{5L}{6}\right)^2\left(\frac{1}{3}\right) = \frac{415}{2,592}L^3$$

$$EIv_6 = \left(\frac{L^2}{4}\right)(L) - \left(\frac{1}{2}\right)\left(\frac{L}{2}\right)(L^2)\left(\frac{1}{3}\right) = \frac{1}{6}L^3$$

Noting that $\delta_{bb} = v_6$, the influence ordinates can be obtained as follows:

$$y_0 = 0$$

$$y_1 = \frac{v_1}{v_6} = \left(\frac{107}{2,592}L^3\right)\left(\frac{6}{L^3}\right) = 0.248$$

$$y_2 = \frac{v_2}{v_6} = \left(\frac{13}{162}L^3\right)\left(\frac{6}{L^3}\right) = 0.481$$

$$y_3 = \frac{v_3}{v_6} = \left(\frac{11}{96}L^3\right)\left(\frac{6}{L^3}\right) = 0.688$$

$$y_4 = \frac{v_4}{v_6} = \left(\frac{23}{162}L^3\right)\left(\frac{6}{L^3}\right) = 0.851$$

$$y_5 = \frac{v_5}{v_6} = \left(\frac{415}{2,592}L^3\right)\left(\frac{6}{L^3}\right) = 0.961$$

$$y_6 = \frac{v_6}{v_6} = 1$$

For the influence line for reaction R_a, we remove the vertical constraint at support A and allow point A to act through a unit displacement in the direction of R_a as shown in Fig. 8-24(e). The ordinates of the influence line may be obtained in a similar manner. However, with the benefit of the influence line for R_b, the computation can be reduced by noting that the deflection curve of the beam due to a unit displacement at point A has the same shape as the one formed by a line passing through points C and B' of the deflection curve due to a unit displacement at point B. However, the absolute values of the ordinates of the former differ from those of the latter by a constant factor. We may therefore obtain AA' from BB' by the relations of similar triangles. Since $AA' = 2$ for $BB' = 1$, we can obtain the ordinates of the influence line for reaction R_a by dividing the vertical ordinates in the shaded part of Fig. 8-24(f) by a factor of 2. Thus the ordinates of the influence line for reaction R_a are obtained from the geometry of the influence line for reaction R_b as represented by the deflection curve in Fig. 8-24(f) as follows:

$y_0 = \frac{2}{2} = 1$

$y_1 = (1.833 - 0.248)/2 = 0.792$

$y_2 = (1.667 - 0.481)/2 = 0.593$

$y_3 = (1.500 - 0.688)/2 = 0.406$

$y_4 = (1.333 - 0.851)/2 = 0.241$

$y_5 = (1.167 - 0.961)/2 = 0.103$

$y_6 = (1 - 1)/2 = 0$

$y_7 = (0.833 - 0.961)/2 = -0.064$

$y_8 = (0.667 - 0.851)/2 = -0.092$

$y_9 = (0.500 - 0.688)/2 = -0.094$

$y_{10} = (0.333 - 0.481)/2 = -0.074$

$y_{11} = (0.167 - 0.248)/2 = -0.041$

$y_{12} = 0$

Example 8-12. The parabolic arch shown in Fig. 8-25(a) is represented by the equation

$$y = \frac{4f}{L^2}(Lx - x^2)$$

The moment of inertia at any section is $I = I_c \sec \beta$, where I_c is the moment of inertia at the crown and β is the angle between a tangent at a point on the arch axis and a horizontal line. Construct the influence line for the horizontal thrust H of the arch.

In order to construct the influence line for the horizontal thrust of the arch, we shall first remove the horizontal constraint at support B and allow point B to act through a unit displacement in the direction of the horizontal force H. According to Müller-Breslau's principle, the deflected shape of the released structure as indicated by the dotted line in Fig. 8-25(a) is the influence line for the horizontal thrust of the arch.

We can also obtain the ordinates of the influence line by computing the deflections of the released system. When a moving vertical load $P = 1$ is applied at point D, which is at a distance kL from the right support of the released structure as shown in Fig. 8-25(b), the horizontal displacement of support B may be denoted by δ_{bd}. If we apply a horizontal unit load at support B of the released structure as shown in Fig. 8-25(c), the support will displace horizontally by an amount δ_{bb}. Then, the horizontal thrust H in the original structure is given by

$$H = \frac{\delta_{bd}}{\delta_{bb}}$$

Note that δ_{bb} is a constant quantity whereas δ_{bd} depends on the distance kL from the right support. Since the horizontal displacement at point B due to a vertical load $P = 1$ at point D is equal to the vertical displacement at point D due to a horizontal load $H = 1$, i.e., $\delta_{bd} = \delta_{db}$, this expression for H gives the vertical ordinates of the influence line provided that δ_{bd} and δ_{bb} can be evaluated.

For a section of the arch axis at a distance x from the left support, we have from Fig. 8-25(d),

$$M = \frac{P(1-k)Lx}{L} = P(1-k)x \qquad \text{for } 0 \le x \le kL$$

(a)

(b)

(c)

(d)

(e)

Figure 8-25

$$M = \frac{PkL(L - x)}{L} = Pk(L - x) \qquad \text{for } kL \le x \le L$$

and from Fig. 8-25(e), $m = y$ for all values of x. Noting that $\sec \beta = ds/dx$, in which ds is measured along the length of the arch axis, δ_{bd} and δ_{bb} may be obtained as follows:*

$$\delta_{bd} = \int_0^L \frac{Mm \; ds}{EI} = \int_0^L \frac{Mm \; ds}{EI_c \sec \beta} = \int_0^L \frac{Mm \; dx}{EI_c}$$

*See detailed explanation of the method of virtual work for computing deflections in Section 9-7.

$$= \frac{1}{EI_c} \int_0^L My \, dx$$

$$= \frac{4Pf}{L^2 EI_c} \left[\int_0^{kL} (Lx - x^2)(1 - k) \, x \, dx + \int_{kL}^L (Lx - x^2)k(L - x) \, dx \right]$$

$$= \frac{PfkL^2}{3EI_c}(1 - 2k^2 + k^3)$$

$$\delta_{bb} = \int_0^L \frac{y^2 \, ds}{EI} = \int_0^L \frac{y^2 \, ds}{EI_c \sec \beta} = \frac{1}{EI_c} \int_0^L y^2 \, dx$$

$$= \frac{16f^2}{EI_c L^4} \int_0^L (Lx - x^2)^2 \, dx = \frac{8f^2 L}{15 \, EI_c}$$

Hence,

$$H = \frac{5PLk}{8f}(1 - 2k^2 + k^4)$$

If the span is divided into six equal divisions, for instance, the influence ordinates for H due to a unit load $P = 1$ moving along the span may be obtained as follows:

for $k = 0$ and $k = 1$, $H = 0$

for $k = \frac{1}{6}$ and $k = \frac{5}{6}$, $H = 0.099L/f$

for $k = \frac{1}{3}$ and $k = \frac{2}{3}$, $H = 0.170L/f$

for $k = \frac{1}{2}$, $H = 0.195L/f$

Since a *downward* vertical load at D will cause an *outward* horizontal displacement at B, an *inward* horizontal thrust will cause an *upward* vertical displacement in the released system. Hence, the influence ordinates are positive.

PROBLEMS

8-1. For the beam shown in Fig. P8-1, draw the influence lines for the following effects: (a) reactions at supports B and C, (b) shears at a section just to the left and another section just to the right of support B, (c) moments at points B, C, E, and F.

Figure P8-1   Figure P8-2

8-2. Construct influence lines for the following effects on the beam shown in Fig. P8-2: (a) reaction at A, (b) reaction at B, (c) shears at C and D, (d) moments at C and D.

8-3. Draw the influence lines for the following effects if a unit load moves from C to A in the structure shown in Fig. P8-3: (a) shears at points E and F, (b) moments at points E and F.

Figure P8-3   Figure P8-4

8-4. Draw the influence lines for the following effects if a unit load moves from D to A of the structure shown in Fig. P8-4: (a) vertical reaction at E, (b) shear to the right of support B, (c) moments at points C and F.

8-5. Construct the influence lines for the following effects on the beam shown in Fig. P8-5: (a) vertical reaction at F, (b) shear at a section just to the left of C, (c) shear at a section just to the right of C, (d) moment at point C, (e) moment at point E.

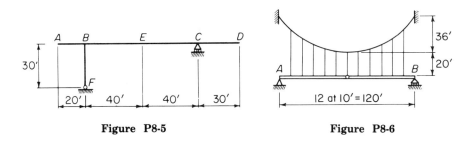

Figure P8-5   Figure P8-6

8-6. Draw the influence line for the reaction at support A of the suspended girder shown in Fig. P8-6

8-7. For the beam with releases shown in Fig. P8-7, draw the influence lines for the following effects, using the concept of a moving unit load: (a) reaction at support B, (b) moment at support B, (c) shear at point G.

Figure P8-7

8-8. For the beam shown in Fig. P8-8, compute the maximum shear and moment at point E due to a uniform live load of 2 kips per foot plus a roving concentrated load of 20 kips.

Figure P8-8

8-9. Construct influence lines for the following effects on the beam shown in Fig. P8-9, using the concept of a moving unit load: (a) reactions at A and B, (b) shears at G and H, (c) moments at G and H.

Figure P8-9

8-10. Repeat Problem 8-7 using the method of virtual displacements.

8-11. Repeat Problems 8-9 using the method of virtual displacements.

8-12. For the compound beam shown in Fig. P8-12, draw the influence lines for the following effects: (a) reaction at support B, (b) shear in panel EF, (c) moment at point F.

Figure P8-12   **Figure P8-13**

8-13. For the girder shown in Fig. P8-13, draw the influence lines for the following effects: (a) shears in panels AB and BC, (b) moments at points C and D.

8-14. For the girder supporting floor beams shown in Fig. P8-14, draw the influence lines for the following effects: (a) reactions at supports B and F, (b) shears in panels BC and EF, (c) moments at points A and D.

Figure P8-14   **Figure P8-15**

8-15. For the semicircular three-hinged arch shown in Fig. P8-15, draw the influence lines for the horizontal reaction H and for the normal force N_d, the shear S_d, and the moment M_d at point D of the arch rib if a vertical unit load moves from the right to the left of the arch.

8-16. The parabolic arch shown in Fig. P8-16 supports a floor system that transmits the floor load to the arch through the vertical struts. Draw the influence line for the horizontal thrust H at the supports B and C.

Figure P8-16

8-17. Draw the influence lines for the normal force, shear, and moment at point D of the three-hinged arch shown in Fig. P8-17. Numerical values of the key ordinates of the influence lines should be given in the diagrams. The equation of the arch rib is $y = x^2/200$.

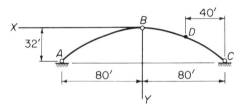

Figure P8-17

8-18. For the truss shown in Fig. P8-18, find the maximum bar forces in members U_2L_3 and L_3L_4 due to a uniform load of 1 kip/ft.

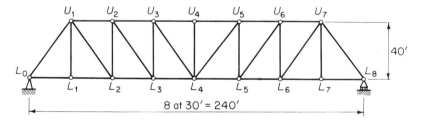

Figure P8-18

8-19. Determine the maximum bar forces in members U_2U_3, U_2L_3, L_2L_3, and U_3L_3 of the truss shown in Fig. P8-19 due to a uniform live load of 6 kips/ft.

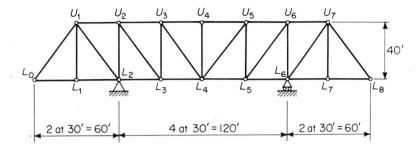

Figure P8-19

8-20. Construct the influence lines for all components of reactions as a unit load moves from A to B on the structure shown in Fig. P8-20.

Figure P8-20

8-21. Construct the influence lines for bar forces in members U_4U_5, L_4L_5, M_4U_5, M_4L_5, U_4M_4, and M_4L_4 of the K-truss shown in Fig. P8-21.

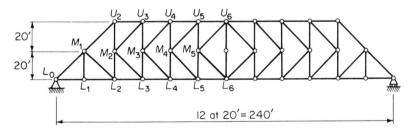

Figure P8-21

8-22. Construct the influence lines for the bar forces in members a, b, and c of the truss shown in Fig. P8-22.

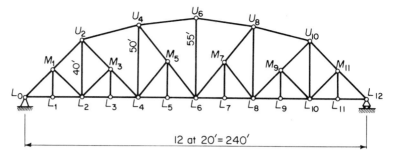

Figure P8-22

8-23. Compute the maximum tensile and/or compressive bar forces in members a and b in the structure shown in Fig. P8-23 due to a moving uniform load of 1 kip/ft.

Figure P8-23

8-24. Construct the influence lines for the bar forces in members a and b and for the reaction A of the stiffening truss of the suspension bridge shown in Fig. P8-24.

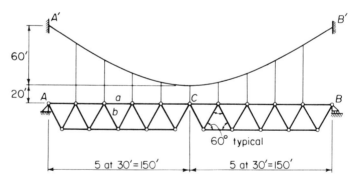

Figure P8-24

8-25 and 8-26. By applying Müller-Breslau's principle, construct influence lines for reactions at supports A and B of the beams shown in Figs. P8-25 and P8-26. Compute the ordinates of the influence lines at 10-ft intervals along the spans. The bending stiffness EI of the beams is constant

Figure P8-25

Figure P8-26

8-27. By applying Müller-Breslau's principle, construct an influence line for the horizontal component of reaction at point G due to a unit load moving from point F to point A of the truss shown in Fig. P8-27. Note that $E = 30 \times 10^3$ ksi and $A = 10$ in.^{2} for all members.

Figure P8-27   Figure P8-28

8-28. The parabolic arch shown in Fig. P8-28 has a moment of inertia at any section equal to $I = I_c \sec \beta$, in which I_c is the moment of inertia at the crown C and β is the angle between the tangent at the section and a horizontal line. Construct an influence line for the moment at point D of the arch. Compute the ordinates of the influence line at the sixth points of the span.

9

Energy Principles

A structure may be considered as a conservative system if no energy is added or taken away from it when it is isolated from its environment. As a structure deforms from one configuration to another under the action of applied loads, *external work* is done on the system by the external forces. On the other hand, *internal work* is done against the deformations in the system by the internal forces during the deformation. Strictly speaking, internal work must be negative because the deformations are imposed on the system and are resisted by the internal forces. According to the principle of conservation of energy, the total energy of an isolated system remains constant. Hence, the algebraic sum of the external and internal work in a structural system must be zero. In common usage, however, we often speak of the equality of external work and internal work which implies that only the absolute values of these quantities are considered. Thus, in a structural system in which displacements are consistent with constraints, the displacements of the system can be related to the external forces by means of the energy relations.

The energy principles presented in this chapter are applicable to conservative deformable systems that are either linearly or nonlinearly elastic. Although these principles have been applied primarily to the computation of deflections of statically determinate structures, we should at least be aware of the broad scope of their application to the analysis of redundant systems. We shall, therefore, present each of the energy theorems in its entirety even if it may not be of immediate interest in the computation of deflections.

358

In a broader sense, however, the strain energy and complementary energy methods may be considered as special cases of a more general principle, i.e., the principle of virtual work which, when applied to deformable systems, may be associated with virtual displacements or virtual forces. Thus, the energy theorems encountered in structural analysis may be grouped into two categories:

A. Theorems related to strain energy:
   1. Principle of virtual displacements
   2. Castigliano's first theorem
   3. Principle of stationary potential energy
B. Theorems related to complementary energy:
   1. Principle of virtual forces
      (Special case: dummy unit load method)
   2. Complementary energy method
      (Special case: Castigliano's second theorem)
   3. Principle of stationary complementary energy

The unifying factor in all these theorems is the principle of virtual work. If only one virtual force is involved, the dummy unit load method can readily be derived from the principle of virtual forces. As a special application of the principle of virtual work, Castigliano's first theorem is obtained from the strain energy of the system while the complementary energy method is derived from the complementary energy of the system. Castigliano's second theorem is merely a special case of the complementary energy method for linear elastic systems. For a more general application of the principle of virtual work, the concepts of stationary potential energy and stationary complementary energy are introduced.

The parallel grouping of these theorems has an important meaning in the analysis of redundant structures. The theorems in group A are used for the displacement method of analysis whereas those in group B are required for the force method of analysis. With traditional emphasis on the force method for the analysis of linear elastic structures, the theorems in group B have historically played the most important part. With the introduction of matrix methods of structural analysis and the use of electronic digital computers, the theorems in group A have become equally important. Hence all these theorems will be discussed briefly in order to illustrate their applications.

9-2 REAL WORK AND COMPLEMENTARY WORK

When an isolated structural system deforms under the action of applied loads, there is no change in the total energy in the isolated system. Thus, according to the principle of conservation of energy, the algebraic sum of the external work W_e and the internal work W_i is equal to zero, i.e.,

$$W_e + W_i = 0 \qquad (9\text{-}1)$$

For the sake of clarity, we shall always denote the internal work on a structural system as negative since the deformations are opposed by the internal forces. On the other hand, the increase in strain energy in a structural system, which is a measure of the internal work, is defined as a positive quantity,

$$U = -W_i \qquad (9\text{-}1a)$$

Thus, it may be stated that in an isolated structural system, the external work due to applied loads must equal the strain energy of the system as the result of deformation, i.e.,

$$W_e = U \qquad (9\text{-}1b)$$

We shall consider the general case of a nonlinear elastic system that may be conceived schematically as consisting of n elements. Let $P_1, P_2, \ldots, P_m$ be a set of m external loads that cause displacements $s_1, s_2, \ldots, s_m$ in the directions of the respective loads as shown in Fig. 9-1. Let $F_1, F_2, \ldots, F_n$ be the internal forces in various elements of the system and $e_1, e_2, \ldots, e_n$ be the deformations in the directions of the respective internal forces. When the external loads are applied gradually to the system, increasing from zero to their full values proportionally, the internal forces will also increase proportionally. Broadly speaking, the external work in a structural system may include the work done by the reactions as well as the applied loads if the supports are deformable. For the sake of simplicity, however, we shall confine our discussion to rigid supports.

If the force-deformation characteristics of all elements of the nonlinear elastic system in Fig. 9-1 can be represented by the curve shown in Fig. 9-2(a),

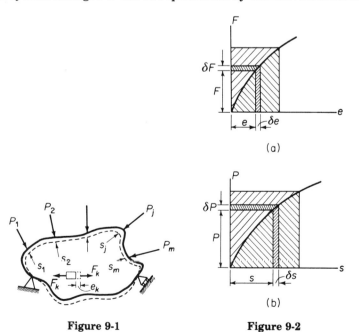

(a)

(b)

Figure 9-1   Figure 9-2

Energy Principles   Chap. 9

the strain energy of an element resulting from the deformation e in the direction of the internal force F is given by $\int F\,de$, or the area under the force-deformation curve. Hence, the total strain energy of the system is equal to

$$U = \sum_{k=1}^{n} \int F_k\,de_k \qquad (9\text{-}2)$$

The external work done on the same system by a force P for a displacement s in the direction of P is given by $\int P\,ds$, or the area under the force-deformation curve in Fig. 9-2(b), which has the same characteristics as that in Fig. 9-2(a). Then, the total external work done on the system is equal to

$$W_e = \sum_{j=1}^{m} \int P_j\,ds_j \qquad (9\text{-}3)$$

From the principle of conservation of energy, we have $W_e = U$, or

$$\sum_{j=1}^{m} \int P_j\,ds_j = \sum_{k=1}^{n} \int F_k\,de_k \qquad (9\text{-}4)$$

Since the external loads are applied gradually to the system in proportion, the internal forces increase from zero to their full values in the same proportion. The deformations and displacements which are related to the forces also increase proportionally from zero to their respective full values. Hence, the lower limits of the integrals in Eqs. (9-2) through (9-4) are all zero, whereas the upper limits represent the respective full values of deformations and displacements when the applied loads reach their full values simultaneously. Although the limits of integration are not shown in these equations, the meaning of these integrals should be fully understood.

Parallel to the development of the concept of real work, the concept of complementary work may be introduced for the derivation of energy theorems related to the complementary energy. The complementary energy resulting from an internal force F and a deformation e in the direction of F is given by $\int e\,dF$, or the area above the force-deformation curve in Fig. 9-2(a), whereas the external complementary work resulting from an external force P for a displacement s in the direction of P is given by $\int s\,dP$, or the area above the force-deformation curve in Fig. 9-2(b). Strictly speaking, the internal complementary work must be negative. Thus, the algebraic sum of the external complementary work C_e and the internal complementary work C_i is equal to zero, i.e.,

$$C_e + C_i = 0 \qquad (9\text{-}5)$$

The increase in complementary energy is a measure of the internal complementary work and is defined as a positive quantity,

$$\bar{U} = -C_i \qquad (9\text{-}5a)$$

Hence,

$$C_e = \bar{U} \qquad (9\text{-}5b)$$

Let us again consider the nonlinear elastic system represented by Fig. 9-1. The total complementary energy of the system is given by

$$\overline{U} = \sum_{k=1}^{n} \int e_k \, dF_k \qquad (9\text{-}6)$$

The total external complementary work done on the same system is equal to

$$C_e = \sum_{j=1}^{m} \int s_j \, dP_j \qquad (9\text{-}7)$$

Then, from $C_e = \overline{U}$, we get

$$\sum_{j=1}^{m} \int s_j \, dP_j = \sum_{k=1}^{n} \int e_k \, dF_k \qquad (9\text{-}8)$$

Without indicating the limits of integration in Eqs. (9-6) through (9-8), it is understood that the lower limits of the integrals are all zero, whereas the upper limits represent the respective full values of external and internal forces which are reached proportionately.

For the special case of linear elasticity as characterized by the linear load-deformation curve in Fig. 9-3, the areas below and above the curve are equal. Hence, the external complementary work on a linearly elastic system is numerically equal to the real work on the system, and the complementary energy and strain energy of the system are interchangeable. In that case, we need be concerned only with the real work and the strain energy of the system. Then, the integrals representing the areas under load-deformation curves are reduced to areas of triangles. If the system shown in Fig. 9-1 is linearly elastic, Eqs. (9-2) and (9-3) become

$$U = \tfrac{1}{2} \sum_{k=1}^{n} F_k e_k \qquad (9\text{-}9)$$

$$W_e = \tfrac{1}{2} \sum_{j=1}^{m} P_j s_j \qquad (9\text{-}10)$$

Because of the relative simplicity in the evaluation of these expressions, linear elasticity is frequently assumed in structural analysis if the material characteristic agrees reasonably well with this assumption.

Figure 9-3

In order to evaluate the strain energy in linear elastic systems, we shall first consider different forms of strain energy that may exist in various structural systems. We are primarily concerned with systems consisting of slender elements such as bars and beams.

Strain energy due to normal stresses. Consider an infinitesimal element of volume $\delta x\, \delta y\, \delta z$ as a free body, as shown in Fig. 9-4, in which uniform stresses σ are acting on the left and right faces of the element. If the normal force $\sigma\, \delta y\, \delta z$ acting on each face increases gradually from zero to its full value, the total deformation is equal to the strain ϵ multiplied by the length δx. The strain energy δU stored in the infinitesimal element is

$$\delta U = \tfrac{1}{2}(\sigma\, \delta y\, \delta z)(\epsilon\, \delta x) = \tfrac{1}{2}\sigma\epsilon\, \delta x\, \delta y\, \delta z$$

Figure 9-4

By applying Hooke's law for linearly elastic materials, $\epsilon = \sigma/E$, where E is the modulus of elasticity, the total strain energy in a structural member of volume V_0 due to a set of normal stresses in the direction of the x-axis becomes

$$U = \iiint_{V_0} \frac{\sigma^2}{2E}\, dx\, dy\, dz \qquad (9\text{-}11)$$

For a structural member subjected to an axial force F only, $\sigma = F/A$ and $\epsilon = e/L$, in which A is the constant cross-sectional area, e is the axial deformation, and L is the length of the member. Thus, the total strain energy in the member subject to an axial force is

$$U = \frac{\sigma^2 AL}{2E} = \frac{F^2 L}{2AE} \qquad (9\text{-}12\text{a})$$

However, the strain energy can also be expressed in terms of the axial deformation e instead of the axial load F, since $e = FL/AE$. Hence,

$$U = \frac{AEe^2}{2L} \qquad (9\text{-}12\text{b})$$

Strain energy in bending. In the case of a member subjected to bending, the bending stresses also are acting in the direction normal to a cross section of the member but are no longer uniformly distributed over the cross-sectional area. However, the total strain energy in bending can still be obtained from Eq. (9-11) if the stress σ is expressed as a function of the distance y by the formula

$$\sigma = -\frac{My}{I}$$

in which M is the moment at a section and I is the moment of inertia about the z-axis for the element shown in Fig. 9-5. Thus, the total energy in a member of volume V_0 subjected to bending becomes

$$U = \iiint_{V_0} \frac{1}{2E}\left(-\frac{My}{I}\right)^2 dx\, dy\, dz$$

For a member of length L and cross-sectional area A, we get

$$U = \int_L \frac{M^2}{2EI^2}\left[\iint_A y^2\, dy\, dz\right] dx$$

By noting $I = \iint_A y^2\, dy\, dz$, we have

$$U = \int_L \frac{M^2\, dx}{2EI} \tag{9-13a}$$

Since the curvature at a section of a structural member may be approximated by d^2v/dx^2, we have $M/EI = d^2v/dx^2$, in which v is the vertical displacement of the beam. Thus, the total bending strain energy of the member can also be expressed in terms of the curvature as follows:

$$U = \int_L \frac{(EId^2v/dx^2)^2\, dx}{2EI} = \int_L \frac{EI}{2}\left(\frac{d^2v}{dx^2}\right)^2 dx \tag{9-13b}$$

Note that Eqs. (9-13) are quite general since the moment M, the curvature d^2v/dx^2, and the bending stiffness EI in these equations may vary from section to section. In the special case of pure bending of a member with constant cross section and material properties, Eqs. (9-13) become

$$U = \frac{M^2L}{2EI} \quad \text{and} \quad U = \frac{EIL}{2}\left(\frac{d^2v}{dx^2}\right)^2$$

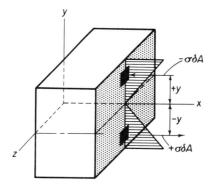

Figure 9-5

Energy Principles   Chap. 9

Strain energy for pure shear.   When an infinitesimal element of volume $\delta x\ \delta y\ \delta z$ is subjected to pure shear as shown in Fig. 9-6, it is noted from the consideration of the summation of the moments of all forces about the z-axis that

$$(\tau_{xy}\ \delta y\ \delta z)(\delta x) = (\tau_{yx}\ \delta x\ \delta z)(\delta y)$$

or

$$\tau_{xy} = \tau_{yx}$$

Denoting the shearing stress by $\tau_{xy} = \tau_{yx} = \tau$ and the corresponding shearing strain by γ, the strain energy in the element resulting from pure shear is

$$\delta U = \tfrac{1}{2}\tau\gamma\ \delta x\ \delta y\ \delta z$$

By applying Hooke's law, $\gamma = \tau/G$ in which G is the modulus of rigidity, the total strain energy in a structural member of volume V_0 due to a set of shearing stresses in the xy-plane is equal to

$$U = \iiint_{V_0} \frac{\tau^2}{2G}\ dx\ dy\ dz \tag{9-14}$$

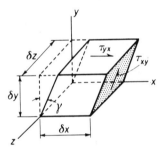

Figure 9-6

When a circular member of length L and constant cross-sectional area A is subjected to a constant torque T, a state of pure shear exists in the member. The shearing stress τ at a point located at a radius r from the center of the circle is given by

$$\tau = \frac{Tr}{J}$$

in which J is the polar moment of inertia. Then, the total strain energy in the circular member subjected to torsion is equal to

$$U = \iiint_{V_0} \frac{1}{2G}\left(\frac{Tr}{J}\right)^2 dx\ dy\ dz = \int_L \frac{T^2}{2GJ^2}\left[\iint_A r^2\ dy\ dz\right] dx$$

Noting that $J = \iint_A r^2\ dy\ dz$, we get

$$U = \int_L \frac{T^2\ dx}{2GJ} = \frac{T^2L}{2GJ} \tag{9-15a}$$

Since the angle of twist per unit length of a circular member is given by $\theta = T/GJ$, or $T = GJ\theta$, the total strain in the member arising from torsion may also be expressed in terms of θ. Thus,

$$U = \frac{(GJ\theta)^2 L}{2GJ} = \frac{GJL\theta^2}{2} \qquad (9\text{-}15b)$$

Strain energy for shear in beams. In the case of a beam subjected to lateral loads, shear as well as bending occurs in the beam. However, the deformation due to shear is usually very small in comparison with that resulting from bending and is negligible except for very deep beams. In any case, the strain energy due to shear can be obtained from Eq. (9-14) since the shearing stresses on the xz- and yz-planes are assumed to be zero. However, the difficulty of its solution is caused by the fact that the variation of shearing stress in a beam depends on the shape of the cross section as well as the depth-span ratio of the beam. For a beam of rectangular cross section as shown in Fig. 9-7(a), for example, it can be shown theoretically that the distribution of shearing stress along the depth of the beam is parabolic as indicated in Fig. 9-7(b). However, if the depth h is many times greater than the width b of the cross section, the distribution of shearing stress along its depth is more complicated and has been found experimentally to have a shape as shown in Fig. 9-7(c).* For an I-beam with a cross section as shown in Fig. 9-8(a), the shearing stress is more likely to have a relatively uniform distribution in the web rather than the theoretical distribution shown in Fig. 9-8(b). In the case of deep beams with large depth-span ratio, the theoretical analysis of the shearing stress is even more complicated and a detailed discussion is beyond the scope of this text. For the sake of simplicity, however, a rational approach may generally be used in the derivation of the expression for strain energy. Let S denote the total shear force acting on the section and A the area of the section that contributes to the resistance of the shear force. The shearing stress τ at any point of the cross section may be expressed in the form

$$\tau = k\frac{S}{A}$$

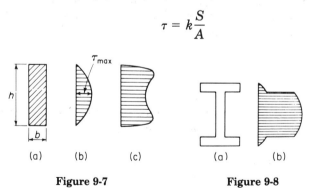

Figure 9-7   Figure 9-8

*See E. G. Coker, "An Optical Determination of the Variation of Stress in a Thin Rectangular Plate," *Proc. Royal Society of London*, ser. A, vol. 86 (1912), p. 291.

in which k is a variable factor depending on the shape of the cross section and the depth-span ratio of the beam. Then, the total strain energy due to shear in a beam of volume V_0 is equal to

$$U = \iiint_{V_0} \frac{1}{2G}\left(k\,\frac{S}{A}\right)^2 dx\,dy\,dz$$

$$= \int_L \frac{S^2}{2GA^2}\left[\iint_A k^2\,dy\,dz\right] dx$$

To simplify the solution of this expression, let us assume that

$$\iint_A k^2\,dy\,dz = CA$$

in which C is a rational constant called the *form factor*. Then

$$U = \int_L \frac{CS^2\,dx}{2GA} = C\int_L \frac{S^2\,dx}{2GA} \tag{9-16}$$

Note that in Eq. (9-16), G, A, and S may vary from section to section of the beam. For beams of ordinary proportions with a rectangular cross section, the form factor may be taken as 1.2. For an ordinary I-beam, the same factor may be used for an approximate solution if A in Eq. (9-16) is taken as the area of the web of the I-beam.

Example 9-1. For a beam of ordinary proportions having a rectangular cross section and subjected to lateral loads, derive an expression for the strain energy due to shear deformation only.

For a rectangular beam with width b and depth h as shown in Fig. 9-9, the distribution of shearing stress is given by

$$\tau = \frac{SQ}{Ib} = \frac{S}{Ib}\int_y^{h/2} by'\,dy' = \frac{S}{2I}\left(\frac{h^2}{4} - y^2\right)$$

in which Q is the statical moment of the shaded area with respect to the neutral axis. Then, from Eq. (9-14), the strain energy due to shear is equal to

$$U = \iiint_{V_0} \frac{\tau^2}{2G}\,dx\,dy\,dz = \int_L \left[\iint_A \frac{\tau^2}{2G}\,dy\,dz\right] dx$$

Figure 9-9

Hence,

$$U = \int_L \left[\int_0^b \int_{-h/2}^{h/2} \frac{S^2}{8GI^2} \left(\frac{h^2}{4} - y^2 \right)^2 dy \, dz \right] dx$$

$$= \int_L \frac{S^2 b}{8GI^2} \left[\int_{-h/2}^{h/2} \left(\frac{h^4}{16} - \frac{h^2 y^2}{2} + y^4 \right) dy \right] dx$$

$$= \int_L \frac{S^2 b}{8GI^2} \left[\frac{h^4 y}{16} - \frac{h^2 y^3}{6} + \frac{y^5}{5} \right]_{-h/2}^{h/2} dx$$

$$= \int_L \frac{S^2 b}{8GI^2} \left[\frac{h^5}{16} - \frac{h^5}{24} + \frac{h^5}{80} \right] dx = \int_L \frac{S^2 b h^5}{240 GI^2} dx$$

Noting that $I = bh^3/12$ and $A = bh$, we obtain,

$$U = \int_L \frac{3S^2}{5GA} dx = 1.2 \int_L \frac{S^2}{2GA} dx$$

Comparing this result with Eq. (9-16), we note that the form factor C is equal to 1.2.

9-4 METHOD OF REAL WORK

By the application of the principle of conservation of energy, we can derive a relationship involving loads, displacements, and elastic and geometrical constants for an elastic structure. However, this relationship in general does not lead to the solution of the displacement in terms of other quantities. For example, if we equate the external work done on a linearly elastic system by the external loads to the strain energy stored in the system as a result of deformation, the expression thus obtained may contain many unknown quantities. The external work done on the system is expressed in terms of the products of the applied loads and the respective displacements. The strain energy of the system can be evaluated if the deformations caused by internal forces are related to the applied loads. In the case of a plane truss, for example, the members are subjected to axial forces only. Let F_k be the bar force in a member of a truss that has a length of L_k and cross-sectional area of A_k. E_k is the modulus of elasticity of the member. Then, the strain energy in the entire truss consisting of n members can be obtained from Eq. (9-12a) as follows:

$$U = \frac{1}{2} \sum_{k=1}^{n} \frac{F_k^2 L_k}{A_k E_k} \tag{9-17a}$$

In the case of a beam of span length L, the strain energy will be given by the sum of the strain energy due to bending and that due to shear as represented by Eqs. (9-13a) and (9-16) respectively. Thus,

$$U = \frac{1}{2} \int_0^L \frac{M^2}{EI} dx + \frac{C}{2} \int_0^L \frac{S^2}{AG} dx \tag{9-17b}$$

$$W_e = \tfrac{1}{2} \sum_{j=1}^{m} P_j S_j$$

Energy Principles   Chap. 9

For beams of ordinary proportions used in structures, the strain energy due to shear is very small in comparison with that due to bending and is usually neglected.

For statically determinate structures, the internal forces can be solved directly from the applied loads. Hence, the displacements $s_j (j = 1, 2, \ldots, m)$ are the only unknowns when we equate Eq. (9-10) to Eq. (9-17a) or (9-17b). Even then, we cannot solve for these displacements in the equation. Only in the special case where a single external load is acting on the structure can the displacement of the point of application of this load in the direction of the load be determined. Thus, for a plane truss, the displacement s of the point of application of a load P in the direction of P may be obtained by equating Eqs. (9-10) and (9-17a) as follows:

$$s = \frac{1}{P} \sum_{j=1}^{n} \frac{F_j^2 L_j}{A_j E_j} \qquad (9\text{-}17c)$$

Similarly, for a beam subjected to a single load P, the displacement of the point of application of P in the direction of P can be obtained by equating Eqs. (9-10) and (9-17b) as follows:

$$s = \frac{1}{P} \left[\int_0^L \frac{M^2 \, dx}{EI} \, dx + C \int_0^L \frac{S^2 \, dx}{AG} \right] \qquad (9\text{-}17d)$$

This method of computing deflections, called the *method of real work*, has only very limited use. *can only have 1 load & can find deflection under this load only*

Example 9-2. A cantilever beam of constant rectangular cross section is subjected to a single vertical load P at the free end, as shown in Fig. 9-10. Compute the vertical deflection Δ at the free end of the beam for the following cases: (a) the shearing deformation is neglected and (b) the shear deformation is not neglected.

We = ½ PΔ

Figure 9-10

Referring to Fig. 9-10, we see that the shear at any section of the beam is $S = -P$ and the moment at any section is given by $M = -Px$. When the shear deformation is neglected, we have

$$\Delta = \frac{1}{P} \int_0^L \frac{M^2 \, dx}{EI} = \frac{1}{P} \int_0^L \frac{P^2 x^2 \, dx}{EI} = \frac{PL^3}{3EI}$$

If the shear deformation is not neglected, the total deformation may be obtained from Eq. (9-17d) by assuming $C = 1.2$ for a rectangular beam of ordinary proportions. Thus,

$$\Delta = \frac{PL^3}{3EI} + \frac{1.2PL}{AG}$$

It can be seen that for beams of ordinary proportions, the first term involving L^3 is much larger than the second term involving L. Hence, it is justifiable to neglect the shear deformation except for beams with large depth-span ratios where shear deformation may constitute a major portion of the deformation.

9-5 STRAIN ENERGY AND COMPLEMENTARY ENERGY METHODS

In Section 9-4, we presented a rather limited application of the method of real work in the computation of deflections. However, the concepts of real work and complementary work may have more general applications in structural analysis if the strain energy of a system is expressed as a function of the displacements and the complementary energy is expressed as a function of the external forces. Theoretically, this is always possible since the internal forces in the system are related to the external forces by the conditions of equilibrium, the deformations can be expressed in terms of the internal forces according to the stress-strain relationship of the material, and the displacements of the external forces are related to the deformations by the conditions of compatibility.

Consider, for example, the deformable system in Fig. 9-1, which in general may be nonlinear elastic. The system is subjected to a set of loads P_1, $P_2, \ldots, P_m$, producing displacements $s_1, s_2, \ldots, s_m$ at the points of application of these loads in the directions of the respective loads. The strain energy U stored in the system during the application of loads may be obtained from Eqs. (9-2) and (9-4) as follows:

$$U = \sum_{k=1}^{n} \int F_k \, de_k = \sum_{j=1}^{m} \int P_j \, ds_j$$

or

$$\delta U = \sum_{k=1}^{n} F_k \, \delta e_k = \sum_{j=1}^{m} P_j \, \delta s_j$$

If one of the displacements, say s_j, is increased by a small amount δs_j in the direction of the load P_j while other displacements remain unchanged, then the increment of strain energy of the system is equal to

$$\delta U = P_j \, \delta s_j \qquad \text{(a)}$$

When the strain energy U is expressed as a function of the displacements, the increment of strain energy may also be expressed as the total differential of U. However, all terms except the one involving s_j will disappear since all other displacements remain unchanged. Hence,

$$\delta U = \frac{\partial U}{\partial s_1} \, \delta s_1 + \frac{\partial U}{\partial s_2} \, \delta s_2 + \cdots + \frac{\partial U}{\partial s_m} \, \delta s_m = \frac{\partial U}{\partial s_j} \, \delta s_j \qquad \text{(b)}$$

By equating Eqs. (a) and (b), we get

$$P_j \, \delta s_j = \frac{\partial U}{\partial s_j} \, \delta s_j$$

or

$$P_j = \frac{\partial U}{\partial s_j} \tag{9-18}$$

This equation gives the external force acting at a specified point if the strain energy is expressed as a function of the displacements.

On the other hand, the complementary energy $\overline{U}$ of the system during the application of the loads may be obtained from Eqs. (9-6) and (9-8) as follows:

$$\overline{U} = \sum_{k=1}^{n} e_k \, dF_k = \sum_{j=1}^{m} \int s_j \, dP_j$$

or

$$\delta\overline{U} = \sum_{k=1}^{n} e_k \, \delta F_k = \sum_{j=1}^{m} s_j \, \delta P_j$$

If one of the loads, say P_j, is increased by a small amount δP_j while other forces remain unchanged, then the increment of complementary energy of the system is equal to

$$\delta\overline{U} = s_j \, \delta P_j \tag{c}$$

When the complementary energy $\overline{U}$ is expressed as a function of the external forces, the increment of complementary energy may also be expressed as the total differential of $\overline{U}$. However, all terms except the one involving P_j will disappear since all other forces remain unchanged. Thus,

$$\delta\overline{U} = \frac{\partial \overline{U}}{\partial P_1} \, \delta P_1 + \frac{\partial \overline{U}}{\partial P_2} \, \delta P_2 + \cdots + \frac{\partial \overline{U}}{\partial P_m} \, \delta P_m = \frac{\partial \overline{U}}{\partial P_j} \, \delta P_j \tag{d}$$

By equating Eqs. (c) and (d), we obtain

$$s_j = \frac{\partial \overline{U}}{\partial P_j} \tag{9-19}$$

This equation gives the displacement acting at a specified point in the direction of the force if the complementary energy is expressed as a function of the external forces.

For the special case of linear elasticity, the strain energy U and the complementary energy $\overline{U}$ of the system are interchangeable. If the strain energy of a linear elastic system is expressed as a function of external forces, Eq. (9-19) may be replaced by

$$s_j = \frac{\partial U}{\partial P_j} \tag{9-20}$$

Equation (9-20) may be regarded as a special case of Eq. (9-19).

The methods of deriving forces, and displacements in the case of linear elasticity, from the strain energy function are called the *strain energy methods;* the method of deriving displacements from the complementary energy function is referred to as the *complementary energy method.* The application of the strain energy methods to linear elastic systems was developed by Castigliano in 1879 without the benefit of the concept of complementary energy. The application of the concept of complementary energy was introduced by Engesser in 1889 and was regarded primarily as a means for the analysis of nonlinear elastic systems. With the traditional emphasis on linear elasticity, the work of Engesser received very little attention during the half-century that followed its development. Only more recently has the general nature of complementary energy been fully recognized. That such a concept permits the representation of the dual roles of the energy principles has been ably expounded by Argyris.*

In the application of these methods to the computation of deflections, we are confronted with the limitation that only the displacements of the points of application of the external forces can be computed. Although these methods represent an improvement over the method of real work since they are applicable to structures subjected to a large number of external forces, they are not general enough for the computation of the deflection at any specified point in any specified direction of a structure. However, the application of these methods may be extended for such a purpose if we realize that they are but special cases of a more general principle, i.e., the principle of virtual work for deformable systems. We shall, therefore, first present the principle of virtual work before discussing in detail the application of the strain energy and complementary energy methods.

9-6 PRINCIPLE OF VIRTUAL WORK

When a rigid system in equilibrium is given an arbitrary virtual displacement, the total virtual work done by all external forces in the system must be zero. The internal forces need not be considered because the distances between any two points in a rigid system must remain constant. Hence, for a rigid system, the principle of virtual work is only used to impose the requirement of equilibrium through the introduction of a virtual displacement.

In the case of a deformable system, we can imagine that the system consists of an infinite number of mass points, the distances between which may be changed. The virtual work done on such a system may be caused by real forces acting through virtual displacements, or by virtual forces acting through real displacements. According to the principle of conservation of energy, the total virtual work done by the internal and external forces on a deformable system must be zero. Hence, the principle of virtual work may be applied to a deformable structural system in two ways. If a structure under the action of

*See J. H. Argyris, "Energy Theorems and Structural Analysis," *Aircraft Engineering,* vol. 26 (1954), pp. 343, 383; vol. 27, (1955), pp. 42, 80, 125, 145.

real forces is subjected to a set of virtual displacements compatible with its constraints, the principle of virtual work gives the requirement of equilibrium. On the other hand, if the system subjected to a set of real displacements is acted on by a set of equilibrating virtual forces, the principle of virtual work leads to the requirements of compatibility. To stress the dual nature of the principle, the former is referred to as the *principle of virtual displacements* whereas the latter is called the *principle of virtual forces.*

The requirements of equilibrium and compatibility of a structural system derived from the energy approach are identical to those obtained from the equilibrium approach. In the application of the principle of virtual work, the only requirements imposed on the system are that the forces acting on the system must be in equilibrium and that the displacements must be compatible with the constraints. Although either the set of forces or displacements can be real while the other set remains virtual, the forces and displacements need not be related causes and effects.

Consider, for example, a deformable system that in general is nonlinearly elastic and may be conceived of schematically as consisting of n elements. If the system is given an infinitesimal variation of displacements compatible with the constraints, i.e., if the system is given a set of virtual displacements in the directions of the respective real forces as shown in Fig. 9-11(a), the increment of strain energy is equal to the sum of the products of the real forces and the respective virtual displacements, or

$$\delta U = \sum_{k=1}^{n} F_k \, \delta e_k \qquad (9\text{-}21a)$$

Note that the external loads are on the structure and the real displacements under the action of these external forces have already taken place when the set of virtual displacements is introduced. Hence, the real force F_k and the virtual

(a)

(b)

Figure 9-11

displacement $\delta e_k \ (k = 1, 2, \ldots, n)$ need not be cause and effect. The set of virtual displacements is entirely independent of the real displacements of the structure. The corresponding increment of external work on the structure is equal to

$$\delta W_e = \sum_{j=1}^{m} P_j \, \delta s_j \tag{9-21b}$$

According to the principle of conservation of energy, the variation of the total work must be zero, i.e., $\delta W_e + \delta W_i = 0$. Hence, $\delta W_e = \delta U$, or

$$\sum_{j=1}^{m} P_j \, \delta s_j = \sum_{k=1}^{n} F_k \, \delta e_k \tag{9-21c}$$

Since the displacements δs_j and δe_k imposed on the system need not be real, they are called *virtual displacements*. As a matter of fact, they may be finite as well as infinitesimal as long as they do not cause a significant change in the geometry of the system. Thus, Eq. (9-21c) may be replaced by

$$\sum_{j=1}^{m} P_j s_j = \sum_{k=1}^{n} F_k e_k \tag{9-21d}$$

Equation (9-21c) or (9-21d) represents the requirement of equilibrium that must be imposed on a system when it is given a set of virtual displacements.

If a structure subjected to a set of real displacements is given an infinitesimal variation of forces, i.e., if the system is subjected to a set of equilibrating virtual forces acting in the directions of the respective real displacements as shown in Fig. 9-11(b), the increment of complementary energy is equal to the sum of the products of the real displacements and the respective virtual forces, or

$$\delta \overline{U} = \sum_{k=1}^{n} e_k \, \delta F_k \tag{9-22a}$$

The real displacements, which may be caused by discrepancy in manufacture, temperature changes, or actual forces, are applied to the structure after the set of virtual forces is introduced. Hence, the real displacement e_k and the virtual force $\delta F_k (k = 1, 2, \ldots, n)$ need not be cause and effect. The set of virtual forces is completely independent of the real forces even if the real displacements in the structure are caused by real forces. The corresponding increment of complementary external work is equal to

$$\delta C_e = \sum_{j=1}^{m} s_j \, \delta P_j \tag{9-22b}$$

By equating δC_e and $\delta \overline{U}$, we have

$$\sum_{j=1}^{m} s_j \, \delta P_j = \sum_{k=1}^{n} e_k \, \delta F_k \tag{9-22c}$$

Since the forces δP_j and δF_k imposed on the system need not be real, they are called *virtual forces*. Indeed, they may be finite as well as infinitesimal as long as they are self-equilibrating. Thus, Eq. (9-22c) may be replaced by

$$\sum_{j=1}^{m} s_j P_j = \sum_{k=1}^{n} e_k F_k \qquad (9\text{-}22\text{d})$$

Equation (9-22c) or (9-22d) represents the requirement of compatibility that must be imposed on a system when it is subjected to a set of virtual forces.

It may be observed that Eqs. (9-21d) and (9-22d) are identical although they have been derived in two different ways. In view of this, we may give a unified definition for the *principle of virtual work* as follows: if a structure is in equilibrium under the action of a set of external forces and is subjected to a set of displacements compatible with the constraints of the structure, the total work done by the external and internal forces during the displacement must be zero. We should point out again that in this statement the set of forces need not be related to the set of displacements as cause and effect but that either set can be real while the other set is virtual. Since the principle of virtual displacements imposes the requirement of equilibrium, it is usually applied to evaluate certain specified forces. On the other hand, the principle of virtual forces imposes the requirement of compatibility, and it is often used to compute certain specified displacements.

One important application of the principle of virtual work is found in the computation of deflections of statically determinate structures. A convenient method of computing deflections may be developed on the basis of a special application of the principle of virtual forces. If a single external virtual force that has a magnitude of unity is placed at a point on a structure before the structure is subjected to real displacements, the displacement of this point in the direction of the unit virtual force is equal to the sum of the products of the real displacements and the respective internal virtual forces that are in equilibrium with the unit virtual force. This method of approach is called the *method of virtual work* or the *dummy unit load method*.[*]

Consider, for example, a virtual force $P = 1$ applied to a structure as shown in Fig. 9-12(a). The displacement of the point of application of this force in the direction of the force may be represented by the deflection Δ. Let f be the internal force in an element of the structure due to the virtual unit force and e be the displacement of the element in the direction of f. Then, according to the principle of virtual work, we have

$$1 \times \Delta = \sum fe \qquad (9\text{-}23\text{a})$$

---

[*]This method was developed independently by J. C. Maxwell in 1864 and O. Mohr in 1874, and is often called the *Maxwell-Mohr method*. Some Amercian publications attributed the method to G. F. Swain, who first introduced the method in American literature in 1883. The versatility of this method and its relationship with other methods based on the geometry of structures have been discussed in H. Cross, "Virtual Work: A Restatement," *Trans. ASCE*, vol. 90 (1926), p. 610.

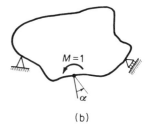

(a)   (b)

Figure 9-12

in which the displacement Δ has the unit of length and the increment of strain energy on the right-hand side of the equation has the unit of force $\times$ length per unit force. Since the displacement e has the unit of length, f is expressed in terms of force per unit force and may be considered as a dimensionless coefficient.

This concept of virtual work can easily be extended to the computation of rotations. If a virtual unit moment $M = 1$ is applied to a structure as shown in Fig. 9-12(b), the rotation about a given point with respect to a given line may be defined by the angle α. Let f be the internal force in an element of the structure due to the unit moment and e be the displacement of the element in the direction of f. Then, from the principle of virtual work, we have

$$1 \times \alpha = \sum fe \qquad (9\text{-}23b)$$

in which the rotation α is in radians or dimensionless, and the increment of strain energy on the right-hand side of the equation has the unit of force $\times$ length per unit moment or is dimensionless. Since the displacement e has the unit of length, f is expressed in terms of force per unit moment or 1/length.

This method of computing deflections is exceedingly general since the displacements e may be produced by any cause (temperature changes, misfit, or external forces). If the displacements e are caused by external forces, the material properties will be involved and the applications will be restricted to the given properties of materials.

Example 9-3. In the truss shown in Fig. 9-13(a), three members have been cut either too long or too short by a small amount as indicated by +0.4 in., +0.2 in., and −0.3 in. for members $L_0 L_1$, $U_1 U_2$, and $U_0 U_1$, respectively, in the figure. Compute the vertical displacement of joint L_2 due to these discrepancies in the lengths of the members.

Since the vertical displacement of joint L_2 is desired, we apply a vertical unit load at that joint. The upward direction is arbitrarily assumed because an upward deflection is anticipated. A positive result will indicate that the assumed sense is correct, while a negative result will indicate a downward deflection.

The internal forces in all members of the truss due to an upward unit load at joint L_2 are solved for and indicated along the members in Fig. 9-13(b). Since the discrepancy in length occurs in members $L_0 L_1$, $U_1 U_2$, and $U_0 U_1$, the change

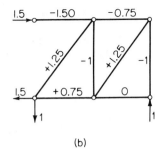

(a)

(b)

Figure 9-13

in length in other members is regarded as zero. Thus, only the internal forces in these members are required in order to compute the deflection. The vertical deflection of joint L_2 is then given by

$$\Delta = \sum fe = (-1.50)(-0.3) + (-0.75)(+0.2) + (0.75)(+0.4)$$

$$= +0.45 - 0.15 + 0.30 = 0.60 \text{ in.}$$

Since the result is positive, the deflection is directed upward as assumed.

Example 9-4. The steel bar shown in Fig. 9-14 has a 10 in. by 20 in. rectangular cross section. The top surface of the bar is maintained at a room temperature of 70°F. while the bottom surface is kept constant at a temperature of 270°F. Assuming linear distribution of temperature through the depth of the beam, determine the vertical displacement of point O at the free end of the beam. The coefficient of linear expansion of steel $\alpha = 0.6 \times 10^{-6}/°F$.

Figure 9-14

The bar is subjected to axial expansion as well as bending as a result of the temperature difference between the top and bottom surfaces. However, the contribution of axial expansion to the vertical deflection is small and negligible. Therefore, only the effect of bending need be considered.

Assuming linear distribution of temperature, the strain at any fiber at a distance y from the neutral axis is given by

$$\epsilon = -(0.6 \times 10^{-6})(270 - 70)y/20 = -0.6 \times 10^{-5}y$$

Thus, the strain is negative for a positive y. Then, the displacement in the same fiber of an element of δx in length is equal to

$$e = \epsilon \, \delta x = -0.6 \times 10^{-5}y \, \delta x$$

If an upward virtual force is applied at point O in Fig. 9-14, the moment at a section at a distance x from O is $m = x$ and the internal force acting in a fiber of area δA at a distance y from the neutral axis is equal to the stress multiplied by the area, or

$$f = \frac{my}{I} \delta A = -\frac{xy}{I} \delta A$$

Then, the vertical deflection at point O may be obtained by integrating over the entire volume V_0 of the bar, i.e.,

$$\Delta = \sum fe = \iiint_{V_0} \left(-\frac{my}{I}\right)(-0.6 \times 10^{-5}y)dA \; dx$$

$$= \int_0^L \frac{0.6 \times 10^{-5}x}{I}\left[\iint_A y^2 \; dA\right] dx$$

$$= \int_0^{120} 0.6 \times 10^{-5}x \; dx = 0.3 \times 10^{-5}x^2 \Big|_0^{120} = 0.0432 \text{ in.}$$

Note that the length of the bar $L = 10$ ft $= 120$ in. The unit of inches must be used in the evaluation of the integral because the depth of the beam has been expressed in terms of inches in the computation of strain used in formulating the integral.

9-7 METHOD OF VIRTUAL WORK FOR LINEAR ELASTIC SYSTEMS

Although no restriction has been placed on the nature of the internal deformations of the structure in the derivation of the method of virtual work, external loads are by far the most common cause of these deformations in actual application. We shall, therefore, develop a procedure for special applications to common structural systems with linearly elastic characteristics.

Consider, for example, an elastic system acted on by a set of external forces $Q_1, Q_2, \ldots, Q_r$ as shown in Fig. 9-15. Prior to the application of these forces, however, let a virtual unit force $P = 1$ be placed at a given point and in a given direction for which the deflection is desired. As the set of external forces is gradually applied to the elastic system increasing from zero to full value and thus causing deformations in the structure, the virtual unit force simply rides along during the deformation. Let the displacements at the points of applica-

Figure 9-15

tion of the external forces in the directions of the respective forces be denoted by $\Delta_1, \Delta_2, \ldots, \Delta_r$ respectively. Then, the external work done on the system from the gradual application of the external forces must equal the increment of strain energy as follows:

$$\frac{1}{2} \sum_{j=1}^{r} Q_j \Delta_j + 1 \times \Delta = \frac{1}{2} \sum Fe + \sum fe \qquad \text{(a)}$$

in which F is the internal force in an element of the structure and e is the corresponding deformation caused by the internal force whereas f is the internal force in the same element due to the virtual unit load. Note that the real work terms include a factor of $1/2$ whereas those representing virtual work do not have such a factor because the virtual unit force $P = 1$ is already on the structure when the external forces are gradually applied. Considering only the real forces, we obtain from the conservation of energy the following relation:

$$\frac{1}{2} \sum_{j=1}^{r} Q_j \Delta_j = \frac{1}{2} \sum Fe \qquad \text{(b)}$$

The virtual work done by the virtual unit force may be obtained by subtracting Eq. (b) from Eq. (a). Thus,

$$1 \times \Delta = \sum fe \qquad \text{(c)}$$

Equation (c) is identical to Eq. (9-23a) except that e is now the result of deformations caused by external forces.

We have already established the force-deformation relations for various types of structural elements. Hence, Eq. (c) can be replaced by the direct relations developed for these structures. Wherever applicable, the notations in Section 9-3 are retained.

1. *Trusses.* In the case of a plane truss, all members are subjected to bar forces only. Hence, for a truss consisting of n members, we have

$$1 \times \Delta = \sum fe = \sum_{k=1}^{n} \frac{f_k F_k L_k}{A_k E_k} \qquad \text{(9-24a)}$$

in which f_k is the bar force in a member caused by a virtual unit load and F_k is the bar force in the same member due to the external forces.

2. *Beams subject to bending.* Consider an element of a beam that has a length of δx and an area of δA. Let m be the bending moment at a section of the element caused by a virtual unit load and M be the moment at the same section due to the external forces. Then,

$$f = -\frac{my}{I} \delta A \quad \text{and} \quad e = \epsilon \, \delta x = \frac{\sigma}{E} \delta x = -\frac{My}{EI} \delta x$$

Integrating over the entire volume V_0 of the beam, we obtain

$$1 \times \Delta = \iint\int_{V_0} \left(-\frac{my}{I}\right)\left(-\frac{My}{EI}\right) dA\ dx$$

$$= \int_L \frac{mM\ dx}{EI} \tag{9-24b}$$

3. *Beams subject to shear.* In the case of a beam element subjected to shear deflection only, we may denote the shear at a section caused by a virtual unit load as s and the shear at the same section resulting from the external forces as S. By considering the average stress at a section, we obtain

$$f = k\frac{s}{A}\ \delta A \quad \text{and} \quad e = k\frac{S}{GA}\ \delta x$$

By using the same simplification in Eq. (8-16), we get

$$1 \times \Delta = \iint\int_{V_0} k^2 \frac{sS}{GA^2} dA\ dx = C \int_L \frac{sS\ dx}{GA} \tag{9-24c}$$

in which C is the form factor, usually taken as 1.2 for rectangular beams and I-beams.

4. *Circular members subject to torsion.* Consider an element of a circular member subjected to torsion that has a length of δx and an area of δA. Let t be the torque at a section of the element caused by the virtual unit load and T the torque at the same section resulting from the external forces. Then,

$$f = \frac{tr}{J}\ \delta A \quad \text{and} \quad e = \gamma\ \delta x = \frac{\tau}{G}\ \delta x = \frac{Tr}{GJ}\ \delta x$$

Integrating over the entire volume V_0 of the bar, we have

$$1 \times \Delta = \iint\int_{V_0} \left(\frac{tr}{J}\right)\left(\frac{Tr}{GJ}\right) dA\ dx$$

$$= \int_L \frac{tT\ dx}{GJ} \tag{9-24d}$$

If the rotations instead of deflections of a structure are desired, the internal force or moment in each of Eqs. (9-24) can be obtained by applying a unit couple about a point in a given direction instead of a unit load. Then, the deflection Δ may be replaced by the rotation in these equations.

Example 9-5. For the truss shown in Fig. 9-16, compute the vertical deflection at point L_2. The areas of the members in square inches are indicated along the members in parentheses in the figure. $E = 30 \times 10^3$ ksi.

The calculation is tabulated in Table 9-1, in which the column f represents the bar forces in all members caused by a virtual unit load acting upward at joint L_2, the column F gives the bar forces in all members resulting from the external

Figure 9-16

Table 9-1

Member	f	F (kips)	L (in.)	A (in.²)	$e = FL/AE$ (in.)	fe (in.)
$U_0 U_1$	-1.50	$+300$	180	6	$+0.30$	-0.45
$U_1 U_2$	-0.75	$+150$	180	3	$+0.30$	-0.225
$L_0 L_1$	$+0.75$	-150	180	3	-0.30	-0.225
$L_1 L_2$	0	0	180	3	0	0
$L_0 U_1$	$+1.25$	-250	300	5	-0.50	-0.625
$L_1 U_1$	-1.00	$+200$	240	4	$+0.40$	-0.40
$L_1 U_2$	$+1.25$	-250	300	5	-0.50	-0.625
$L_2 U_2$	-1.00	0	240	4	0	0
					$\Delta =$	-2.55

load of 200 kips at joint U_2. The other columns in the table are self-explanatory. The final result is obtained from the sum of all values in the column fe. The negative sign indicates that the assumed upward direction is incorrect and that the deflection should be downward.

Example 9-6. Compute the deflection and rotation at the free end of the cantilever beam in Fig. 9-17(a). The bending stiffness EI of the beam is constant.

In computing the deflection Δ, we apply a downward unit load at the free end as shown in Fig. 9-17(b). At any section of the beam, we have

$$M = -Px \quad \text{and} \quad m = -x$$

(a)　　　　　　　　(b)　　　　　　　　(c)

Figure 9-17

Hence,

$$\Delta = \int_0^L \frac{(-Px)(-x)\,dx}{EI} = \frac{Px^3}{3EI}\bigg|_0^L = \frac{PL^3}{3EI}$$

For the computation of the rotation α, we apply a counterclockwise unit moment at the free end as shown in Fig. 9-17(c). Then, at any section, $m = -1$ while M remains the same. Hence,

$$\alpha = \int_0^L \frac{(-Px)(-1)\,dx}{EI} = \frac{Px^2}{2EI}\bigg|_0^L = \frac{PL^2}{2EI}$$

9-8 CASTIGLIANO'S THEOREMS

In Section 9-3 the strain energy for various forms of linear elastic systems was expressed as a function of either the internal forces or deformations. These forces and deformations can in turn be expressed as a function of the external forces or displacements from the conditions of equilibrium and compatibility. Thus, the strain energy function may be used to derive the external forces or the displacements of their points of application. This application of the strain energy of linear elastic systems was first observed by Castigliano, who called it the *theorem of the differential coefficients of the internal work*. He stated the theorem as follows.*

Part 1. If the internal work of a framed structure is expressed as a function of the relative displacements of the external forces applied at its nodes, the resulting expression is such that its differential coefficients with regard to these displacements give the values of the corresponding forces.

Part 2. If, on the contrary, the internal work of a framed structure is expressed as a function of the external forces, the resulting expression is such that its differential coefficients give the relative displacements of their points of application.

For the sake of clarity, we shall henceforth refer to part 1 of the theorem as *Castigliano's first theorem* and part 2 as *Castigliano's second theorem*. The "differential coefficients" in the statement of the theorems are the partial derivatives in Eqs. (9-18) and (9-20). We should point out again that the first theorem is applicable to all conservative systems whereas the second theorem is applicable only to linear elastic systems.

Parallel to the principle of virtual work, the first theorem imposes the requirement of equilibrium while the second theorem expresses the requirement of compatibility. With the traditional emphasis on the force method of analysis, the first theorem has been almost forgotten, but the second theorem

---

*This theorem has been stated verbatim according to the translation of A. Castigliano, *Théorème de l'Équilibre des Systèmes Élastiques et ses Applications*, 1879; Eng. trans. E. S. Andrews, *Elastic Stresses in Structures* (London: Scott, Greenwood & Son, 1919), p. 15.

has been used extensively for the computation of deflections of statically determinate structures and for the requirement of compatibility for statically indeterminate structures.*

Actually, Castigliano's theorems may generally be used in the analysis of statically indeterminate structures, examples of which will be given in Chapter 10. The second theorem may also be used for computing the deflections of statically determinate structures, although any problem that can be solved by this method can also be solved by the dummy unit load method. Nevertheless, we shall illustrate the application of Castigliano's second theorem to the computation of deflections.

Let Δ_j denote the deflection at a given point along a given direction in which a force P_j acts. Then, the strain energy relations for linear elastic systems may be obtained from Sections 9-3 and 9-4 and the corresponding deflections computed as follows:

1. *Trusses:*

$$U = \frac{1}{2} \sum_{k=1}^{n} \frac{F_k^2 L_k}{A_k L_k}$$

Hence,

$$\Delta_j = \frac{\partial U}{\partial P_j} = \sum_{k=1}^{n} \frac{F_k L_k}{A_k E_k} \frac{\partial F_k}{\partial P_j} \tag{9-25a}$$

2. *Beams subject to bending:*

$$U = \int_L \frac{M^2 \, dx}{2EI}$$

Hence,

$$\Delta_j = \int_L \frac{M \, dx}{EI} \frac{\partial M}{\partial P_j} \tag{9-25b}$$

3. *Beams subject to shear:*

$$U = C \int_L \frac{S^2 \, dx}{2GA}$$

Hence,

$$\Delta_j = C \int_L \frac{S \, dx}{GA} \frac{\partial S}{\partial P_j} \tag{9-25c}$$

---

*A case in point is that in all but the more recent publications, part 1 of the original theorem does not appear at all. Part 2 appears in two forms: when applied to statically determinate structures, it is called "Castigliano's first theorem," and when applied to statically indeterminate structures, it is called "Castigliano's second theorem." This truncation of Castigliano's theorems of internal work is not followed in this text.

4. *Circular members subject to torsion:*

$$U = \int_L \frac{T^2 \, dx}{2GJ}$$

Hence,

$$\Delta_j = \int_L \frac{T \, dx}{GJ} \frac{\partial T}{\partial P_j} \tag{9-25d}$$

The similarity between this method and the dummy unit load method is striking. It may be demonstrated later that indeed $\partial F_k/\partial P_j = f$, $\partial M/\partial P_j = m$, and so on. We can take advantage of this similarity and extend the usefulness of Castigliano's second theorem. If we desire to determine the deflection at a point in a given direction for which no load is acting, it is possible to assume an arbitrary load at the given point in the given direction and include its effect in the strain energy and its partial derivative. The arbitrary load may then be set equal to zero in evaluating the summation or integration in Eqs. (9-25). This is equivalent to the introduction of a dummy unit load at that point in the given direction. Furthermore, Eqs. (9-25) may be used to compute the angular rotation at a point of a structure with respect to a given line if an arbitrary moment instead of a force is applied at the desired location.

In order to demonstrate the equivalence of this method and the dummy unit load method, let us consider as an example a truss subjected to a set of loads $P_1, P_2, \ldots, P_n$. Let the bar force in a member k caused by the external loads be denoted by F_k, and the bar force in a member due to all loads except P_j be denoted by $\overline{F}_k$. If $P_j = 1$ is applied to the truss while all other external loads are removed, the resulting bar force in member k may be denoted by f_k. The bar force in member k due to the load P_j is therefore equal to $f_k P_j$. Thus,

$$F_k = \overline{F}_k + f_k P_j$$

Since $\overline{F}_k$ is independent of P_j, we obtain from the differentiation of F_k with respect to P_j

$$\frac{\partial F_k}{\partial P_j} = f_k \tag{9-26a}$$

Similarly, we may denote for other cases the moment, shear, and torque as follows:

$$M = \overline{M} + mP_j$$
$$S = \overline{S} + sP_j$$
$$T = \overline{T} + tP_j$$

in which $\overline{M}$, $\overline{S}$, and $\overline{T}$ are the corresponding portions of moment, shear, and torque independent of P_j and m, s, and t are the moment, shear, and torque due to $P_j = 1$. Then, by taking the partial derivative of the pertinent quantity with respect to P_j, we have

$$\frac{\partial M}{\partial P_j} = m \qquad \qquad (9\text{-}26b)$$

$$\frac{\partial S}{\partial P_j} = s \qquad \qquad (9\text{-}26c)$$

$$\frac{\partial T}{\partial P_j} = t \qquad \qquad (9\text{-}26d)$$

If we compare Eqs. (9-25) and (9-26) with Eqs. (9-24), it is obvious that both methods lead to identical results.

Example 9-7. For the truss shown in Fig. 9-18(a), compute the relative displacement between joints B and D for a vertical load of 200 kips at joint G. The areas of the members in square inches are indicated along the members in parentheses in the figure. $E = 30 \times 10^3$ ksi.

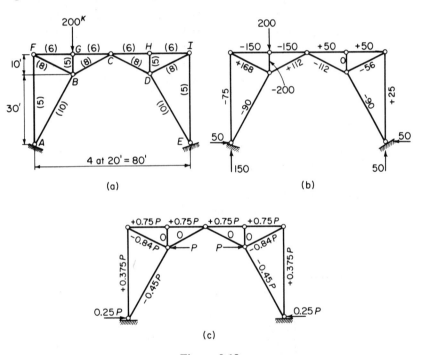

Figure 9-18

Since no external force is acting between B and D for which the relative displacement is required, a pair of equal, opposite, and colinear forces P is added to joints B and D as shown in Fig. 9-18(c). The senses of direction indicated for the forces P are arbitrarily assumed and will cause an increase in the distance between joints B and D. A positive answer for the displacement will indicate that the assumed increase is correct; otherwise a decrease in the distance is indicated. The bar forces in the truss caused by a vertical load of 200 kips at joint G alone are given in Fig. 9-18(b) and the bar forces in the truss resulting from the assumed loads P are given in Fig. 9-18(c). The remaining steps of computation are shown in Table 9-2.

Table 9-2

Member	L (in.)	A (in.²)	F	$\partial F/\partial P$	FL/AE $(P=0)$	$(FL/AE)(\partial F/\partial P)$ (in.)
AB	432	10	$-90 - 0.45P$	-0.45	-0.130	$+0.0585$
BC	268	8	$+112 + 0$	0	$+0.125$	0
CD	268	8	$-112 + 0$	0	-0.125	0
DE	432	10	$-90 - 0.45P$	-0.45	-0.130	$+0.0585$
FG	240	6	$-150 + 0.75P$	$+0.75$	-0.200	-0.150
GC	240	6	$-150 + 0.75P$	$+0.75$	-0.200	-0.150
CH	240	6	$+50 + 0.75P$	$+0.75$	$+0.067$	$+0.050$
HI	240	6	$+50 + 0.75P$	$+0.75$	$+0.067$	$+0.050$
AF	480	5	$-75 + 0.375P$	$+0.375$	-0.240	-0.090
BG	120	5	$-200 + 0$	0	-0.160	0
DH	120	5	$0 + 0$	0	0	0
EI	480	5	$+25 + 0.375P$	$+0.375$	$+0.080$	$+0.030$
BF	268	8	$+168 - 0.84P$	-0.84	$+0.188$	-0.158
DI	268	8	$-56 - 0.84P$	-0.84	-0.063	$+0.053$
					$\Delta =$	-0.248

Example 9-8. A cantilever girder made of a circular tube has a 90-deg. bend in the horizontal x-plane as shown in Fig. 9-19. A vertical load P in line with the z-axis (normal to the xy-plane) is applied at the free end A of the girder. Determine the vertical deflection of point A assuming that the bending stiffness EI and torsional stiffness GJ of the tube are constant.

Figure 9-19

For segment AB of the girder, the moment at a section that is at a distance y from point A is given by

$$M = -Py \quad \text{and} \quad \partial M/\partial P = -y$$

The segment BC is subjected to torsion as well as bending. At a section that is at

386   Energy Principles   Chap. 9

a distance x from point B, we have

$$M = -Px \quad \text{and} \quad \partial M/\partial P = -x$$

$$T = -Pd \quad \text{and} \quad \partial T/\partial P = -d$$

Hence,

$$\Delta = \int_0^d \frac{(-Py)(-y)\ dy}{EI} + \int_0^h \frac{(-Px)(-x)\ dx}{EI} + \int_0^h \frac{(-Pd)(-d)\ dx}{GJ}$$

$$= \frac{Py^3}{3EI}\bigg|_0^d + \frac{Px^3}{3EI}\bigg|_0^h + \frac{Pd^2x}{GJ}\bigg|_0^h$$

$$= \frac{P(d^3 + h^3)}{3EI} + \frac{Pd^2h}{GJ}$$

9-9 DEFLECTIONS OF NONLINEAR ELASTIC SYSTEMS

The deflections of nonlinear elastic systems may be computed by means of the dummy unit load method or the complementary energy method. The complementary energy of a system such as the one shown in Fig. 9-1 is given by

$$\overline{U} = \sum_{k=1}^n \int e_k\ dF_k$$

in which e_k is the deformation of an element k and F_k is the internal force in the same element caused by the external loads. By means of the complementary energy method, the deflection at point j in the direction of the force P_j is given by Eq. (9-25) as follows:

$$\Delta_j = \frac{\partial \overline{U}}{\partial P_j} = \sum_{k=1}^n e_k \frac{\partial F_k}{\partial P_j} \tag{9-27}$$

To demonstrate the equivalence of the complementary energy method and the dummy unit load method, let $\overline{F}_k$ be the internal force in an element k caused by all loads except P_j. If $P_j = 1$ is applied to the system while all other external loads are removed, the resulting internal force in the element k may be denoted by f_k. The internal force in an element k due to the load P_j is therefore equal to $f_k P_j$. Thus,

$$F_k = \overline{F}_k + f_k P_j$$

Since $\overline{F}_k$ is independent of P_j, we obtain from the differentiation of F_k with respect to P_j

$$\frac{\partial F_k}{\partial P_j} = f_k \tag{a}$$

By substituting Eq. (a) into Eq. (9-27), we obtain

$$\Delta_j = \sum_{k=1}^n e_k f_k$$

This is identical to Eq. (9-23a), which was obtained by the principle of virtual work.

The difficulty in the solution of a nonlinear elastic system lies in the fact that the stress-strain curve of the material may be complicated and cannot be expressed by a simple equation. In some cases, the relation between stress σ and strain ϵ may be represented by a parabolic curve

$$\sigma = C\epsilon^{1/n} \tag{b}$$

in which C and n are constants. However, even in a simple case like this, we should be aware of the additional complications that do not exist in linear elastic systems. For example, if Eq. (b) is expressed in the following form

$$\epsilon = \frac{\sigma^n}{C^n} \tag{c}$$

and if n is even, Eq. (c) implies that ϵ is positive regardless of the sign of σ, and this is physically impossible. Therefore, the right-hand side of Eq. (c) must be preceded by a postive sign for $+\sigma$ and a negative sign for $-\sigma$.

Example 9-9. For the nonlinear elastic system shown in Fig. 9-20(a), determine the horizontal and vertical components of displacement of joint O if the stress-strain relation of the material for the members is given by the parabolic curve $\sigma = 1,000\sqrt{\epsilon}$ ksi. The cross-sectional area of each member is 5 in.^{2}, and the load $P = 100$ kips.

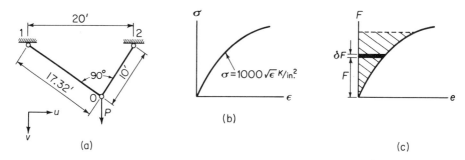

Figure 9-20

Let the horizontal and vertical components of displacement of joint O be denoted by u and v with positive directions indicated in the figure. Let F be the bar force in a member and e be the elongation in that member whose length and cross-sectional area are denoted by L and A, respectively. Then, from the given stress-strain curve $\sigma = 1,000\sqrt{\epsilon}$ ksi, shown in Fig. 9-20(b), we have

$$\epsilon - 10^{-6}\sigma^3$$

The force-deformation relation may be represented by the curve in Fig. 9-20(c), which is given by

$$e = \epsilon L = 10^{-6}\sigma^2 L = 10^{-6}\left(\frac{F}{A}\right)^2 L = \frac{10^{-6}L}{A^2}F^2$$

Energy Principles   Chap. 9

Let the quantities pertaining to members 01 and 02 be denoted by subscripts 1 and 2, respectively. Assuming that the bar forces F_1 and F_2 are in tension, then from the conditions of equilibrium of joint O we obtain

$$\sum F_x = 0, \qquad F_1 \cos 30° = F_2 \cos 60°$$

$$\sum F_y = 0, \qquad F_1 \sin 30° + F_2 \sin 60° = P$$

Thus, $F_1 = 0.5P$ and $F_2 = 0.866P$. The elongations of the members can be obtained from the force-deformation relation as follows:

$$e_1 = \frac{(10^{-6})(17.32)(12)}{5^2} F_1^2 = 8.32 \times 10^{-6} F_1^2 = 2.08 \times 10^{-6} P^2$$

$$e_2 = \frac{(10^{-6})(10)(12)}{5^2} F_2^2 = 4.8 \times 10^{-6} F_2^2 = 3.6 \times 10^{-6} P^2$$

By using Eq. (9-27), we obtain

$$v = e_1 \frac{\partial F_1}{\partial P} + e_2 \frac{\partial F_2}{\partial P} = (2.08 \times 10^{-6} P^2)(0.5) + (3.6 \times 10^{-6} P^2)(0.866)$$

$$= 1.04 \times 10^{-6} P^2 + 2.94 \times 10^{-6} P^2 = 3.98 \times 10^{-6} P^2$$

In order to determine the horizontal displacement u, we first assume a fictitious force Q in the positive direction of u. Then, from the equilibrium of joint O, we get

$$F_1 = 0.5P + 0.866Q, \qquad F_2 = 0.866P - 0.5Q$$

Thus, by taking the partial derivatives of F_1 and F_2 with respect to Q, we have

$$\frac{\partial F_1}{\partial Q} = 0.866 \quad \text{and} \quad \frac{\partial F_2}{\partial Q} = -0.5$$

We can now evaluate e_1 and e_2 by letting $Q = 0$ in F_1 and F_2. Thus, e_1 and e_2 are identical to the respective values obtained previously when P alone is acting. Then,

$$u = e_1 \frac{\partial F_1}{\partial Q} + e_2 \frac{\partial F_2}{\partial Q} = (2.08 \times 10^{-6} P^2)(0.866) + (3.6 \times 10^{-6} P^2)(-0.5)$$

$$= 1.80 \times 10^{-6} P^2 - 1.8 \times 10^{-6} P^2 = 0$$

Note that in the calculation of v, we must retain P as a variable until the last step, whereas in the computation of u, we can let $P = 100$ kips from the beginning. In general, if there are n loads, we consider only load P_j as a variable when the displacement s_j at the point of application of P_j in the direction of P_j is required. In this problem, $P = 100$ kips and we finally obtain

$$v = 4.14 \times 10^{-6} P^2 = 0.0414 \text{ in.}$$

$$u = 0$$

For nonlinear systems with a large number of members, the calculation can be carred out systematically in tabulated form. As an example, the computations of v and u in this problem are given in Tables 9-3 and 9-4, respectively.

Table 9-3

Member	F	$\dfrac{\partial F}{\partial P} = f$	e	$e\dfrac{\partial F}{\partial P} = ef$
01	$0.5P$	0.5	$2.08 \times 10^{-6}P^2$	$1.04 \times 10^{-6}P^2$
02	$0.866P$	0.866	$3.60 \times 10^{-6}P^2$	$2.94 \times 10^{-6}P^2$
				$v = 3.98 \times 10^{-6}P^2$

Table 9-4

Member	F	$\dfrac{\partial F}{\partial P} = f$	$\begin{array}{c} e \\ (Q = 0) \end{array}$	$e\dfrac{\partial F}{\partial Q} = ef$
01	$0.5P + 0.866Q$	0.866	$2.08 \times 10^{-6}P^2$	$1.80 \times 10^{-6}P^2$
02	$0.866P - 0.5Q$	-0.500	$3.6 \times 10^{-6}P^2$	$-1.80 \times 10^{-6}P^2$
				$u = 0$

9-10 PRINCIPLE OF STATIONARY POTENTIAL ENERGY

The principle of minimum potential energy can be derived from the principle of virtual work if the latter is obtained first from the principle of conservation of energy. For deformable systems, however, the requirement of minimum potential energy is not necessarily satisfied unless the system is linearly elastic. If a potential energy function is said to be stationary when all of its partial derivatives equal zero, we can at least demonstrate that for a deformable system in equilibrium, the potential energy is stationary. If the system in equilibrium is linearly elastic, we can further show that the potential energy is a minimum.

In the case of deformable systems, both external and internal forces contribute to the total potential energy. For the purpose of structural analysis, it is convenient to define a potential Ω of the external forces in such a manner that it is strictly associated with the applied external forces only. Consider, for example, two identical bars subjected to identical loads but placed in different positions, as shown in Fig. 9-21. If we consider the influence of the outside environment, say gravitation, the potential of the external forces in Fig. 9-21(a) is different from that in Fig. 9-21(b). However, if we consider as the

(a)   (b)   **Figure 9-21**

potential of the external forces the potential capacity of performing external work by the applied forces P and Q, then the potential due to the external forces will be the same in each case. Therefore, we can simplify the formulation of the total potential energy of a structural system by introducing a concise definition of the potential external forces.

Consider a conservative deformable system in equilibrium under a set of forces $P_1, P_2, \ldots, P_m$ as shown in Fig. 9-22. If displacements $s_1, s_2, \ldots, s_m$ are produced at the points of application of these forces in the direction of the respective forces, the work done by the external forces is given by Eq. (9-3). Let the potential of the external forces be defined as $\Omega = -W_e$. The potential of the internal forces is equal to the strain energy U and is given by Eq. (9-2). Thus, the total potential energy of the system is

$$V = \Omega + U \qquad (9\text{-}28)$$

If the system is given a small displacement consistent with constraints, we have

$$\delta V = \delta \Omega + \delta U$$

or

$$\delta V = -\sum_{j=1}^{m} P_j \delta s_j + \sum_{k=1}^{n} F_k \delta e_k \qquad (a)$$

By the principle of virtual displacements, i.e., Eq. (9-21c), we get from Eq. (a)

$$\delta V = \delta \Omega + \delta U = 0 \qquad (b)$$

Hence, the change in total potential energy must be zero when a deformable system in equilibrium is given a virtual displacement compatible with its constraints.

Figure 9-22

If the total potential energy of a conservative system is expressed as a function of r displacements or displacement parameters $q_1, q_2, \ldots, q_r$, which represent r degrees of freedom, and if the system is given a set of virtual displacements consistent with its constraints, the conditions of equilibrium are given by

$$\delta V = \frac{\partial V}{\partial q_1} \delta q_1 + \frac{\partial V}{\partial q_2} \delta q_2 + \cdots + \frac{\partial V}{\partial q_r} \delta q_r = 0 \qquad (9\text{-}29)$$

Since $\delta q_1, \delta q_2, \ldots, \delta q_r$ are not all zero and are independent of each other, it is necessary that

$$\frac{\partial V}{\partial q_1} = \frac{\partial V}{\partial q_2} = \cdots = \frac{\partial V}{\partial q_r} = 0 \qquad (9\text{-}30)$$

It can be stated, therefore, that of all possible configurations compatible with the constraints of a deformable system, the total potential energy of the configuration that satisfies the conditions of equilibrium is stationary. This is the *principle of stationary potential energy* for deformable systems.

Let us now consider a special case in which the displacement s_j is increased by a small amount δs_j in the direction of the load P_j while the other displacements remain unchanged. Then, Eq. (b) becomes

$$\delta V = \delta \Omega + \delta U = -P_j \delta s_j + \frac{\partial U}{\partial s_j} \delta s_j = 0$$

Then,

$$P_j = \frac{\partial U}{\partial s_j}$$

This result is identical to Eq. (9-18). Hence, Castigliano's first theorem may be considered as a special case derived from the principle of stationary potential energy. In application, the two approaches are strikingly similar. In the method based on the principle of stationary potential energy, a set of equations of equilibrium are obtained from Eqs. (9-30) whereas according to Castigliano's first theorem, one equation of equilibrium is obtained at a time from the partial derivative of the strain energy corresponding to a particular displacement. The latter approach differs from the former only in form, and they are interchangeable.

It may be interesting to note that the stationary value of the total potential energy of a linear elastic system always corresponds to a relative minimum when the equilibrium is stable. Consider, for example, a linear elastic system of volume V_0 whose internal potential energy or strain energy is given by

$$U = \iiint_{V_0} \frac{1}{2} \sigma \epsilon \, dx \, dy \, dz = \iiint_{V_0} \frac{E}{2} \epsilon^2 \, dx \, dy \, dz$$

If the system is given a virtual displacement, the total strain energy is

$$U + \delta U = \iiint_{V} \frac{E}{2} (\epsilon + \delta \epsilon)^2 \, dx \, dy \, dz$$

$$= \iiint_{V} \frac{E}{2} [\epsilon^2 + 2\epsilon \, \delta \epsilon + (\delta \epsilon)^2] \, dx \, dy \, dz$$

Thus, the change in strain energy is equal to

$$\delta U = \iiint_{V_0} E\epsilon \,\delta\epsilon \, dx \, dy \, dz + \iiint_{V_0} \frac{E}{2}(\delta\epsilon)^2 \, dx \, dy \, dz$$

$$= \iiint_{V_0} E\epsilon \,\delta\epsilon \, dx \, dy \, dz + \zeta \tag{c}$$

in which ζ is a positive quantity of higher order since it contains the $(\delta\epsilon)^2$ term. Using the expression for external potential energy $\Omega = -W_e$ and the expression for internal potential energy in Eq. (c), we obtain from Eq. (b) that

$$\delta V = -\sum P \,\delta s + \iiint_{V_0} E\epsilon \,\delta\epsilon \, dx \, dy \, dz + \zeta$$

If the virtual displacement is infinitesimal, the second-order term ζ approaches zero as a limit. For small finite virtual displacements, the term ζ may be neglected. Since ζ is always greater than zero for all displacements, it means that a small virtual displacement causing a deformable system to depart from its position of equilibrium always produces an increase in potential energy. Hence, the *principle of minimum potential energy* for linear elastic systems can be stated as follows: Of all possible configurations compatible with the constraints of a linear elastic system, the configuration that satisfies the conditions of equilibrium has a minimum total potential energy.

The property of minimum potential energy of conservative systems in equilibrium can also be used to advantage in obtaining the approximate solutions of displacements of complex structural systems. If the deflected shape of the system that satisfies the boundary conditions can be approximated by an infinite series, the coefficients of the terms of the series may be determined by the condition that the total potential energy be a minimum for a configuration in stable equilibrium. Note that $q_1, q_2, \ldots, q_r$ in Eqs. (9-29) and (9-30) can be parameters of displacements, such as the coefficients in an infinite series representing displacements, instead of actual displacements. Hence, if we take a finite number of terms in the series, the coefficients of these terms can be determined from Eqs. (9-30). Although the accuracy of an approximate solution depends on the rapidity of convergence of the series and the number of terms taken, this method provides a simple means of reducing the number of displacement parameters specifying the displacements of a complex system.

Example 9-10. Obtain an approximate deflection curve for a simple beam of constant EI subjected to a concentrated load P, as shown in Fig. 9-23, by means of the principle of minimum potential energy.

Figure 9-23

The deflection curve of the beam can be approximated by a trigonometric series that satisfies the boundary conditions. Usually, the simplest series used for such a purpose is either a sine or cosine series. Consider, for instance, a sine series of the form

$$v = c_1 \sin \frac{\pi x}{L} + c_2 \sin \frac{2\pi x}{L} + \cdots + c_n \sin \frac{n \pi x}{L} = \sum_{j=1}^{n} c_j \sin \frac{j \pi x}{L} \qquad (a)$$

in which $c_1, c_2, \ldots, c_n$ are arbitrary constants to be determined. Since $v = 0$ when $x = 0$ and $x = L$, the boundary conditions of the beam are satisfied. The integer j represents the number of half sine waves in the span length L. As examples, the first three terms in the series are plotted in Figs. 9-24(a), (b), and (c), respectively. Thus, the deflection curve of the beam is equal to the superposition of these shapes provided that $c_1, c_2, \ldots, c_n$ are first obtained by the prinicple of minimum potential energy.

(a)

(b)

(c)   **Figure 9-24**

The potential energy of the external force is equal to $\Omega = -Pv_p$, in which v_p is the vertical deflection under the load at $x = a$. Hence,

$$\Omega = -P \sum_{j=1}^{n} c_j \sin \frac{j \pi a}{L} \qquad (b)$$

The potential energy of the internal forces expressed as a function of displacements is given by Eq. (8-13b) as follows:

$$U = \frac{EI}{2} \int_0^L \left(\frac{d^2 v}{dx^2} \right)^2 dx \qquad (c)$$

Noting that

$$\frac{d^2 v}{dx^2} = - \sum_{j=1}^{n} \left(\frac{j \pi}{L} \right)^2 c_j \sin \frac{j n \pi}{L}$$

we get

$$\left(\frac{d^2v}{dx^2}\right)^2 = \frac{\pi^4}{L^4}\left[\sum_{j=1}^{n} j^2 c_j \sin\frac{jn\pi}{L}\right]^2 \qquad \text{(d)}$$

The square of the sum of the terms inside the brackets consists of either square terms in the form of

$$j^4 c_j^2 \sin^2\frac{j\pi x}{L} \qquad (j = 1, 2, \ldots, n)$$

or product terms for $k \neq j$ in the form of

$$2j^2 k^2 c_j c_k \sin\frac{j\pi x}{L} \sin\frac{k\pi x}{L} \qquad (j = 1, 2, \ldots, n, \qquad k = 1, 2, \ldots, n)$$

It can be demonstrated by direct integration that

$$\int_0^L \sin^2\frac{j\pi x}{L}\,dx = \frac{L}{2}$$

and

$$\int_0^L \sin\frac{j\pi x}{L} \sin\frac{k\pi x}{L}\,dx = 0 \qquad (j \neq k)$$

Hence, when we substitute Eq. (d) into Eq. (c), only the square terms remain. Then, we have

$$U = \left(\frac{EI}{2}\right)\left(\frac{\pi^4}{L^4}\right)\left(\frac{L}{2}\right)\sum_{j=1}^{n} j^4 c_j^2 \qquad \text{(e)}$$

The total potential energy of the system is then equal to the sum of Eqs. (b) and (e), or

$$V = -P\sum_{j=1}^{n} c_j \sin\frac{j\pi a}{L} + \frac{\pi^4 EI}{4L^3}\sum_{j=1}^{n} j^4 c_j^2$$

By the principle of stationary potential energy, we obtain for the general case

$$\frac{\partial V}{\partial c_j} = 0, \qquad P\sin\frac{j\pi a}{L} = \frac{\pi^4 EI}{2L^3} j^4 c_j$$

Hence, the general expression for the coefficient c_j is

$$c_j = \frac{2PL^3}{\pi^4 j^4 EI}\sin\frac{j\pi a}{L} \qquad \text{(f)}$$

Substituting Eq. (f) into Eq. (a), we get

$$v = \frac{2PL^3}{\pi^4 EI}\sum_{j=1}^{n}\frac{1}{j^4}\sin\frac{j\pi a}{L}\sin\frac{j\pi x}{L} \qquad \text{(g)}$$

To illustrate the application of Eq. (g), let us consider $a = L/2$ and take the first three terms of the series. Then,

$$v = \frac{2PL^3}{\pi^4 EI} \left[\sin^2 \frac{\pi}{2} + \frac{1}{2^4} \sin^2 \pi + \frac{1}{3^4} \sin^2 \frac{3\pi}{2} \right]$$

$$= \frac{2PL^3}{\pi^4 EI} \left[1 + 0 + \frac{1}{81} \right] = \frac{PL^3}{48.6 EI}$$

It can be seen that the series converges very rapidly and, in general, a very few terms of the series will give results sufficiently accurate for practical purposes.

9-11 PRINCIPLE OF STATIONARY COMPLEMENTARY ENERGY

In the application of the principle of stationary potential energy, it has been shown that, if a conservative deformable system is given a variation of displacements during which the conditions of geometrical compatibility are maintained, the equations of equilibrium may be derived from the requirement of stationary potential energy. We shall now consider another application that is analogous to this principle. If a conservative deformable system is given a variation of internal forces during which the conditions of equilibrium are maintained, the equations of compatibility may be obtained from the requirement of stationary complementary energy.

Consider again a conservative deformable system in equilibrium under the action of a set of forces $P_1, P_2, \ldots, P_m$, producing displacments $s_1, s_2, \ldots, s_m$ at the points of application of these forces in the direction of the respective forces, as shown in Fig. 9-22. If the system is statically indeterminate, it is possible to produce many sets of internal forces, each of which will hold the system in equilibrium while the external forces are kept constant. Note that the deformations e are now interpreted as functions of the internal forces F, which may be varied during the equilibrium without varying the external forces. However, there is only one set of internal forces that satisfies the conditions of compatibility also. From the principle of virtual forces, i.e., Eqs. (9-22a) and (9-22c), we have

$$\delta \overline{U} = \sum_{k=1}^{n} e_k \, \delta F_k = \sum_{j=1}^{m} s_j \, \delta P_j \qquad \text{(a)}$$

The set of internal forces that satisfies the requirements of compatibility must also satisfy Eq. (a) with $\delta P_j = 0$ $(j = 1, 2, \ldots m)$. Hence,

$$\delta \overline{U} = \sum_{k=1}^{n} e_k \, \delta F_k = 0 \qquad \text{(b)}$$

or

$$\delta \overline{U} = 0 \qquad \text{(9-31)}$$

Equation (9-31) states that of all possible states of internal forces satisfying the conditions of equilibrium of a system, the one that satisfies the conditions of compatibility causes the variation of complementary energy to vanish. This is called the *complementary energy theorem*.

In the analysis of redundant structures, the complementary energy $\overline{U}$ may be expressed as a function of the redundant forces. For a system with r redundances $X_1, X_2, \ldots, X_r$, we have

$$\delta\overline{U} = \frac{\partial\overline{U}}{\partial X_1}\,\delta X_1 + \frac{\partial\overline{U}}{\partial X_2}\,\delta X_2 + \cdots + \frac{\partial\overline{U}}{\partial X_r}\,\delta X_r = 0 \qquad (9\text{-}32)$$

Since $\delta X_1, \delta X_2, \ldots, \delta X_r$ are not all zero and are independent of each other, it is necessary that

$$\frac{\partial\overline{U}}{\partial X_1} = \frac{\partial\overline{U}}{\partial X_2} = \cdots = \frac{\partial\overline{U}}{\partial X_r} = 0 \qquad (9\text{-}33)$$

In other words, of all possible states of internal forces satisfying the conditions of equilibrium, the one that also satisfies the conditions of compatibility makes the complementary energy function stationary. This is known as the *principle of stationary complementary energy*. Except for the special case of linear elastic systems, the stationary value of complementary energy is not always a minimum. However, in the application of this principle, it is immaterial whether the stationary value is a relative maximum or minimum.

For a given redundant structure, we can always establish the equations of equilibrium first. If the structure has r redundant forces $X_1, X_2, \ldots, X_r$, the complementary energy $\overline{U}$ can be expressed as a function of the redundant forces only since the other forces may be eliminated by using the relation of forces in the equations of equilibrium. Then, the compatibility conditions, which are as numerous as the redundant forces, can be obtained by Eqs. (9-32), with one equation corresponding to a redundant force.

Example 9-11. Determine the bar forces in the redundant nonlinear elastic system shown in Fig. 9-25(a) if the stress-strain relation of the material for all members is given by the parabolic curve $\sigma = 1{,}000\sqrt{\epsilon}$ ksi. The cross-sectional areas of the members in square inches are indicated along the members.

Since the structure is symmetrical, let all quantities pertaining to members 01 and 03 be denoted by the subscript 1 and those pertaining to member 02 be denoted by the subscript 2. Assuming that all bar forces are in tension, then from the equation of equilibrium. $\Sigma\,F_y = 0$, we have

$$(2F_1)(\tfrac{4}{5}) + F_2 = P$$

(a)

(b)   **Figure 9-25**

The structure is statically indeterminate to the first degree. We shall, therefore, consider one bar force, say F_2, as the redundant force. Then, the other bar force can be obtained in terms of F_2 from the equation of equilibrium as follows:

$$F_1 = \frac{1}{1.6}(P - F_2)$$

The elongation of a member can be expressed in terms of the bar force from the stress-strain relation $\sigma = 1{,}000\sqrt{\epsilon}$. Then,

$$e = \epsilon L = 10^{-6}\sigma^2 L = 10^{-6}\left(\frac{F}{A}\right)^2 L = \frac{10^{-6}L}{A^2}F^2$$

Thus,

$$e_1 = \frac{(10^{-6})(25)(12)}{(5)^2}F_1^2 = 12 \times 10^{-6}F_1^2 = 4.68 \times 10^{-6}(P - F_2)^2$$

$$e_2 = \frac{(10^{-6})(20)(12)}{(4)^2}F_2^2 = 15 \times 10^{-6}F_2^2$$

Then,

$$\frac{\partial \bar{U}}{\partial F_2} = 2e_1\frac{\partial F_1}{\partial F_2} + e_2\frac{\partial F_2}{\partial F_2} = (10^{-6})\left[(2)(4.68)(P - F_2)^2\frac{1}{1.6} + 15F_2^2(1)\right]$$

or

$$\frac{\partial \bar{U}}{\partial F_2} = (10^{-6})[-5.86(P - F_2)^2 + 15F_2^2] = 0$$

Multiplying through by a factor of $10^6/5.86$ leads to the quadratic equation

$$1.56F_2^2 + 2PF_2 - P^2 = 0$$

the roots of which are $F_2 = 0.385P$ and $-1.667P$. The corresponding values of F_1 are obtained as follows:

$$F_1 = \frac{1}{1.6}(P - F_2) = 0.385P \text{ and } + 1.667P$$

Note that each set of results represents a state of stress that is in equilibrium and automatically satisfies the requirement of compatibility. However, physically, there cannot be two sets of forces both of which satisfy the requirement of compatibility as well as conditions of equilibrium. In other words, the solution must be unique. The explanation for the multiplicity of answers lies in the fact that in computing the deformation e in a member, we take the square of the stress-strain relation $\sigma = 1{,}000\sqrt{\epsilon}$ as given by the solid portion of the parabolic curve in Fig. 9-25(b), but the same deformation e could have been obtained by taking the square of a fictitious stress-strain relation $\sigma = -1{,}000\sqrt{\epsilon}$ as represented by the dotted portion of the parabolic curve in Fig. 9-25(b). The set of bar forces $F_1 = 0.385P$ and $F_2 = 0.385P$ corresponds to the former case while the set $F_1 = 1.667P$ and $F_2 = -1.667P$ corresponds to the latter. Hence, only the set $F_1 = 0.385P$ and $F_2 = 0.385P$ is consistent with the given stress-strain relation.

Generally, nonlinear stress-strain relations lead to a multiplicity of answers. If the strain is a function of an odd power of stress, or the stress is a function of an odd power of strain, this situation may not occur. However, there is always one and only one set of answers that satisfies all requirements. We must therefore observe the uniqueness of the solution and select only the correct one from the multiplicity of roots obtained by the complementary energy theorem.

PROBLEMS

9-1. By the method of real work, determine the slope at end B of the beam due to a couple M applied at end B, as shown in Fig. P9-1. The bending stiffness EI of the beam is constant.

Figure P9-1   Figure P9-2

9-2. By the method of real work, determine the deflection at the center of the span of the simple beam shown in Fig. P9-2. The bending stiffness of the beam is constant.

9-3 to 9-5. By the method of virtual work, compute the vertical deflection at point C of each of the beams shown in Figs. P6-3 to P6-5 at the end of Chapter 6.

9-6. By the method of virtual work, compute the horizontal and vertical displacements of joint D of the frame shown in Fig. P6-18 at the end of Chapter 6.

9-7. By the method of virtual work, compute the horizontal displacement at joint E of the frame shown in Fig. P6-20 at the end of Chapter 6.

9-8 and 9-9. By the method of virtual work, find the vertical displacement at joint B of each of the trusses shown in Figs. P6-24 and P6-25 at the end of Chapter 6.

9-10. By the method of virtual work, calculate the displacement of joint L_3 in a direction perpendicular to member $U_2 L_3$ of the truss shown in Fig. P6-26 at the end of Chapter 6.

9-11 and 9-12. By the method of virtual work, determine the horizontal and vertical displacements at joint G of the trusses shown in Figs. P9-11 ($A = 8$ in.^{2} for all members), and P9-12 ($A = 10$ in.^{2} for all members). $E = 30 \times 10^3$ ksi for both.

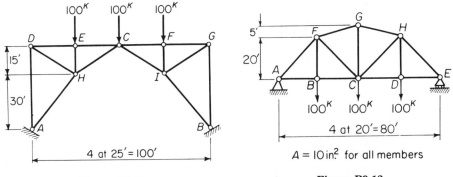

Figure P9-11   Figure P9-12

9-13 and **9-14.** Using Castigliano's second theorem, compute the slope at point A of the beam shown in Figs. P9-13 and P9-14. The bending stiffness EI of the beams is constant.

Figure P9-13   Figure P9-14

9-15 and **9-16.** Using Castigliano's second theorem, compute the relative displacement of joints H and I of the trusses shown in Figs. P9-15 and P9-16. $E = 30 \times 10^3$ ksi.

$E = 30 \times 10^3$ ksi
$A = 4\,\text{in.}^2$ for all members
except bottom chord
$A = 20\,\text{in}^2$ for bottom chord

Figure P9-15

$E = 30 \times 10^3$ ksi
$A = 10\,\text{in.}^2$ for all members

Figure P9-16

9-17 and **9-18.** If the material used for all members in a truss has a stress-strain relation $\sigma = 500\sqrt{\epsilon}$, determine the vertical displacement at point C of the trusses shown in Fig. P9-17 and P9-18.

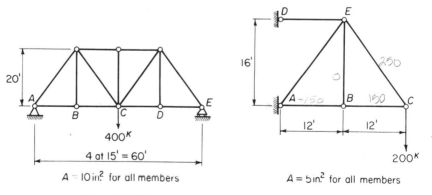

$A = 10\,\text{in.}^2$ for all members

Figure P9-17

$A = 5\,\text{in.}^2$ for all members

Figure P9-18

9-19 and **9-20.** Using the principle of minimum potential energy, determine the horizontal and vertical components of joint O in each truss shown in Fig. P9-19 and

P9-20. The areas of the members in square inches are given along the members. The stress-strain relation of the material is linear with $E = 30 \times 10^3$ ksi.

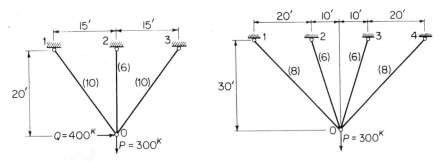

Figure P9-19   Figure P9-20

9-21 and 9-22. If the material used for all members in a system has a stress-strain relation $\sigma = 2,000\sqrt{\epsilon}$, determine the bar forces in each of the structural systems shown in Figs. P9-19 and P9-20. Use the principle of stationary complementary energy.

10

Introduction to Elastic Analysis of Redundant Systems

In previous chapters dealing with statically determinate structures, we have emphasized the use of traditional methods of analysis, the origins of which may be traced back more than a century. In this chapter, we shall briefly summarize the basic concepts of the traditional methods used in the analysis of redundant systems as a prelude to matrix methods of structural analysis, which are treated in the remaining chapters of this text. We shall see that for redundant systems the equations of equilibrium alone are not sufficient for the determination of the unknowns in a system. Additional equations must be obtained from the conditions of geometrical compatibility of displacements in the system. For this reason, the geometrical compatibility is sometimes considered as the "equilibrium" of displacements. Furthermore, additional equations must be obtained from the force-deformation relations. If the stress-strain relation of the material is linearly elastic, the equations representing the force-deformation relations are also linear functions of unknown reactions or internal forces. Thus, the analysis of linear structural systems may be reduced to the solution of a large system of linear simultaneous equations, giving rise to the development of matrix methods of structural analysis.

Although matrix algebra as a field of mathematics is at least as old as many principles used in structural mechanics, such as the principle of virtual work, it is only within the past three or four decades that matrix methods have been developed for structural analysis. Beginning around the mid 1940s the need arose for accurate methods to analyze systems of increasing complexity such as modern aircraft structures. While matrix methods provided the means for systematizing analyses, only the coincident emergence of the digital computer, capable of performing arithmetic operations with large matrices, made this analytical approach practicable. Today, general purpose computer codes that incorporate matrix methods may be used routinely to analyze very large and complex structures with ever increasing computational efficiency.

Two distinct approaches for the solution of linear elastic structural systems are the *stiffness* (or *displacement*) and *flexibility* (or *force*) methods. Within the context of matrix formulations, the flexibility method was the first to appear in technical literature, but it requires that redundant forces be identified in statically indeterminate systems, and it often involves more matrix operations than the stiffness method. The stiffness method, which was introduced a few years later, does not require that one distinguish between statically determinate and indeterminate structures, and it is generally considered to be more systematic than the flexibility method. Consequently, the stiffness method was found to be more readily incorporated into general purpose computer codes, and for that reason it has enjoyed much greater popularity than the flexibility method. Within the past thirty years both approaches have undergone enormous expansion and refinement. Of particular importance is the extension of these methods to the analysis of continua, which may be considered to comprise assemblages of deformable *finite elements* interconnected along their boundaries. Thus a plate or a shell, for example, may be envisioned as an assemblage of rectangular or triangular finite elements interconnected at their vertices, just as members of a frame or truss are joined at their end points. The same general approach used to evaluate displacements and internal forces in structures comprising bars, beams, and columns is applied to find the deformation and stresses in the finite element model of a continuum.

10-2 INFLUENCE COEFFICIENTS FOR LINEAR SYSTEMS

In the analysis of linear elastic structures, we can express either the displacements in terms of forces or the forces in terms of displacements, obtaining a set of simultaneous linear equations. In the force method, the unknowns in the set of equations are forces and the coefficients are displacements per unit force; in the displacement method, the unknowns in the set of equations are displacements and the coefficients are forces per unit displacement. The coefficients of these simultaneous linear equations are called *influence coefficients*.

Let us first consider a linear spring with one degree of freedom. Let a force P be applied to the spring causing a displacement s. The force-displacement relation of the spring may be given by

$$P = ks$$

in which k is called the *spring constant* or the *stiffness coefficient* of the spring, given by $k = P/s$, which is the force required to produce a unit displacement in the spring. On the other hand, the force-displacement relation may also be expressed in the form

$$s = fP$$

in which f is called the *flexibility coefficient* of the spring and $f = s/P$ is the displacement caused by a unit force in the spring. For this simple case with one degree of freedom, it is seen that

$$k = \frac{1}{f}$$

That is, the stiffness coefficient is the inverse of the flexibility coefficient and vice versa.

For a structural system with more than one degree of freedom, the relations between the stiffness and flexibility coefficients of individual members are no longer so simple. However, the stiffness of the system as a whole is the inverse of the flexibility of the entire system. In other words, the coefficients for one set of simultaneous linear equations involving forces as unknowns can be obtained from the solution of another set of simultaneous equations involving displacements as unknowns.

Consider, for instance, the linear system in Fig. 10-1, on which forces $P_1, P_2, \ldots, P_n$ are applied at points $1, 2, \ldots, n$. By the principle of superposition, the displacement at any point in a given direction is the sum of the displacements in that direction caused by each force acting separately. Let f_{ij} be a flexibility coefficient denoting the displacement at joint i in the direction of the line of action of P_i due to a unit force at joint j in the direction of s_j. Then, the displacements at various points in the lines of action of the respective forces can be expressed as follows:

$$s_1 = f_{11}P_1 + f_{12}P_2 + f_{13}P_3 + \cdots + f_{1n}P_n$$
$$s_2 = f_{21}P_1 + f_{22}P_2 + f_{23}P_3 + \cdots + f_{2n}P_n$$
$$s_3 = f_{31}P_1 + f_{32}P_2 + f_{33}P_3 + \cdots + f_{3n}P_n \qquad (10\text{-}1)$$
$$\vdots$$
$$s_n = f_{n1}P_1 + f_{n2}P_2 + f_{n3}P_3 + \cdots + f_{nn}P_n$$

We can also express forces in terms of displacements for the linear system in Fig. 10-1. The force at any point in a given direction is the sum of the force

Figure 10-1

Introduction to Elastic Analysis of Redundant Systems   Chap. 10

in that direction corresponding to each displacement applied separately. Let k_{ij} be a stiffness coefficient denoting the force at joint i in the direction of the line of action of P_i due to a unit displacement at joint j in the direction of s_j while all other displacements are prevented. Then, the forces at various points in the respective given directions can be expressed as follows:

$$P_1 = k_{11}s_1 + k_{12}s_2 + k_{13}s_3 + \cdots + k_{1n}s_n$$

$$P_2 = k_{21}s_1 + k_{22}s_2 + k_{23}s_3 + \cdots + k_{2n}s_n$$

$$P_3 = k_{31}s_1 + k_{32}s_2 + k_{33}s_3 + \cdots + k_{3n}s_n \qquad (10\text{-}2)$$

$$\vdots$$

$$P_n = k_{n1}s_1 + k_{n2}s_2 + k_{n3}s_3 + \cdots + k_{nn}s_n$$

One important characteristic of linear structural systems as implied by Eqs. (10-1) and (10-2), is that the *principle of superposition* can be used for their solutions. This principle, which has wide applications in structural analysis, simply states that if several causes act simultaneously on a system and if each effect is directly proportional to its cause, then the total effect is the sum of the individual effects. For instance, the strain in a structural member resulting from several applied forces is the algebraic sum of the strains caused by the forces applied separately if each strain is linearly related to the force causing it. In view of the fact that plane sections before deformation are assumed to remain plane after deformation without significant error for a member subject to axial force, twisting moment, or bending moment, the strain in each case is indeed directly proportional to the corresponding applied force. On the other hand, stress is proportional to strain only in the elastic range of the material. Hence the stress in a structural member resulting from several applied forces is the algebraic sum of their effects only if Hooke's law holds true. Similarly, the deflections of beams subjected to several vertical loads can also be obtained by the principle of superposition. Again, this approach is possible because the deflection caused by each load is directly proportional to the curvature thus produced in the elastic range of the material. Hence, the analysis of linear structural systems can often be simplified by using the principle of super-position.

10-3 MAXWELL-BETTI THEOREM OF RECIPROCAL DISPLACEMENTS

In the study of deflections of linear elastic structures, we may observe a very useful relation indicating the reciprocity of deflections at different locations. We shall consider as an example the deflections of a simple beam. Let δ_{ab} be the deflection at point A due to a vertical load P acting at point B, and δ_{ba} be the deflection at point B due to a vertical load P acting at point A as shown in Fig.

10-2. By the method of virtual work, we obtain

$$\delta_{ab} = \int_0^L \frac{M_b m_a \, dx}{EI}$$

$$\delta_{ba} = \int_0^L \frac{M_a m_b \, dx}{EI}$$

in which M_a and M_b are the moments at a section of the beam due to the vertical force P acting at points A and B respectively, and m_a and m_b are the moments at the same section due to a downward unit load acting at points A and B respectively. Since moments in a beam are linear functions of external loads, we note that $M_b = Pm_b$ and $M_a = Pm_a$. Hence,

$$\delta_{ab} = \int_0^L \frac{Pm_a m_b \, dx}{EI} = \delta_{ba}$$

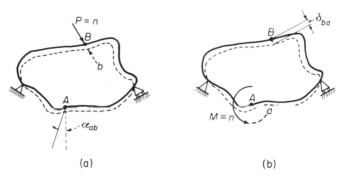

(a)

(b)   Figure 10-2

It should be noted that this relation is not confined to the vertical deflections of beams. Let us consider a more general case such as the linear elastic system in Fig. 10-3. If the direction of rotation of the moment M in Fig. 10-3(b) and the direction of the force P in Fig. 10-3(a) are defined as the a and b directions respectively, a force $P = n$ kips acting alone at B will cause a rotation α_{ab} at point A in the a direction, whereas a moment $M = n$ ft-kips acting alone at A will cause a deflection δ_{ba} at point B in the b direction. Then,

(a)   (b)

Figure 10-3

from the method of virtual work, we have

$$1 \times \alpha_{ab} = \sum f_a e_b \qquad \text{and} \qquad 1 \times \delta_{ba} = \sum f_b e_a$$

where

f_a = the internal force in an element due to a fictitious unit moment at point A in the a direction,

e_b = the displacement of the element in the direction of f_a due to an external force $P = n$ acting at point B in the b direction,

f_b = the internal force in an element due to a fictitious unit load at point B in the b direction,

e_a = the displacement of the element in the direction of f_b due to an external force $M = n$ acting at point A in the a direction.

Note that e_a and e_b can be expressed in terms of f_a and f_b since the internal forces and moments are linear functions of external force and moments and the displacements and rotations are linear functions of internal forces and moments. Consider, for example, a truss in which all members are subjected to axial forces only. Then,

$$1 \times \alpha_{ab} = \sum f_a e_b = \sum f_a \frac{n f_b L}{AE}$$

$$1 \times \delta_{ba} = \sum f_b e_a = \sum f_b \frac{n f_a L}{AE}$$

The units in these expressions should be carried out consistently. In the expression $1 \times \alpha_{ab}$, the unit moment has the unit of force $\times$ length and the rotation is a dimensionless quantity; whereas in the expression $1 \times \delta_{ba}$, the unit load has the unit of force and the deflection has the unit of length. If the internal forces f_a and f_b and the deformations e_a and e_b are obtained accordingly, we can equate the two expressions obtained from the principle of virtual work as follows

$$1 \times \alpha_{ab} = 1 \times \delta_{ba}$$

Hence, we have *numerically*

$$\alpha_{ab} = \delta_{ba}$$

Another interpretation of the above equality is that for $n = 1$, α_{ab} represents the rotation at A per unit force ($P = 1$) at B, and δ_{ba} represents the deflection at B per unit moment ($M = 1$) at A. Then, the quantity on each side of the equal sign has the unit for $1/\text{force}$.

In general, the reciprocal relation of displacements may be stated as follows: In a linear elastic structure, the displacement of point A in the a direction due to a load acting at a point B in the b direction is equal to the displacement of point B in the given b direction due to a load of the same magnitude acting at point A in the a direction. This is known as *Maxwell's theorem of reciprocal displacements*. The theorem is very general since the term "displacement" may refer to rotation or linear displacement and the term "load" means either moment or force.

A further generalization of the theorem has been made by Betti, and the modified form is usually called the *Maxwell-Betti theorem*. Let two sets of forces $P_1, P_2, \ldots, P_j, \ldots, P_m$ and $P'_1, P'_2, \ldots, P'_k, \ldots, P'_n$ act on a linear elastic system. When these two sets of forces are acting on the system separately as shown in Fig. 10-4, each set causes deformations in the system. Let

δ_{jk} = displacement of the point of application of force P_j in the direction of this force caused by the application of P'_k,

δ'_{kj} = displacement of the point of application of force P'_k in the direction of this force caused by the application of P_j.

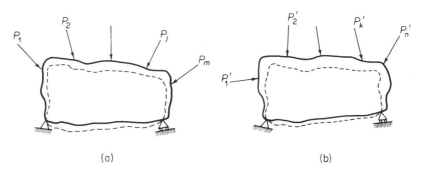

(a)   (b)

Figure 10-4

According to the principle of virtual work, δ_{jk} may be interpreted as being the external virtual work due to a unit load acting at the point of application of P_j in the direction of P_j as a result of the deformation caused by the application of P'_k. Then, $P_j \delta_{jk}$ = the external virtual work due to P_j as a result of the deformation caused by the application of P'_k. By summing these terms for $k = 1, 2, \ldots, n$, we obtain the external virtual work due to P_j as a result of the deformation caused by the application of the set of loads $P'_1, P'_2, \ldots, P'_n$. The total external virtual work due to all loads $P_1, P_2, \ldots, P_m$ in the first set as a result of the deformation caused by the application of all loads in the second set $P'_1, P'_2, \ldots, P'_n$ is equal to the summation of the terms for $j = 1, 2, \ldots, m$ and $k = 1, 2, \ldots, n$. Hence,

$$W_e = \sum_{j=1}^{m} \sum_{k=1}^{n} P_j \delta_{jk}$$

Similarly, the total external virtual work due to all loads $P'_1, P'_2 \ldots, P'_n$ in the second set as a result of the deformation caused by the application of all loads in the first set $P_1, P_2, \ldots, P_m$ is equal to

$$W_e = \sum_{k=1}^{n} \sum_{j=1}^{m} P'_k \delta'_{kj}$$

For a linear elastic system, the order of application of the set of loads is irrelevant since the principle of superposition is valid. Hence, the total external virtual work by one set of loads due to the deformation caused by the other set is identical to the total external virtual work done by the second set of loads due to the deformation caused by the first set. That is,

$$\sum_{j=1}^{m} \sum_{k=1}^{n} P_j \delta_{jk} = \sum_{k=1}^{n} \sum_{j=1}^{m} P_k' \delta_{kj}' \qquad (10\text{-}3)$$

This is the *Betti theorem* or *Maxwell-Betti theorem*, which states that in a linear elastic system, the external virtual work done by a set of forces P_m during the deformation caused by another set of forces P_n' is equal to the external virtual work done by the set of forces P_n' during the deformation caused by the set of forces P_m.

An important special case of the theorem is obtained when each set of loads consists of the same number of loads and the lines of application of one set of loads are, respectively, the directions of displacements of the other set. Furthermore, if all forces of the first set except P_j and all forces of the second set except P_k' equal zero, we obtain from Eq. (10-3)

$$P_j \delta_{jk} = P_k' \delta_{kj}$$

When $P_j = P_k' = P$, the expression is reduced to *Maxwell's theorem of reciprocal displacements* as follows:

$$\delta_{jk} = \delta_{kj} \qquad (10\text{-}4)$$

Example 10-1. Determine the horizontal displacement at joint I of the truss shown in Fig. 10-5 due to a downward vertical load of 15 kips at (a) joint E and (b) joint F. The areas of the members of the truss in square inches are indicated along the members in parentheses. $E = 30 \times 10^3$ ksi.

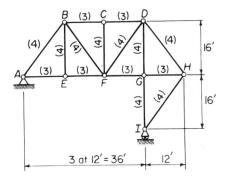

3 at 12' = 36'   12'   **Figure 10-5**

Let the horizontal displacements at joint I of the truss due to a vertical load of 15 kips at joints E and F be directed to the left and denoted by u_{ie} and u_{if}, respectively. Let the downward vertical displacements at joints E and F due to a horizontal force of 15 kips acting to the left at joint I be v_{ei} and v_{fi}, respectively. According to Maxwell's theorem of reciprocal displacements, we have

$$u_{ie} = v_{ei} \qquad \text{and} \qquad u_{if} = v_{fi}$$

We can therefore compute the deflections at two points of a truss for one position of loading instead of the deflection at one point of the truss for two different positions of loading. The computation is carried out step by step in Table 10-1. Since the results for v_{ei} and v_{fi} are found to be

$$v_{ei} = -0.012 \text{ in. } (\uparrow), \qquad v_{fi} = +0.0534 \text{ in } (\downarrow)$$

By using Maxwell's theorem, we finally obtain

$$u_{ie} = -0.012 \text{ in. } (\rightarrow), \qquad u_{if} = +0.534 \text{ in. } (\leftarrow)$$

Note that a positive result indicates that the assumed sense of direction is correct and a negative result indicates that it should be reversed.

Table 10-1

Member	L (in.)	A (in.^{2})	15 kips horizontal at I		1 vertical at E		1 vertical at F	
			F (kips)	e (in.)	f	fe (in.)	f	fe (in.)
AB	240	4	+ 8.33	+0.0167	−0.833	−0.014	−0.417	−0.0078
BC	144	3	+10.00	+0.0160	−0.250	−0.004	−0.500	+0.0080
CD	144	3	+10.00	+0.0160	−0.250	−0.004	−0.500	+0.0080
DH	240	4	+25.00	+0.0500	0	0	0	0
GH	144	3	−30.00	−0.048	0	0	0	0
FG	144	3	−30.00	−0.048	0	0	0	0
EF	144	3	−20.00	−0.032	+0.500	−0.016	+0.250	−0.0080
AE	144	3	−20.00	−0.032	+0.500	−0.016	+0.250	−0.0080
BE	192	4	0	0	+1.000	0	0	0
BF	240	4	− 8.33	−0.0167	−0.417	+0.007	+0.417	−0.0078
CF	192	4	0	0	0	0	0	0
DF	240	4	+ 8.33	+0.0167	+0.417	+0.007	+0.833	+0.0156
HI	240	4	+25.00	+0.0500	0	0	0	0
DG	192	4	−26.67	−0.0427	−0.333	+0.014	−0.667	+0.0267
GI	192	4	−26.67	−0.0427	−0.333	+0.014	−0.667	+0.0267
					$v_{ei} = -0.012$		$v_{fi} = +0.0534$	

10-4 THE FORCE METHOD

✴In the force method, the reactions and internal forces of a statically determinate structure are obtained from the consideration of the equilibrium of the structure. The reactions and internal forces can, in general, be expressed as unknowns of a set of linear simultaneous equations. For statically indeterminate structures, the requirements of geometrical compatability are based on the simple principle that the deformations of the individual elements in a system must be compatible with the over-all deformation of the entire system, and vice versa. Hence, a study of the geometry of structural systems becomes necessary in the solution of redundant systems.

Consider, for instance, the beam in Fig. 10-6(a). If the neutral axis of the beam is not strained during bending, there must be a slight horizontal displacement of support A toward the left as the beam deflects downward under the action of the vertical load P. It can be demonstrated, however, that the horizontal displacement of any element in the beam is very small in comparison with its vertical displacement and is therefore negligible. Furthermore, the shape of the deflected beam is also governed by the supporting conditions. At support A, the beam is free to rotate but not to displace vertically. This implies that at support A the moment as well as the vertical displacement equals zero. At support B, the beam is neither free to rotate nor to displace vertically. Thus, at support B the slope and the vertical displacement of the beam are both zero. The conditions of forces or moments at the supporting points are called *force boundary conditions*, whereas the conditions of rotations and displacements at the supports are known as *displacement boundary conditions*. The boundary conditions of a structure are important in sketching its deflected shape qualitatively as well as for computing the displacements quantitatively.

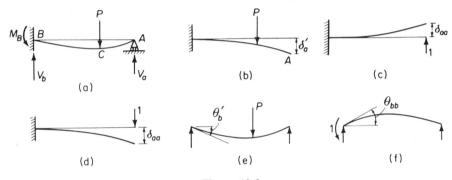

Figure 10-6

Now that we have described the geometry of the deflected structure, we shall attempt to analyze the redundant structure in the light of the condition of geometrical compatibility. Since there are three unknown components of reaction for the structure in Fig. 10-6(a) and only two equations of equilibrium available, the third one being a trivial statement that the forces and reactions in the horizontal direction are identically zero, the structure is statically indeterminate to the first degree. We shall therefore remove a redundance, say reaction V_a at support A, to make the structure determinate. The resulting structure, as shown in Fig. 10-6(b), is known as the *released* structure of the original system. Since point A of the released structure will deflect by an amount of δ_a' under the action of the external load P, this point must eventually be brought back by the same amount in order to satisfy the geometrical boundary conditions of the original system. This is accomplished by assuming a unit load acting upward at point A of the released structure while the external load is removed as shown in Fig. 10-6(c). If the vertical upward displacement of point A due to a unit upward load at A is denoted by δ_{aa}, then the force necessary to restore point A to the undeformed position must be the unknown vertical reaction at A. Thus, the reaction can be obtained as follows:

$$V_a = \frac{\delta_a'}{\delta_{aa}} \qquad \text{(a)}$$

Note that the sense of direction of the unit load is arbitrarily assumed. If the assumed sense is correct, the reaction V_a will be positive. If the unit load is assumed to be acting downward and the vertical downward displacement of point A due to a unit downward load is denoted by δ_{aa} as indicated in Fig. 10-6(d), the condition of zero displacement at point A in the original system requires

$$\delta_a' + V_a \delta_{aa} = 0 \qquad \text{or} \qquad V_a = \frac{-\delta_a'}{\delta_{aa}}$$

It should be pointed out that in a redundant system, any component of reaction may be chosen as a redundant. For the structure in Fig. 10-6(a), the moment M_b at the fixed end may be chosen as a redundant. In that case, the released structure will deflect as shown in Fig. 10-6(e) under the external load P, and the beam undergoes a rotation θ_b' at the end B as a result of the removal of the redundant M_b. Then, a unit couple may be applied at end B of the released structure, causing a rotation of θ_{bb} at end B as shown in Fig. 10-6(f). Thus,

$$M_b = \frac{\theta_b'}{\theta_{bb}} \qquad \text{(b)}$$

If we know only how to compute the displacements of the released structures due to the external loads as well as a unit load, Eq. (a) or (b) will provide the additional equation needed for the solution of the remaining unknown components of reaction.

If more than one redundance is involved in a structural system, the same principle may still be applied. Consider, for example, the continuous beam in Fig. 10-7(a), which is statically indeterminate to the second degree. If reactions R_b and R_c are removed as redundances, the vertical displacements at points B

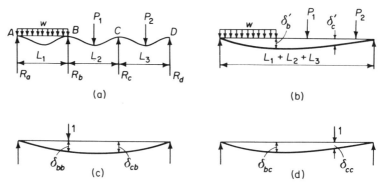

(a)

(b)

(c)

(d)

Figure 10-7

Introduction to Elastic Analysis of Redundant Systems   Chap. 10

and C of the released structure under the external loads will be δ_b' and δ_c', respectively, as shown in Fig. 10-7(b). Let δ_{bb} and δ_{cb} be the vertical displacements at B and C, respectively, due to a unit vertical load at B, and δ_{bc} and δ_{cc} be the vertical displacements at B and C, respectively, due to a unit vertical load at C, as shown in Figs. 10-7(c) and (d). Then, two equations of geometrical compatibility may be written since the vertical displacements at points B and C in the original redundant system must both be zero. Thus,

$$\delta_b' + R_b\delta_{bb} + R_c\delta_{bc} = 0 \qquad\qquad \text{(a)}$$

$$\delta_c' + R_b\delta_{cb} + R_c\delta_{cc} = 0 \qquad\qquad \text{(b)}$$

The simultaneous solution of Eqs. (a) and (b) gives the redundant reactions R_b and R_c in terms of displacements of the released structure. Hence, the remaining unknown components of reaction may be determined from the equations of equilibrium.

We may conclude, therefore, that the conditions of geometrical compatibility will in general lead to a set of simultaneous equations with as many unknowns as the number of redundances in a redundant system. This set of equations, together with the equations of equilibrium, will enable us to solve all the unknowns involved in the system. Before we can do so, however, we must know how to select a released system which is statically determinate by removing the appropriate redundances, and to compute the displacements of this statically determinate system under various loads. Although the first step involves judgment based on experience if we are to select a released system that requires a minimum of numerical computations, the second step can be handled systematically and separately.

Example 10-2.   Compute the redundant reactions R_1, R_2, and R_3 for the continuous beam in Fig. 10-8(a) by the force method. The bending stiffness EI of the beam is constant. Both downward forces and downward deflections are considered as negative.

The beam is statically indeterminate to the third degree. Let us ignore for the moment the conditions of symmetry for the problem in order to preserve the generality of our discussion, i.e., we first treat the problem as if either the loading or the structure were asymmetric. Thus, the reactions R_1, R_2, and R_3 are considered as redundances. We shall first remove the redundances and the released structure will deflect under the action of the external load as shown in Fig. 10-8(b). Next, place a unit load at points 1, 2, and 3 of the released structure successively as shown in Fig. 10-8(c), (d), and (e), respectively. Denoting the deflections of the auxiliary structure as shown, the conditions of compatibility require that

$$v_1' = v_{11}R_1 + v_{12}R_2 + v_{13}R_3$$

$$v_2' = v_{21}R_1 + v_{22}R_2 + v_{23}R_3 \qquad\qquad \text{(a)}$$

$$v_3' = v_{31}R_1 + v_{32}R_2 + v_{33}R_3$$

Note that since the downward uniform load is considered as negative, *all* displacements in Eqs. (a) are opposite to the senses of direction of the respective forces. Hence, no negative signs appear in the equations.

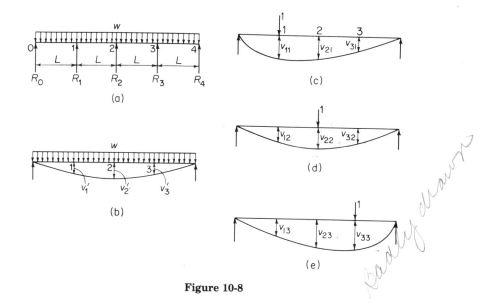

Figure 10-8

The deflection curve of a simple beam of span length $4L$ subjected to a uniform load $-w$ can readily be obtained by successive integrations as follows:

$$v = \frac{1}{24EI}[2w(4L)x^3 - w(4L)^3x - wx^4]$$

For $x = L$, $2L$, and $3L$, we obtain the displacements at points 1, 2, and 3 of the auxiliary structure as follows:

$$v_1' = -\frac{57wL^4}{24EI}, \qquad v_2' = -\frac{80wL^4}{24EI}, \qquad v_3' = -\frac{57wL^4}{24EI}$$

The coefficients of Eqs. (a) may be obtained from the deflections of the released structure with a unit load acting at the desired position. From Example 6-3, we note that for a simple beam of span length $4L$ subjected to a concentrated load P acting at distance a and b from the left and right supports, respectively, the deflection curve is given by

$$v = \frac{Pb}{24EIL}[x^3 - (16L^2 - b^2)x], \qquad 0 \leq x \leq a$$

$$v = \frac{Pb}{24EIL}\left[x^3 - \frac{4L}{b}(x - a)^3 - (16L^2 - b^2)x\right], \qquad a \leq x \leq L$$

For a unit load $P = 1$ at point 1 as shown in Fig. 10-8(c), $a = L$ and $b = 3L$. We have, for $x = L$, $2L$, and $3L$ respectively,

$$v_{11} = -\frac{3L^3}{4EI}, \qquad v_{21} = -\frac{11L^3}{12EI}, \qquad v_{31} = -\frac{7L^3}{12EI}$$

For a unit load $P = 1$ at point 2 as shown in Fig. 10-8(d), $a = 2L$ and $b = 2L$. We obtain, for $x = L$, $2L$, and $3L$, respectively.

$$u_{12} = -\frac{11L^3}{12EI}, \qquad u_{22} = -\frac{4L^3}{3EI}, \qquad u_{32} = -\frac{11L^3}{12EI}$$

For a unit load $P = 1$ at point 3 as shown in Fig. 10-8(e), $a = 3L$ and $b = L$, we get, for $x = L, 2L$, and $3L$, respectively.

$$u_{13} = -\frac{7L^3}{12EI}, \qquad u_{23} = -\frac{11L^3}{12EI}, \qquad u_{33} = -\frac{3L_3}{4EI}$$

In examining the displacements $v_i'(i = 1, 2, 3)$ and $v_{ij}(i, j = 1, 2, 3)$, we observe that the solution can be greatly simplified by considering the conditions of symmetry for the problem. Thus, $v_1' = v_3'$, $v_{21} = v_{23}$, $v_{11} = v_{33}$, and $v_{ij} = v_{ji}(i, j = 1, 2, 3)$; also $R_1 = R_3$ and $R_0 = R_4$. Then Eqs. (a) become:

$$v_1' = (v_{11} + v_{13})R_1 + v_{12}R_2$$

$$v_2' = 2v_{12}R_1 + v_{22}R_2$$

(b)

as the third equation becomes redundant. From the values of v_i' and v_{ij} computed previously, we get

$$R_1 = R_3 = \frac{8}{7}wL = 1.143 \ wL$$

$$R_2 = \frac{13}{14}wL = 0.928 \ wL$$

The remaining reactions can be obtained from the conditions of equilibrium. Again, noting the conditions of symmetry,

$$R_0 = R_4 = \frac{1}{2}(4 \ wL - R_1 - R_2 - R_3)$$

$$= \frac{11}{28} \ wL = 0.393 \ wL$$

10-5 THE DISPLACEMENT METHOD

In the displacement method, the displacements of the joints of a structure are selected as unknowns, whereby a sufficient number of equations will be sought to relate and solve the unknown displacements. Consequently, the degree of statical indeterminacy or redundancy is no longer important in the solution. Instead, we want to know the number of unknown displacements as indicated by the degrees of freedom in the idealized structural system. Hence, the number of degrees of freedom for a structure is sometimes referred to as the *degree of kinematic indeterminacy* of the system.

Consider, for example, a ship on the high seas. If the ship is regarded as a floating rigid body with no external constraints, as shown in Fig. 10-9(a), its displacements may be described by the surge u, the heave v, and the sway w in the x, y, and z directions, respectively, and its rotations may be defined by the roll φ_x, the yaw φ_y, and the pitch φ_z about the x, y, and z-axes, respectively,

(a)

(b)   Figure 10-9

as shown in Fig. 10-9(b). Since the motion of the ship can be specified by six displacement components u, v, w, φ_x, φ_y, and φ_z, it is said to have six degrees of freedom. On the other hand, a locomotive moving on a track can be specified by one variable. Hence, it has only one degree of freedom.

In general, a rigid system in space may have at most six degrees of freedom, whereas a coplanar rigid system may have up to three degrees of freedom. Thus, a rigid system can be restrained in a fixed position relative to the surrounding environment or foundation by a sufficient number of constraining forces at supporting points to counteract its tendency to move. However, the supports themselves may be either rigid or deformable. The former does not permit any displacement of the supporting points; the latter allows such displacements. In reality, structural supports may displace slightly owing to the settlement of the foundation or other causes but may be assumed to be rigid for most practical purposes. In cases where such an assumption cannot be made, the support itself may have various degrees of freedom. Consider, for example, the supporting springs in Fig. 10-10, which are permitted to displace in a vertical direction only. In Fig. 10-10(a), the location of the mass M can be defined by a vertical displacement v. In Fig. 10-10(b), a spring is placed under each of the two masses. Hence, the locations of the masses M_1 and M_2 must be specified by two vertical displacements v_1 and v_2. In Fig. 10-10(c), the rigid

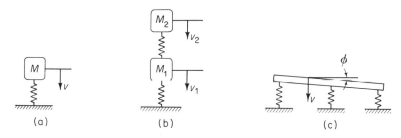

(a)   (b)   (c)

Figure 10-10

system is supported by three springs. However, the motion of the rigid body may be specified by a vertical displacement v referring to some point of the body and a rotation φ. Hence, the system has two degrees of freedom.

The internal constraints of a stable system may also be released to permit rigid-body movements. Consider the truss structure shown in Fig. 10-11(a). If the bottom diagonal is removed as shown in Fig. 10-11(b), the movement of the top panel of the truss relative to a fixed line, say line y-y, can be specified by either a horizontal displacement u or a rotation φ. Hence, the system in Fig. 10-11(b) has one degree of freedom. Similarly, the system in Fig. 10-11(c), in which both diagonals have been removed, has two degrees of freedom.

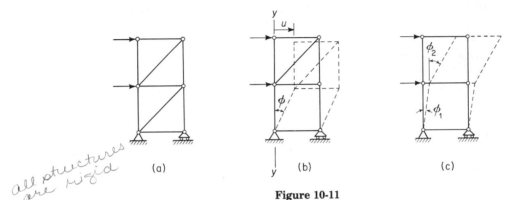

all structures are rigid

Figure 10-11

When a structural system is treated as a deformable body, it no longer possesses a finite number of displacement components. Consider the simple beam in Fig. 10-12(a), which is regarded as a rigid system in the analysis of forces or moments. On the other hand, when treated as a deformable system in displacement computation, every point on the neutral axis of the beam except at the supports moves from its initial position to another position that defines the final configuration of the beam. Hence, the system has an infinite number of degrees of freedom. However, for practical purposes, the beam can be effectively approximated by a finite number of displacement components as shown in Fig. 10-12(b), in which the displacements at only four points of the beam are considered. Then the system may be regarded as having a finite number of degrees of freedom.

The number of degrees of freedom chosen for an approximated system depends to a large extent on the desired accuracy of the solution. In the study of vibration of beams subjected to pulsating vertical loads, for example, it may be assumed that the mass of a beam is concentrated at the selected points. Since

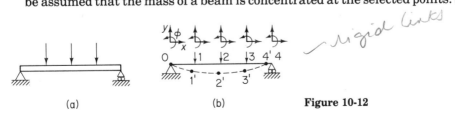

rigid links

Figure 10-12

the horizontal displacements at these points of a beam are small compared with the corresponding vertical displacements, the horizontal displacements are negligible. Furthermore, the rotations at these points are unimportant and are usually neglected. Thus, the number of degrees of freedom in such a problem is drastically reduced. For the beam in Fig. 10-12(b), only three vertical displacements are considered, and hence the system is assumed to have three degrees of freedom in vibration analysis.

The concept of approximating a deformable system by a finite set of displacement components is very useful in displacement computation. The points on a structure arbitrarily chosen for this purpose are called *nodal points*. For framed structures it is logical to select the joints as nodal points. Thus, the degrees of freedom of such systems are approximated by the number of unknown displacement components at the nodal points. For the pin-connected truss in Fig. 10-13(a), for example, there are eight nodal points, each of which can be specified by two displacement components, i.e., horizontal and vertical displacements. Since three of the displacement components are zero, there are 13 unknown displacements and the system has 13 degrees of freedom. Similarly, for the rigid frame in Fig. 10-13(b), there are six nodal points, each of which can be specified by three displacement components, i.e., rotation as well as horizontal and vertical displacements. Since the nodal points A, B, and C are completely fixed, there are nine unknown displacement components resulting from the three remaining nodal points. Hence, the system has nine degrees of freedom if all components of displacements are considered as important.

Figure 10-13

Example 10-3. Compute the displacement components at joint O of the simple truss in Fig. 10-14(a). The areas of the members in square inches are indicated along the members. $E = 30 \times 10^3$ ksi.

This truss is a statically indeterminate structure that will be solved by the displacement method. Hence, we are no longer interested in the degree of statical indeterminacy of the system. Instead, we should determine the degrees of kinematic indeterminacy, which are the same as the degrees of freedom. Since only one joint in the structure is free to move, and the movement can be defined by the horizontal and vertical components of displacement of this joint, the structure has two degrees of freedom or kinematic indeterminacy. Let the horizontal and vertical displacements at joint O be denoted by u and v, respectively, with positive directions indicated in the figure. From the conditions of equilibrium of joint O, we have

$$P = k_{11}u + k_{12}v$$
$$Q = k_{21}u + k_{22}v$$

(a)

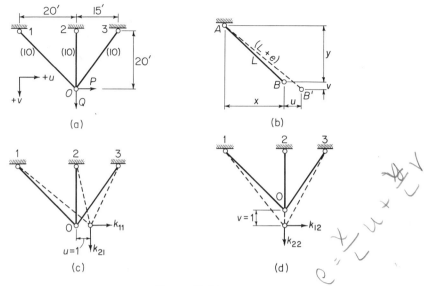

Figure 10-14

where

k_{11} = the force at joint O in the direction of P due to a unit displacement in the direction of u while the displacement in the direction of v is prevented,

k_{12} = the force at joint O in the direction of P due to a unit displacement in the direction of v while the displacement in the direction of u is prevented,

k_{21} = the force at joint O in the direction of Q due to a unit displacement in the direction of u while the displacement in the direction of v is prevented,

k_{22} = the force at joint O in the direction of Q due to a unit displacement in the direction of v while the displacement in the direction of u is prevented.

In order to evaluate these coefficients, let us establish the relation between the displacement of joints and the deformation of members in a system. Consider first a single member of length L whose horizontal and vertical projections are x and y, respectively, as shown in Fig. 10-14(b). If joint A of the member is hinged and joint B moves to point B' as the result of an elongation e in the member, the horizontal and vertical displacements of end B may be denoted by u and v respectively. From the relations of right triangles, we have

$$L^2 = x^2 + y^2 \tag{b}$$

and

$$(L + e)^2 = (x + u)^2 + (y + v)^2 \tag{c}$$

Expanding Eq. (c), we obtain

$$L^2 + 2Le + e^2 = x^2 + 2xu + u^2 + y^2 + 2yv + v^2$$

Since the deformation of a member is very small in comparison with its length, the higher-order terms of deformation and displacements are negligible. Then, Eq. (c) becomes

$$L^2 + 2Le = x^2 + 2xu + y^2 + 2vy$$

Subtracting Eq. (b) from this equation, we obtain

$$2Le = 2xu + 2yv$$

or

$$e = \frac{x}{L}u + \frac{y}{L}v \tag{d}$$

in which x/L and y/L are the direction cosines of the lines representing the member.

Let us denote the quantities pertaining to members 01, 02, and 03 of the truss shown in Fig. 10-14(a) by subscripts 1, 2, and 3, respectively. Assuming that the bar forces are in tension and that joint O displaces in the positive directions of u and v, we obtain from Eq. (d)

$$e_1 = \frac{20}{20\sqrt{2}}u + \frac{20}{20\sqrt{2}}v = 0.707u + 0.707v$$

$$e_2 = 0 + \frac{20}{20}v = v \tag{e}$$

$$e_3 = -\frac{15}{25}u + \frac{20}{25}v = -0.6u + 0.8v$$

These are the conditions of compatibility of the system. Using for force-deformation relation $e = FL/EA$, Eqs. (e) become

$$\frac{F_1(20\sqrt{2})(12)}{(30 \times 10^3)(10)} = 0.707u + 0.707v$$

$$\frac{F_2(20)(12)}{(30 \times 10^3)(10)} = v$$

$$\frac{F_3(25)(12)}{(30 \times 10^3)(10)} = -0.6u + 0.8v$$

or

$$F_1 = 625u + 625v$$

$$F_2 = 1,250v \tag{f}$$

$$F_3 = -600u + 800v$$

Hence, the bar forces in the truss can be obtained from Eqs. (f) after the displacement components u and v are obtained.

We can also make use of Eqs. (f) in determining the bar forces due to a unit displacement $u = 1$ or $v = 1$ at joint O. For $u = 1$ and $v = 0$ as shown in Fig.

10-14(c), we have

$$F_1 = 625, \qquad F_2 = 0, \qquad F_3 = -600$$

Then, from the equations of equilibrium of joint O, we get

$$k_{11} = (0.707)(625) - (0.6)(-600) = 802 \text{ kips/in.}$$

$$k_{21} = (0.707)(625) + (1)(0) + (0.8)(-600) = -38 \text{ kips/in.}$$

Similarly, for $u = 0$ and $v = 1$ as shown in Fig. 10-14(d), we have

$$F_1 = 625, \qquad F_2 = 1,250, \qquad F_3 = 800$$

Then, from the equilibrium of joint O, we obtain

$$k_{12} = (0.707)(625) - (0.6)(800) = -38 \text{ kips/in.}$$

$$k_{22} = (0.707)(625) + (1)(1,250) + (0.8)(800) = 2,332 \text{ kips/in.}$$

After these coefficients are obtained, the displacement components u and v can be computed from the solution of Eqs. (a). That is,

$$P = 802u - 38v$$

$$Q = -38u + 2,332v$$

For $P = 100$ kips and $Q = 200$ kips, we find $u = 0.129$ in. and $v = 0.088$ in. The bar forces in the truss are then found from Eqs. (f) to be $F_1 = 135$ kips, $F_2 = 110$ kips and $F_3 = -7$ kips.

Example 10-4. Find the horizontal displacements of the joints for the rigid frame in Fig. 10-15(a), assuming that the flexural stiffnesses of the girders are rigid ($EI = $ infinity) in comparison with the vertical members, all of which have the same EI ($E = 30$ ksi and $I = 500$ in.^{4}).

Since the girders are assumed to be rigid there is no rotation of joints, but the frame will displace laterally under the action of the horizontal forces P_1 and P_2. Hence, this rigid frame has two degrees of freedom, resulting in a horizontal displacement d_1 for both joint 1 and joint 4 at level 1, and a horizontal displacement of d_2 for both joint 2 and joint 5 at level 2.

The end moments of the vertical members due to joint translation are given in Table 7-4 of Chapter 7. Thus, for the vertical member shown in Fig. 10-15(b), the end moment is given by

$$M = \frac{6EI}{L^2} \Delta$$

Noting the joint of inflection at the mid-point of length L, the end shear is

$$S = \frac{M}{L/2} = \frac{12EI}{L^3} \Delta$$

Note also that the designer's sign convention is used for moments and shears in Fig. 10-15(b) when it is viewed from right to left.

The horizontal force at each level of the rigid frame is resisted equally by the end shears from two vertical members of the same EI. If one of the girders in the

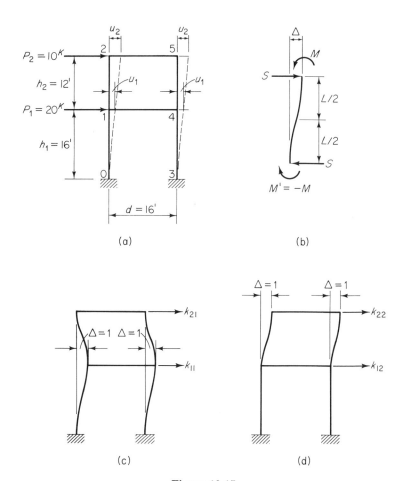

Figure 10-15

rigid frame is permitted to move horizontally, then the joints at both ends of the girder will have the same displacement. Hence, the effect of two vertical members will be double that of each vertical member. Referring to Figs. 10-15(c) and (d), the stiffness influence coefficients for the rigid frame are defined as follows;

k_{11} = the force at level 1 in the direction of P_1 to cause a unit displacement at level 1.

k_{21} = the force at level 2 in the direction of P_2 to prevent the displacement at level 2 as a result of a unit displacement at level 1.

k_{22} = the force at level 2 in the direction of P_2 to cause a unit displacement at level 2.

k_{12} = the force at level 1 in the direction of P_1 to prevent the displacement at level 1 as a result of a unit displacement at level 2.

Considering the sign convention in Fig. 10-15(b) and the displacement configuration in Figs. 10-15(c) and (d), we have

$$k_{11} = 2\left(\frac{12EI}{h_2^3}\right) + 2\left(\frac{12EI}{h_1^3}\right) = \frac{189EI}{9000}$$

$$k_{21} = -2\left(\frac{12EI}{h_2^3}\right) = -\frac{EI}{72}$$

$$k_{22} = 2\left(\frac{12EI}{h_2^3}\right) = \frac{EI}{72}$$

$$k_{12} = -2\left(\frac{12EI}{h_2^3}\right) = -\frac{EI}{72}$$

Then, the equation of equilibrium at each level can be expressed in terms of the stiffness influence coefficients. These equations for levels 1 and 2 are, respectively,

$$k_{11}u_1 + k_{12}u_2 = P_1$$

$$k_{21}u_1 + k_{22}u_2 = P_2$$

or

$$\frac{189EI}{9000}u_1 - \frac{EI}{72}u_2 = 20$$

$$-\frac{EI}{72}u_1 + \frac{EI}{72}u_2 = 10$$

from which we obtain

$$u_1 = \frac{16,875}{4EI} = \frac{(16,875)(12^3)}{(4)(30,000)(500)} = 0.486 \text{ in.}$$

$$u_2 = \frac{19,755}{4EI} = 0.567 \text{ in.}$$

Example 10-5. Determine the moments at the interior supports 1, 2 and 3 of the continuous beam in Fig. 10-8(a) of Example 10-2 by the displacement method.

The deflected shape of the beam is shown in Fig. 10-16(a) with the angular displacements (rotations) at the supports designated by θ_0, θ_1, θ_2, θ_3, and θ_4. Due to the symmetry of the beam and loading, it is obvious that $\theta_0 = \theta_4$, $\theta_1 = \theta_3$, and $\theta_2 = 0$. Furthermore, since the beam is simply supported at joints 0 and 4, i.e., the moments M_0 and M_4 equal zero, we need not find θ_0 and θ_4 if we take into account the support conditions at joints 0 and 4 when we determine the rotational stiffnesses of the exterior spans.

Referring to Eqs. (7-2) and (7-3) in Chapter 7, we define the rotational stiffness at joint j in a beam (i, j) of span length L as the end moment at joint j which causes a unit rotation at end j. If the far end i of the beam is simply supported or hinged, the rotational stiffness at end j is given by

$$K_{ji} = \frac{M}{\theta_{ji}} = \frac{3EI}{L}$$

(a)

(b)

Figure 10-16

Where M is the moment applied at joint j and θ_{ji} is the rotation at end j. If the far end i of the beam is fixed, then the rotational stiffness at end j is

$$K_{ji} = \frac{M}{\theta_{ji}} = \frac{4EI}{L}$$

The fixed-end moments for a beam (i, j) of span length L under a uniform load w can be found from Tables 7-2 and 7-3 in Chapter 7. For a beam with end i being simply supported, the fixed-end moment at end j is

$$M^f_{ji} = -\frac{wL^2}{8}$$

If both ends of the beams are fixed, then the fixed-end moments at i and j are, respectively,

$$M^F_{ij} = -\frac{wL^2}{12} \qquad \text{and} \qquad M^F_{ji} = -\frac{wL^2}{12}$$

Note that the designer's sign convention is used in the development of these expressions in Chapter 7.

Due to the symmetry of the continuous beam in Fig. 10-16(a), we need to find only M_1 and M_2 at supports 1 and 2, respectively. The direction of rotation θ_1 at joint 1 is chosen according to the assumed deflected shape of the beam. A positive result will confirm that the assumed direction is correct, and a negative result will indicate that the opposite is true. As noted earlier, $\theta_2 = 0$ at joint 2. When the spans are isolated as free-body diagrams as shown in Fig. 10-16(b), each end moment may be regarded as the superposition of the fixed-end moment and a moment caused by the rotation at that joint. For the exterior span 1–0, $\theta_{10} = \theta_1$; then the moment caused by the rotation at joint 1 is $k_{10}\theta_{10}$. Hence,

$$M_{10} = M^f_{10} + K_{10}\theta_{10} = -\frac{wL^2}{8} + \frac{3EI}{L}\theta_1 \qquad (a)$$

For the interior span 1–2, $\theta_{12} = \theta_1$ and $\theta_{21} = 0$. The moment produced by the rotation at each end will be carried over to the far end by a carry-over factor of $-\frac{1}{2}$.

Thus,

$$M_{12} = M_{12}^F + \left(K_{12}\theta_{12} - \frac{1}{2}K_{21}\theta_{21}\right)$$

$$= -\frac{wL^2}{12} - \frac{4EI}{L}\theta_1 \qquad\qquad\qquad (b)$$

$$M_{21} = M_{21}^F + \left(K_{21}\theta_{21} - \frac{1}{2}K_{12}\theta_{12}\right)$$

$$= -\frac{wL^2}{12} + \frac{2EI}{L}\theta_1 \qquad\qquad\qquad (c)$$

From the equilibrium of moments at each joint in Fig. 10-16(b), we have $M_{10} = M_{12}$ at joint 1. Substituting Eqs. (a) and (b) into the relation, we obtain

$$-\frac{wL^2}{8} + \frac{3EI}{L}\theta_1 = -\frac{wL^2}{12} - \frac{4EI}{L}\theta_1$$

from which

$$\theta_1 = \frac{wL^3}{168EI}$$

The condition of $M_{21} = M_{23}$ at joint 2 leads to a zero identity because of symmetry, but this condition is not needed for computing M_{21} since $\theta_2 = 0$. Thus, the moment at support 1 can be obtained from either Eq. (a) or (b), i.e.,

$$M_1 = M_{10} = M_{12} = -\frac{3}{28}wL^2$$

and the moment at support 2 is computed by Eq. (c), i.e.,

$$M_2 = M_{21} = -\frac{1}{14}wL^2$$

The results of M_1 and M_2 can be checked by using the reactions obtained in Example 10-2. Thus, for $R_0 = (11/28)wL$ and $R_1 = (8/7)wL$,

$$M_1 = \frac{11}{28}wL^2 - \frac{1}{2}wL^2 = -\frac{3}{28}wL^2$$

$$M_2 = \frac{22}{28}wL^2 + \frac{8}{7}wL^2 - 2wL^2 = -\frac{1}{14}wL^2$$

As expected, the results are identical whether the problem is solved by the force method or the displacement method.

This example illustrates a special application of the displacement (stiffness) method in the sense that the angular displacements (rotations) at the supports are computed first, and the moments at the supports are then obtained from these displacements. Such an approach linking the end rotations to end moments of each member in continuous beams or rigid frames is referred to as the *slope-deflection method*. A more general and systematic approach that involves the construction of a set of stiffness coefficients for the entire structure by synthesizing those for individual members will be introduced in Chapter 12.

In the development of Castigliano's theorems in Section 9-8, we observed that they are applicable to the analysis of linearly elastic systems. Consider, for example, a linear elastic system subject to a set of loads $P_1, P_2, \ldots, P_m$, producing displacements $s_1, s_2, \ldots, s_m$ at the points of application of these loads in the directions of the respective loads. Let U be the strain energy function which may be used to derive the external forces or the displacements at their points of application. Then, according to Castigliano's first theorem,

$$P_j = \frac{\partial U}{\partial s_j} \qquad (j = 1, 2, \ldots, m) \tag{10-5}$$

and from Castigliano's second theorem,

$$s_j = \frac{\partial U}{\partial P_j} \qquad (j = 1, 2, \ldots, m) \tag{10-6}$$

For the displacement method of analysis, Castigliano's first theorem may be used to express the conditions of equilibrium; for the force method of analysis, Castigliano's second theorem may be used to express the conditions of compatibility. With traditional emphasis on the force method of analysis, the second theorem has been cast in a more important role than the first theorem. Castigliano himself contributed to such an unbalanced emphasis by stressing the numerous applications of the second theorem and called it the *theorem of least work*.[*] He stated that, among all the statically possible states of stress in a structure subjected to a variation of stress during which the conditions of equilibrium are maintained, the correct one is that which makes the strain energy of the system a minimum.

Consider, for example, a linearly elastic system with r redundant forces $X_1, X_2, \ldots, X_r$, the points of application of which remain unchanged in their positions during deformation under the action of external loads. According to Castigliano's second theorem

$$\frac{\partial U}{\partial X_j} = 0 \qquad (j = 1, 2, \ldots, r) \tag{10-7a}$$

This set of equations is interpreted as follows: Of all possible sets of values that the redundant forces in the system may assume, the correct set of values is that which makes the strain energy U a minimum. Since one equation is obtained for each redundant force, a set of equations corresponding to the conditions of compatibility will result.

Castigliano further extended the theorem of least work to systems that are self-strained. In that case, the point of application of a redundant force X_j

---

[*]See A. Castigliano, *Théorème de l' Équilibre des Systèmes Élastiques et ses Applications,* 1879; Eng. trans, E. S. Andrews, *Elastic Stresses in Structures* (London: Scott, Greenwood & Son, 1919), p. 18.

may be displaced by an amount λ_j in the direction of the force. Hence,

$$\frac{\partial U}{\partial X_j} = \lambda_j \qquad (j = 1, 2, \ldots, r) \tag{10-7b}$$

For example, the self-straining may be caused by the settlement of the support of a redundant reaction by an amount of $-\lambda_j$ or by the initial misfit of a member by an amount λ_j too short. In the former, the negative sign of λ_j indicates that the direction of the settlement is opposite to that of the redundant reaction; in the latter, λ_j is positive for a member too short because the tension caused by the stretching of the member to its desired length is in the same direction as the deformation.

In examining Eq. (10-7b), it appears that the interpretation of minimum strain energy is rather artificial although the equation itself is as useful as Eq. (10-7a) for obtaining the conditions of compatibility for redundant systems. Southwell suggested that Castigliano's theorem of least work, in effect, means that the strain energy of a linearly elastic system that is initially unstrained will have less strain energy stored in it when subjected to a load system than it would have if it were self-strained.[*] Charlton further argued that a true principle of least work should be associated with the determination of the equations of equilibrium of self-straining systems.[†] Hence, if certain prescribed deflections are introduced to a linear elastic structure, the other deflections assume values such that the strain energy of the structure is a minimum. Actually, Eqs. (10-7) represent a theorem imposing the conditions of compatibility and need not be associated with a minimum of strain energy. Hence, the theorem should not be given a different name, especially not the misnomer "the theorem of least work." In this text, we shall refer to it as Castigliano's second theorem.

Example 10-6. Determine the bar forces and joint displacements in the truss shown in Example 10-3 using Castigliano's first theorem if $P = 100$ kips and $Q = 200$ kips.

For this problem, the conditions of compatibility have been previously established in Example 10-3 as follows:

$$e_1 = 0.707u + 0.707v$$

$$e_2 = v \tag{a}$$

$$e_3 = -0.6u + 0.8v$$

and from the force-deformation relation $e = FL/AE$, the internal forces have been obtained as follows:

$$F_1 = 625u + 625v$$

---

[*]See R. V. Southwell, "On Castigliano's Theorem of Least Work and the Principle of St. Venant," *Philosophical Magazine* (London), 6th ser., vol. 45 (1923), p. 193

[†]See T. M. Charlton, *Energy Principles in Applied Statics* (London: Blackie & Son, 1959), p. 24.

$$F_2 = 1{,}250v$$

$$F_3 = -600u + 800v \qquad \text{(b)}$$

The strain energy of the linear elastic system is given by

$$U = \tfrac{1}{2} \sum Fe = \tfrac{1}{2}F_1 e_1 + \tfrac{1}{2}F_2 e_2 + \tfrac{1}{2}F_3 e_3$$

in which

$$\tfrac{1}{2}F_1 e_1 = \tfrac{1}{2}(625u + 625v)(0.707u + 0.707v) = 221u^2 + 442uv + 221v^2$$

$$\tfrac{1}{2}F_2 e_2 = \tfrac{1}{2}(1{,}250v)v = 625v^2$$

$$\tfrac{1}{2}F_3 e_3 = \tfrac{1}{2}(-600u + 800v)(-0.6u + 0.8v) = 180u^2 - 480uv + 320v^2$$

Hence,

$$U = 401u^2 - 38uv + 1{,}166v^2 \qquad \text{(c)}$$

By using Castigliano's first theorem, we obtain

$$P = \frac{\partial U}{\partial u} = 802u - 38v$$

and

$$\qquad \text{(d)}$$

$$Q = \frac{\partial U}{\partial v} = -38u + 2{,}332v$$

Equations (d) are the equation of equilibrium expressed in terms of displacements and stiffness coefficients. For $P = 100$ kips and $Q = 200$ kips we obtain from the solution of Eqs. (d) that $u = 0.129$ in. and $v = 0.088$ in.

The bar forces are computed from Eqs. (b) after u and v are evaluated. Thus, $F_1 = 135$ kips, $F_2 = 110$ kips and $F_3 = -7$ kips.

Example 10-7. Derive the equation of compatibility for the continuous truss shown in Fig. 10-17(a) if the center support is considered as a redundance.

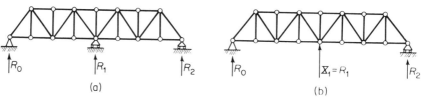

(a)   (b)

Figure 10-17

Let the center support be removed and replaced by a force $X_1 = R_1$ as shown in Fig. 10-17(b). The released structure is statically equivalent to the original structure. Then, the bar force in a member of the original truss due to the external loads may be given by

$$F = F' + X_1 f_1 \qquad \text{(a)}$$

in which F' is the bar force in the same member of the released structure due to the external loads when $X_1 = 0$, and f_1 is the bar force in the same member of the released structure due to $X_1 = 1$ with no other external loads.

According to Eq. (9-17a), the strain energy in the original truss is as follows:

$$U = \frac{1}{2} \sum \frac{F^2 L}{AE} \qquad (b)$$

By using Castigliano's second theorem, we obtain

$$\frac{\partial U}{\partial X_1} = \sum \frac{FL}{AE} \frac{\partial F}{\partial X_1} = 0 \qquad (c)$$

From Eq. (9-26a), we have

$$\frac{\partial F}{\partial X_1} = f_1 \qquad (d)$$

Substituting Eqs. (a) and (d) into Eq. (c), we get

$$\sum \frac{F'L f_1}{AE} + X_1 \sum \frac{f_1^2 L}{AE} = 0 \qquad (e)$$

This is the equation of compatibility for the statically indeterminate truss. We note from the principle of virtual work,

$$\delta_1' = \sum \frac{F'L f_1}{AE} \qquad \text{and} \qquad \delta_{11} = \frac{f_1^2 L}{AE}$$

in which δ_1' is the vertical deflection of point 1 of the released structure due to external loads when $R_1 = 0$, and δ_{11} is the vertical deflection of point 1 of the released structure due to $R_1 = 1$ without other external loads. Thus, the redundant reaction of the truss may be obtained from Eq. (e) as follows:

$$X_1 = -\frac{\displaystyle\sum \frac{F'L f_1}{AE}}{\displaystyle\sum \frac{f_1^2 L}{AE}} = -\frac{\delta_1'}{\delta_{11}} \qquad (f)$$

Example 10-8. For the rigid frame in Fig. 10-18(a), determine the redundant forces by Castigliano's second theorem. The bending stiffness EI is constant for all members.

The rigid frame is statically indeterminate to three degrees and we can select any three stress resultants as redundances. The components of reaction at support D, for example, may be chosen as redundances as shown in Fig. 10-18(b). After the redundances are obtained, the stress resultants at any section of the frame can readily be determined. Using Castigliano's second theorem, the equations of compatibility will be obtained automatically without the necessity of matching the displacements at the point where the redundances are introduced. Thus, it is just as simple to choose as redundances the stress resultants at an intermediate point as those at a support of the frame. Owing to the symmetry of this problem, there is much to be gained by choosing redundant forces that preserve the symmetry of the released structure, for example, selecting the stress resultants at the midpoint of member BC as redundances, as shown in Fig.

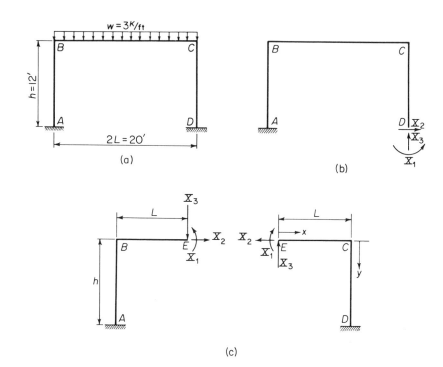

Figure 10-18

10-18(c). From the condition of symmetry, it is obvious that the shear force $X_3 = 0$ because its existence would violate the symmetry of the structure and the loading. Thus, we need only two equations of compatibility instead of three for the statically equivalent structure shown in Fig. 10-18(c).

The strain energy due to axial force and shear is small in comparison with that due to bending and can therefore be neglected in establishing the strain energy expression. Thus,

$$U = \Sigma \int \frac{M^2 \, ds}{EI}$$

By using Castigliano's second theorem, we have

$$\frac{\partial U}{\partial X_1} = 0 \quad \text{or} \quad \Sigma \int \frac{M \, ds}{EI} \frac{\partial M}{\partial X_1} = 0 \qquad \text{(a)}$$

$$\frac{\partial U}{\partial X_2} = 0 \quad \text{or} \quad \Sigma \int \frac{M \, ds}{EI} \frac{\partial M}{\partial X_2} = 0 \qquad \text{(b)}$$

At a point between E and C of the frame, we have

$$M = X_1 - \frac{wx^2}{2}$$

$$\frac{\partial M}{\partial X_1} = 1 \quad \text{and} \quad \frac{\partial M}{\partial X_2} = 0$$

At a point between C and D of the frame, we get

$$M = X_1 - X_2 y - \frac{wL^2}{2}$$

$$\frac{\partial M}{\partial X_1} = 1 \quad \text{and} \quad \frac{\partial M}{\partial X_2} = -y$$

Because of the symmetry, the moment at a point in EB is identical to that in EC, and the moment at a point in BA is the same as that in CD. Since EI is constant throughout the entire frame, it may be eliminated from Eqs. (a) and (b). Then, Eqs. (a) and (b) may be expressed as functions of X_1 and X_2 as follows:

$$\Sigma \int M \frac{\partial M}{\partial X_1} \, ds = 2 \int_0^L \left(X_1 - \frac{wx^2}{2}\right)(1) \, dx + 2 \int_0^h \left(X_1 - X_2 y - \frac{wL^2}{2}\right)(1) \, dy$$

$$= 2\left[X_1 x - \frac{wx^3}{6}\right]_0^L + 2\left[X_1 y - X_2 \frac{y^2}{2} - \frac{wL^2 y}{2}\right]_0^h = 0$$

or

$$2(L + h)X_1 - h^2 X_2 - wL^3\left(\frac{1}{3} + \frac{h}{L}\right) = 0 \tag{a'}$$

$$\Sigma \int M \frac{\partial M}{\partial X_2} \, ds = 2 \int_0^L \left(X_1 - \frac{wx^2}{2}\right)(0) \, dx + 2 \int_0^h \left(X_1 - X_2 y - \frac{wL^2}{2}\right)(-y) \, dy$$

$$= -2\left[X_1\left(\frac{y^2}{2}\right) - X_2\left(\frac{y^3}{3}\right) - \frac{wL^2 y^2}{4}\right]_0^h = 0$$

or

$$-h^2 X_1 + \frac{2h^3}{3}X_2 + \frac{wL^2 h^2}{2} = 0 \tag{b'}$$

By substituting the values of $w = 3$ kips/ft, $L = 10$ ft, and $h = 12$ ft into Eqs. (a') and (b'), we get

$$44X_1 - 144X_2 = 4{,}600$$

$$-144X_1 + 1{,}152X_2 = -21{,}600$$

from which we obtain $X_1 = 73.1$ ft-kips and $X_2 = -9.6$ kips.

10-7 CHOICE OF REDUNDANT FORCES

In analyzing statically indeterminate systems, the amount of computation often can be minimized through a judicious choice of redundant forces. Consider the problem originally analyzed in Example 10-2 and shown again in Fig. 10-19(a). Again, let us ignore for the moment the conditions of symmetry to preserve the generality of the problem, i.e., we suppose either the loading or the structure is asymmetric. If we were to proceed (in the manner followed in Example 10-2) by choosing three of the vertical sections of redundant forces, we

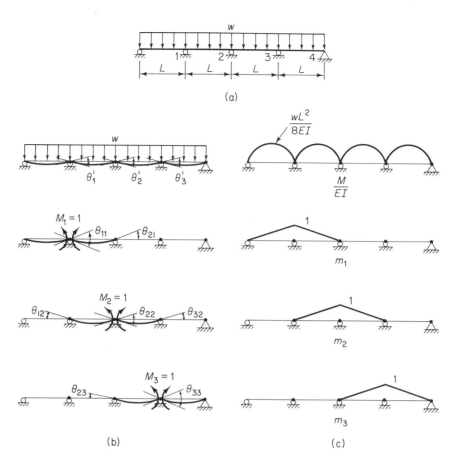

(a)

(b)   (c)

Figure 10-19

would be required to solve the three compatibility equations,

$$v_1' = v_{11}R_1 + v_{12}R_2 + v_{13}R_3$$

$$v_2' = v_{21}R_1 + v_{22}R_2 + v_{23}R_3 \qquad \text{(a)}$$

$$v_3' = v_{31}R_1 + v_{32}R_2 + v_{33}R_3$$

in which, as shown previously in Figure 10-8, all coefficients are nonzero.

Suppose, alternatively, we were to choose as redundant forces the bending moments at the same three reaction points. We would then be required to write compatibility conditions for the three rotations at these points. Hence,

$$\theta_1' = \theta_{11}M_1 + \theta_{12}M_2 + \theta_{13}M_3$$

$$\theta_2' = \theta_{21}M_1 + \theta_{22}M_2 + \theta_{23}M_3 \qquad \text{(b)}$$

$$\theta_3' = \theta_{31}M_1 + \theta_{32}M_2 + \theta_{33}M_3$$

In these equations θ_1', θ_2' and θ_3' are the relative rotations of members of the released structure at supporting points 1, 2, and 3, respectively, due to the applied distributed load. The terms θ_{ij} are the relative rotations between members at joint i due to a unit bending moment applied at joint j and, of course, $\theta_{ji} = \theta_{ij}$. These rotations are shown in Figure 10-19(b).

Note that in this alternative formulation the equations simplify somewhat, because $\theta_{13} = \theta_{31} = 0$. That is, for the released structure, a moment applied at joint 1 creates no relative rotation at joint 3 (and vice versa) owing to the presence of the hinges which stop the propagation of bending moments. In addition, if the beam were loaded only over part of its span, then some of the terms on the left side of Eq. (b) might be zero; for example, if the load were confined to the first span, then both θ_2' and θ_3' would equal zero.

If the coefficients are computed by using the method of virtual work, the resulting integrals for θ_i' and θ_{ij} are often simpler to evaluate when bending moments have been chosen as the redundant forces. This simplification is evident from the bending moments shown in Fig. 10-19(c). Note that

$$\theta_i' = \int \frac{Mm_i}{EI}\, dx \qquad (i = 1, 2, 3) \tag{c}$$

and

$$\theta_{ij} = \int \frac{m_i m_j}{EI}\, dx \qquad (i, j, = 1, 2, 3) \tag{d}$$

where the integration takes place over the entire structure, but m_i is nonzero over only two out of four spans in the present case. Thus, computation of θ_i' and θ_{ii} (i.e., where $i = j$) involves integration over one-half the structure, and computation of $\theta_{ij}(i \neq j)$ involves integration over only one-quarter the structure. Moreover, where the integrand is nonzero it takes a simple form, which may be easily evaluated. Table 10-2, which includes expressions for integrals formed by products of common bending moment functions, may be used to aid in the computations.

Finally, it should be mentioned that considerable simplification can accrue by exploiting conditions of symmetry. It may be seen from Fig. 10-19 that if both the loading and structure are symmetric, then $\theta_1' = \theta_3'$, $\theta_{11} = \theta_{33}$, $\theta_{12} = \theta_{32}$ (and in general $\theta_{ij} = \theta_{ji}$), and $M_1 = M_3$. This means that we need perform computations over only one-half the structure; indeed Eqs. (b) reduce to

$$\theta_1' = \theta_{11} M_1 + \theta_{12} M_2$$
$$\theta_2' = 2\theta_{21} M_1 + \theta_{22} M_2 \tag{e}$$

as the third equation becomes redundant. When confronted with a symmetric structure, one should choose redundants (whether forces or moments) that preserve symmetry. The computations simplify considerably, especially if the loading also is symmetric.

10-8 SIGN CONVENTIONS AND TABLES FOR BEAM MOMENTS

As noted in Section 3-2, the selection of sign conventions for axial forces, shear and moments is a matter of convenience. In dealing with beams bending in a single principal plane, it is convenient to define a bending moment at a section of a beam as positive if it tends to bend the beam into a concave curvature

Table 10-2 EVALUATION OF INTEGRALS $\int_0^L m_i m_j\, dx$

m_j \ m_i	m ▭ L	m ◁ L	m ▷ L	m △ a|b L
M ▭ L	mML	$\dfrac{mML}{2}$	$\dfrac{mML}{2}$	$\dfrac{mML}{2}$
M ◁ L	$\dfrac{mML}{2}$	$\dfrac{mML}{3}$	$\dfrac{mML}{6}$	$\dfrac{mM}{6}(L+b)$
M ◁ L	$\dfrac{mML}{2}$	$\dfrac{mML}{6}$	$\dfrac{mML}{3}$	$\dfrac{mM}{6}(L+a)$
M ◱ N L	$\dfrac{mL}{2}(M+N)$	$\dfrac{mL}{6}(2M+N)$	$\dfrac{mL}{6}(M+2N)$	$\dfrac{mM}{6}(L+b)$ $+\dfrac{mM}{6}(L+a)$
M △ $L/2\ \ L/2$	$\dfrac{mML}{2}$	$\dfrac{mML}{4}$	$\dfrac{mML}{4}$	$\dfrac{mM}{12b}(3L^2-4a^2)$
M △ c|d L	$\dfrac{mML}{2}$	$\dfrac{mM}{6}(L+d)$	$\dfrac{mM}{6}(L+c)$	For $c>a$, $\dfrac{mML}{6}\left[2-\dfrac{(c-a)^2}{bc}\right]$ For $c<a$, $\dfrac{mML}{6}\left[2-\dfrac{(a-c)^2}{ad}\right]$
Second degree parabola $(Q>M;\ Q>N)$ M ⌣ N $L/2\ \ L/2$	$\dfrac{mL}{6}(M+4Q+N)$	$\dfrac{mL}{6}(M+2Q)$	$\dfrac{mL}{6}(2Q+N)$	$\dfrac{m}{6L}(Mb^2+Na^2)$ $+\dfrac{mQ}{3L}(L^2+ab)$

causing tension in the bottom of the beam, and as negative otherwise. This is referred to as the *designer's sign convention*. If a member is either inclined or vertical, such as those in a rigid frame, the sign convention is also fully explained in Section 3-2. The designer's sign convention has been adopted up to this point in the text, including Tables 7-2, 7-3, and 7-4 for fixed-end moments in beams due to vertical loads and joint rotation or translation (Chapter 7), as well as Table 10-2 for evaluation of integrals involving products of beam moments in this chapter.

Since these tables are also useful for matrix methods of structural analysis in the subsequent chapters, it is important to note that the sign convention for beam moments in the matrix methods is different from the designer's sign convention. In later chapters, a bending moment at a section of a beam is defined as positive if it is counter clockwise, and as negative if it is clockwise (or, in general, positive in the direction of a positive global axis). This new sign convention for beam moments is a natural consequence of the definitions adopted for the matrix methods of structural analysis. Once the difference in the two sign conventions for beam moments is recognized, it is easy to convert from one convention to another when the need arises.

PROBLEMS

10-1. By using the force method of analysis, determine the horizontal reaction at support D of the frame shown in Fig. P10-1. $E = 30 \times 10^3$ ksi.

Figure P10-1   **Figure P10-2**

10-2. By using the force method of analysis, compute the moment at support B of the continuous beam shown in Fig. P10-2. $E = 30 \times 10^3$ ksi.

10-3. By using the displacement method of analysis, determine the horizontal and vertical displacements of joint O of the system shown in Fig. P10-3. The areas of the members in square inches are given along the members. $E = 30 \times 10^3$ ksi.

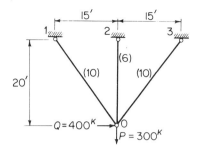

Figure P10-3

10-4. By using the displacement method of analysis, compute the vertical displacement of joint O of the system shown in Fig. P10-4. The area of the members in square inches are given along the members. $E = 30 \times 10^3$ ksi.

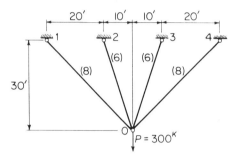

Figure P10-4

10-5 and **10-6.** By using the force method of analysis, determine the vertical reaction at support B of the structures shown in Figs. P10-5 and P10-6. $E = 30 \times 10^3$ ksi.

Figure P10-5

Figure P10-6

10-7 and **10-8.** Work Problems 10-3 and 10-4 using Castigliano's first theorem.

10-9 and **10-10.** Work Problems 10-5 and 10-6 using Castigliano's second theorem.

10-11 and **10-12.** Work Problems 10-1 and 10-2 using Castigliano's second theorem.

10-13. Find the reactions for the beam in Fig. P10-13, considering the vertical reactions at supports 1 and 2 as redundances in the application of the force method.

Figure P10-13

10-14. Find the reactions for the beam in Fig. P10-13, considering the vertical reaction and the moment at support 3 as redundances in the application of the force method.

11

Matrix Methods of Structural Analysis

11-1 MATRIX NOTATION AND OPERATIONS

The primary objective of this chapter is to introduce the stiffness and flexibility methods in the context of matrix algebra. Because we wish to emphasize fundamental concepts and the relationship between the two methods, we will concentrate on very simple systems composed of linearly elastic springs here. In subsequent chapters, we shall employ the methods to treat more realistic structural systems.

Since the analysis of linear structural systems often leads to a large system of linear equations, it is convenient to formulate such problems in matrix notation. Before introducing the concept of matrix methods, however, we shall briefly review matrix notation and operations. We shall designate matrices with boldface letters within brackets such as $[\mathbf{A}]$ and braces, $\{\mathbf{B}\}$.

A set of numbers or elements arranged in a rectangular array of m rows and n columns in the form

$$[\mathbf{A}] = \begin{bmatrix} a_{11} & a_{12} & \cdots & a_{1n} \\ a_{21} & a_{22} & \cdots & a_{2n} \\ \vdots & & & \\ a_{m1} & a_{m2} & \cdots & a_{mn} \end{bmatrix}$$

is called an $m \times n$ *matrix*. The numbers m and n are called the dimensions of the matrix. It is convenient to denote the matrix $[\mathbf{A}]$ in the abbreviated form

$$[\mathbf{A}] = [a_{ij}], \qquad i = 1, 2, \ldots, m, \qquad j = 1, 2, \ldots, n$$

in which a_{ij} denotes the element in the ith row and the jth column of $[\mathbf{A}]$. Matrices composed of a single row are called *row vectors*, and matrices composed of a single column are called *column vectors*. A row vector of $1 \times n$ is denoted by $[a_1, a_2, \ldots, a_n]$; a column vector of $m \times 1$ is denoted by $\{a_1, a_2, \ldots, a_m\}$. If the dimensions of a matrix are $m = n$, the matrix is called a *square matrix* of order m. The elements $a_{11}, a_{22}, \ldots, a_{mm}$ are called the *elements of the principal diagonal*. A square matrix whose elements are zero, except for those along the principal diagonal, is called a *diagonal matrix* and is sometimes designated by $\lceil \ \rfloor$. The special case of a diagonal matrix having all principal diagonal elements equal to unity is called a *unit matrix* or an *identity matrix* and is denoted by $[\mathbf{I}]$. A matrix of any dimensions whose elements all equal zero is called a *zero matrix*, and is designated by $[\mathbf{0}]$.

The interchange of rows and columns in a matrix is called the transpose of the matrix. The transpose of an $m \times n$ matrix $[\mathbf{A}] = [a_{ij}]$ is given by an $n \times m$ matrix $[\mathbf{A}]^T = [a_{ji}]$, or explicitly

$$[\mathbf{A}] = \begin{bmatrix} a_{11} & a_{12} & \cdots & a_{1n} \\ a_{21} & a_{22} & \cdots & a_{2n} \\ \vdots & & & \\ a_{m1} & a_{m2} & \cdots & a_{mn} \end{bmatrix} \quad \text{and} \quad [\mathbf{A}]^T = \begin{bmatrix} a_{11} & a_{21} & \cdots & a_{m1} \\ a_{12} & a_{22} & \cdots & a_{m2} \\ \vdots & & & \\ a_{1n} & a_{2n} & \cdots & a_{mn} \end{bmatrix}$$

The special case when either m or n equals one means that the transpose of a row vector is a column vector, and vice versa; i.e.,

$$[a_1, a_2, \ldots, a_n]^T = \{a_1, a_2, \ldots, a_n\}$$

Two matrices $[\mathbf{X}]$ and $[\mathbf{Y}]$ are equal only if they have the same dimensions and if their corresponding elements are equal. A matrix $[\mathbf{Z}]$ whose elements are the sums of the corresponding elements of $[\mathbf{X}]$ and $[\mathbf{Y}]$, having the same dimensions, is called the sum of $[\mathbf{X}]$ and $[\mathbf{Y}]$. Thus for $[\mathbf{Z}] = [\mathbf{X}] + [\mathbf{Y}]$,

$$\begin{bmatrix} z_{11} & z_{12} & \cdots & z_{1n} \\ z_{21} & z_{22} & \cdots & z_{2n} \\ \vdots & & & \\ z_{m1} & z_{m2} & \cdots & z_{mn} \end{bmatrix} = \begin{bmatrix} x_{11} + y_{11} & x_{12} + y_{12} & \cdots & x_{1n} + y_{1n} \\ x_{21} + y_{21} & x_{22} + y_{22} & \cdots & x_{2n} + y_{2n} \\ \vdots & & & \\ x_{m1} + y_{m1} & x_{m2} + y_{m2} & \cdots & x_{mn} + y_{mn} \end{bmatrix}$$

A matrix $[\mathbf{W}]$ whose elements are obtained by multiplying each of the elements of matrix $[\mathbf{X}]$ by a scalar k is called the product of the scalar k and the matrix $[\mathbf{X}]$. Thus for $[\mathbf{W}] = k[\mathbf{X}]$,

$$\begin{bmatrix} w_{11} & w_{12} & \cdots & w_{1n} \\ w_{21} & w_{22} & \cdots & w_{2n} \\ \vdots & & & \\ w_{m1} & w_{m2} & \cdots & w_{mn} \end{bmatrix} = \begin{bmatrix} kx_{11} & kx_{12} & \cdots & kx_{1n} \\ kx_{21} & kx_{22} & \cdots & kx_{2n} \\ \vdots & & & \\ kx_{m1} & kx_{m2} & \cdots & kx_{mn} \end{bmatrix}$$

Multiplication of two matrices $[\mathbf{X}]$ and $[\mathbf{Y}]$ is defined only if the number of columns of the former matrix equals the number of rows of the latter. Let $[\mathbf{X}]$

be an $m \times n$ matrix and $[\mathbf{Y}]$ be an $n \times p$ matrix. Then $[\mathbf{X}]$ can be *post-multiplied* by $[\mathbf{Y}]$ and the product $[\mathbf{Z}] = [\mathbf{X}][\mathbf{Y}]$ is an $m \times p$ matrix. The elements of $[\mathbf{Z}]$ are defined by

$$z_{ij} = [x_{i1}, x_{i2}, \ldots, x_{in}]\{y_{1j}, y_{2j}, \ldots, y_{nj}\}$$

$$= x_{i1}y_{1j} + x_{i2}y_{2j} + x_{in}y_{nj} = \sum_{k=1}^{n} x_{ik}y_{kj}$$

$$i = 1, 2, \ldots, m; \qquad j = 1, 2, \ldots, p$$

In general, the commutative law for multiplication of scalars does not hold for matrix multiplication; and in the above example, $[\mathbf{Y}]$ cannot be post-multiplied by $[\mathbf{X}]$. However, for square matrices of the same order, there are exceptions to this general rule. For example, if $[\mathbf{X}]$ is an $m \times m$ matrix and if $[\mathbf{I}]$ is a unit matrix of the same order, it can be shown that

$$[\mathbf{X}][\mathbf{I}] = [\mathbf{I}][\mathbf{X}] = [\mathbf{X}]$$

If a square matrix $[\mathbf{A}]$ is post-multiplied by a square matrix $[\mathbf{B}]$ of the same order, such that $[\mathbf{A}][\mathbf{B}] = [\mathbf{I}]$, then $[\mathbf{B}]$ is said to be the *inverse* of $[\mathbf{A}]$, and is denoted by $[\mathbf{B}] = [\mathbf{A}]^{-1}$. Furthermore,

$$[\mathbf{A}][\mathbf{A}]^{-1} = [\mathbf{A}]^{-1}[\mathbf{A}] = [\mathbf{I}]$$

For a square matrix of order m, the transpose is also a square matrix of the same order. The determinant whose elements are the elements of a square matrix $[\mathbf{A}]$ without disarrangement is said to be the *determinant of the matrix*, and is denoted by $|\mathbf{A}|$, that is,

$$|\mathbf{A}| = \begin{vmatrix} a_{11} & a_{12} & \cdots & a_{1m} \\ a_{21} & a_{22} & \cdots & a_{2m} \\ \vdots & & & \\ a_{m1} & a_{m2} & \cdots & a_{mm} \end{vmatrix}$$

The *adjoint* of $[\mathbf{A}]$ is defined as the transpose of the matrix formed by the cofactors (minors with signs) in place of the original element. Let $[\mathbf{C}]$ be the adjoint of $[\mathbf{A}]$. Then

$$[\mathbf{C}] = \begin{bmatrix} c_{11} & c_{21} & \cdots & c_{m1} \\ c_{12} & c_{22} & \cdots & c_{m2} \\ \vdots & & & \\ c_{1m} & c_{2m} & \cdots & c_{mm} \end{bmatrix}$$

where

$$c_{ij} = (-1)^{i+j} \times \text{minor of } a_{ij}$$

If $|\mathbf{A}| = 0$, the matrix $[\mathbf{A}]$ is said to be *singular* and does not possess an inverse. From a theorem on the expansion of determinants, it can be shown that for $|\mathbf{A}| \neq 0$,

$$[\mathbf{A}]^{-1} = \frac{[\mathbf{C}]}{|\mathbf{A}|}$$

It should also be noted that the transpose of an inverse is identical to the inverse of the transpose of a matrix.

11-2 MATRIX REPRESENTATION OF LINEAR EQUATIONS

For a system of m linearly independent equations in m variables given in the form

$$a_{11}x_1 + a_{12}x_2 + \cdots + a_{1m}x_m = b_1$$
$$a_{21}x_1 + a_{22}x_2 + \cdots + a_{2m}x_m = b_2$$
$$\vdots$$
$$a_{m1}x_1 + a_{m2}x_2 + \cdots + a_{mm}x_m = b_m$$

the coefficients can be detached from the variables in the matrix representation as follows:

$$\begin{bmatrix} a_{11} & a_{12} & \cdots & a_{1m} \\ a_{21} & a_{22} & \cdots & a_{2m} \\ \vdots & & & \\ a_{m1} & a_{m2} & \cdots & a_{mm} \end{bmatrix} \begin{Bmatrix} x_1 \\ x_2 \\ \vdots \\ x_m \end{Bmatrix} = \begin{Bmatrix} b_1 \\ b_2 \\ \vdots \\ b_m \end{Bmatrix}$$

Let $[\alpha_{ij}]$ be the inverse of the detached coefficients $[a_{ij}]$ such that

$$\begin{bmatrix} a_{11} & a_{12} & \cdots & a_{1m} \\ a_{21} & a_{22} & \cdots & a_{2m} \\ \vdots & & & \\ a_{m1} & a_{m2} & \cdots & a_{mm} \end{bmatrix} \begin{bmatrix} \alpha_{11} & \alpha_{12} & \cdots & \alpha_{1m} \\ \alpha_{21} & \alpha_{22} & \cdots & \alpha_{2m} \\ \vdots & & & \\ \alpha_{m1} & \alpha_{m2} & \cdots & \alpha_{mm} \end{bmatrix} = \begin{bmatrix} 1 & 0 & \cdots & 0 \\ 0 & 1 & \cdots & 0 \\ \vdots & & & \\ 0 & 0 & \cdots & 1 \end{bmatrix}$$

Then the variables in the system of equations are given correspondingly by

$$\begin{Bmatrix} x_1 \\ x_2 \\ \vdots \\ x_m \end{Bmatrix} = \begin{bmatrix} 1 & 0 & \cdots & 0 \\ 0 & 1 & \cdots & 0 \\ \vdots & & & \\ 0 & 0 & \cdots & 1 \end{bmatrix} \begin{Bmatrix} x_1 \\ x_2 \\ \vdots \\ x_m \end{Bmatrix}$$

or

$$\begin{Bmatrix} x_1 \\ x_2 \\ \vdots \\ x_m \end{Bmatrix} = \begin{bmatrix} \alpha_{11} & \alpha_{12} & \cdots & \alpha_{1m} \\ \alpha_{21} & \alpha_{22} & \cdots & \alpha_{2m} \\ \vdots & & & \\ \alpha_{m1} & \alpha_{m1} & \cdots & \alpha_{mm} \end{bmatrix} \begin{Bmatrix} b_1 \\ b_2 \\ \vdots \\ b_m \end{Bmatrix} = \begin{Bmatrix} \overline{b}_1 \\ \overline{b}_2 \\ \vdots \\ \overline{b}_m \end{Bmatrix}$$

in which

$$x_i = \bar{b}_i = \sum_{k=1}^{m} \alpha_{ik} b_k, \qquad i = 1, 2, \ldots, m$$

In compact notation, the system of m linear equations and its solution can be expressed as follows:

$$[\mathbf{A}]\{\mathbf{x}\} = \{\mathbf{b}\}$$

and

$$\{\mathbf{x}\} = [\mathbf{I}]\{\mathbf{x}\} = [\alpha]\{\mathbf{b}\} = \{\bar{\mathbf{b}}\}$$

11-3 GENERALIZED COORDINATES AND FORCES

In previous chapters we have solved for the deformation of trusses and frames, and there the translations and rotations at the joints (*nodes* or *nodal points*) of members were central to the discussion. While it might seem logical to attach significance to the displacements of the nodes of structures, we must now offer a precise rationale for doing so. This is motivated by our desire to describe the behavior of a structure in terms of force and displacement vectors having finite dimensions. We wish to assure that if the displacements are known at the finite number of nodal points on a structure, then the internal forces and displacements (or stresses and strains) may be computed unambiguously at all of the infinite number of points lying between any two nodal points.

Accordingly, we define the set of *generalized coordinates* (or *generalized displacements*) of a structure as the set of displacements required to describe the structure's configuration. We refer to *generalized forces* as those forces or moments which correspond to the generalized coordinates. The unconstrained generalized coordinates of the node points correspond to the degrees of freedom of the structure. Thus, for each translational degree of freedom at a node point on the structure there corresponds a force at that point in the direction of the specified degree of freedom; similarly, for each rotational degree of freedom there corresponds a moment.

We shall elaborate on this idea, without offering formal proof, by referring first to the planar two-bar truss shown in Fig. 11-1(a). Under a load applied at node 2 (the only point on the structure at which an arbitrarily directed load may be placed while producing only axial member forces), the joint will exhibit displacements u_2 and v_2 in the x and y directions, respectively. Nodes 1 and 3 are, of course, restrained against displacement. Insofar as nodal displacements are concerned, therefore, u_2 and v_2 completely define the configuration of the truss. Moreover, the displacement of any material point of the structure may be expressed in terms of u_2 and v_2 by recognizing that the bars remain straight as they deform. Thus a point that is located a distance x along the horizontal member of length L will displace an amount $u(x) = u_2 x/L$ in the x direction and $v(x) = v_2 x/L$ in the y direction.

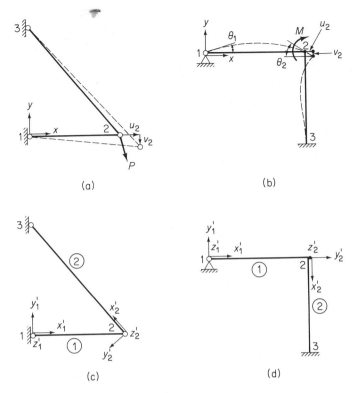

Figure 11-1

Now consider a simple planar frame, as shown in Fig. 11-1(b), which is subjected to a concentrated moment at node 2 and thus exhibits both bending and axial deformation of its members. We recall that the displacement of a material point within a flexural member is related in general to the rotation of the cross section as well as to the translation of the centroid of the cross section. Because node 1 is restrained against translation and node 3 is completely restrained, the translations u_2, v_2 and the rotations θ_1, θ_2 are the only nonzero nodal displacements. The cross-sectional rotation and translation at any point of the frame may be determined from these four generalized coordinates, as will be explained in Chapter 12.

Three important points may be further noted. First, for plane frameworks, the displacements of each unrestrained node are defined by two translations and one rotation, although for plane trusses only the two joint translations enter the formulation. Second, for systems exhibiting bending deformations, such as the frame in Fig. 11-1(b), the transverse deflections due to axial deformation often are negligible compared with deflections associated with rotations of the joints. In such cases translational degrees of freedom at the nodes usually may be either reduced in number or neglected entirely, and hence the total number of generalized coordinates entering the formulation may be reduced significantly. This simply implies that bending deformation may be accurately estimated while assuming the member to be axially inextensible. Finally, as regards generalized forces, the truss in Fig. 11-1(a) will admit two such forces (corresponding to u_2 and v_2), which simply will be the horizontal and vertical components of the load P applied at node 2. Similarly the generalized forces for the frame in Fig. 11-1(b) are associated with translations u_2 and v_2 and rotations θ_1 and θ_2. Generalized forces play an important role in cases where members are loaded between their ends. Just as the joint displacements of a member that is loaded at its ends determine directly the displacements between the joints, so may the generalized forces at the joints be used to represent loading applied between the joints. The most important consequence is our ability to formulate matrix analyses in terms of generalized forces and displacements regardless of how the actual loading is distributed over the structure.

11-4 LOCAL AND GLOBAL COORDINATE SYSTEMS

To describe the deformations of the horizontal members shown in Figs. 11-1(a) and (b), we referred to the location of the point of interest along the members as x, since the coordinate system was located at the left end of each member. If we also wish to describe the displacements of points in the remaining member of either structure in terms of its joint displacements, we might logically do so by defining a new coordinate system originating at one of the end points as shown in Figs. 11-1(c) and (d). For several reasons we shall find it convenient to define a single *global coordinate system* for an entire structure along with a set of *local coordinate systems* for the members comprising the structure. The global coordinate system generally will be designated as the x–y–z right-handed system where, for planar structures, the z-axis is normal to the plane of the members. Each local coordinate system will be designated as x'–y'–z', where x' will be directed along the member's axis and y' and z' will be directed along principal axes of the cross section. For planar structures z' will have the same sense as z.

We shall henceforth define positive translations and rotations at the ends of a member in the positive directions of the coordinate axes. The same definition will apply to positive generalized forces (forces and moments). Occasions will often arise when we must express nodal displacements and forces in terms of both local and global axes. When we discuss the behavior of an individual structural element, we shall usually find it convenient to use the local (member) coordinate system. When we discuss the interaction of the members comprising the structure, however, it will be necessary to use a common (global) coordinate system. As we shall subsequently see, the transformation between local and global coordinate systems is a routine occurrence in the application of matrix methods.

To facilitate the transformation of coordinates, we first assume that *all* generalized displacements in a structure are unrestrained. Later the constraint conditions are prescribed to prevent any rigid-body movement. For general three-dimensional frameworks, the generalized displacements of each node are then defined by three translations and three rotations, while for space trusses they are defined by three translations only. Hence, the vector incorporating all generalized displacements is larger (i.e., it has more rows) than that incorporating only the unconstrained generalized displacements. Strictly speaking, we refer to the set of all generalized displacements as comprising the degrees of freedom of the system, while the set of unconstrained generalized displacements comprises the *active* degrees of freedom of the system.

11-5 SYSTEM STIFFNESS AND FLEXIBILITY MATRICES

Let us consider a structure that is restrained against rigid-body motion and whose deformation may be characterized by n generalized coordinates Δ_1, $\Delta_2, \ldots, \Delta_n$, representing n *active* degrees of freedom. That is, the structure must be kinematically stable and remain in equilibrium. Thus, for a plane structure which must have at least three components of reaction, n is at least three degrees of freedom less than that of a structure completely unrestrained against rigid-body motion. If we consider the system to be linearly elastic and to undergo small displacements when subjected to the generalized forces P_1, $P_2, \ldots, P_n$ corresponding to $\Delta_1, \Delta_2, \ldots, \Delta_n$, then we may write the relationship between forces and displacements in matrix form as

$$
\begin{Bmatrix} \Delta_1 \\ \Delta_2 \\ \vdots \\ \Delta_n \end{Bmatrix} = \begin{bmatrix} f_{11} & f_{12} & \cdots & f_{1n} \\ f_{21} & f_{22} & \cdots & f_{2n} \\ \vdots & \vdots & \vdots & \vdots \\ f_{n1} & f_{n2} & \cdots & f_{nn} \end{bmatrix} \begin{Bmatrix} P_1 \\ P_2 \\ \vdots \\ P_n \end{Bmatrix} \tag{11-1a}
$$

The terms f_{ij} represent *deflection influence coefficients*, or *flexibility coefficients*, relating the displacement Δ_i to the force P_j. Indeed f_{ij} is numerically equal to Δ_i when $P_j = 1$ while all other applied forces are equal to zero. We may write Eq. (11-1a) in compact notation as

$$
\{\Delta_f\} = [\mathscr{F}]\{P_f\} \tag{11-1b}
$$

Thus, the displacement and force vectors, $\{\Delta_f\}$ and $\{P_f\}$, are related through the *global flexibility matrix* or *system flexibility matrix* $[\mathscr{F}]$. The subscript f indicates that the displacements and forces are those pertaining to the free (i.e., unrestrained) nodes; restrained nodes, at which displacements are zero, are the reaction points.

We can just as readily write the relationship between generalized displacements and forces for a structure restrained against rigid-body motion in the following form:

$$
\begin{Bmatrix} P_1 \\ P_2 \\ \vdots \\ P_n \end{Bmatrix} = \begin{bmatrix} k_{11} & k_{12} & \cdots & k_{1n} \\ k_{21} & k_{22} & \cdots & k_{2n} \\ \vdots & \vdots & \vdots & \vdots \\ k_{n1} & k_{n2} & \cdots & k_{nn} \end{bmatrix} \begin{Bmatrix} \Delta_1 \\ \Delta_2 \\ \vdots \\ \Delta_n \end{Bmatrix} \tag{11-2a}
$$

in which the terms k_{ij} are the *stiffness coefficients*. The term k_{ij} is numerically equal to the force P_i associated with $\Delta_j = 1$ while all other displacements are set equal to zero. Since these generalized displacements represent only the *active* degrees of freedom of the system, i.e., the displacements which are non-zero, we may express Eq. (11-2a) simply as

$$\{\mathbf{P}_f\} = [\mathbf{K}_{ff}]\{\Delta_f\} \qquad (11\text{-}2b)$$

in which $[\mathbf{K}_{ff}]$ is called the *reduced global stiffness matrix* or *reduced system stiffness matrix*. If the elements of $[\mathbf{K}_{ff}]$ are known, and all the displacements comprising $\{\Delta_f\}$ are prescribed, then we may solve Eq. (11-2b) directly for the forces $\{\mathbf{P}_f\}$. Conversely, if all the applied forces are prescribed and (necessarily) all the displacements are unknown, we may solve Eq. (11-2b) to obtain

$$\{\Delta_f\} = [\mathbf{K}_{ff}]^{-1}\{\mathbf{P}_f\} \qquad (11\text{-}3)$$

where $[\mathbf{K}_{ff}]^{-1}$ is the inverse of $[\mathbf{K}_{ff}]$. Comparing Eqs. (11-1b) and (11-3), we see that

$$[\mathcal{F}] = [\mathbf{K}_{ff}]^{-1} \qquad (11\text{-}4)$$

that is, the system flexibility matrix is equal to the inverse of the reduced system stiffness matrix.

In the sequel we shall often refer to both the system stiffness matrix $[\mathbf{K}]$ and the *reduced* system stiffness matrix $[\mathbf{K}_{ff}]$. The distinction between the two is as follows: $[\mathbf{K}]$ represents the relationship between *all* generalized forces (including reactions) that act on the structure and *all* generalized displacements (including those that are prescribed, usually as zero, at the reactions); thus

$$\{\mathbf{P}\} = [\mathbf{K}]\{\Delta\} \qquad (11\text{-}5)$$

where $\{\mathbf{P}\}$ and $\{\Delta\}$ are the vectors of all generalized forces and displacements, respectively. Because $\{\Delta\}$ includes rigid-body movement, $[\mathbf{K}]$ does not possess an inverse. $[\mathbf{K}_{ff}]$, however, represents the relationship between applied forces (i.e., forces *exclusive* of reactions) and all nonprescribed generalized displacements, as implied by Eq. (11-2b). We shall demonstrate later that $[\mathbf{K}_{ff}]$ may be easily extracted from $[\mathbf{K}]$.

It may be recalled from the discussion in Chapter 10 that, according to the Maxwell-Betti reciprocal theorem, a force P_i, acting through a displacement caused by force P_j, does the same amount of work as force P_j does while acting through a displacement caused by P_i. Thus

$$P_i(f_{ij}P_j) = P_j(f_{ji}P_i)$$

or

$$f_{ij} = f_{ji} \qquad (11\text{-}6)$$

The reciprocal theorem thus ensures that for a linearly elastic structure undergoing small displacements, the flexibility matrix $[\mathcal{F}]$ is *symmetric*. Similarly, because of Eq. (11-4), $k_{ij} = k_{ji}$; that is, the reduced stiffness matrix $[\mathbf{K}_{ff}]$ also is symmetric. These symmetry properties add greatly to the efficiency of computing the flexibility and stiffness matrices, storing them in a computer, and solving the force-displacement equations.

It should be noted that very seldom are *all* the forces that act on a structure known at the outset. Rather, some forces are usually known, while other (reactions) are unknown. Similarly, some displacements (those at the reaction points) usually are known, while others are unknown. Thus, we are usually confronted with a mixture of known and unknown quantities on either side of the force-displacement equations, Eq. (11-5). This may be handled routinely, but it is important to remember that at every point on the structure (i.e., corresponding to every degree of freedom), *either* a generalized force *or* a generalized displacement (but not both) *must* be prescribed.

Example 11-1. For the truss with three active degrees of freedom shown in Fig. 11-2(a), the unconstrained displacements in the directions of P_1, P_2, and P_3 are Δ_1, Δ_2, and Δ_3, respectively. Determine symbolically (a) the system flexibility matrix, (b) the reduced system stiffness matrix, and (c) the system stiffness matrix.

(a)

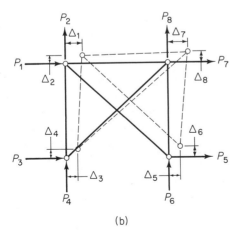

(b)

Figure 11-2

Let f_{ij} represent the flexibility coefficient which equals Δ_i for $P_j = 1$ while all other applied forces are equal to zero. Noting that P_1, P_2, and P_3 are known applied forces while the components of reactions are unknown, the relationship between displacements and forces can be expressed in terms of the system flexibility matrix as follows:

$$\begin{Bmatrix} \Delta_1 \\ \Delta_2 \\ \Delta_3 \end{Bmatrix} = \begin{bmatrix} f_{11} & f_{12} & f_{13} \\ f_{21} & f_{22} & f_{23} \\ f_{31} & f_{32} & f_{33} \end{bmatrix} \begin{Bmatrix} P_1 \\ P_2 \\ P_3 \end{Bmatrix}$$

or

$$\{\mathbf{\Delta}_f\} = [\mathscr{F}]\{\mathbf{P}_f\}$$

Similarly, let k_{ij} represent the stiffness coefficient which equals the force P_i for $\Delta_j = 1$ while all other displacements are set equal to zero. If we consider only the applied forces for which $\Delta_j \neq 0$, we have the relationship between forces and displacements in terms of the reduced system stiffness matrix as follows:

$$\begin{Bmatrix} P_1 \\ P_2 \\ P_3 \end{Bmatrix} = \begin{bmatrix} k_{11} & k_{12} & k_{13} \\ k_{21} & k_{22} & k_{23} \\ k_{31} & k_{32} & k_{33} \end{bmatrix} \begin{Bmatrix} \Delta_1 \\ \Delta_2 \\ \Delta_3 \end{Bmatrix}$$

or

$$\{\mathbf{P}_f\} = [\mathbf{K}_{ff}]\{\mathbf{\Delta}_f\}$$

However, if we include the reactions and associated displacements, as shown in Fig. 11-2(b), the unrestrained structure has eight degrees of freedom. Thus, the relationship between forces and displacements in terms of the system stiffness matrix is:

$$\begin{Bmatrix} P_1 \\ P_2 \\ P_3 \\ P_4 \\ P_5 \\ P_6 \\ P_7 \\ P_8 \end{Bmatrix} = \begin{bmatrix} k_{11} & k_{12} & k_{13} & k_{14} & k_{15} & k_{16} & k_{17} & k_{18} \\ k_{21} & k_{22} & k_{23} & k_{24} & k_{25} & k_{26} & k_{27} & k_{28} \\ k_{31} & k_{32} & k_{33} & k_{34} & k_{35} & k_{36} & k_{37} & k_{38} \\ k_{41} & k_{42} & k_{43} & k_{44} & k_{45} & k_{46} & k_{47} & k_{48} \\ k_{51} & k_{52} & k_{53} & k_{54} & k_{55} & k_{56} & k_{57} & k_{58} \\ k_{61} & k_{62} & k_{63} & k_{64} & k_{65} & k_{66} & k_{67} & k_{68} \\ k_{71} & k_{72} & k_{73} & k_{74} & k_{75} & k_{76} & k_{77} & k_{78} \\ k_{81} & k_{82} & k_{83} & k_{84} & k_{85} & k_{86} & k_{87} & k_{88} \end{bmatrix} \begin{Bmatrix} \Delta_1 \\ \Delta_2 \\ \Delta_3 \\ \Delta_4 \\ \Delta_5 \\ \Delta_6 \\ \Delta_7 \\ \Delta_8 \end{Bmatrix}$$

or

$$\{\mathbf{P}\} = [\mathbf{K}]\{\mathbf{\Delta}\}$$

Note that the system flexibility matrix $[\mathscr{F}]$ is the inverse of the reduced system stiffness matrix $[\mathbf{K}_{ff}]$. Consequently, the unknown displacements associated with the applied forces P_1, P_2, and P_3 in Fig. 11-2(a) can be obtained from the relationship involving the system flexibility matrix $[\mathscr{F}]$. On the other hand, the displacements at the supports of a structure are usually prescribed, i.e., $\Delta_4 = 0$, $\Delta_5 = 0, \ldots, \Delta_8 = 0$, but the components of reactions $P_4, P_5, \ldots, P_8$ are unknown. More generally $\Delta_4, \Delta_5, \ldots, \Delta_8$ may be prescribed values other than zero, e.g., the supports may settle vertically or shift horizontally. Then, a rigid body movement may take place, and $[\mathbf{K}]$ does not possess an inverse.

Since the force-displacement relationship involving the system stiffness matrix contains a mixture of known and unknown quantities on either side of the

Matrix Methods of Structural Analysis   Chap. 11

equation, it is convenient to partition the system stiffness matrix according to these known and unknown quantities. For example, the known applied forces P_1, P_2, and P_3 are associated with unknown displacements Δ_1, Δ_2, and Δ_3, respectively, while unknown reactions P_4, P_5, . . . , P_8 are associated with known prescribed values of Δ_4, Δ_5, . . . ,Δ_8, respectively. Thus, at every node of the truss in Fig. 11-2(b), either a generalized force or a generalized displacement must be prescribed, but neither none nor both of force and displacement in the same direction may be specified at any node. Furthermore, if we prescribe $\Delta_4 = 0$, . . . , $\Delta_8 = 0$, we can extract $[\mathbf{K}_{ff}]$ from $[\mathbf{K}]$ by eliminating all stiffness coefficients associated with Δ_4, . . . , Δ_8 and with P_4, . . . , P_8. This simple extraction process holds, however, only when all these displacements are prescribed to be zero. If at least one nonzero displacement is prescribed, a more general procedure must be used to extract $[\mathbf{K}_{ff}]$ from $[\mathbf{K}]$.

11-6 THE STIFFNESS METHOD

The objective of developing the stiffness method is to formulate and solve the stiffness equations, Eq. (11-2b). We do this by constructing the system stiffness matrix $[\mathbf{K}]$, from which $[\mathbf{K}_{ff}]$ may be derived, by assembling information concerning the stiffness of all members that the structure comprises.

We shall demonstrate the basic steps in this chapter by referring first to conceptually very simple structural assemblies involving linearly elastic springs, deferring to Chapter 12 the application of this method to trusses and frames.* It should be noted from the outset that, because the equations of interest relate applied forces to displacements, the three fundamental concepts of deformable body mechanics must be employed; that is, for both the structure as a whole and the individual components of the structure,

1. forces must satisfy equilibrium,
2. stress-strain (or force-deformation) relations must be satisfied, and
3. deformations must be geometrically compatible.

Consider the single elastic spring, shown in Fig. 11-3(a), which can resist only axial forces. We may first identify the generalized coordinates of this one-element structure as Δ_1 and Δ_2, the axial displacements at the ends of the spring. Corresponding to the two generalized coordinates, Δ_1 and Δ_2, are two generalized forces, P_1 and P_2. We may then express the relationship between forces and displacements as

$$\begin{Bmatrix} P_1 \\ P_2 \end{Bmatrix} = \begin{bmatrix} k_{11} & k_{12} \\ k_{21} & k_{22} \end{bmatrix} \begin{Bmatrix} \Delta_1 \\ \Delta_2 \end{Bmatrix} \qquad (11\text{-}7)$$

The immediate question at hand is: What are the coefficients k_{ij} $(i, j = 1, 2)$ of the stiffness matrix in terms of the elastic properties of the system (i.e., the

*The use of springs to explain matrix methods follows H. C. Martin, *Introduction to Matrix Methods of Structural Analysis*, (New York: McGraw-Hill 1966).

(a)

(b)

$P_1 \xrightarrow{\quad} \bullet \xrightarrow{\quad} F$ $F \xleftarrow{\quad} \bullet \xleftarrow{\quad} P_2$
Node 1   Node 2

(c)   (d)   **Figure 11-3**

spring constant k)? Before answering this question, let us emphasize that the one-element structure is a special case forming the basis for treating an assemblage of springs. Hence, the stiffness matrix Eq. (11-7) is referred to as the *element stiffness matrix*. By considering the elastic spring as a free body in Fig. 11-3(b), the internal spring force F must satisfy the force-deformation relationship

$$F = k\delta \quad \text{or} \quad k = \frac{F}{\delta}$$

where δ is the displacement (positive for elongation) of the spring corresponding to the internal force (positive for tension), and k is called the spring constant, which is defined as the force required to produce a unit displacement between the ends of the spring.

To find the coefficients k_{ij} of the stiffness matrix, we first note that if node 2 is restrained ($\Delta_2 = 0$), then the relative displacement between nodes 1 and 2 equals $\Delta_1 = -\delta$ and the spring force is $P_1 = -F$ as shown in Fig. 11-3(c). Then,

$$k = \frac{F}{\delta} = \frac{-P_1}{-\Delta_1} = \frac{P_1}{\Delta_1}$$

or

$$P_1 = k\Delta_1 \tag{11-8a}$$

Alternatively, if node 1 is restrained ($\Delta_1 = 0$), we observe from Fig. 11-3(d) that $\Delta_2 = \delta$ and $P_2 = F$. Hence,

$$P_2 = k\Delta_2 \tag{11-8b}$$

Note also that in Fig. 11-3(a) P_1 and P_2 must satisfy equilibrium; i.e.,

$$P_1 = -P_2$$

Thus, for the case $\Delta_2 = 0$,

$$P_2 = -k\Delta_1 \tag{11-8c}$$

and for the case $\Delta_1 = 0$,

$$P_1 = -k\Delta_2 \tag{11-8d}$$

In the general case for which neither Δ_1 nor Δ_2 is set equal to zero, we may combine Eqs. (11-8) and write

$$\begin{Bmatrix} P_1 \\ P_2 \end{Bmatrix} = \begin{bmatrix} k & -k \\ -k & k \end{bmatrix} \begin{Bmatrix} \Delta_1 \\ \Delta_2 \end{Bmatrix} \qquad (11\text{-}9)$$

Comparing Eqs. (11-9) and (11-7), we find that the element stiffness matrix for a single spring is

$$[\mathbf{K}] = \begin{bmatrix} k_{11} & k_{12} \\ k_{21} & k_{22} \end{bmatrix} = k \begin{bmatrix} 1 & -1 \\ -1 & 1 \end{bmatrix} \qquad (11\text{-}10)$$

It may be recalled that in formulating Eqs. (11-8), we employed the force-deformation relationship for the spring. Also, equilibrium of forces was satisfied. Compatibility conditions were not employed explicitly, as the system comprises only a single structural element. However, satisfaction of internal compatibility of the spring was tacitly assumed through the use of the force-deformation relationship.

Note also that the element stiffness matrix in Eq. (11-10) is also the system stiffness matrix for the one-element structure. It does not possess an inverse, implying that the spring would undergo arbitrarily large displacements if it were subjected to a combination of prescribed forces $\{P_1, P_2\}$. As we shall observe subsequently in more detail, the stiffness matrix is invertible only so long as arbitrary rigid-body motion of the structure has been eliminated. In other words, if either Δ_1 or Δ_2 were prescribed, then the remaining displacement could be calculated.

Because the system considered above comprises a single spring, the relationship between applied loads and resulting displacements could be derived in a straightforward manner. The corresponding relationship, i.e., the system stiffness matrix, for systems comprising multiple elements may be constructed systematically. The methods of assembling the system stiffness matrix and for solving the stiffness equations are described in the sequel.

11-7 FORMULATION OF THE SYSTEM STIFFNESS MATRIX

Now let us consider a simple assemblage of two springs having, in general, different spring constants k_1 and k_2, as shown in Fig. 11-4(a). In principle, an assemblage of more than two elements can be treated in the same way. The generalized coordinates required to define the axial deformation of the assemblage are Δ_1, Δ_2, and Δ_3, and the corresponding generalized forces are P_1, P_2, and P_3. We wish to determine the system stiffness matrix $[\mathbf{K}]$ that relates $\{P_1, P_2, P_3\}$ to $\{\Delta_1, \Delta_2, \Delta_3\}$; that is, we wish to find the elements k_{ij} in

$$\begin{Bmatrix} P_1 \\ P_2 \\ P_3 \end{Bmatrix} = \begin{bmatrix} k_{11} & k_{12} & k_{13} \\ k_{21} & k_{22} & k_{23} \\ k_{31} & k_{32} & k_{33} \end{bmatrix} \begin{Bmatrix} \Delta_1 \\ \Delta_2 \\ \Delta_3 \end{Bmatrix} \qquad (11\text{-}11)$$

Figure 11-4

Formulation of [**K**] from basic principles. We proceed by considering equilibrium of forces at the nodes, compatibility of deformations, and the force-deformation relationships for the individual elements. First, referring to the free-body diagrams of Figs. 11-4(b) and (c), we may express equilibrium at each node in terms of the applied loads P_1, P_2, and P_3 and the internal spring forces F_1 and F_2; i.e.,

$$P_1 + F_1 = 0$$
$$P_2 - F_1 + F_2 = 0$$
$$P_3 - F_2 = 0$$

or, in matrix form

$$\begin{Bmatrix} P_1 \\ P_2 \\ P_3 \end{Bmatrix} = \begin{bmatrix} -1 & 0 \\ 1 & -1 \\ 0 & 1 \end{bmatrix} \begin{Bmatrix} F_1 \\ F_2 \end{Bmatrix} \qquad (11\text{-}12\text{a})$$

Symbolically, we may write Eq. (11-12a) as

$$\{\mathbf{P}\} = [\mathbf{B}]\{\mathbf{F}\} \qquad (11\text{-}12\text{b})$$

where $\{\mathbf{P}\}$ is the vector of loads including both applied forces and reactions, $\{\mathbf{F}\}$ is the vector of unknown member forces, and [**B**] is defined as the *system statics matrix*.

If we define the elongation of the two springs as δ_1 and δ_2, as in Fig. 11-4(b), then we may express these quantities in terms of the nodal displacements Δ_1, Δ_2, and Δ_3 as

$$\delta_1 = \Delta_2 - \Delta_1$$
$$\delta_2 = \Delta_3 - \Delta_2$$

Matrix Methods of Structural Analysis   Chap. 11

This compatibility condition may be written in matrix form as

$$\begin{Bmatrix} \delta_1 \\ \delta_2 \end{Bmatrix} = \begin{bmatrix} -1 & 1 & 0 \\ 0 & -1 & 1 \end{bmatrix} \begin{Bmatrix} \Delta_1 \\ \Delta_2 \\ \Delta_3 \end{Bmatrix} \qquad (11\text{-}13a)$$

or, symbolically, as

$$\{\boldsymbol{\delta}\} = [\mathbf{A}]\{\boldsymbol{\Delta}\} \qquad (11\text{-}13b)$$

where $\{\boldsymbol{\delta}\}$ is the vector of element deformations (elongations here), $\{\boldsymbol{\Delta}\}$ is the vector of nodal displacements including those at reaction points, and $[\mathbf{A}]$ is termed the *system kinematics matrix*.

Finally the force-deformation relationship for the elements may be expressed as

$$F_1 = k_1 \delta_1$$

$$F_2 = k_2 \delta_2$$

In matrix form,

$$\begin{Bmatrix} F_1 \\ F_2 \end{Bmatrix} = \begin{bmatrix} k_1 & 0 \\ 0 & k_2 \end{bmatrix} \begin{Bmatrix} \delta_1 \\ \delta_2 \end{Bmatrix} \qquad (11\text{-}14a)$$

or

$$\{\mathbf{F}\} = [\mathcal{K}]\{\boldsymbol{\delta}\} \qquad (11\text{-}14b)$$

where $[\mathcal{K}]$ is formed by listing the member stiffnesses along the main diagonal; it is therefore termed the *matrix of member stiffnesses*. Note that this matrix specifies the relationship between internal forces and internal deformations of all the unassembled springs in the system. It is not to be confused with the element stiffness matrix which relates the generalized forces and generalized displacements of the nodes at the ends of an individual spring in the system.

By substituting Eqs. (11-13) into Eqs. (11-14), and substituting the resultant into Eqs. (11-12), we obtain

$$\begin{Bmatrix} P_1 \\ P_2 \\ P_3 \end{Bmatrix} = \begin{bmatrix} -1 & 0 \\ 1 & -1 \\ 0 & 1 \end{bmatrix} \begin{bmatrix} k_1 & 0 \\ 0 & k_2 \end{bmatrix} \begin{bmatrix} -1 & 1 & 0 \\ 0 & -1 & 1 \end{bmatrix} \begin{Bmatrix} \Delta_1 \\ \Delta_2 \\ \Delta_3 \end{Bmatrix} \qquad (11\text{-}15a)$$

or

$$\{\mathbf{P}\} = [\mathbf{B}][\mathcal{K}][\mathbf{A}]\{\boldsymbol{\Delta}\} \qquad (11\text{-}15b)$$

The matrix multiplication in Eq. (11-15a) may be carried out to yield

$$\begin{Bmatrix} P_1 \\ P_2 \\ P_3 \end{Bmatrix} = \begin{bmatrix} k_1 & -k_1 & 0 \\ -k_1 & k_1 + k_2 & -k_2 \\ 0 & -k_2 & k_2 \end{bmatrix} \begin{Bmatrix} \Delta_1 \\ \Delta_2 \\ \Delta_3 \end{Bmatrix} \qquad (11\text{-}16a)$$

This may be written symbolically as

$$\{\mathbf{P}\} = [\mathbf{K}]\{\boldsymbol{\Delta}\} \qquad (11\text{-}16b)$$

where, in view of Eq. (11-15b), we find

$$[\mathbf{K}] = [\mathbf{B}][\mathcal{K}][\mathbf{A}] \tag{11-17}$$

It is apparent from Eqs. (11-15) that

$$[\mathbf{B}] = [\mathbf{A}]^T \tag{11-18}$$

which is a general property, the proof of which is provided in Section 11-14. Thus the system matrix $[\mathbf{K}]$ may be expressed in terms of the matrix of member stiffnesses $[\mathcal{K}]$ as

$$[\mathbf{K}] = [\mathbf{A}]^T[\mathcal{K}][\mathbf{A}] = [\mathbf{B}][\mathcal{K}][\mathbf{B}]^T \tag{11-19}$$

The foregoing development included the equilibrium relationship between all external forces $\{\mathbf{P}\}$ (which normally include reactions as well as applied loads) and internal forces $\{\mathbf{F}\}$, as expressed by Eqs. (11-12); and the corresponding compatibility conditions that relate generalized displacements at all nodes (including nodes that would be reaction points) $\{\boldsymbol{\Delta}\}$ and internal deformations $\{\boldsymbol{\delta}\}$, as given by Eqs. (11-13).

We could have equally well imposed boundary conditions from the outset and constructed the formulation around $\{\mathbf{P}_f\}$ and $\{\boldsymbol{\Delta}_f\}$; i.e., Eq. (11-12a) is reduced to

$$\{\mathbf{P}_f\} = [\mathbf{B}]\{\mathbf{F}\} \tag{11-20a}$$

and Eq. (11-13a) becomes

$$\{\boldsymbol{\delta}\} = [\mathbf{A}]\{\boldsymbol{\Delta}_f\} \tag{11-20b}$$

with $[\mathbf{A}]$ and $[\mathbf{B}]$ being reformulated appropriately, but still possessing the property indicated by Eq. (11-18). This approach would have led to the formulation of $[\mathbf{K}_{ff}]$ instead of $[\mathbf{K}]$ as given by Eq. (11-17). Consider, for example, the system shown in Fig. 11-4(a) for which P_1 and P_2 are known applied loads, while $\Delta_3 = 0$ is a prescribed displacement; thus P_3 is an unknown reaction. Then, as indicated by the equilibrium conditions associated with the free bodies shown in Fig. 11-4(b),

$$\begin{Bmatrix} P_1 \\ P_2 \end{Bmatrix} \equiv \{\mathbf{P}_f\} = \begin{bmatrix} -1 & 0 \\ 1 & -1 \end{bmatrix} \begin{Bmatrix} F_1 \\ F_2 \end{Bmatrix}$$

Also, compatibility requirements indicate that

$$\begin{Bmatrix} \delta_1 \\ \delta_2 \end{Bmatrix} \equiv \{\boldsymbol{\Delta}_f\} = \begin{bmatrix} -1 & 1 \\ 0 & -1 \end{bmatrix} \begin{Bmatrix} \Delta_1 \\ \Delta_2 \end{Bmatrix}$$

Hence,

$$[\mathbf{B}] = [\mathbf{A}]^T = \begin{bmatrix} -1 & 0 \\ 1 & -1 \end{bmatrix}$$

and, according to Eq. (11-17) and the foregoing argument,

$$[\mathbf{K}_{ff}] = \begin{bmatrix} -1 & 0 \\ 1 & -1 \end{bmatrix} \begin{bmatrix} k_1 & 0 \\ 0 & k_2 \end{bmatrix} \begin{bmatrix} -1 & 1 \\ 0 & -1 \end{bmatrix} = \begin{bmatrix} k_1 & -k_1 \\ -k_1 & (k_1 + k_2) \end{bmatrix}$$

This expression for $[\mathbf{K}_{ff}]$ agrees, of course, with the first two rows and columns of $[\mathbf{K}]$ given by Eq. (11-16a). As we shall see later, there is an advantage to formulating $[\mathbf{K}]$ and extracting $[\mathbf{K}_{ff}]$ from it, particularly if boundary restraints are subject to change or if nonzero displacements are prescribed at some nodes.

Formulation of $[\mathbf{K}]$ by the direct stiffness method. It is possible to circumvent much of the preceding formalism and matrix operations in deriving the system stiffness matrix by employing the so-called *direct stiffness method*. This method, while necessarily still incorporating the conditions of force equilibrium, displacement compatibility and force-displacement relationships, permits the system stiffness matrix to be formulated through the direct superposition of stiffness matrices for the individual structural elements. To see how this works, let us return to the previous example and write the stiffness matrix appearing in Eqs. (11-16), while denoting above each column the pertinent generalized coordinate and next to each row the corresponding generalized force:

$$[\mathbf{K}] = \begin{matrix} & \Delta_1 & \Delta_2 & \Delta_3 & \\ & \begin{bmatrix} k_1 & -k_1 & 0 \\ -k_1 & k_1 + k_2 & -k_2 \\ 0 & -k_2 & k_2 \end{bmatrix} & \begin{matrix} P_1 \\ P_2 \\ P_3 \end{matrix} \end{matrix} \qquad (11\text{-}21)$$

Also, in view of Eq. (11-10), we may write the element stiffness matrices $[\mathbf{k}^{(1)}]$ and $[\mathbf{k}^{(2)}]$ for the two individual springs that the assemblage comprises as

$$[\mathbf{k}^{(1)}] = \begin{matrix} & \Delta_1 & \Delta_2 & \\ & \begin{bmatrix} k_1 & -k_1 \\ -k_1 & k_1 \end{bmatrix} & \begin{matrix} P_1 \\ P_2 \end{matrix} \end{matrix}$$

and

$$[\mathbf{k}^{(2)}] = \begin{matrix} & \Delta_2 & \Delta_3 & \\ & \begin{bmatrix} k_2 & -k_2 \\ -k_2 & k_2 \end{bmatrix} & \begin{matrix} P_2 \\ P_3 \end{matrix} \end{matrix}$$

If we wish to assign to these element stiffness matrices the same order as pertains to the system stiffness matrix, then we may write

$$[\mathbf{k}^{(1)}] = \begin{matrix} & \Delta_1 & \Delta_2 & \Delta_3 & \\ & \begin{bmatrix} k_1 & -k_1 & 0 \\ -k_1 & k_1 & 0 \\ 0 & 0 & 0 \end{bmatrix} & \begin{matrix} P_1 \\ P_2 \\ P_3 \end{matrix} \end{matrix} \qquad (11\text{-}22a)$$

and

$$[\mathbf{k}^{(2)}] = \begin{matrix} & \Delta_1 & \Delta_2 & \Delta_3 & \\ & \begin{bmatrix} 0 & 0 & 0 \\ 0 & k_2 & -k_2 \\ 0 & -k_2 & k_2 \end{bmatrix} & \begin{matrix} P_1 \\ P_2 \\ P_3 \end{matrix} \end{matrix} \qquad (11\text{-}22b)$$

Having $[\mathbf{k}^{(1)}]$ and $[\mathbf{k}^{(2)}]$ in this form, we may add Eqs. (11-22) directly to obtain

$$[\mathbf{k}^{(1)}] + [\mathbf{k}^{(2)}] = \begin{matrix} \Delta_1 & \Delta_2 & \Delta_3 \\ \begin{bmatrix} k_1 & -k_1 & 0 \\ -k_1 & k_1 + k_2 & -k_2 \\ 0 & -k_2 & k_2 \end{bmatrix} & & \end{matrix}\begin{matrix} P_1 \\ P_2 \\ P_3 \end{matrix} \qquad (11\text{-}23)$$

Since Eqs. (11-21) and (11-23) are identical, we conclude that the system stiffness matrix $[\mathbf{K}]$ for the structural assemblage may be formed by the superposition of the stiffness matrices for the individual structural elements. Thus, provided the order of the element stiffness matrices is identical to that of the system stiffness matrix, we may express $[\mathbf{K}]$ in general as

$$[\mathbf{K}] = [\mathbf{k}^{(1)}] + [\mathbf{k}^{(2)}] + \cdots + [\mathbf{k}^{(M)}] = \sum_{m=1}^{M} [\mathbf{k}^{(m)}] \qquad (11\text{-}24)$$

where M represents the total number of structural elements. Henceforth, we shall use this direct stiffness method to formulate $[\mathbf{K}]$.

11-8 SOLUTION OF THE STIFFNESS EQUATIONS

The objective of structural analysis is to solve for the displacements and the internal forces induced by applied loads or prescribed nodal displacements, given appropriate boundary conditions. By way of demonstration, let us again consider the two-spring assemblage of Fig. 11-4(a) and let us suppose that node 3 is fixed against displacement. Having prescribed $\Delta_3 = 0$, we must view the force P_3 as being unknown, i.e., it is a reaction. Conversely, as the displacements of nodes 1 and 2 are *not* prescribed, the forces P_1 and P_2 *must* be prescribed. Thus, given

$$\begin{Bmatrix} P_1 \\ P_2 \\ \text{---} \\ P_3 \end{Bmatrix} = \left[\begin{array}{cc:c} k_1 & -k_1 & 0 \\ -k_1 & k_1 + k_2 & -k_2 \\ \hdashline 0 & -k_2 & k_2 \end{array}\right] \begin{Bmatrix} \Delta_1 \\ \Delta_2 \\ \text{---} \\ \Delta_3 \end{Bmatrix} \qquad (11\text{-}25)$$

we have known quantities (P_1, P_2, and Δ_3) as well as unknown quantities (Δ_1, Δ_2, and P_3) appearing on both sides of the equations. In practice such will almost always be the case. The *partitioning* of the force and displacement vectors in Eq. (11-25) has been made to delineate known and unknown quantities. By virtue of the nodal numbering scheme and the constraint imposed on node 3, it so happens that the known forces appear above the partition in the force vector while the unknown reaction appears below the partition. The converse is true for the elements of the displacement vector. The rows of the stiffness matrix are partitioned to agree with the vector partitioning, while the columns are partitioned to maintain square matrices (one 2×2 matrix and one 1×1

matrix) along the principal diagonal. Note that if a different displacement, say Δ_2, were specified, then it would be necessary to rearrange the matrices until the partitioned form were similar to that described above. We shall address this issue later in more detail.

While it is a fairly simple matter to solve these three equations for the three unknowns, it is useful to formalize the approach. Following the partitioning scheme, we may rewrite Eq. (11-25) as

$$\begin{Bmatrix} P_1 \\ P_2 \end{Bmatrix} = \begin{bmatrix} k_1 & -k_1 \\ -k_1 & k_1 + k_2 \end{bmatrix} \begin{Bmatrix} \Delta_1 \\ \Delta_2 \end{Bmatrix} + \begin{bmatrix} 0 \\ -k_2 \end{bmatrix} \{\Delta_3\} \qquad (11\text{-}26a)$$

and

$$\{P_3\} = \begin{bmatrix} 0 & -k_2 \end{bmatrix} \begin{Bmatrix} \Delta_1 \\ \Delta_2 \end{Bmatrix} + [k_2]\{\Delta_3\} \qquad (11\text{-}26b)$$

Equation (11-26a) may be solved for the unknown displacements as

$$\begin{bmatrix} k_1 & -k_1 \\ -k_1 & k_1 + k_2 \end{bmatrix} \begin{Bmatrix} \Delta_1 \\ \Delta_2 \end{Bmatrix} = \begin{Bmatrix} P_1 \\ P_2 \end{Bmatrix} - \begin{bmatrix} 0 \\ -k_2 \end{bmatrix} \{\Delta_3\}$$

or

$$\begin{Bmatrix} \Delta_1 \\ \Delta_2 \end{Bmatrix} = \begin{bmatrix} k_1 & -k_1 \\ -k_1 & k_1 + k_2 \end{bmatrix}^{-1} \left(\begin{Bmatrix} P_1 \\ P_2 \end{Bmatrix} - \begin{bmatrix} 0 \\ -k_2 \end{bmatrix} \{\Delta_3\} \right) \qquad (11\text{-}27a)$$

Now the vector $\{\Delta_1, \Delta_2\}$ may be substituted in Eq. (11-26b) to determine

$$\{P_3\} = \begin{bmatrix} 0, & -k_2 \end{bmatrix} \begin{bmatrix} k_1 & -k_1 \\ -k_1 & k_1 + k_2 \end{bmatrix}^{-1} \left(\begin{Bmatrix} P_1 \\ P_2 \end{Bmatrix} - \begin{bmatrix} 0 \\ -k_2 \end{bmatrix} \{\Delta_3\} \right) + [k_2]\{\Delta_3\} \qquad (11\text{-}27b)$$

Note that the *reduced stiffness matrix*, that appears in the first term on the right side of Eq. (11-26a), does possess an inverse, because arbitrary rigid body motion has been eliminated through the specification of displacements (a single displacement, Δ_3, in this case). For this simple problem, the inverse matrix may be evaluated by hand computation, and it is found to be

$$\begin{bmatrix} k_1 & -k_1 \\ -k_1 & k_1 + k_2 \end{bmatrix}^{-1} = \begin{bmatrix} \dfrac{1}{k_1} + \dfrac{1}{k_2} & \dfrac{1}{k_2} \\[2mm] \dfrac{1}{k_2} & \dfrac{1}{k_2} \end{bmatrix} \qquad (11\text{-}28)$$

It is worth noting that Eqs. (11-27) may be solved for any combination of $\{P_1, P_2\}$ and $\{\Delta_3\}$. Certainly $\{\Delta_3\}$ need not be set equal to zero. In the special case, however, for which $\Delta_3 = 0$, we find after employing Eq. (11-28),

$$\begin{Bmatrix} \Delta_1 \\ \Delta_2 \end{Bmatrix} = \begin{bmatrix} \dfrac{1}{k_1} + \dfrac{1}{k_2} & \dfrac{1}{k_2} \\[2mm] \dfrac{1}{k_2} & \dfrac{1}{k_2} \end{bmatrix} \begin{Bmatrix} P_1 \\ P_2 \end{Bmatrix} \qquad (11\text{-}29a)$$

and

$$\{P_3\} = [0, -k_2] \begin{bmatrix} \dfrac{1}{k_1} + \dfrac{1}{k_2} & \dfrac{1}{k_2} \\ \dfrac{1}{k_2} & \dfrac{1}{k_2} \end{bmatrix} \begin{Bmatrix} P_1 \\ P_2 \end{Bmatrix}$$

or

$$\{P_3\} = [-1, -1] \begin{Bmatrix} P_1 \\ P_2 \end{Bmatrix} = -P_1 - P_2 \qquad (11\text{-}29\text{b})$$

Equation (11-29b) indicates that the reaction P_3 is in equilibrium with the sum of applied forces P_2 and P_3.

For the special case in which Δ_3 is prescribed to be nonzero while $P_1 = P_2 = 0$, we obtain from Eqs. (11-27)

$$\begin{Bmatrix} \Delta_1 \\ \Delta_2 \end{Bmatrix} = - \begin{bmatrix} \dfrac{1}{k_1} + \dfrac{1}{k_2} & \dfrac{1}{k_2} \\ \dfrac{1}{k_2} & \dfrac{1}{k_2} \end{bmatrix} \begin{bmatrix} 0 \\ -k_2 \end{bmatrix} \{\Delta_3\}$$

or

$$\begin{Bmatrix} \Delta_1 \\ \Delta_2 \end{Bmatrix} = \begin{bmatrix} 1 \\ 1 \end{bmatrix} \{\Delta_3\} = \begin{Bmatrix} \Delta_3 \\ \Delta_3 \end{Bmatrix} \qquad (11\text{-}30\text{a})$$

and

$$\{P_3\} = -[0, -k_2] \begin{bmatrix} \dfrac{1}{k_1} + \dfrac{1}{k_2} & \dfrac{1}{k_2} \\ \dfrac{1}{k_2} & \dfrac{1}{k_2} \end{bmatrix} \begin{bmatrix} 0 \\ -k_2 \end{bmatrix} \{\Delta_3\} + [k_2]\{\Delta_3\}$$

or

$$\{P_3\} = -[k_2]\{\Delta_3\} + [k_2]\{\Delta_3\} = \{0\} \qquad (11\text{-}30\text{b})$$

Equations (11-30) confirm the conclusion we might have reached without solving the stiffness equations: $\Delta_1 = \Delta_2 = \Delta_3$ pertains to *specified* rigid body motion, which incurs no reactive forces, i.e., $P_3 = 0$.

11-9 INTERNAL NODAL FORCES

Having determined the generalized displacements at each node of the system, we may find the internal force in each spring element. In order to make the computational procedures more automatic, particularly for application to complex systems, we introduce the concept of *internal nodal forces* of a spring element which are defined as the generalized forces (in the same direction as the local generalized coordinates) at the end nodes when the spring element is treated as a free body. Basically, we attempt to replace the internal force F_1 of the first spring in Fig. 11-4(b) by a pair of internal nodal forces $F_1^{(1)}$ and $F_2^{(1)}$ at nodes 1 and 2, respectively, as shown in Fig. 11-5(a). Thus, $F_1^{(1)} = -F_1$ and $F_2^{(1)} = F_1$. We can similarly replace the internal force F_2 of the second spring in Fig. 11-4(b) by internal nodal forces $F_2^{(2)}$ and $F_3^{(2)}$ in Fig. 11-5(b) such that $F_2^{(2)} = -F_2$ and $F_3^{(2)} = F_2$.

(a)

(b)

(c)

(d)   **Figure 11-5**

The internal nodal forces are generally different from the generalized applied forces at the nodes of the assemblage. For this particular case, we note that

$$P_1 = F_1^{(1)}$$

$$P_2 = F_2^{(1)} + F_2^{(2)}$$

$$P_3 = F_3^{(2)}$$

In other words, the generalized applied force at each node of the assemblage equals the vector sum of the internal nodal forces of all spring elements connected to that node. Therefore, the use of internal nodal forces for each spring element (as opposed to the internal force in that spring element) will simplify the formulation of the equations of equilibrium at the nodes of a spring assemblage, particularly if the assemblage consists of nodes connected to a large number of springs.

Consider again the first spring, defined by nodes 1 and 2, as a free body in Fig. 11-5(a). We may express the internal nodal forces $F_1^{(1)}$ and $F_2^{(1)}$ in terms of the displacements Δ_1 and Δ_2 through the element stiffness equation, i.e.,

$$\begin{Bmatrix} F_1^{(1)} \\ F_2^{(1)} \end{Bmatrix} = \begin{bmatrix} k_1 & -k_1 \\ -k_1 & k_1 \end{bmatrix} \begin{Bmatrix} \Delta_1 \\ \Delta_2 \end{Bmatrix} \tag{11-31a}$$

Similarly, for the second spring defined by nodes 2 and 3, we get

$$\begin{Bmatrix} F_2^{(2)} \\ F_3^{(2)} \end{Bmatrix} = \begin{bmatrix} k_2 & -k_2 \\ -k_2 & k_2 \end{bmatrix} \begin{Bmatrix} \Delta_2 \\ \Delta_3 \end{Bmatrix} \qquad (11\text{-}31\text{b})$$

By expanding the stiffness matrices in Eqs. (11-31) to order of 3×3 and summing, we obtain

$$\begin{Bmatrix} P_1 \\ P_2 \\ P_3 \end{Bmatrix} = \begin{Bmatrix} F_1^{(1)} \\ F_2^{(1)} + F_2^{(2)} \\ F_3^{(2)} \end{Bmatrix} = \begin{bmatrix} k_1 & -k_1 & 0 \\ -k_1 & k_1 + k_2 & -k_2 \\ 0 & -k_2 & k_2 \end{bmatrix} \begin{Bmatrix} \Delta_1 \\ \Delta_2 \\ \Delta_3 \end{Bmatrix}$$

This result is identical to Eq. (11-16a).

Suppose we now consider the first spring as a free body and define the internal force in the spring as F corresponding to a displacement $\Delta(x)$ as shown in Fig. 11-5(c). We find that to satisfy equilibrium,

$$F = -F_1^{(1)}$$

and hence, from the first of Eqs. (11-31a),

$$F = -k_1(\Delta_1 - \Delta_2) = k_1(\Delta_2 - \Delta_1) \qquad (11\text{-}32)$$

Alternatively, we could have expressed the internal force, shown in Fig. 11-5(d), as

$$F = F_2^{(1)}$$

and, through the use of the second of Eqs. (11-31a), we would have again obtained Eq. (11-32).

It also is worth noting that the displacement $\Delta(x)$ at any point a distance x from the left end along the spring, as shown in Fig. 11-5(c), may be expressed as

$$\Delta(x) = \Delta_1 + (\Delta_2 - \Delta_1)\frac{x}{L} \qquad (11\text{-}33)$$

where L is the length of the spring. The remaining right-end portion of the spring, with length $L - x$, is shown in Fig. 11-5(d).

The internal force in the second spring can also be related to the internal nodal forces in a similar manner. The displacement $\Delta(x)$ at any point a distance x along the second spring can also be computed accordingly.

11-10 TRANSFORMATION OF THE STIFFNESS MATRIX

The preceding two-spring assemblage comprised colinear elements, and therefore a single coordinate system sufficed. We were able to express directly the stiffness matrix of each spring in terms of that single (global) coordinate system. Usually, however, not all the elements in a structure have the same orientation, and we must transform the element stiffness equations from local to global coordinate systems before assembling them into the system stiffness equations.

To demonstrate the transformation, consider the system shown in Fig. 11-6, in which the springs previously considered are no longer colinear. In addition to specifying the global x–y axes system, we also indicate two sets of local axes, x_1'–y_1' (which happens to coincide with the x–y system) for spring 1 and x_2'–y_2' for spring 2. We can immediately express the relationship between internal nodal axial forces and axial displacements for each spring in terms of local coordinates, as shown in Fig. 11-7(a). That is, for either member (designated as member m) having end points i (the origin of x_m'–y_m') and j, we may write

$$\begin{Bmatrix} F_{x'i} \\ F_{x'j} \end{Bmatrix} = k_m \begin{bmatrix} 1 & -1 \\ -1 & 1 \end{bmatrix} \begin{Bmatrix} \Delta_{x'i} \\ \Delta_{x'j} \end{Bmatrix} \tag{11-34}$$

where the nodal forces and displacements are referred to the member's local coordinate system. In conformity with the designation of internal nodal forces, a superscript (m) would have to be added to each nodal force or displacement in Eq. (11-34). However, for the sake of simplicity, such superscripts have been dropped, since the "prime" notation for the local coordinates sufficiently differentiates them from the internal force and the internal deformation. Note, therefore, that the forces $F_{x'i}$ and $F_{x'j}$ are internal to the system, i.e., they are not externally applied loads. But, as far as the spring is concerned, these forces play the same role as P_1 and P_2 played in Fig. 11-3. Clearly, however, force $F_{x'2}$ and displacement $\Delta_{x'2}$, for example, will be different for each of the two springs joined at node 2 because they refer to different directions as well as different spring constants for each spring.

Figure 11-6

Figure 11-7

Our objective is to transform Eq. (11-34) in terms of the global coordinate system so that forces and displacements may be related for both springs. To do this, we first expand Eq. (11-34) to incorporate forces and displacements in the local y' directions. Then we may write

$$\begin{Bmatrix} F_{x'i} \\ F_{y'i} \\ F_{x'j} \\ F_{y'j} \end{Bmatrix} = k_m \begin{bmatrix} 1 & 0 & -1 & 0 \\ 0 & 0 & 0 & 0 \\ -1 & 0 & 1 & 0 \\ 0 & 0 & 0 & 0 \end{bmatrix} \begin{Bmatrix} \Delta_{x'i} \\ \Delta_{y'i} \\ \Delta_{x'j} \\ \Delta_{y'j} \end{Bmatrix} \qquad (11\text{-}35a)$$

or

$$\{\overline{\mathbf{F}}'\} = [\mathbf{k}']\{\mathbf{\Delta}'\} \qquad (11\text{-}35b)$$

where the bar over the force vector is to designate internal nodal forces, as opposed to element forces (i.e., internal forces in spring elements) that have been previously designated by the force vector $\{\mathbf{F}\}$; the prime refers to the local coordinate system. Obviously, forces $F_{y'i}$ and $F_{y'j}$ are zero and all forces are unrelated to the displacements $\Delta_{y'i}$ and $\Delta_{y'j}$. This expansion, however, permits a straightforward transformation between forces referred to global coordinates and those referred to local coordinates. From Fig. 11-7(b) we may infer that at node i

$$F_{x'i} = F_{xi} \cos \theta_m + F_{yi} \sin \theta_m \qquad (11\text{-}36a)$$

Similarly,

$$F_{y'i} = -F_{xi} \sin \theta_m + F_{yi} \cos \theta_m \qquad (11\text{-}36b)$$

in which θ_m represents the angle between x and x'. Similar expressions may be written for the forces at node j. Denoting

$$\lambda = \cos \theta_m \quad \text{and} \quad \mu = \sin \theta_m \qquad (11\text{-}37)$$

we may write Eqs. (11-36) at node i and their counterparts for node j as

$$\begin{Bmatrix} F_{x'i} \\ F_{y'i} \\ F_{x'j} \\ F_{y'j} \end{Bmatrix} = \begin{bmatrix} \lambda & \mu & 0 & 0 \\ -\mu & \lambda & 0 & 0 \\ 0 & 0 & \lambda & \mu \\ 0 & 0 & -\mu & \lambda \end{bmatrix} \begin{Bmatrix} F_{xi} \\ F_{yi} \\ F_{xj} \\ F_{yj} \end{Bmatrix} \qquad (11\text{-}38a)$$

or

$$\{\overline{\mathbf{F}}'\} = [\mathbf{T}]\{\overline{\mathbf{F}}\} \qquad (11\text{-}38b)$$

in which $[\mathbf{T}]$ is termed the *transformation matrix*. Furthermore, we note that

$$F_{xi} = F_{x'i} \cos \theta_m - F_{y'i} \sin \theta_m$$

$$F_{yi} = F_{x'i} \sin \theta_m + F_{y'i} \cos \theta_m$$

By including their counterparts for node j, we obtain

$$\begin{Bmatrix} F_{xi} \\ F_{yi} \\ F_{xj} \\ F_{yj} \end{Bmatrix} = \begin{bmatrix} \lambda & -\mu & 0 & 0 \\ \mu & \lambda & 0 & 0 \\ 0 & 0 & \lambda & -\mu \\ 0 & 0 & \mu & \lambda \end{bmatrix} \begin{Bmatrix} F_{x'i} \\ F_{y'i} \\ F_{x'j} \\ F_{y'j} \end{Bmatrix} \tag{11-39a}$$

or

$$\{\overline{\mathbf{F}}\} = [\mathbf{T}]^T\{\overline{\mathbf{F}}'\} \tag{11-39b}$$

Thus, by solving for $\{\overline{\mathbf{F}}\}$ in Eqs. (11-38b) and observing the relations in Eqs. (11-39b), we get

$$\{\overline{\mathbf{F}}\} = [\mathbf{T}]^{-1}\{\overline{\mathbf{F}}'\} = [\mathbf{T}]^T\{\overline{\mathbf{F}}'\} \tag{11-40}$$

That is, the inverse of the transformation matrix is equal to its transpose, a fortuitous circumstance for computational purposes.

We may transform displacements from global to local coordinates in precisely the same manner. Then

$$\begin{Bmatrix} \Delta_{x'i} \\ \Delta_{y'i} \\ \Delta_{x'j} \\ \Delta_{y'j} \end{Bmatrix} = \begin{bmatrix} \lambda & \mu & 0 & 0 \\ -\mu & \lambda & 0 & 0 \\ 0 & 0 & \lambda & \mu \\ 0 & 0 & -\mu & \lambda \end{bmatrix} \begin{Bmatrix} \Delta_{xi} \\ \Delta_{yi} \\ \Delta_{xj} \\ \Delta_{yj} \end{Bmatrix} \tag{11-41}$$

or

$$\{\mathbf{\Delta}'\} = [\mathbf{T}]\{\mathbf{\Delta}\} \tag{11-42}$$

Recalling Eq. (11-35b) which states that

$$\{\overline{\mathbf{F}}'\} = [\mathbf{k}']\{\mathbf{\Delta}'\} \tag{11-35b}$$

we may substitute Eqs. (11-38b) and (11-42) into this equation and get

$$[\mathbf{T}]\{\overline{\mathbf{F}}\} = [\mathbf{k}'][\mathbf{T}]\{\mathbf{\Delta}\}$$

Pre-multiplying this result by $[\mathbf{T}]^{-1}(= [\mathbf{T}]^T)$, we obtain

$$\{\overline{\mathbf{F}}\} = [\mathbf{k}]\{\mathbf{\Delta}\} \tag{11-43}$$

where

$$[\mathbf{k}] = [\mathbf{T}]^T[\mathbf{k}'][\mathbf{T}] \tag{11-44}$$

Equation (11-43) expresses the relationship between element nodal forces and displacements in terms of a global coordinate system. Thus, the element stiffness matrix [k] referred to the global coordinate system is obtained through Eq. (11-44) by transforming the element stiffness matrix [k'] expressed in local coordinates. We shall see the utility of Eqs. (11-43) and (11-44) in the examples that follow. For the simple spring (element m) being considered, the matrix multiplication indicated by Eqs. (11-44) leads to the multiplication of matrices in Eqs. (11-38a), (11-35a), and (11-39a) with the following result:

$$[\mathbf{k}^{(m)}] = k_m \begin{array}{c} \quad\;\Delta_{xi} \qquad \Delta_{yi} \qquad \Delta_{xj} \qquad \Delta_{yj} \\ \begin{bmatrix} \lambda^2 & \lambda\mu & -\lambda^2 & -\lambda\mu \\ \lambda\mu & \mu^2 & -\lambda\mu & -\mu^2 \\ -\lambda^2 & -\lambda\mu & \lambda^2 & \lambda\mu \\ -\lambda\mu & -\mu^2 & \lambda\mu & \mu^2 \end{bmatrix} \begin{array}{l} F_{xi} \\ F_{yi} \\ F_{xj} \\ F_{yj} \end{array} \end{array} \qquad (11\text{-}45)$$

The displacement and force components are placed above the columns and beside the rows as reminders of the meaning of the individual stiffness components in $[\mathbf{k}^{(m)}]$. It should also be recalled that λ and μ will change from member to member; for simplicity, however, we have chosen not to subscript these symbols.

Example 11-2. For the two-spring system shown in Fig. 11-8(a), construct the system stiffness matrix, and find the displacements and internal forces due to a vertical load P applied at node 2.

(a)

(b)

(c)

Figure 11-8

Matrix Methods of Structural Analysis   Chap. 11

We begin by formulating the element stiffness matrices in local coordinates $[\mathbf{k}']$ and the associated transformation matrix $[\mathbf{T}]$ for each element. For spring 1, in Fig. 11-8(b), $\lambda_1 = 1$ and $\mu_1 = 0$, while for spring 2, in Fig. 11-8(c), $\lambda_2 = \sqrt{3}/2$ and $\mu_2 = 0.5$. We then may perform the multiplication indicated by Eq. (11-44) or, alternatively, we may find $[\mathbf{k}]$ directly from Eq. (11-45). In either case, we obtain for spring 1

$$[\mathbf{k}^{(1)}] = k_1 \begin{array}{cccc} \Delta_{x1} & \Delta_{y1} & \Delta_{x2} & \Delta_{y2} \\ \begin{bmatrix} 1 & 0 & -1 & 0 \\ 0 & 0 & 0 & 0 \\ -1 & 0 & 1 & 0 \\ 0 & 0 & 0 & 0 \end{bmatrix} & \begin{array}{c} F_{x1}^{(1)} \\ F_{y1}^{(1)} \\ F_{x2}^{(1)} \\ F_{y2}^{(1)} \end{array} \end{array}$$

and for spring 2

$$[\mathbf{k}^{(2)}] = \frac{k_2}{4} \begin{array}{cccc} \Delta_{x2} & \Delta_{y2} & \Delta_{x3} & \Delta_{y3} \\ \begin{bmatrix} 3 & \sqrt{3} & -3 & -\sqrt{3} \\ \sqrt{3} & 1 & -\sqrt{3} & -1 \\ -3 & -\sqrt{3} & 3 & \sqrt{3} \\ -\sqrt{3} & -1 & \sqrt{3} & 1 \end{bmatrix} & \begin{array}{c} F_{x2}^{(2)} \\ F_{y2}^{(2)} \\ F_{x3}^{(2)} \\ F_{y3}^{(2)} \end{array} \end{array}$$

We have added to the nodal force components a superscript indicating the pertinent element on which the forces act. It is also important to note that although Δ_{x2}, for example, is one and the same displacement for springs 1 and 2 (implying compatibility), in general, the sum of $F_{x2}^{(1)}$ and $F_{x2}^{(2)}$ must be equal to the external force P_{x2} applied in the x direction at node 2 (implying equilibrium). These conditions of compatibility and equilibrium are imposed when we combine element stiffness matrices. Recognizing that the system stiffness matrix will be of order six, we expand the foregoing matrices to facilitate their addition. Then

$$[\mathbf{k}^{(1)}] = k_1 \begin{array}{cccccc} \Delta_{x1} & \Delta_{y1} & \Delta_{x2} & \Delta_{y2} & \Delta_{x3} & \Delta_{y3} \\ \begin{bmatrix} 1 & 0 & -1 & 0 & 0 & 0 \\ 0 & 0 & 0 & 0 & 0 & 0 \\ -1 & 0 & 1 & 0 & 0 & 0 \\ 0 & 0 & 0 & 0 & 0 & 0 \\ 0 & 0 & 0 & 0 & 0 & 0 \\ 0 & 0 & 0 & 0 & 0 & 0 \end{bmatrix} & \begin{array}{c} F_{x1}^{(1)} \\ F_{y1}^{(1)} \\ F_{x2}^{(1)} \\ F_{y2}^{(1)} \\ F_{x3}^{(1)} \\ F_{y3}^{(1)} \end{array} \end{array}$$

and

$$[\mathbf{k}^{(2)}] = \frac{k_2}{4} \begin{array}{cccccc} \Delta_{x1} & \Delta_{y1} & \Delta_{x2} & \Delta_{y2} & \Delta_{x3} & \Delta_{y3} \\ \begin{bmatrix} 0 & 0 & 0 & 0 & 0 & 0 \\ 0 & 0 & 0 & 0 & 0 & 0 \\ 0 & 0 & 3 & \sqrt{3} & -3 & -\sqrt{3} \\ 0 & 0 & \sqrt{3} & 1 & -\sqrt{3} & -1 \\ 0 & 0 & -3 & -\sqrt{3} & 3 & \sqrt{3} \\ 0 & 0 & -\sqrt{3} & -1 & \sqrt{3} & 1 \end{bmatrix} & \begin{array}{c} F_{x1}^{(2)} \\ F_{y1}^{(2)} \\ F_{x2}^{(2)} \\ F_{y2}^{(2)} \\ F_{x3}^{(2)} \\ F_{y3}^{(2)} \end{array} \end{array}$$

Now suppose, for the sake of simplicity, we set $k_1 = k_2 = k$. The system stiffness matrix, which is the sum of $[\mathbf{k}^{(1)}]$ and $[\mathbf{k}^{(2)}]$, is then

$$
\begin{array}{cccccc}
\Delta_{x1} & \Delta_{y1} & \Delta_{x2} & \Delta_{y2} & \Delta_{x3} & \Delta_{y3}
\end{array}
$$

$$
[\mathbf{K}] = \frac{k}{4}
\begin{bmatrix}
4 & 0 & -4 & 0 & 0 & 0 \\
0 & 0 & 0 & 0 & 0 & 0 \\
-4 & 0 & 7 & \sqrt{3} & -3 & -\sqrt{3} \\
0 & 0 & \sqrt{3} & 1 & -\sqrt{3} & -1 \\
0 & 0 & -3 & -\sqrt{3} & 3 & \sqrt{3} \\
0 & 0 & -\sqrt{3} & -1 & \sqrt{3} & 1
\end{bmatrix}
\begin{array}{l}
P_{x1} \\
P_{y1} \\
P_{x2} \\
P_{y2} \\
P_{x3} \\
P_{y3}
\end{array}
$$

Note that we have now indicated each row by symbols P_{x1}, etc., implying the relationship between displacements and *externally* applied loads.

To facilitate the solution of the stiffness equations, we interchange the first two rows and columns with the third and fourth. We may then write

$$
\begin{Bmatrix}
P_{x2} \\
P_{y2} \\
\text{---} \\
P_{x1} \\
P_{y1} \\
P_{x3} \\
P_{y3}
\end{Bmatrix}
= \frac{k}{4}
\left[
\begin{array}{cc:cccc}
7 & \sqrt{3} & -4 & 0 & -3 & -\sqrt{3} \\
\sqrt{3} & 1 & 0 & 0 & -\sqrt{3} & -1 \\
\hdashline
-4 & 0 & 4 & 0 & 0 & 0 \\
0 & 0 & 0 & 0 & 0 & 0 \\
-3 & -\sqrt{3} & 0 & 0 & 3 & \sqrt{3} \\
-\sqrt{3} & -1 & 0 & 0 & \sqrt{3} & 1
\end{array}
\right]
\begin{Bmatrix}
\Delta_{x2} \\
\Delta_{y2} \\
\text{---} \\
\Delta_{x1} \\
\Delta_{y1} \\
\Delta_{x3} \\
\Delta_{y3}
\end{Bmatrix}
$$

where we have partitioned the force and displacement vectors according to known and unknown quantities. We may then write

$$
\begin{Bmatrix}
P_{x2} \\
P_{y2}
\end{Bmatrix}
= \frac{k}{4}
\begin{bmatrix}
7 & \sqrt{3} \\
\sqrt{3} & 1
\end{bmatrix}
\begin{Bmatrix}
\Delta_{x2} \\
\Delta_{y2}
\end{Bmatrix}
+ \frac{k}{4}
\begin{bmatrix}
-4 & 0 & -3 & -\sqrt{3} \\
0 & 0 & -\sqrt{3} & -1
\end{bmatrix}
\begin{Bmatrix}
\Delta_{x1} \\
\Delta_{y1} \\
\Delta_{x3} \\
\Delta_{y3}
\end{Bmatrix}
$$

and

$$
\begin{Bmatrix}
P_{x1} \\
P_{y1} \\
P_{x3} \\
P_{y3}
\end{Bmatrix}
= \frac{k}{4}
\begin{bmatrix}
-4 & 0 \\
0 & 0 \\
-3 & -\sqrt{3} \\
-\sqrt{3} & -1
\end{bmatrix}
\begin{Bmatrix}
\Delta_{x2} \\
\Delta_{y2}
\end{Bmatrix}
+ \frac{k}{4}
\begin{bmatrix}
4 & 0 & 0 & 0 \\
0 & 0 & 0 & 0 \\
0 & 0 & 3 & \sqrt{3} \\
0 & 0 & \sqrt{3} & 1
\end{bmatrix}
\begin{Bmatrix}
\Delta_{x1} \\
\Delta_{y1} \\
\Delta_{x3} \\
\Delta_{y3}
\end{Bmatrix}
$$

The specific loading conditions and boundary conditions that are imposed dictate that

$$
\begin{Bmatrix} P_{x2} \\ P_{y2} \end{Bmatrix} = \begin{Bmatrix} 0 \\ -P \end{Bmatrix}
\quad \text{and} \quad
\begin{Bmatrix} \Delta_{x1} \\ \Delta_{y1} \\ \Delta_{x3} \\ \Delta_{y3} \end{Bmatrix} = \begin{Bmatrix} 0 \\ 0 \\ 0 \\ 0 \end{Bmatrix}
$$

Therefore, we have

$$
\begin{Bmatrix} 0 \\ -P \end{Bmatrix} = \frac{k}{4}
\begin{bmatrix} 7 & \sqrt{3} \\ \sqrt{3} & 1 \end{bmatrix}
\begin{Bmatrix} \Delta_{x2} \\ \Delta_{y2} \end{Bmatrix}
\tag{a}
$$

and

$$
\begin{Bmatrix} P_{x1} \\ P_{y1} \\ P_{x3} \\ P_{y3} \end{Bmatrix} = \frac{k}{4}
\begin{bmatrix}
-4 & 0 \\
0 & 0 \\
-3 & -\sqrt{3} \\
-\sqrt{3} & -1
\end{bmatrix}
\begin{Bmatrix} \Delta_{x2} \\ \Delta_{y2} \end{Bmatrix}
\tag{b}
$$

Equation (a) may be solved for $\{\Delta_{x2}, \Delta_{y2}\}$:

$$\begin{Bmatrix} \Delta_{x2} \\ \Delta_{y2} \end{Bmatrix} = \frac{4}{k}\begin{bmatrix} 7 & \sqrt{3} \\ \sqrt{3} & 1 \end{bmatrix}^{-1}\begin{Bmatrix} 0 \\ -P \end{Bmatrix} = \frac{1}{k}\begin{bmatrix} 1 & -\sqrt{3} \\ -\sqrt{3} & 7 \end{bmatrix}\begin{Bmatrix} 0 \\ -P \end{Bmatrix} = \frac{P}{k}\begin{Bmatrix} \sqrt{3} \\ -7 \end{Bmatrix} \qquad \text{(c)}$$

These displacements may then be substituted into Eq. (b) to find $\{P_{x1}, P_{y1}, P_{x3}, P_{y3}\}$, which is found to be $\{-\sqrt{3}P, 0, \sqrt{3}P, P\}$.

The internal spring forces may be determined through satisfaction of equilibrium for each element in the assemblage. Alternatively, and more generally, we may use the displacement vector (now fully known) along with the element stiffness matrices to determine the forces acting on each element. That is, by substituting the values of $\{\Delta\}$ in Eq. (c) into Eq. (11-43) for the elements related to node 2 (springs 1 and 2 in this case) we can compute $\{\mathbf{F}\} = [\mathbf{k}]\{\Delta\}$ for each of these springs. For example, the nodal forces acting on spring 2 may be determined from

$$\begin{Bmatrix} F_{x2} \\ F_{y2} \\ F_{x3} \\ F_{y3} \end{Bmatrix} = \frac{k}{4}\begin{bmatrix} 3 & \sqrt{3} & -3 & -\sqrt{3} \\ \sqrt{3} & 1 & -\sqrt{3} & -1 \\ -3 & -\sqrt{3} & 3 & \sqrt{3} \\ -\sqrt{3} & -1 & \sqrt{3} & 1 \end{bmatrix}\begin{Bmatrix} \dfrac{\sqrt{3}P}{k} \\ \dfrac{-7P}{k} \\ 0 \\ 0 \end{Bmatrix} = P\begin{Bmatrix} -\sqrt{3} \\ -1 \\ \sqrt{3} \\ 1 \end{Bmatrix}$$

Figure 11-9(a) indicates that these nodal forces in spring 2 are in equilibrium, as they necessarily must be, and that the internal force F in spring 2 shown in Fig. 11-9(b) is the resultant of $\sqrt{3}P$ and P and is equal to $2P$ (tension). Nodal forces and the internal force may be determined for spring 1 in a similar manner.

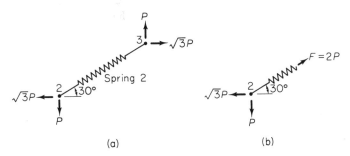

(a)   (b)

Figure 11-9

Example 11-3. Consider the same system as described in the previous example, except now possessing an additional member, spring 3, as shown in Fig. 11-10. We

Figure 11-10

again wish to find the displacements at node 2 and the internal forces in the elements.

The formulation of element stiffness matrices follows the precedure described in Example 11-2. Indeed $[\mathbf{k}^{(1)}]$ and $[\mathbf{k}^{(2)}]$ are identical to those computed previously except that in their expanded form they must now accommodate Δ_{x4} and Δ_{y4}, the displacements (of zero value) at the newly created node 4. For spring 3 (having $\theta_3 = 90°$ and hence $\lambda_3 = 0$, $\mu_3 = 1$) the expanded stiffness matrix in global coordinates is

$$[\mathbf{k}^{(3)}] = k_3 \begin{array}{cccccccc} \Delta_{x1} & \Delta_{y1} & \Delta_{x2} & \Delta_{y2} & \Delta_{x3} & \Delta_{y3} & \Delta_{x4} & \Delta_{y4} \end{array}
\begin{bmatrix}
0 & 0 & 0 & 0 & 0 & 0 & 0 & 0 \\
0 & 0 & 0 & 0 & 0 & 0 & 0 & 0 \\
0 & 0 & 0 & 0 & 0 & 0 & 0 & 0 \\
0 & 0 & 0 & 1 & 0 & 0 & 0 & -1 \\
0 & 0 & 0 & 0 & 0 & 0 & 0 & 0 \\
0 & 0 & 0 & 0 & 0 & 0 & 0 & 0 \\
0 & 0 & 0 & 0 & 0 & 0 & 0 & 0 \\
0 & 0 & 0 & -1 & 0 & 0 & 0 & 1
\end{bmatrix}
\begin{array}{l}
F_{x1}^{(3)} \\
F_{y1}^{(3)} \\
F_{x2}^{(3)} \\
F_{y2}^{(3)} \\
F_{x3}^{(3)} \\
F_{y3}^{(3)} \\
F_{x4}^{(3)} \\
F_{y4}^{(3)}
\end{array}$$

This stiffness matrix may be combined with the sum of $[\mathbf{k}^{(1)}]$ and $[\mathbf{k}^{(2)}]$, that sum being $[\mathbf{K}]$ in Example 11-2. Thus, by adding a new member to the original system, we need merely add the stiffness matrix for that member to the original system stiffness matrix, accounting, of course, for additional degrees of freedom.

If we now suppose, again for convenience, that $k_1 = k_2 = k_3 = k$, then we find

$$[\mathbf{K}] = \frac{k}{4} \begin{array}{cccccccc} \Delta_{x2} & \Delta_{y2} & \Delta_{x1} & \Delta_{y1} & \Delta_{x3} & \Delta_{y3} & \Delta_{x4} & \Delta_{y4} \end{array}
\begin{bmatrix}
7 & \sqrt{3} & -4 & 0 & -3 & -\sqrt{3} & 0 & 0 \\
\sqrt{3} & 5 & 0 & 0 & -\sqrt{3} & -1 & 0 & -4 \\
-4 & 0 & 4 & 0 & 0 & 0 & 0 & 0 \\
0 & 0 & 0 & 0 & 0 & 0 & 0 & 0 \\
-3 & -\sqrt{3} & 0 & 0 & 3 & \sqrt{3} & 0 & 0 \\
-\sqrt{3} & -1 & 0 & 0 & \sqrt{3} & 1 & 0 & 0 \\
0 & 0 & 0 & 0 & 0 & 0 & 0 & 0 \\
0 & -4 & 0 & 0 & 0 & 0 & 0 & 4
\end{bmatrix}
\begin{array}{l}
P_{x2} \\
P_{y2} \\
P_{x1} \\
P_{y1} \\
P_{x3} \\
P_{y3} \\
P_{x4} \\
P_{y4}
\end{array}$$

Since the prescribed displacements $\{\Delta_{x1}, \Delta_{y1}, \Delta_{x3}, \Delta_{y3}, \Delta_{x4}, \Delta_{y4}\}$ form a null vector, because all supports are rigidly restrained, we may write

$$\begin{Bmatrix} 0 \\ -P \end{Bmatrix} = \frac{k}{4} \begin{bmatrix} 7 & \sqrt{3} \\ \sqrt{3} & 5 \end{bmatrix} \begin{Bmatrix} \Delta_{x2} \\ \Delta_{y2} \end{Bmatrix}$$

Hence,

$$\begin{Bmatrix} \Delta_{x2} \\ \Delta_{y2} \end{Bmatrix} = \frac{4}{k} \begin{bmatrix} 7 & \sqrt{3} \\ \sqrt{3} & 5 \end{bmatrix}^{-1} \begin{Bmatrix} 0 \\ -P \end{Bmatrix} = \frac{1}{8k} \begin{bmatrix} 5 & -\sqrt{3} \\ -\sqrt{3} & 7 \end{bmatrix} \begin{Bmatrix} 0 \\ -P \end{Bmatrix} = \frac{P}{8k} \begin{Bmatrix} \sqrt{3} \\ -7 \end{Bmatrix}$$

By comparing these results with those of the previous example, we find that due to the addition of the third spring, displacements have been reduced to one-eighth of the values pertaining to the previous two-spring case. Nodal forces acting on each spring may be determined through the product of the displacement vector and the element stiffness matrices as described previously.

It is important to note that when we employ the stiffness method we need make no distinction between statically determinate and indeterminate systems. The system of Example 11-2 was statically determinate, but that of Example 11-3 was not. Yet, apart from having to formulate one additional element stiffness matrix, the latter example involved no additional computational effort. Indeed, computational effort is related to the number of active degrees of freedom in the system, and often a more highly redundant system is easier to analyze than one having fewer redundant forces but having more degrees of freedom.

Examples 11-2 and 11-3 illustrate that the zero-valued nodal degrees of freedom at fixed supports play no active role in the computation of displacements. Accordingly, rather than partition the stiffness matrices and carry out the matrix algebra indicated in Example 11-2, we could have merely deleted those rows and columns of $[\mathbf{K}]$ pertaining to the fixed displacements and thus acquired $[\mathbf{K}_{ff}]$. Any displacements that are prescribed to be nonzero must, of course, be retained.

As we shall see in Chapter 12, the procedure illustrated above may be adequately generalized to treat most structural analysis problems. We now summarize the formulation and solution procedure for the direct stiffness method and, at the same time, set the stage for later discussion by listing the following steps:

1. Establish the generalized coordinates which define the deformed shape of the system.

2. Evaluate for each structural component (say the mth component) the element stiffness matrix $[\mathbf{k}^{(m)}]$, usually referred first to local coordinates and then transformed relative to a global coordinate system, which relate an appropriate subset of generalized forces and displacements.

3. After redimensioning the element stiffness matrices, so that their order coincides with that of the system stiffness matrix $[\mathbf{K}]$, sum the element stiffness matrices to obtain

$$[\mathbf{K}] = \sum_{m=1}^{M} [\mathbf{k}^{(m)}] \quad (M = \text{total number of elements})$$

4. After specifying the applied loads and nodal displacements (including support restraints), partition $[\mathbf{K}]$ and solve for the unknown quantities.

5. Obtain the element internal forces using the displacements determined in Step 4 and the element stiffness matrices established in Step 2. That is,

$$\{\overline{\mathbf{F}}\} = [\mathbf{k}^{(m)}]\{\mathbf{\Delta}\}$$

Note that the matrix addition referred to in Step 3 may be easily automated without requiring that one actually write out each element stiffness matrix as part of the full system stiffness matrix. Although that procedure was followed in the preceding examples, it is a relatively simple matter to "fill in" the system matrix with the coefficients of the element stiffness matrices. Note also that for systems with identical elements but different orientations, the stiffness matrix for one element may be obtained from that of the other element through proper transformation of coordinates.

With respect to Step 4, we may formalize the solution procedure for a general situation in the following way. Suppose the stiffness equations

$$\{P\} = [K]\{\Delta\}$$

are partitioned to have the form

$$\left\{\begin{array}{c} P_f \\ \hline P_s \end{array}\right\} = \left[\begin{array}{c:c} K_{ff} & K_{fs} \\ \hline K_{sf} & K_{ss} \end{array}\right] \left\{\begin{array}{c} \Delta_f \\ \hline \Delta_s \end{array}\right\} \tag{11-46}$$

in which $\{P_f\}$ represents the vector of prescribed generalized forces corresponding to the vector of unknown generalized displacements $\{\Delta_f\}$, while $\{P_s\}$ represents the vector of unknown generalized forces (reactions) corresponding to the vector of prescribed generalized displacements $\{\Delta_s\}$ (which includes support displacements, often specified to be zero).

Writing Eq. (11-46) as

$$\{P_f\} = [K_{ff}]\{\Delta_f\} + [K_{fs}]\{\Delta_s\} \tag{11-47a}$$

$$\{P_s\} = [K_{sf}]\{\Delta_f\} + [K_{ss}]\{\Delta_s\} \tag{11-47b}$$

we may solve for the unknown quantities $\{\Delta_f\}$ and $\{P_s\}$ as

$$\{\Delta_f\} = [K_{ff}]^{-1}(\{P_f\} - [K_{fs}]\{\Delta_s\}) \tag{11-48a}$$

and

$$\{P_s\} = [K_{sf}][K_{ff}]^{-1}\{P_f\} - ([K_{sf}][K_{ff}]^{-1}[K_{fs}] - [K_{ss}])\{\Delta_s\} \tag{11-48b}$$

Thus the solution is obtained by forming the system stiffness matrix, partitioning it appropriately, and performing the matrix operations indicated by Eqs. (11-48).

Example 11-4. The system of the three parallel springs shown in Fig. 11-11 supports a rigid platform which is subjected to a vertical force P and a moment M at point O. Recognizing that, if horizontal displacement is prevented, the platform has

Figure 11-11

only two active degrees of freedom, e.g., the vertical displacement Δ at point O and a small uniform rotation θ, derive the two stiffness equations and solve for the displacements and spring forces.

Referring to the free-body diagram in Fig. 11-12(a), we can obtain the necessary equations for solving this problem according to the basic principles in the analysis of statically indeterminate systems. Let F_1, F_2, and F_3 be the internal forces and δ_1, δ_2, and δ_3 be the displacements of springs 1, 2, and 3, respectively. Then, the conditions of equilibrium can be expressed in terms of the system statics matrix, i.e.,

$$\begin{Bmatrix} P \\ M \end{Bmatrix} = \begin{bmatrix} 1 & 1 & 1 \\ -L & 0 & L \end{bmatrix} \begin{Bmatrix} F_1 \\ F_2 \\ F_3 \end{Bmatrix}$$

The conditions of compatibility lead to the relation involving the system kinematics matrix, i.e.,

$$\begin{Bmatrix} \delta_1 \\ \delta_2 \\ \delta_3 \end{Bmatrix} = \begin{bmatrix} 1 & -L \\ 1 & 0 \\ 1 & L \end{bmatrix} \begin{Bmatrix} \Delta \\ \theta \end{Bmatrix}$$

The force-deformation relationship may be expressed in terms of the matrix of member stiffnesses, i.e.,

$$\begin{Bmatrix} F_1 \\ F_2 \\ F_3 \end{Bmatrix} = \begin{bmatrix} k_1 & 0 & 0 \\ 0 & k_2 & 0 \\ 0 & 0 & k_3 \end{bmatrix} \begin{Bmatrix} \delta_1 \\ \delta_2 \\ \delta_3 \end{Bmatrix}$$

Thus, according to Eq. (11-15b), we obtain through matrix multiplication,

$$\begin{Bmatrix} P \\ M \end{Bmatrix} = \begin{bmatrix} k_1 + k_2 + k_3 & -(k_3 - k_1)L \\ -(k_3 - k_1)L & (k_1 + k_3)L^2 \end{bmatrix} \begin{Bmatrix} \Delta \\ \theta \end{Bmatrix}$$

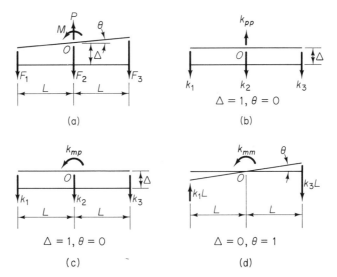

Figure 11-12

By inverting the reduced system stiffness matrix, we find

$$
\left\{ \begin{array}{c} \Delta \\ \theta \end{array} \right\} = \left[\begin{array}{cc} \dfrac{k_1 + k_3}{k_1 k_2 + k_2 k_3 + 4 k_1 k_3} & \dfrac{k_1 - k_3}{(k_1 k_2 + k_2 k_3 + 4 k_1 k_3)L} \\[3mm] \dfrac{k_1 - k_3}{(k_1 k_2 + k_2 k_3 + 4 k_1 k_3)L} & \dfrac{k_1 + k_2 + k_3}{(k_1 k_2 + k_2 k_3 + 4 k_1 k_3)L^2} \end{array} \right] \left\{ \begin{array}{c} P \\ M \end{array} \right\}
$$

or

$$
\Delta = \frac{PL(k_1 + k_3) + M(k_1 - k_3)}{(k_1 k_2 + k_2 k_3 + 4 k_1 k_3)L}
$$

$$
\theta = \frac{PL(k_1 - k_3) + M(k_1 + k_2 + k_3)}{(k_1 k_2 + k_2 k_3 + 4 k_1 k_3)L^2}
$$

Consequently, the internal forces are found to be

$$
F_1 = \frac{2PLk_1 k_3 - Mk_1(k_2 + 2k_3)}{(k_1 k_2 + k_2 k_3 + 4 k_1 k_3)L}
$$

$$
F_2 = \frac{PLk_2(k_1 + k_3) + Mk_2(k_1 - k_3)}{(k_1 k_2 + k_2 k_3 + 4 k_1 k_3)L}
$$

$$
F_3 = \frac{2PLk_1 k_3 + Mk_3(2k_1 + k_2)}{(k_1 k_2 + k_2 k_3 + 4 k_1 k_3)L}
$$

This problem also may be solved by finding the coefficients of the stiffness equations directly. Because the generalized coordinates Δ and θ at node O will define the active degrees of freedom of the system, the two stiffness equations for the constrained system are

$$
\left\{ \begin{array}{c} P \\ M \end{array} \right\} = \left[\begin{array}{cc} k_{pp} & k_{pm} \\ k_{mp} & k_{mm} \end{array} \right] \left\{ \begin{array}{c} \Delta \\ \theta \end{array} \right\}
$$

where the coefficients in the reduced system stiffness matrix are

k_{pp} = force in the direction of P due to $\Delta = 1$ and $\theta = 0$

k_{pm} = force in the direction of P due to $\Delta = 0$ and $\theta = 1$

k_{mp} = moment in the direction of M due to $\Delta = 1$ and $\theta = 0$

k_{mm} = moment in the direction of M due to $\Delta = 0$ and $\theta = 1$.

Since $k_{pm} = k_{mp}$, we need to derive only the coefficients k_{pp}, k_{mp}, and k_{mm} from the free-body diagrams shown in Fig. 11-12(b), (c) and (d). Thus, from Fig. 11-12(b) in which $\delta_1 = \delta_2 = \delta_3 = \Delta = 1$, we obtain from $\Sigma F_y = 0$,

$$
k_{pp} = k_1 + k_2 + k_3
$$

From Fig. 11-12(c), we find from $\Sigma M_0 = 0$

$$
k_{mp} + k_1 L - k_3 L = 0
$$

or

$$
k_{mp} = (-k_1 + k_3)L = k_{pm}
$$

Finally, from Fig. 11-12(d), in which $\delta_1 = -L\theta$, $\delta_2 = 0$, and $\delta_3 = L\theta$, we get from $\Sigma M_0 = 0$

$$k_{mm} - k_1 L^2 - k_3 L^2 = 0$$

or

$$k_{mm} = (k_1 + k_3)L^2$$

Consequently, the displacements at point 0 are given by

$$\begin{Bmatrix} \Delta \\ \theta \end{Bmatrix} = \begin{bmatrix} k_1 + k_2 + k_3 & (-k_1 + k_3)L \\ (-k_1 + k_3)L & (k_1 + k_3)L^2 \end{bmatrix}^{-1} \begin{Bmatrix} P \\ M \end{Bmatrix}$$

The remaining steps for finding displacements and spring forces are identical to those discussed previously.

Example 11-5. Formulate the stiffness matrices for the individual springs and derive the system stiffness matrix for the assemblage shown in Fig. 11-13(a). Furthermore, devise a transformation procedure for obtaining the system stiffness matrix for the configuration shown in Fig. 11-13(b) from the matrix previously derived.

(a)   (b)   **Figure 11-13**

The free-body diagrams of the individual springs are shown in Fig. 11-14. For spring 1 in Fig. 11-14(a), $\theta_1 = 90°$, $\lambda_1 = \cos\theta_1 = 0$ and $\mu_1 = \sin\theta_1 = 1$; for spring 2 in Fig. 11-14(b), $\theta_2 = 0°$, $\lambda_2 = 1$ and $\mu_2 = 0$. Similarly, for spring 3 in Fig. 11-14(c), $\theta_3 = 45°$, $\lambda_3 = \sqrt{2}/2$ and $\mu_3 = \sqrt{2}/2$; thus $\lambda_3^2 = 1/2$, $\lambda_3\mu_3 = 1/2$ and $\mu_3^2 = 1/2$. From Eq. (11-45), we find the element stiffness matrix for each individual spring:

$$[\mathbf{k}^{(1)}] = k_1 \begin{array}{c} \begin{array}{cccc} \Delta_{x3} & \Delta_{y3} & \Delta_{x1} & \Delta_{y1} \end{array} \\ \begin{bmatrix} 0 & 0 & 0 & 0 \\ 0 & 1 & 0 & -1 \\ 0 & 0 & 0 & 0 \\ 0 & -1 & 0 & 1 \end{bmatrix} \end{array}$$

$$[\mathbf{k}^{(2)}] = k_2 \begin{array}{c} \begin{array}{cccc} \Delta_{x1} & \Delta_{y1} & \Delta_{x2} & \Delta_{y2} \end{array} \\ \begin{bmatrix} 1 & 0 & -1 & 0 \\ 0 & 0 & 0 & 0 \\ -1 & 0 & 1 & 0 \\ 0 & 0 & 0 & 0 \end{bmatrix} \end{array}$$

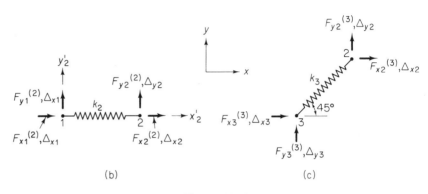

(a)

(b)   (c)

Figure 11-14

$$[\mathbf{k}^{(3)}] = k_3 \begin{array}{c} \begin{array}{cccc} \Delta_{x3} & \Delta_{y3} & \Delta_{x2} & \Delta_{y2} \end{array} \\ \begin{bmatrix} 1/2 & 1/2 & -1/2 & -1/2 \\ 1/2 & 1/2 & -1/2 & -1/2 \\ -1/2 & -1/2 & 1/2 & 1/2 \\ -1/2 & -1/2 & 1/2 & 1/2 \end{bmatrix} \end{array}$$

Then, the system stiffness matrix may be obtained by superposition

$$[\mathbf{K}] = \begin{array}{c} \begin{array}{cccccc} \Delta_{x1} & \Delta_{y1} & \Delta_{x2} & \Delta_{y2} & \Delta_{x3} & \Delta_{y3} \end{array} \\ \begin{bmatrix} k_2 & 0 & -k_2 & 0 & 0 & 0 \\ 0 & k_1 & 0 & 0 & 0 & -k_1 \\ -k_2 & 0 & k_2 + k_3/2 & k_3/2 & -k_3/2 & -k_3/2 \\ 0 & 0 & k_3/2 & k_3/2 & -k_3/2 & -k_3/2 \\ 0 & 0 & -k_3/2 & -k_3/2 & k_3/2 & k_3/2 \\ 0 & -k_1 & -k_3/2 & -k_3/2 & k_3/2 & k_1 + k_3/2 \end{bmatrix} \end{array} \begin{array}{c} P_{x1} \\ P_{y1} \\ P_{x2} \\ P_{y2} \\ P_{x3} \\ P_{y3} \end{array}$$

If we rotate the configuration in Fig. 11-13(a) by 180°, we obtain the configuration shown in Fig. 11-13(b). Note that during the rotation, the global coordinates associated with the former become $\bar{x}$ and $\bar{y}$ in Fig. 11-15(a). To retain the global coordinates x and y relative to the new configuration as shown in Fig. 11-15(b), we note that $\theta = 180°$ between $(\bar{x}, \bar{y})$ and (x, y). Thus, for $\lambda = \cos \theta = -1$

Figure 11-15

and $\mu = \sin \theta = 0$, the transformation matrix $[\mathbf{T}]$ for the system is found to be

$$[\mathbf{T}] = \begin{bmatrix} -1 & 0 & 0 & 0 & 0 & 0 \\ 0 & -1 & 0 & 0 & 0 & 0 \\ 0 & 0 & -1 & 0 & 0 & 0 \\ 0 & 0 & 0 & -1 & 0 & 0 \\ 0 & 0 & 0 & 0 & -1 & 0 \\ 0 & 0 & 0 & 0 & 0 & -1 \end{bmatrix}$$

Then, the system stiffness matrix $[\mathbf{K}_b]$ for the configuration in Fig. 11-13(b) can be obtained from the system stiffness matrix $[\mathbf{K}_a]$ corresponding to the configuration in Fig. 11-13(a) as follows:

$$[\mathbf{K}_b] = [\mathbf{T}]^T [\mathbf{K}_a][\mathbf{T}] = [\mathbf{K}_a]$$

That is, the system stiffness matrix for the configuration in Fig. 11-13(b) is identical to that in Fig. 11-13(a).

11-12 THE FLEXIBILITY METHOD*

In the preceding sections, we found that the stiffness method is based on our expressing the governing equations in terms of nodal degrees of freedom which, once determined may be used to find internal forces in all structural elements. Because the primary unknowns are displacements, the stiffness method is often referred to as the *displacement method.*

By contrast, the *flexibility method* is often referred to as the *force method,* because the primary variables to be solved are the member forces. As we have seen previously, however, we can calculate all internal forces and reactions without considering compatibility of deformation only when the structure is statically determinate. For statically indeterminate structures, we are confronted with a greater number of unknown forces than equations of equilibrium. Thus, for prescribed loading, a unique set of redundant forces is re-

---

*The notation and development of the flexibility method used in this chapter and in Chapter 13 are similar to those presented by W. McGuire and R. W. Gallagher, *Matrix Structural Analysis,* (New York: John Wiley, 1979).

quired to satisfy compatibility of nodal displacements while still maintaining equilibrium.

In deploying the flexibility method we first express the *static equilibrium equations* at each joint of the structure and, if the structure is statically determinate, we may solve these equations directly for member forces and reactions. If the structure is statically indeterminate, however, we must supplement the equilibrium equations with *kinematic equations,* which relate internal member displacements to nodal degrees of freedom. The kinematic equations then may be expressed in terms of forces by considering the *flexibility* (i.e., the force-deformation relationship) of each member. In what follows, we shall introduce the basic features of the matrix flexibility method, while deferring to Chapter 13 certain refinements associated with greater generality and practical applications.

Statically determinate structures. First, we refer to the statically determinate structure in Fig. 11-16(a), accounting for the particular support conditions that exist. Based on the equations of equilibrium for the joints, as shown in Fig. 11-16(b), we may write

$$\begin{Bmatrix} P_2 \\ P_3 \\ P_4 \end{Bmatrix} = \begin{bmatrix} 1 & -1 & 0 \\ 0 & 1 & -1 \\ 0 & 0 & 1 \end{bmatrix} \begin{Bmatrix} F_1 \\ F_2 \\ F_3 \end{Bmatrix} \tag{11-49}$$

(a)

(b)

Figure 11-16

We have placed all the (known) applied loads on the left side of Eq. (11-49) and all the (unknown) internal forces on the right side. Necessarily, only one applied load appears in each equation, whereas the unknown member forces may appear in more than one equation. Provided the structure is kinematically stable, as in the present case, the square matrix on the right side of Eq. (11-49) may be inverted. Hence,

$$\begin{Bmatrix} F_1 \\ F_2 \\ F_3 \end{Bmatrix} = \begin{bmatrix} 1 & -1 & 0 \\ 0 & 1 & -1 \\ 0 & 0 & 1 \end{bmatrix}^{-1} \begin{Bmatrix} P_2 \\ P_3 \\ P_4 \end{Bmatrix} = \begin{bmatrix} 1 & 1 & 1 \\ 0 & 1 & 1 \\ 0 & 0 & 1 \end{bmatrix} \begin{Bmatrix} P_2 \\ P_3 \\ P_4 \end{Bmatrix} \qquad (11\text{-}50)$$

This represents the solution to the problem. Note that, instead of inverting the matrix, it might have been easier to solve Eq. (11-49) in some alternative way. However, equilibrium equations for more complicated structures may be solved more conveniently by using a computer code that incorporates a matrix inversion routine.

We may write Eq. (11-49) symbolically as

$$\{\mathbf{P}_f\} = [\mathbf{B}]\{\mathbf{F}\} \qquad (11\text{-}51)$$

where, as we have noted previously, $\{\mathbf{P}_f\}$ is the vector of applied loads (i.e., loads exclusive of unknown reactions), $\{\mathbf{F}\}$ is the vector of unknown member forces, and $[\mathbf{B}]$ is the system statics matrix. For a *statically determinate, kinematically stable structure,* $[\mathbf{B}]$ is square and nonsingular. Accordingly, we may write

$$\{\mathbf{F}\} = [\mathbf{B}]^{-1}\{\mathbf{P}_f\} \qquad (11\text{-}52)$$

Note that the determination of internal forces represents the end of the analysis for many practical problems, unless displacements must be computed. As we have just demonstrated, the internal forces can be obtained from the equilibrium equations alone if the system is statically determinate. If the system is statically indeterminate, or if displacements must be computed, it is necessary to invoke conditions of compatiblity and force-deformation in addition to equilibrium.

Statically indeterminate structures. Now consider the statically indeterminate structure shown in Fig. 11-17. Only two nodes, at which loads P_2 and P_3, now are unrestrained. The nodal equilibrium equations previously written for nodes 2 and 3 are

$$\{\mathbf{P}_f\} \equiv \begin{Bmatrix} P_2 \\ P_3 \end{Bmatrix} = \begin{bmatrix} 1 & -1 & \vdots & 0 \\ 0 & 1 & \vdots & -1 \end{bmatrix} \begin{Bmatrix} F_1 \\ F_2 \\ \text{---} \\ F_3 \end{Bmatrix} = [\mathbf{B}]\{\mathbf{F}\} \qquad (11\text{-}53)$$

As for any statically indeterminate structure, the rectangular matrix on the right side of Eq. (11-53) cannot be inverted because it has more rows than columns; that is, there are more unknowns than equations. Compared with the preceding statically determinate problem, we have one fewer equilibrium equation (associated with node 4, where now an unknown reaction acts) while we still have three unknown internal forces. If spring 3, for example, were

Figure 11-17

removed as a redundance, the resulting released structure would be statically determinate.

We have partitioned the unknown force vector so as to identify F_3 as the redundant force (we could have designated any one of the internal forces as the redundance), and we have partitioned the matrix of coefficients such that the part to the left of the partition is square. We may thus express Eq. (11-53) symbolically as

$$\{\mathbf{P}_f\} = [\mathbf{B}]\{\mathbf{F}\} = [\mathbf{B}_0 \vdots \mathbf{B}_x]\begin{Bmatrix} \mathbf{F}_0 \\ --- \\ \mathbf{F}_x \end{Bmatrix} \quad (11\text{-}54)$$

where $\{\mathbf{F}_0\}$ is the vector of member forces associated with the released (statically determinate) structure, i.e., the structure created when the redundant forces are ignored; and $\{\mathbf{F}_x\}$ is the vector of redundant forces. $[\mathbf{B}_0]$ is a square and (for a kinematically stable structure) nonsingular matrix, and $[\mathbf{B}_x]$ is, in general, a rectangular matrix having as many rows as $[\mathbf{B}_0]$ and as many columns as $\{\mathbf{F}_x\}$ has rows. In the present case, comparing Eqs. (11-53) and (11-54), we have

$$\{\mathbf{F}_0\} = \begin{Bmatrix} F_1 \\ F_2 \end{Bmatrix} \qquad \{\mathbf{F}_x\} = \{F_3\} \qquad (11\text{-}55a)$$

$$[\mathbf{B}_0] = \begin{bmatrix} 1 & -1 \\ 0 & 1 \end{bmatrix} \quad \text{and} \quad [\mathbf{B}_x] = \begin{bmatrix} 0 \\ -1 \end{bmatrix} \qquad (11\text{-}55b)$$

We may express $\{\mathbf{F}_0\}$ in terms of $\{\mathbf{P}_f\}$ and $\{\mathbf{F}_x\}$. That is, from Eq. (11-54),

$$\{\mathbf{F}_0\} = [\mathbf{B}_0]^{-1}(\{\mathbf{P}_f\} - [\mathbf{B}_x]\{\mathbf{F}_x\}) \qquad (11\text{-}56a)$$

or

$$\{\mathbf{F}_0\} = [\mathbf{C}_0]\{\mathbf{P}_f\} + [\mathbf{C}_x]\{\mathbf{F}_x\} \qquad (11\text{-}56b)$$

where

$$[\mathbf{C}_0] = [\mathbf{B}_0]^{-1} \qquad (11\text{-}56c)$$

and

$$[\mathbf{C}_x] = -[\mathbf{B}_0]^{-1}[\mathbf{B}_x] = -[\mathbf{C}_0][\mathbf{B}_x] \qquad (11\text{-}56d)$$

For the present case,

$$\begin{Bmatrix} F_1 \\ F_2 \end{Bmatrix} = \begin{bmatrix} 1 & 1 \\ 0 & 1 \end{bmatrix}\begin{Bmatrix} P_2 \\ P_3 \end{Bmatrix} + \begin{bmatrix} 1 \\ 1 \end{bmatrix}\{F_3\} \qquad (11\text{-}57)$$

We now wish to express the redundant force vector $\{\mathbf{F}_x\}$ (or $\{F_3\}$ in this case) in terms of $\{\mathbf{F}_0\}$ (or $\{F_1, F_2\}$) by satisfying conditions of geometric compatibility. First we seek to formalize the kinematic relationship between the deformation of a spring element and its generalized coordinates. Suppose we again designate $\{\boldsymbol{\delta}\}$ as the vector of relative displacements between two ends of a structural

Matrix Methods of Structural Analysis   Chap. 11

member. For the simple spring elements considered here, $\{\boldsymbol{\delta}\} = \{\delta_1, \delta_2, \delta_3\}$. By defining $[\mathbf{A}]$ as the system kinematics matrix relating the vector of relative displacements $\{\boldsymbol{\delta}\}$ in terms of the vector of nodal displacements $\{\boldsymbol{\Delta}_f\}$ corresponding to the *active* degrees of freedom of the system, we may write

$$\{\boldsymbol{\delta}\} = [\mathbf{A}]\{\boldsymbol{\Delta}_f\} \tag{11-58}$$

For the example under consideration, we then have

$$\{\boldsymbol{\delta}\} = \begin{Bmatrix} \delta_1 \\ \delta_2 \\ \delta_3 \end{Bmatrix} = \begin{bmatrix} 1 & 0 \\ -1 & 1 \\ 0 & -1 \end{bmatrix} \begin{Bmatrix} \Delta_2 \\ \Delta_3 \end{Bmatrix} = [\mathbf{A}]\{\boldsymbol{\Delta}_f\} \tag{11-59}$$

It may be seen, by comparing Eqs. (11-53) and (11-59) that $[\mathbf{A}]^T = [\mathbf{B}]$, as we observed previously in discussing the stiffness method. This relationship is useful from a practical viewpoint, in that we need not derive both the global statics matrix $[\mathbf{B}]$ and the kinematics matrix $[\mathbf{A}]$ independently.

To exploit further the relationship between $[\mathbf{B}]$ and $[\mathbf{A}]$, we may partition $\{\boldsymbol{\delta}\}$ and $[\mathbf{A}]$ in the same pattern as we partitioned $\{\mathbf{F}\}$ and $[\mathbf{B}]$ in Eq. (11-54), i.e., let

$$\{\boldsymbol{\delta}\} = \begin{Bmatrix} \boldsymbol{\delta}_0 \\ \hline \boldsymbol{\delta}_x \end{Bmatrix} = \begin{bmatrix} \mathbf{A}_0 \\ \hline \mathbf{A}_x \end{bmatrix} \{\boldsymbol{\Delta}_f\} = [\mathbf{A}]\{\boldsymbol{\Delta}_f\} \tag{11-60}$$

Thus, as we partitioned $\{\mathbf{F}\}$ into $\{\mathbf{F}_0\}$, which comprises the unknown forces of the released system, and $\{\mathbf{F}_x\}$, which comprises the redundant forces, we may similarly partition $\{\boldsymbol{\delta}\}$. For the particular case being considered,

$$\{\boldsymbol{\delta}_0\} = \begin{Bmatrix} \delta_1 \\ \delta_2 \end{Bmatrix} \quad \text{and} \quad \{\boldsymbol{\delta}_x\} = \{\delta_3\} \tag{11-61a}$$

and

$$[\mathbf{A}_0] = \begin{bmatrix} 1 & 0 \\ -1 & 1 \end{bmatrix} \quad \text{and} \quad [\mathbf{A}_x] = [0 \ -1] \tag{11-61b}$$

By comparing Eqs. (11-55) and (11-61), we see that $[\mathbf{A}_0] = [\mathbf{B}_0]^T$ and $[\mathbf{A}_x] = [\mathbf{B}_x]^T$, properties which apply in general. Of course, it will always be essential that the entries in $\{\boldsymbol{\delta}\}$ and $\{\boldsymbol{\Delta}_f\}$ have the same order as the entries in $\{\mathbf{F}\}$ and $\{\mathbf{P}_f\}$, respectively; that is, the first entry in $\{\boldsymbol{\delta}\}$ is δ_1 (the deformation of spring 1) while the first entry in $\{\mathbf{F}\}$ is F_1 (the force in spring 1), etc.

We may write the upper partition of Eq. (11-60) as

$$\{\boldsymbol{\delta}_0\} = [\mathbf{A}_0]\{\boldsymbol{\Delta}_f\}$$

from which

$$\{\boldsymbol{\Delta}_f\} = [\mathbf{A}_0]^{-1}\{\boldsymbol{\delta}_0\} = [[\mathbf{B}_0]^T]^{-1}\{\boldsymbol{\delta}_0\} = [\mathbf{C}_0]^T\{\boldsymbol{\delta}_0\} \tag{11-62}$$

The lower partition of Eq. (11-60) yields

$$\{\boldsymbol{\delta}_x\} = [\mathbf{A}_x]\{\boldsymbol{\Delta}_f\} = [\mathbf{B}_x]^T\{\boldsymbol{\Delta}_f\}$$

which, when combined with Eq. (11-62), permits us to express $\{\boldsymbol{\delta}_x\}$ in terms of $\{\boldsymbol{\delta}_0\}$, i.e.,

$$\{\boldsymbol{\delta}_x\} = [\mathbf{B}_x]^T[\mathbf{C}_0]^T\{\boldsymbol{\delta}_0\} = -[\mathbf{C}_x]^T\{\boldsymbol{\delta}_0\} \tag{11-63}$$

We have now expressed conditions of equilibrium, Eq. (11-56b), and of compatibility, Eqs. (11-62) and (11-63), in forms that will be most useful. We have yet to specify the third essential ingredient, the force-deformation relationships. We do this now by noting that the deformation (i.e., the relative displacement between the ends of the member) of any structural element may be related to its internal force. For each of the three springs in our example, $F = k\delta$ or $\delta = fF$, where $f = 1/k$ is referred to as the flexibility of the spring. Hence we may write for the mth spring

$$\delta_m = f_m F_m \qquad (m = 1, 2, 3) \tag{11-64a}$$

In more general terms, we may write for the mth element of a structure

$$\{\boldsymbol{\delta}_m\} = [\mathbf{f}_m]\{\mathbf{F}_m\} \tag{11-64b}$$

Here $[\mathbf{f}_m]$ is the *member flexibility matrix,* which may be, and often is, of order greater than one for elements that are more complicated than the springs considered here. Noting that $\{\boldsymbol{\delta}\}$ and $\{\mathbf{F}\}$ actually comprise the vectors $\{\boldsymbol{\delta}_m\}$ and $\{\mathbf{F}_m\}$ of all M members ($m = 1, 2, \ldots, M$), we may write the combined member flexibility equations as

$$\{\boldsymbol{\delta}\} = [\mathbf{f}]\{\mathbf{F}\} \tag{11-65}$$

in which

$$\{\boldsymbol{\delta}\} = \begin{Bmatrix} \delta_1 \\ \delta_2 \\ \vdots \\ \delta_M \end{Bmatrix} \quad \{\mathbf{F}\} = \begin{Bmatrix} F_1 \\ F_2 \\ \vdots \\ F_M \end{Bmatrix} \quad \text{and} \quad [\mathbf{f}] = \begin{bmatrix} [\mathbf{f}_1] & & & \\ & [\mathbf{f}_2] & & \\ & & \ddots & \\ & & & [\mathbf{f}_M] \end{bmatrix}$$

where $[\mathbf{f}]$ is termed the *matrix of member flexibilities.* Because we previously partitioned $\{\boldsymbol{\delta}\}$ and $\{\mathbf{F}\}$ as $\{\boldsymbol{\delta}_0, \boldsymbol{\delta}_x\}$ and $\{\mathbf{F}_0, \mathbf{F}_x\}$, we may write Eq. (11-65) as

$$\begin{Bmatrix} \boldsymbol{\delta}_0 \\ \hline \boldsymbol{\delta}_x \end{Bmatrix} = \begin{bmatrix} [\mathbf{f}_{00}] & \vdots & [\mathbf{f}_{0x}] \\ \hline [\mathbf{f}_{x0}] & \vdots & [\mathbf{f}_{xx}] \end{bmatrix} \begin{Bmatrix} \mathbf{F}_0 \\ \hline \mathbf{F}_x \end{Bmatrix} \tag{11-66}$$

which, for the present example, is

$$\begin{Bmatrix} \delta_1 \\ \delta_2 \\ \hline \delta_3 \end{Bmatrix} = \begin{bmatrix} 1/k_1 & 0 & \vdots & 0 \\ 0 & 1/k_2 & \vdots & 0 \\ \hline 0 & 0 & \vdots & 1/k_3 \end{bmatrix} \begin{Bmatrix} F_1 \\ F_2 \\ \hline F_3 \end{Bmatrix} \tag{11-67}$$

These are the force-deformation relationships we sought.

We may now combine the three essential pieces—equilibrium, compatibility, and force-deformation—to solve for the unknown forces and, if we wish, the unknown displacements. First we add to the equilibrium conditions, Eq. (11-56b), the identity $\{\mathbf{F}_x\} = [\mathbf{I}]\{\mathbf{F}_x\}$ to obtain

$$\begin{Bmatrix} \mathbf{F}_0 \\ \hline \mathbf{F}_x \end{Bmatrix} = \begin{bmatrix} [\mathbf{C}_0] & \vdots & [\mathbf{C}_x] \\ \hline [\mathbf{0}] & \vdots & [\mathbf{I}] \end{bmatrix} \begin{Bmatrix} \mathbf{P}_f \\ \hline \mathbf{F}_x \end{Bmatrix} \tag{11-68}$$

Also, Eqs. (11-62) and (11-63) may be combined into a single compatibility relation, i.e.,

$$\begin{Bmatrix} \boldsymbol{\Delta}_f \\ \hline \mathbf{0} \end{Bmatrix} = \begin{bmatrix} [\mathbf{C}_0]^T & \vdots & [\mathbf{0}] \\ \hline [\mathbf{C}_x]^T & \vdots & [\mathbf{I}] \end{bmatrix} \begin{Bmatrix} \boldsymbol{\delta}_0 \\ \hline \boldsymbol{\delta}_x \end{Bmatrix} \tag{11-69}$$

We may then substitute the force-deformation relationship, Eq. (11-66), and the equilibrium equations, Eq. (11-68), into Eq. (11-69) to obtain

$$\begin{Bmatrix} \boldsymbol{\Delta}_f \\ \hline \mathbf{0} \end{Bmatrix} = \begin{bmatrix} [\mathbf{C}_0]^T & \vdots & [\mathbf{0}] \\ \hline [\mathbf{C}_x]^T & \vdots & [\mathbf{I}] \end{bmatrix} \begin{bmatrix} [\mathbf{f}_{00}] & \vdots & [\mathbf{f}_{0x}] \\ \hline [\mathbf{f}_{x0}] & \vdots & [\mathbf{f}_{xx}] \end{bmatrix} \begin{bmatrix} [\mathbf{C}_0] & \vdots & [\mathbf{C}_x] \\ \hline [\mathbf{0}] & \vdots & [\mathbf{I}] \end{bmatrix} \begin{Bmatrix} \mathbf{P}_f \\ \hline \mathbf{F}_x \end{Bmatrix}$$

or

$$\begin{Bmatrix} \boldsymbol{\Delta}_f \\ \hline \mathbf{0} \end{Bmatrix} = \begin{bmatrix} [\mathscr{F}_{pp}] & \vdots & [\mathscr{F}_{px}] \\ \hline [\mathscr{F}_{xp}] & \vdots & [\mathscr{F}_{xx}] \end{bmatrix} \begin{Bmatrix} \mathbf{P}_f \\ \hline \mathbf{F}_x \end{Bmatrix} \tag{11-70}$$

in which

$$[\mathscr{F}_{pp}] = [\mathbf{C}_0]^T [\mathbf{f}_{00}][\mathbf{C}_0] \tag{11-71a}$$

$$[\mathscr{F}_{px}] = [\mathscr{F}_{xp}]^T = [\mathbf{C}_0]^T [\mathbf{f}_{00}][\mathbf{C}_x] + [\mathbf{C}_0]^T [\mathbf{f}_{0x}] \tag{11-71b}$$

$$[\mathscr{F}_{xx}] = [\mathbf{C}_x]^T [\mathbf{f}_{00}][\mathbf{C}_x] + [\mathbf{C}_x]^T [\mathbf{f}_{0x}] + [\mathbf{f}_{x0}][\mathbf{C}_x] + [\mathbf{f}_{xx}] \tag{11-71c}$$

The lower partition of Eqs. (11-70) leads to the evaluation of the redundant forces; i.e.,

$$\{\mathbf{F}_x\} = -[\mathscr{F}_{xx}]^{-1}[\mathscr{F}_{xp}]\{\mathbf{P}_f\} \tag{11-72}$$

When this expression is substituted into the upper partition of Eq. (11-68), we obtain the remaining unknown forces

$$\{\mathbf{F}_0\} = ([\mathbf{C}_0] - [\mathbf{C}_x][\mathscr{F}_{xx}]^{-1}[\mathscr{F}_{xp}])\{\mathbf{P}_f\} \tag{11-73}$$

Finally, the joint displacements may be found by substituting Eq. (11-72) into the upper partition of Eq. (11-70) to obtain

$$\{\boldsymbol{\Delta}_f\} = ([\mathscr{F}_{pp}] - [\mathscr{F}_{px}][\mathscr{F}_{xx}]^{-1}[\mathscr{F}_{xp}])\{\mathbf{P}_f\}$$

or

$$\{\boldsymbol{\Delta}_f\} = [\mathscr{F}]\{\mathbf{P}_f\} \tag{11-74a}$$

where

$$[\mathscr{F}] = [\mathscr{F}_{pp}] - [\mathscr{F}_{px}][\mathscr{F}_{xx}]^{-1}[\mathscr{F}_{xp}] \tag{11-74b}$$

is the *system flexibility matrix;* it is equal to the inverse of the reduced system stiffness matrix $[\mathbf{K}_{ff}]$.

We may now complete the example by performing the preceding matrix operations. Recall that

$$[\mathbf{C}_0] = \begin{bmatrix} 1 & 1 \\ 0 & 1 \end{bmatrix}$$

$$[\mathbf{C}_x] = [\mathbf{C}_0][\mathbf{B}_x] = \begin{bmatrix} 1 \\ 1 \end{bmatrix}$$

$$[\mathbf{f}_{00}] = \begin{bmatrix} 1/k_1 & 0 \\ 0 & 1/k_2 \end{bmatrix}$$

$$[\mathbf{f}_{0x}] = [\mathbf{f}_{x0}]^T = \begin{bmatrix} 0 \\ 0 \end{bmatrix}$$

and

$$[\mathbf{f}_{xx}] = [1/k_3]$$

Then, from Eqs. (11-71),

$$[\mathscr{F}_{pp}] = \begin{bmatrix} 1/k_1 & 1/k_1 \\ 1/k_1 & (1/k_1 + 1/k_2) \end{bmatrix}$$

$$[\mathscr{F}_{px}] = [\mathscr{F}_{xp}]^T = \begin{bmatrix} 1/k_1 \\ (1/k_1 + 1/k_2) \end{bmatrix}$$

and

$$[\mathscr{F}_{xx}] = [(1/k_1 + 1/k_2 + 1/k_3)]$$

We now consider for simplicity the case in which $k_1 = k_2 = k_3 = k$. Then from Eq. (11-72), we obtain

$$\{\mathbf{F}_x\} \equiv F_3 = -\frac{1}{3}P_2 - \frac{2}{3}P_3$$

and, from Eqs. (11-73),

$$\{\mathbf{F}_0\} = \begin{Bmatrix} F_1 \\ F_2 \end{Bmatrix} = \begin{Bmatrix} \frac{2}{3}P_2 + \frac{1}{3}P_3 \\ -\frac{1}{3}P_2 + \frac{1}{3}P_3 \end{Bmatrix}$$

Finally, from Eqs. (11-74),

$$\{\mathbf{\Delta}_f\} = \begin{Bmatrix} \Delta_2 \\ \Delta_3 \end{Bmatrix} = \frac{1}{k} \begin{Bmatrix} \frac{2}{3}P_2 + \frac{1}{3}P_3 \\ \frac{1}{3}P_2 + \frac{2}{3}P_3 \end{Bmatrix}$$

Matrix Methods of Structural Analysis   Chap. 11

The foregoing development has employed conditions of equilibrium, compatibility and force-deformation, Eqs. (11-68), (11-69), and (11-70), respectively, to establish the final set of equations for internal forces and nodal displacements. In contrast with the stiffness method, which leads to governing equations expressed in terms of generalized displacements, the flexibility method leads to equations expressed in terms of internal forces, Eqs. (11-72) and (11-73). Displacements may be computed from Eqs. (11-74), but they are not the primary unknowns. Of course, as noted previously, the flexibility method does require that we distinguish whether a structure is statically determinate or indeterminate. Primarily for this reason, this method has not been as highly developed for automatic computation as has the stiffness method.

We may summarize the solution procedure for the flexibility method as follows:

1. Express equations of equilibrium at each node in the direction corresponding to each unrestrained degree of freedom. Through these equations, relating applied external loads $\{P_f\}$ to unknown internal forces $\{F\}$, we establish the global statics matrix $[B]$.

2. Identify redundant internal forces and partition $\{F\}$ as $\{F_0 \vdots F_x\}$ and $[B]$ as $[B_0 \vdots B_x]$; $\{F_0\}$ must have the same dimension as $\{P_f\}$, and $\{F_x\}$ must be selected to maintain a kinematically stable structure, such that $[B_0]$ is square and nonsingular. We may then compute $[C_0] = [B_0]^{-1}$ and $[C_x] = -[B_0]^{-1}[B_x]$.

3. Form the matrix of member flexibilities $[f]$, relating the member deformations to the corresponding internal forces. By ordering these deformations and forces according to the order of $\{F_0 \vdots F_x\}$, we may partition $[f]$ according to Eq. (11-66).

4. Compute the matrices $[\mathcal{F}_{pp}]$, $[\mathcal{F}_{px}] = [\mathcal{F}_{xp}]^T$ and $[\mathcal{F}_{xx}]$ according to Eqs. (11-71).

5. Compute the internal forces $\{F_0\}$ and $\{F_x\}$ from Eqs. (11-72) and (11-73) and, if desired, the nodal displacements $\{\Delta_f\}$ from Eqs. (11-74).

We shall employ the foregoing procedure in Chapter 13 to analyze trusses and frames. We conclude the present discussion with an example of a simple assemblage of springs.

Example 11-6. We return to the system described in Example 11-3, now treating the problem by the flexibility method. Again, we wish to find the internal forces, reactions and displacements of the system shown in Fig. 11-18(a), assuming $k_1 = k_2 = k_3 = k$.

Figure 11-18

We consider equilibrium only of the node that is not restrained, node 2, as shown in Fig. 11-18(b). The relevant equilibrium equations are

$$\begin{Bmatrix} P_{x2} \\ P_{y2} \end{Bmatrix} = \begin{bmatrix} 1 & -\sqrt{3}/2 & \vdots & 0 \\ 0 & -1/2 & \vdots & -1 \end{bmatrix} \begin{Bmatrix} F_1 \\ F_2 \\ \hline F_3 \end{Bmatrix}$$

where now

$$\{\mathbf{P}_f\} = \begin{Bmatrix} P_{x2} \\ P_{y2} \end{Bmatrix} = \begin{Bmatrix} 0 \\ -P \end{Bmatrix} \qquad \{\mathbf{\Delta}_f\} = \begin{Bmatrix} \Delta_{x2} \\ \Delta_{y2} \end{Bmatrix}$$

$$\{\mathbf{F}_0\} = \begin{Bmatrix} F_1 \\ F_2 \end{Bmatrix} \qquad \{\mathbf{F}_x\} = \{F_3\}$$

$$[\mathbf{B}_0] = \begin{bmatrix} 1 & -\sqrt{3}/2 \\ 0 & -1/2 \end{bmatrix} \qquad [\mathbf{B}_x] = \begin{bmatrix} 0 \\ -1 \end{bmatrix}$$

We then find

$$[\mathbf{C}_0] = [\mathbf{B}_0]^{-1} = \begin{bmatrix} 1 & -\sqrt{3} \\ 0 & -2 \end{bmatrix}$$

$$[\mathbf{C}_x] = -[\mathbf{C}_0][\mathbf{B}_x] = \begin{bmatrix} -\sqrt{3} \\ -2 \end{bmatrix}$$

We observe that the redundant force has been taken as F_3, the force in spring 3. Note also that

$$\{\mathbf{\delta}\} = \begin{Bmatrix} \mathbf{\delta}_0 \\ \hline \mathbf{\delta}_x \end{Bmatrix} = \begin{Bmatrix} \delta_1 \\ \delta_2 \\ \hline \delta_3 \end{Bmatrix}$$

and thus

$$[\mathbf{f}] = \begin{bmatrix} [\mathbf{f}_{00}] & \vdots & [\mathbf{f}_{0x}] \\ \hline [\mathbf{f}_{x0}] & \vdots & [\mathbf{f}_{0x}] \end{bmatrix} = \begin{bmatrix} 1/k & 0 & \vdots & 0 \\ 0 & 1/k & \vdots & 0 \\ \hline 0 & 0 & \vdots & 1/k \end{bmatrix}$$

Matrix Methods of Structural Analysis   Chap. 11

Hence,

$$[\mathscr{F}_{pp}] = [\mathbf{C}_0]^T[\mathbf{f}_{00}][\mathbf{C}_0] = \frac{1}{k}\begin{bmatrix} 1 & -\sqrt{3} \\ -\sqrt{3} & 7 \end{bmatrix}$$

$$[\mathscr{F}_{px}] = [\mathbf{C}_0]^T[\mathbf{f}_{00}][\mathbf{C}_x] + [\mathbf{C}_0]^T[\mathbf{f}_{0x}] = \frac{1}{k}\begin{bmatrix} -\sqrt{3} \\ 7 \end{bmatrix}$$

$$[\mathscr{F}_{xx}] = [\mathbf{C}_x]^T[\mathbf{f}_{00}][\mathbf{C}_x] + [\mathbf{C}_x]^T[\mathbf{f}_{0x}] + [\mathbf{f}_{x0}][\mathbf{C}_x] + [\mathbf{f}_{xx}] = \frac{8}{k}$$

We may therefore compute

$$\{\mathbf{F}_x\} = -[\mathscr{F}_{xx}]^{-1}[\mathscr{\bar F}_{xp}]\{\mathbf{P}_f\}$$

or

$$F_3 = \frac{7}{8}P$$

and

$$\{\mathbf{F}_0\} = ([\mathbf{C}_0] - [\mathbf{C}_x][\mathscr{F}_{xx}]^{-1}[\mathscr{F}_{xp}])\{\mathbf{P}_f\}$$

or

$$\begin{Bmatrix} F_1 \\ F_2 \end{Bmatrix} = P\begin{Bmatrix} \sqrt{3}/8 \\ 1/4 \end{Bmatrix}$$

Finally,

$$\{\mathbf{\Delta}_f\} = ([\mathscr{F}_{pp}] - [\mathscr{F}_{px}][\mathscr{F}_{xx}]^{-1}[\mathscr{F}_{xp}])\{\mathbf{P}_f\} = [\mathscr{F}]\{\mathbf{P}_f\}$$

or

$$\begin{Bmatrix} \Delta_{x2} \\ \Delta_{y2} \end{Bmatrix} = \frac{P}{k}\begin{Bmatrix} \sqrt{3}/8 \\ -7/8 \end{Bmatrix}$$

Having determined the internal member forces, we may find the reactions, which do not directly enter the formulation, by writing the equilibrium equations for nodes 1, 3 and 4.

11-14 CONCLUDING REMARKS

In concluding this chapter, we elaborate on some points raised earlier. First, we previously observed an important relationship between the system kinematics matrix [**A**] and the system statics matrix [**B**], namely

$$[\mathbf{B}] = [\mathbf{A}]^T \tag{11-75a}$$

and, further

$$[\mathbf{B}_0] = [\mathbf{A}_0]^T \tag{11-75b}$$

and

$$[\mathbf{B}_x] = [\mathbf{A}_x]^T \tag{11-75c}$$

These relationships may be derived by noting that the sum of real external work W_e and real internal work W_i is zero. External work, performed by applied loads $\{\mathbf{P}_f\}$ acting through corresponding displacements $\{\mathbf{\Delta}_f\}$ may be expressed as

$$W_e = \frac{1}{2}\{\mathbf{P}_f\}^T\{\mathbf{\Delta}_f\} \tag{11-76}$$

Internal work, performed by member forces $\{\mathbf{F}\}$ acting against displacements $\{\boldsymbol{\delta}\}$ may be denoted by

$$W_i = -\frac{1}{2}\{\mathbf{F}\}^T\{\boldsymbol{\delta}\} \tag{11-77}$$

Using the conditions of equilibrium, Eq. (11-54), and noting $\{\mathbf{P}_f\}^T = \{\mathbf{F}\}^T[\mathbf{B}]^T$, Eq. (11-76) becomes

$$W_e = \frac{1}{2}\{\mathbf{F}\}^T[\mathbf{B}]^T\{\mathbf{\Delta}_f\} = \frac{1}{2}\{\mathbf{F}_0 \vdots \mathbf{F}_x\}^T[\mathbf{B}_0 \vdots \mathbf{B}_x]^T\{\mathbf{\Delta}_f\} \tag{11-78}$$

Also, using the condition of compatibility, Eq. (11-60), we may write Eq. (11-77) as

$$W_i = -\frac{1}{2}\{\mathbf{F}\}^T[\mathbf{A}]\{\mathbf{\Delta}_f\} = -\frac{1}{2}\{\mathbf{F}_0 \vdots \mathbf{F}_x\}^T\left[\frac{\mathbf{A}_0}{\mathbf{A}_x}\right]\{\mathbf{\Delta}_f\} \tag{11-79}$$

Setting $W_e + W_i = 0$, or $W_e = -W_i$, we obtain the desired relationships expressed by Eqs. (11-75).

As a second point, we wish to emphasize that, while the stiffness and flexibility methods might appear to be more disparate than they are similar, both methods embody precisely the same conditions, i.e.,

equilibrium	$\{\mathbf{P}_f\} = [\mathbf{B}]\{\mathbf{F}\}$	(11-80)
compatibility	$\{\boldsymbol{\delta}\} = [\mathbf{A}]\{\mathbf{\Delta}_f\}$	(11-81)
force-displacement	$\{\mathbf{F}\} = [\mathcal{K}]\{\boldsymbol{\delta}\}$	(11-82a)
or	$\{\boldsymbol{\delta}\} = [\mathbf{f}]\{\mathbf{F}\}$	(11-82b)

$$\text{(where } [\mathbf{f}]^{-1} = [\mathcal{K}])$$

In Section 11-7, we combined these conditions to obtain the system stiffness equations

$$\{\mathbf{P}\} = [\mathbf{K}]\{\mathbf{\Delta}\} \qquad\qquad (11\text{-}83a)$$

or, alternatively, in the absence of prescribed nonzero displacements,

$$\{\mathbf{P}_f\} = [\mathbf{K}_{ff}]\{\mathbf{\Delta}_f\} \qquad\qquad (11\text{-}83b)$$

Although the primary variables in the flexibility method are internal forces rather than nodal displacements, we used the foregoing conditions in Section 11-12 to obtain, in addition to the expressions relating internal forces to applied loads, the flexibility equations

$$\{\mathbf{\Delta}_f\} = [\mathscr{F}]\{\mathbf{P}_f\} \qquad\qquad (11\text{-}84)$$

From Eqs. (11-83b) and (11-84)

$$[\mathscr{F}] = [\mathbf{K}_{ff}]^{-1} \qquad\qquad (11\text{-}85)$$

as stated previously.

Although the flexibility method preceded the stiffness method in the development of the matrix methods of structural analysis, the latter has acquired an increasingly dominant role because it is more amenable to automatic computation. This is largely due to the need to distinguish between statically determinate and indeterminate systems when employing the flexibility method. The computational effort associated with the stiffness method is related to the nodal degrees of freedom; thus the stiffness method is often preferred in treating highly indeterminate problems where relatively few generalized displacements might exist. On the other hand, the flexibility method may provide computational advantages where structures have many degrees of freedom, but are either statically determinate or possess only a few redundant forces.

PROBLEMS

→**11-1.** For the system comprising three springs in series, as shown in Fig. P11-1, derive the system stiffness matrix by two methods:
(a) by formulating the matrix of member stiffness $[\mathscr{K}]$ and the system statics matrix $[\mathbf{B}]$, and then employing Eq. (11-19); and
(b) by combining stiffness matrices of the individual springs.

Figure P11-1

→**11-2.** For the system shown in Fig. P11-1, find the nodal displacements and the internal forces in the springs if node 4 is restrained and axial forces P_i ($i = 1, 2, 3$) are applied at nodes 1, 2 and 3. Investigate the behavior of the system when either $k_2 = 0$ or $k_2 = \infty$.

→**11-3.** For the system shown in Fig. P11-1, find the nodal displacements and the internal forces in the springs if nodes 2 and 4 are restrained and axial forces are applied at nodes 1 and 3. Investigate the behavior of the system when either $k_2 = 0$ or $k_2 = \infty$.

11-4. For the system shown in Fig. P11-1, find the nodal displacements and the internal forces in the springs if nodes 1 and 4 are restrained and an axial force P_2 is applied at node 2 while the axial displacement Δ_3 is prescribed at node 3.

11-5. Using the results of Problem 11-1, express the system stiffness matrix for an assemblage of N springs in series, as shown in Fig. P11-5(a). For any particular case, such as for $N = 5$, write the system stiffness matrix considering the two different nodal numbering schemes shown in Fig. P11-5(b). Which one of the schemes would be preferable?

(a)

(b)

Figure P11-5

11-6. The system of three parallel springs shown in Fig. P11-6 supports a rigid platform which is subjected to a vertical force P and a moment M at point O. Recognizing that, if horizontal displacement is prevented, the platform has only two degrees of freedom, e.g., the vertical displacements Δ at point O and a uniform rotation θ, derive the stiffness equations and solve for the displacements and spring forces.

Figure P11-6

11-7. Using the results of Example 11-4 express the stiffness matrix for an assemblage of N equally spaced parallel springs, as shown in Fig. P11-7.

Matrix Methods of Structural Analysis   Chap. 11

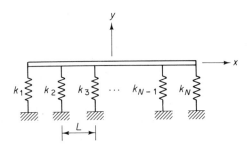

Figure P11-7

11-8. Considering nodes 1, 2, 3 and 4 to be restrained, derive the two stiffness equations relating forces and displacements at node O, assuming the prescribed forces at node O to be in the directions of the global coordinates for both the x–y and the $\bar{x}$–$\bar{y}$ coordinate systems shown in Fig. P11-8.

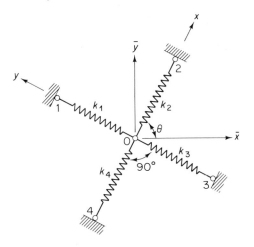

Figure P11-8

11-9. Using the results in Example 11-5, formulate the system stiffness matrices for the assemblages shown in Fig. P11-9(a) and (b).

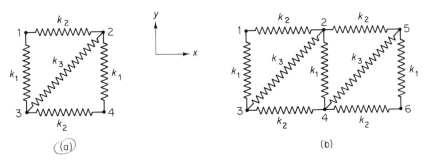

Figure P11-9

11-10 and 11-11. Solve Problems 11-2 and 11-3 using the flexibility method.

11-12. Solve Problem 11-4 by the flexibility method. Note that this problem may be solved in terms of an axial force P_3 (applied at node 3) whose magnitude ultimately may be determined from Eq. (11-74a).

11-13. Consider the nodal equilibrium equations expressing $\{P_f\}$ and $\{F\}$ presented as the first equations in Example 11-6. Demonstrate that by solving these equations in a traditional manner (e.g., by Gauss elimination) for the nonredundant forces in terms of the applied nodal loads and the redundant force, the matrices $[C_0]$ and $[C_x]$ may be determined without formally inverting $[B_0]$.

11-14. Solve Example 11-4 by the flexibility method.

11-15. For the systems comprising springs of equal stiffness shown in Fig. P11-15, demonstrate that $[A] = [B]^T$.

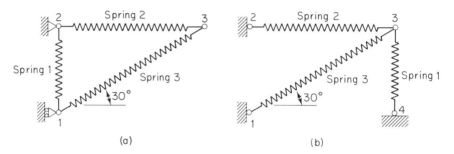

Figure P11-15

11-16. For the systems shown in Fig. P11-15, find the system flexibility matrix $[\mathscr{F}]$ and, through inversion of this matrix, find the reduced system stiffness matrix $[K_{ff}]$.

11-17. For the system shown in Fig. P11-15(a), demonstrate that if spring 1 is eliminated, the system is unstable.

11-18. For the system shown in Fig. P11-18,
  (a) find the internal forces and nodal displacements by considering either spring 1 or spring 2 to be the redundant member; and
  (b) demonstrate that spring 3 is not an admissible choice as the redundant member.

Figure P11-18

12

The Direct Stiffness Method

12-1 FORMULATION OF THE STIFFNESS EQUATIONS

The previous chapter presented the basic concepts associated with the stiffness and flexibility methods of structural analysis, leaving the application of these methods to traditional structures for subsequent chapters. The present chapter deals with the application of the direct stiffness method to structural systems comprising bar and beam elements.

As the central step in this method is the formulation of the stiffness equations, we begin by deriving the stiffness matrices for bar and beam elements. The analysis of trusses, beams and frames that follows requires the synthesis of the system stiffness matrix by combining the transformed element stiffness matrices of the members that constitute the structure. Particular attention is paid to the treatment of distributed transverse loads acting on beams and the analysis of self-strained structures, i.e., structures which undergo changes in temperature or incorporate members of imperfect dimensions. Finally, we conclude the chapter by describing simplifications that accrue from conditions of symmetry when they exist, and by carrying out the solution through methods of condensation and substructuring.

12-2 STIFFNESS MATRICES FOR BAR ELEMENTS

Because bars and beam-columns comprise the primary structural elements in the vast majority of civil engineering structures, we begin with the derivation of the stiffness matrices for these elements. Although bars and beam-columns differ in the sense that the former undergo only axial extension or compression while the latter also exhibit bending deformation, both are considered to be one-dimensional. If we know the generalized forces and displacements along the axis (i.e., along one dimension) of the member, we can deduce the member's behavior over the cross-section (i.e., in the two remaining dimensions).

Formulation of [k'] in local coordinates. Consider a bar of length L, constant cross-sectional area A, and Young's modulus E, as shown in Fig. 12-1(a). The end points are designated as i and j, and a local coordinate axis x' is directed from i to j along the axis of the bar. The bar force $F_{x'}$ is defined as positive for axial tension. Thus, the internal nodal forces are $F_{x'i} = -F_{x'}$ at end i and $F_{x'j} = F_{x'}$ at end j in Fig. 12-1(b). We wish to find the relationship between the generalized forces $F_{x'i}$ and $F_{x'j}$ directed axially at the end points, and the corresponding generalized displacements u_i' and u_j'. That is, we wish to establish the element stiffness matrix [k'], such that

$$\{\mathbf{F}'\} = [\mathbf{k}']\{\mathbf{u}'\} \qquad (12\text{-}1)$$

where

$$\{\mathbf{F}'\} = \begin{Bmatrix} F_{x'i} \\ F_{x'j} \end{Bmatrix} \text{ and } \{\mathbf{u}'\} = \begin{Bmatrix} u_i' \\ u_j' \end{Bmatrix} \qquad (12\text{-}2)$$

(a)

(b)

Figure 12-1

Here we have designated the displacements and the subscripts of the forces with primes to indicate their reference to the local coordinate x'; moreover, forces and displacements are considered positive when they act in the positive x' direction, as shown in Fig. 12-1(b).

One way of deriving [k'] is to recall that due to a constant axial force $F_{x'}$ (positive for tension), the axial stress $F_{x'}/A$ and strain du'/dx' are constant

The Direct Stiffness Method   Chap. 12

throughout the bar, i.e., from Hooke's law

$$F_{x'} = EA \frac{du'}{dx'} = \text{constant} \qquad (12\text{-}3a)$$

or

$$\frac{d^2 u'}{dx'^2} = 0 \qquad (12\text{-}3b)$$

Sequential integration of this equation leads to the general solution

$$u'(x') = C_1 x' + C_2 \qquad (12\text{-}4)$$

in which the constants of integration may be determined by requiring that at the boundaries (nodes i and j), u' must satisfy

$$u'(0) = u_i' \qquad \text{and} \qquad u'(L) = u_j' \qquad (12\text{-}5)$$

We then find that

$$C_1 = \frac{1}{L}(u_j' - u_i') \qquad \text{and} \qquad C_2 = u_i'$$

Thus the solution to Eq. (12-3b) subject to the boundary conditions, Eqs. (12-5), is

$$u'(x') = u_i'\left(1 - \frac{x'}{L}\right) + u_j'\frac{x'}{L} \qquad (12\text{-}6)$$

Now, substituting Eq. (12-6) into Eq. (12-3a), we find

$$F_{x'} = \frac{EA}{L}(u_j' - u_i')$$

To satisfy equilibrium,

$$F_{x'i} = -F_{x'} \text{ at } x' = 0$$

and

$$F_{x'j} = F_{x'} \text{ at } x' = L$$

Therefore, we find that

$$F_{x'i} = \frac{EA}{L}(u_i' - u_j')$$

and

$$F_{x'j} = \frac{EA}{L}(-u_i' + u_j')$$

That is,

$$\begin{Bmatrix} F_{x'i} \\ F_{x'j} \end{Bmatrix} = \frac{EA}{L}\begin{bmatrix} 1 & -1 \\ -1 & 1 \end{bmatrix}\begin{Bmatrix} u_i' \\ u_j' \end{Bmatrix} \qquad (12\text{-}7)$$

Comparing Eqs. (12-1) and (12-7), we find that

$$[\mathbf{k}'] = \frac{EA}{L} \begin{bmatrix} 1 & -1 \\ -1 & 1 \end{bmatrix} \tag{12-8}$$

Transformation of [k'] to global coordinates. As we indicated previously, the treatment of structures comprising assemblages of elements generally requires that forces and displacements be referred to a global coordinate system. Thus, the element stiffness matrices must be transformed to refer to the global coordinate system.

We begin by assigning two additional axes, y' and z' that are orthogonal to each other and to x'. The x'–y'–z' axes then constitute a local cartesian coordinate system. We may consider three forces to act at node i, namely, $F_{x'i}$, $F_{y'i}$, and $F_{z'i}$; corresponding to these forces are displacements u'_i, v'_i, and w'_i. (Of course, $F_{y'i}$ and $F_{z'i}$ are both zero because the bar can sustain only an axial force, but we retain them symbolically.) We may similarly associate with node j the forces $F_{x'j}$, $F_{y'j}$, $F_{z'j}$ and the displacements u'_j, v'_j, and w'_j. Then, an expanded form of Eq. (12-7) may be written as

$$\{\mathbf{F}'\} = [\mathbf{k}']\{\mathbf{\Delta}'\} \tag{12-9}$$

where

$$\{\mathbf{F}'\} = \begin{Bmatrix} F_{x'i} \\ F_{y'i} \\ F_{z'i} \\ F_{x'j} \\ F_{y'j} \\ F_{z'j} \end{Bmatrix} \qquad \{\mathbf{\Delta}'\} = \begin{Bmatrix} u'_i \\ v'_i \\ w'_i \\ u'_j \\ v'_j \\ w'_j \end{Bmatrix}$$

and

$$[\mathbf{k}'] = \begin{bmatrix} 1 & 0 & 0 & -1 & 0 & 0 \\ 0 & 0 & 0 & 0 & 0 & 0 \\ 0 & 0 & 0 & 0 & 0 & 0 \\ -1 & 0 & 0 & 1 & 0 & 0 \\ 0 & 0 & 0 & 0 & 0 & 0 \\ 0 & 0 & 0 & 0 & 0 & 0 \end{bmatrix} \tag{12-10}$$

The rows and columns containing only zero elements indicate that $F_{y'i}$, $F_{z'i}$, $F_{y'j}$, and $F_{z'j}$ are equal to zero, since the bar can sustain only an axial force.

Now consider the bar element shown in Fig. 12-2(a) where the generalized forces and displacements are referred to the global coordinate system, x–y–z. We define $\theta_{xx'}$, $\theta_{yx'}$, and $\theta_{zx'}$ as the angles formed by the local x'-axis and the global x-, y-, and z-axes, respectively. These angles are shown in Fig. 12-2(b). We similarly define sets of angles $\theta_{xy'}$, $\theta_{yy'}$, $\theta_{zy'}$ and $\theta_{xz'}$, $\theta_{yz'}$, $\theta_{zz'}$, between the local y'- and z'-axes, respectively, and the global axes.

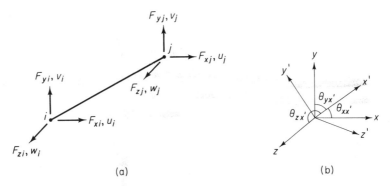

Figure 12-2

We observe that at node i,

$$F_{x'i} = F_{xi} \cos \theta_{xx'} + F_{yi} \cos \theta_{yx'} + F_{zi} \cos \theta_{zx'}$$
$$F_{y'i} = F_{xi} \cos \theta_{xy'} + F_{yi} \cos \theta_{yy'} + F_{zi} \cos \theta_{zy'} \qquad (12\text{-}11)$$
$$F_{z'i} = F_{xi} \cos \theta_{xz'} + F_{yi} \cos \theta_{yz'} + F_{zi} \cos \theta_{zz'}$$

Similarly, we may also write the transformation between forces referred to local and global coordinates for node j. If we adopt the notation

$$\begin{array}{lll} \lambda_{x'} = \cos \theta_{xx'} & \lambda_{y'} = \cos \theta_{xy'} & \lambda_{z'} = \cos \theta_{xz'} \\ \mu_{x'} = \cos \theta_{yx'} & \mu_{y'} = \cos \theta_{yy'} & \mu_{z'} = \cos \theta_{yz'} \\ \nu_{x'} = \cos \theta_{zx'} & \nu_{y'} = \cos \theta_{zy'} & \nu_{z'} = \cos \theta_{zz'} \end{array} \qquad (12\text{-}12)$$

then we may write Eqs. (12-11) for both nodes i and j as

$$\begin{Bmatrix} F_{x'i} \\ F_{y'i} \\ F_{z'i} \\ F_{x'j} \\ F_{y'j} \\ F_{z'j} \end{Bmatrix} = \begin{bmatrix} \lambda_{x'} & \mu_{x'} & \nu_{x'} & 0 & 0 & 0 \\ \lambda_{y'} & \mu_{y'} & \nu_{y'} & 0 & 0 & 0 \\ \lambda_{z'} & \mu_{z'} & \nu_{z'} & 0 & 0 & 0 \\ 0 & 0 & 0 & \lambda_{x'} & \mu_{x'} & \nu_{x'} \\ 0 & 0 & 0 & \lambda_{y'} & \mu_{y'} & \nu_{y'} \\ 0 & 0 & 0 & \lambda_{z'} & \mu_{z'} & \nu_{z'} \end{bmatrix} \begin{Bmatrix} F_{xi} \\ F_{yi} \\ F_{zi} \\ F_{xj} \\ F_{yj} \\ F_{zj} \end{Bmatrix} \qquad (12\text{-}13)$$

or simply

$$\{\mathbf{F'}\} = [\mathbf{T}]\{\mathbf{F}\} \qquad (12\text{-}14)$$

in which $[\mathbf{T}]$ is the transformation matrix, which may be written as

$$[\mathbf{T}] = \begin{bmatrix} [\mathbf{\Lambda}] & [\mathbf{0}] \\ [\mathbf{0}] & [\mathbf{\Lambda}] \end{bmatrix} \qquad (12\text{-}15)$$

where

$$[\mathbf{\Lambda}] = \begin{bmatrix} \lambda_{x'} & \mu_{x'} & \nu_{x'} \\ \lambda_{y'} & \mu_{y'} & \nu_{y'} \\ \lambda_{z'} & \mu_{z'} & \nu_{z'} \end{bmatrix} \qquad (12\text{-}16)$$

As we observed in Chapter 11 in deriving the transformation matrix with reference to a cartesian coordinate system in a plane,

$$[\mathbf{T}]^{-1} = [\mathbf{T}]^T \tag{12-17}$$

We may similarly express the relationship between displacements referred to local and global coordinates as

$$\{\boldsymbol{\Delta}'\} = [\mathbf{T}]\{\boldsymbol{\Delta}\} \tag{12-18}$$

where

$$\{\boldsymbol{\Delta}\} = \begin{Bmatrix} u_i \\ v_i \\ w_i \\ u_j \\ v_j \\ w_j \end{Bmatrix} \tag{12-19}$$

The elements of $\{\boldsymbol{\Delta}\}$ are generalized displacements referred to the x–y–z coordinate system, and they correspond to the generalized forces $F_{xi}, F_{yi}, \ldots, F_{zj}$.

Using Eqs. (12-14) and (12-18), we now may write Eq. (12-9) as

$$[\mathbf{T}]\{\mathbf{F}\} = [\mathbf{k}'][\mathbf{T}]\{\boldsymbol{\Delta}\}$$

Then

$$\{\mathbf{F}\} = [\mathbf{T}]^{-1}[\mathbf{k}'][\mathbf{T}]\{\boldsymbol{\Delta}\}$$

or

$$\{\mathbf{F}\} = [\mathbf{k}]\{\boldsymbol{\Delta}\} \tag{12-20}$$

where, utilizing Eq. (12-17), we define the element stiffness matrix referred to the global coordinate system as

$$[\mathbf{k}] = [\mathbf{T}]^T[\mathbf{k}'][\mathbf{T}] \tag{12-21}$$

We may represent $[\mathbf{k}]$ explicitly for the bar element as

$$[\mathbf{k}] = \frac{EA}{L} \begin{matrix} \quad u_i \quad\quad v_i \quad\quad w_i \quad\quad u_j \quad\quad v_j \quad\quad w_j \\ \begin{bmatrix} \lambda_{x'}^2 & & & & & \\ \lambda_{x'}\mu_{x'} & \mu_{x'}^2 & & \text{symmetric} & & \\ \lambda_{x'}\nu_{x'} & \mu_{x'}\nu_{x'} & \nu_{x'}^2 & & & \\ -\lambda_{x'}^2 & -\lambda_{x'}\mu_{x'} & -\lambda_{x'}\nu_{x'} & \lambda_{x'}^2 & & \\ -\lambda_{x'}\mu_{x'} & -\mu_{x'}^2 & -\mu_{x'}\nu_{x'} & \lambda_{x'}\mu_{x'} & \mu_{x'}^2 & \\ -\lambda_{x'}\nu_{x'} & -\mu_{x'}\nu_{x'} & -\nu_{x'}^2 & \lambda_{x'}\nu_{x'} & \mu_{x'}\nu_{x'} & \nu_{x'}^2 \end{bmatrix} \begin{matrix} F_{xi} \\ F_{yi} \\ F_{zi} \\ F_{xj} \\ F_{yj} \\ F_{zj} \end{matrix} \end{matrix} \tag{12-22}$$

where we have written symbols for displacements above the columns and forces next to the rows as a reminder of the meaning of each element of $[\mathbf{k}]$.

Note that because $F_{y'i} = F_{z'i} = F_{y'j} = F_{z'j} = 0$ for the bar element, $[\mathbf{k}]$ is related only to $\lambda_{x'}$, $\mu_{x'}$, and $\nu_{x'}$, and is not related to $\lambda_{y'}$, ..., $\nu_{z'}$. For simplicity, therefore, we may drop the subscript x' on the elements of $[\mathbf{k}]$ for the bar element. Furthermore, the steps leading to $[\mathbf{k}]$ could have been simplified if null rows and columns (those with all zero elements) were discarded in the matrix operations. Considering only the pertinent relations in Eq. (12-12), we adopt the simplified notation

$$
\begin{aligned}
\lambda &= \lambda_{x'} = \cos\theta_{xx'} \\
\mu &= \mu_{x'} = \cos\theta_{yx'} \\
\nu &= \nu_{x'} = \cos\theta_{zx'}
\end{aligned}
\tag{12-12a}
$$

Thus, conforming to Eq. (12-7) instead of Eq. (12-10), we obtain, in place of Eq. (12-13),

$$
\left\{\begin{matrix} F_{x'i} \\ F_{x'j} \end{matrix}\right\} = \begin{bmatrix} \lambda & \mu & \nu & 0 & 0 & 0 \\ 0 & 0 & 0 & \lambda & \mu & \nu \end{bmatrix} \left\{\begin{matrix} F_{xi} \\ F_{yi} \\ F_{zi} \\ F_{xj} \\ F_{yj} \\ F_{zj} \end{matrix}\right\}
\tag{12-13a}
$$

in which the transformation matrix is now

$$
[\mathbf{T}] = \begin{bmatrix} \lambda & \mu & \nu & 0 & 0 & 0 \\ 0 & 0 & 0 & \lambda & \mu & \nu \end{bmatrix}
\tag{12-15a}
$$

Then, Eq. (12-21) for the global stiffness matrix of a member becomes

$$
[\mathbf{k}] = \begin{bmatrix} \lambda & 0 \\ \mu & 0 \\ \nu & 0 \\ 0 & \lambda \\ 0 & \mu \\ 0 & \nu \end{bmatrix} \left(\frac{EA}{L}\right) \begin{bmatrix} 1 & -1 \\ -1 & 1 \end{bmatrix} \begin{bmatrix} \lambda & \mu & \nu & 0 & 0 & 0 \\ 0 & 0 & 0 & \lambda & \mu & \nu \end{bmatrix}
\tag{12-21a}
$$

which leads directly to the result in Eq. (12-22).

For a planar truss (e.g., one lying in the x–y plane), the forces and displacements in the direction normal to the plane (the z-direction) may be assumed to be zero. Hence $[\mathbf{k}]$ reverts to a 4×4 matrix when null rows and columns are discarded as a result of $\nu_{x'} = 0$. In such a case

$$
[\mathbf{k}] = \frac{EA}{L} \begin{matrix} u_i & v_i & u_j & v_j \\ \begin{bmatrix} \lambda^2 & & & \text{symmetric} \\ \lambda\mu & \mu^2 & & \\ -\lambda^2 & -\lambda\mu & \lambda^2 & \\ -\lambda\mu & -\mu^2 & \lambda\mu & \mu^2 \end{bmatrix} & \begin{matrix} F_{xi} \\ F_{yi} \\ F_{xj} \\ F_{yj} \end{matrix} \end{matrix}
\tag{12-23}
$$

We now consider a beam element, which can sustain bending and twisting deformation as well as axial extension or compression. The element has length L and uniform cross-sectional properties, i.e., the area A, the bending moments of inertia $I_{y'}$ and $I_{z'}$, the torsional constant J, and the Young's modulus E and shear modulus G, are constants. As shown in Fig. 12-3, six generalized forces and displacements pertain to each end, nodes i and j, of the member. (For clarity, however, we have indicated only the three forces and translations at node i and the three moments and rotations at node j.) A local right-hand coordinate system is defined such that x' runs along the member's axis from i to j, while y' and z' coincide with principal bending axes. Because of this particular orientation of y' and z', it is possible to describe the bending moments and shearing forces in the x'–y' plane in terms of displacements occurring only in that plane. The same can be said for the x'–z' plane; i.e., bending deformations in the two principal planes are, by definition, independent.

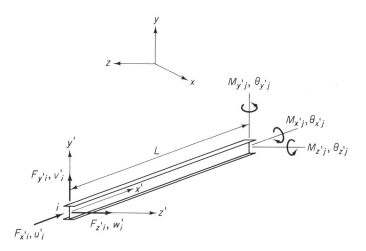

Figure 12-3

Formulation of $[\mathbf{k'}]$ in local coordinates. It is our immediate objective to derive the relationships between the twelve generalized forces and corresponding displacements. That is, we wish to determine the 12×12 element stiffness matrix $[\mathbf{k'}]$, in terms of the local coordinates, such that

$$\{\mathbf{F'}\} = [\mathbf{k'}]\{\mathbf{\Delta'}\} \tag{12-24}$$

where, in terms of the force and displacement vectors at nodes i and j,

$$\{\mathbf{F'}\} = \begin{Bmatrix} \mathbf{F'_i} \\ \mathbf{F'_j} \end{Bmatrix} \quad \text{and} \quad \{\mathbf{\Delta'}\} = \begin{Bmatrix} \mathbf{\Delta'_i} \\ \mathbf{\Delta'_j} \end{Bmatrix} \tag{12-25}$$

At node i,

$$\{\mathbf{F}'_i\} = \begin{Bmatrix} F_{x'i} \\ F_{y'i} \\ F_{z'i} \\ M_{x'i} \\ M_{y'i} \\ M_{z'i} \end{Bmatrix} \quad \text{and} \quad \{\mathbf{\Delta}'_i\} = \begin{Bmatrix} u'_i \\ v'_i \\ w'_i \\ \theta_{x'i} \\ \theta_{y'i} \\ \theta_{z'i} \end{Bmatrix} \qquad (12\text{-}26)$$

The nodal force and displacement vectors $\{\mathbf{F}'_j\}$ and $\{\mathbf{\Delta}'_j\}$ are similarly defined.

Axial Stiffness. We begin by noting that the derivation employed previously for the bar element is also valid for relating $F_{x'i}$ and $F_{x'j}$ to u'_i and u'_j for the beam. This derivation is valid provided deformations are small enough to allow any coupling between axial and bending forces (and displacements) to be ignored. Thus, the axial deformation of the beam is governed by Eq. (12-3b).

$$\frac{d^2 u'}{dx'^2} = 0 \qquad (12\text{-}3\text{b})$$

Following the same line of reasoning described previously, we may write

$$\begin{Bmatrix} F_{x'i} \\ F_{x'j} \end{Bmatrix} = \frac{EA}{L} \begin{bmatrix} 1 & -1 \\ -1 & 1 \end{bmatrix} \begin{Bmatrix} u'_i \\ u'_j \end{Bmatrix} \qquad (12\text{-}27)$$

Noting that $F_{x'i}$ and $F_{x'j}$ occupy the first and seventh positions in $\{\mathbf{F}'\}$, and that u'_i and u'_j occupy corresponding positions in $\{\mathbf{\Delta}'\}$, we see that Eq. (12-27) provides the stiffness coefficients $k'_{1,1}$, $k'_{1,7} = k'_{7,1}$ and $k'_{7,7}$.

Torsional Stiffness. For a member subjected to a uniform torque, the angle of twist varies uniformly between the ends of the member; i.e.,

$$M_{x'} = GJ \frac{d\theta_{x'}}{dx'} = \text{constant} \qquad (12\text{-}28\text{a})$$

or

$$\frac{d^2 \theta_{x'}}{dx'^2} = 0 \qquad (12\text{-}28\text{b})$$

Equations (12-28), which govern the twist of the member, are identical in form to Eqs. (12-3), which govern the axial deformation. Accordingly, the solution of Eq. (12-28b) is

$$\theta_{x'}(x') = C_1 x' + C_2$$

By virtue of the boundary conditions

$$\theta_{x'}(0) = \theta_{x'i} \quad \text{and} \quad \theta_{x'}(L) = \theta_{x'j}$$

the constants of integration C_1 and C_2 may be determined. We thus find

$$\theta_{x'}(x') = \theta_{x'i}\left(1 - \frac{x'}{L}\right) + \theta_{x'j}\left(\frac{x'}{L}\right) \qquad (12\text{-}29)$$

The relationship between torque and the two angles of twist $\theta_{x'i}$ and $\theta_{x'j}$ may be found by substituting Eq. (12-29) into Eq. (12-28a); thus

$$M_{x'} = \frac{GJ}{L}(\theta_{x'j} - \theta_{x'i})$$

Now equilibrium requires that

$$M_{x'i} = -M_{x'} \text{ at } x' = 0$$

and

$$M_{x'j} = M_{x'} \text{ at } x' = L$$

We may write these two conditions as

$$\begin{Bmatrix} M_{x'i} \\ M_{x'j} \end{Bmatrix} = \frac{GJ}{L} \begin{bmatrix} 1 & -1 \\ -1 & 1 \end{bmatrix} \begin{Bmatrix} \theta_{x'i} \\ \theta_{x'j} \end{Bmatrix} \tag{12-30}$$

Because the differential equations governing the axial and twisting deformations are identical in form, it should come as no surprise that the stiffness matrices of Eqs. (12-27) and (12-30) differ only in terms of the factors EA/L versus GJ/L. Because $M_{x'i}$ and $M_{x'j}$ occupy the fourth and tenth positions in $\{\mathbf{F}'\}$, and in view of Eq. (12-26), Eq. (12-30) provides the stiffness coefficients $k'_{4,4}$, $k'_{4,10} = k'_{10,4}$, and $k'_{10,10}$.

Bending Stiffness. We first restrict our attention to the x'–y' plane as shown in Fig. 12-4(a). For a member having uniform flexural rigidity, loaded only at its end points, and undergoing no shear deformation, the governing differential equation is

$$\frac{d^4v'}{dx'^4} = 0 \tag{12-31}$$

The general solution to Eq. (12-31) may be obtained by successive integration to obtain

$$v'(x') = C_1 x'^3 + C_2 x'^2 + C_3 x' + C_4 \tag{12-32}$$

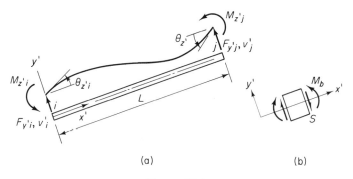

(a)   (b)

Figure 12-4

The Direct Stiffness Method   Chap. 12

The constants of integration, $C_1, \ldots, C_4$, may be found in terms of the displacements and rotations at the ends of the member. That is, the boundary conditions for bending in the x'–y' plane are

$$v'(0) = v_i' \qquad v'(L) = v_j'$$

$$\frac{dv'(0)}{dx'} = \theta_{z'i} \qquad \frac{dv'(L)}{dx'} = \theta_{z'j} \tag{12-33}$$

Requiring Eq. (12-32) to satisfy Eqs. (12-33), we find

$$v'(x') = \left[-\frac{2}{L^3}(v_j' - v_i') + \frac{1}{L^2}(\theta_{z'j} + \theta_{z'i}) \right] x'^3$$

$$+ \left[\frac{3}{L^2}(v_j' - v_i') - \frac{1}{L}(\theta_{z'j} + 2\theta_{z'i}) \right] x'^2 + \theta_{z'i}x' + v_i' \tag{12-34a}$$

or, alternatively,

$$v'(x') = v_i'\left[1 - 3\left(\frac{x'}{L}\right)^2 + 2\left(\frac{x'}{L}\right)^3 \right] + v_j'\left[3\left(\frac{x'}{L}\right)^2 - 2\left(\frac{x'}{L}\right)^3 \right]$$

$$+ \theta_{z'i}L\left(\frac{x'}{L}\right)\left[\left(\frac{x'}{L}\right)^2 - 2\left(\frac{x'}{L}\right) + 1 \right] + \theta_{z'j}L\left(\frac{x'}{L}\right)^2\left[\left(\frac{x'}{L}\right) - 1 \right] \tag{12-34b}$$

Either of Eqs. (12-34) provides the displacement $v'(x')$ at any location between the ends of the member in terms of specified translations v_i' and v_j' and rotations $\theta_{z'i}$ and $\theta_{z'j}$ at the ends. In order to prescribe these displacements, however, it is necessary to exert moments $M_{z'i}$ and $M_{z'j}$ and transverse forces $F_{y'i}$ and $F_{y'j}$ at the ends. Recall that expressions for bending moment and shear force are

$$M_b = EI_{z'}\frac{d^2v'}{dx'^2} \tag{12-35}$$

and

$$S = EI_{z'}\frac{d^3v'}{dx'^3} \tag{12-36}$$

Then, by using the expression for $v'(x)$ given by Eq. (12-34b), we may write

$$M_b(x') = v_i'\frac{6EI_{z'}}{L^2}\left(-1 + \frac{2x'}{L}\right) + v_j'\frac{6EI_{z'}}{L^2}\left(1 - \frac{2x'}{L}\right)$$

$$+ \theta_{z'i}\frac{2EI_{z'}}{L}\left(3\frac{x'}{L} - 2\right) + \theta_{z'j}\frac{2EI_{z'}}{L}\left(3\frac{x'}{L} - 1\right) \tag{12-37}$$

and

$$S(x') = v_i'\frac{12EI_{z'}}{L^3} - v_j'\frac{12EI_{z'}}{L^3} + \theta_{z'i}\frac{6EI_{z'}}{L^2} + \theta_{z'j}\frac{6EI_{z'}}{L^2} \tag{12-38}$$

We next recognize that at the ends of the member $(x' = 0, L)$

$$F_{y'i} = S(0) \qquad F_{y'j} = -S(L)$$
$$M_{z'i} = -M_b(0) \qquad M_{z'j} = M_b(L) \qquad (12\text{-}39)$$

The signs that appear in Eqs. (12-39) are established by comparing the sign convention associated with the generalized forces in Fig. 12-4(a) with the sign convention associated with the shear force and bending moment in Fig. 12-4(b). Evaluating Eqs. (12-37) and (12-38) at $x' = 0$ to determine $F_{y'i}$ and $M_{z'i}$, we may write

$$F_{y'i} = \frac{12EI_{z'}}{L^3}v_i' - \frac{12EI_{z'}}{L^3}v_j' + \frac{6EI_{z'}}{L^2}\theta_{z'i} + \frac{6EI_{z'}}{L^2}\theta_{z'j} \qquad (12\text{-}40)$$

and

$$M_{z'i} = \frac{6EI_{z'}}{L^2}v_i' - \frac{6EI_{z'}}{L^2}v_j' + \frac{4EI_{z'}}{L}\theta_{z'i} + \frac{2EI_{z'}}{L}\theta_{z'j} \qquad (12\text{-}41)$$

After determining $F_{y'j}$ and $M_{z'j}$ similarly (at $x = L$), we may express the complete set of generalized forces in terms of the generalized displacements as

$$\begin{Bmatrix} F_{y'i} \\ M_{z'i} \\ F_{y'j} \\ M_{z'j} \end{Bmatrix} = \frac{EI_{z'}}{L^3} \begin{bmatrix} 12 & 6L & -12 & 6L \\ 6L & 4L^2 & -6L & 2L^2 \\ -12 & -6L & 12 & -6L \\ 6L & 2L^2 & -6L & 4L^2 \end{bmatrix} \begin{Bmatrix} v_i' \\ \theta_{z'i} \\ v_j' \\ \theta_{z'j} \end{Bmatrix} \qquad (12\text{-}42)$$

The coefficients appearing in the square matrix in Eq. (12-42) provide the desired relationships between generalized forces (transverse forces and moments) and corresponding displacements associated with bending deformation in the $x'-y'$ plane. According to Eq. (12-26), these generalized forces and displacements occupy the second, sixth, eighth, and twelfth positions in $\{\mathbf{F'}\}$ and $\{\mathbf{\Delta'}\}$. Therefore, Eq. (12-42) furnishes the coefficients to the stiffness matrix $[\mathbf{k'}]$ in these rows and columns; i.e., $k_{2,2}$, $k_{2,6}$, etc.

Thus far we have confined our attention to bending deformation in the $x'-y'$ plane. We may formulate a similar analysis for bending in the $x'-z'$ plane, thereby providing relationships between generalized forces $F_{z'i}$, $M_{y'i}$, $F_{z'j}$ and $M_{y'j}$ and the generalized displacements w_i', $\theta_{y'i}$, w_j', and $\theta_{y'j}$ in Fig. 12-5(a) with the sign convention associated with the shear force and bending moment in Fig. 12-5(b). These relationships may be expressed as

$$\begin{Bmatrix} F_{z'i} \\ M_{y'i} \\ F_{z'j} \\ M_{y'j} \end{Bmatrix} = \frac{EI_{y'}}{L^3} \begin{bmatrix} 12 & -6L & -12 & -6L \\ -6L & 4L^2 & 6L & 2L^2 \\ -12 & 6L & 12 & 6L \\ -6L & 2L^2 & 6L & 4L^2 \end{bmatrix} \begin{Bmatrix} w_i' \\ \theta_{y'i} \\ w_j' \\ \theta_{y'j} \end{Bmatrix} \qquad (12\text{-}43)$$

The coefficients appearing Eq. (12-43) furnish the elements of the third, fifth, ninth and eleventh rows and columns of the stiffness matrix $[\mathbf{k'}]$.

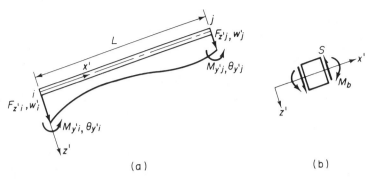

(a)   (b)

Figure 12-5

Complete member stiffness matrix in local coordinates. We may combine the results of the foregoing analyses to arrive at the element stiffness matrix $[\mathbf{k}']$ in Eq. (12-44a). We have listed the generalized forces and displacements along the top and side of $[\mathbf{k}']$ as a reminder of the meaning of each coefficient.

It is often convenient to cast the element stiffness matrix in such a form that all entries are dimensionless. This may be done by dividing moments by a characteristic length, such as the length of the beam element, and by multiplying the rotations by the same length. Thus, the generalized forces become $M_{x'i}/L$, $M_{y'i}/L$, etc., in addition to $F_{x'i}$, $F_{y'i}$, etc., all having units of force. The attendant generalized displacements are $\theta_{x'i}L$, $\theta_{y'i}L$, etc., as well as u_i', v_i', etc., all having dimensions of length. The resulting stiffness matrix is given in Eq. (12-44b).

The 12×12 stiffness matrix defined by Eqs. (12-44) on pages 504 and 505 must be employed when solving three-dimensional flexure-torsion problems. For treating two-dimensional problems in which member torsion is absent, we may delete the rows and columns corresponding to the twisting rotations and out-of plane translations. If, for example, deformation is confined to the $x'-y'$-plane, the member stiffness matrix may be reduced to order 6×6; i.e.,

$$
[\mathbf{k}'] = \frac{EI_{z'}}{L^3}
\begin{bmatrix}
\dfrac{AL^2}{I_{z'}} & & & & & \\[2mm]
0 & 12 & & \text{symmetric} & & \\[2mm]
0 & 6L & 4L^2 & & & \\[2mm]
-\dfrac{AL^2}{I_{z'}} & 0 & 0 & \dfrac{AL^2}{I_{z'}} & & \\[2mm]
0 & -12 & -6L & 0 & 12 & \\[2mm]
0 & 6L & 2L^2 & 0 & -6L & 4L^2
\end{bmatrix}
\begin{matrix}
F_{x'i} \\[2mm]
F_{y'i} \\[2mm]
M_{z'i} \\[2mm]
F_{x'j} \\[2mm]
F_{y'j} \\[2mm]
M_{z'j}
\end{matrix}
\qquad (12\text{-}45a)
$$

with column headings $u_i'\quad v_i'\quad \theta_{z'i}\quad u_j'\quad v_j'\quad \theta_{z'j}$.

$$
[\mathbf{k}'] =
\begin{array}{c}
\begin{array}{cccccccccccc}
u_i' & v_i' & w_i' & \theta_{xi} & \theta_{yi} & \theta_{zi} & u_j' & v_j' & w_j' & \theta_{xj} & \theta_{yj} & \theta_{zj}
\end{array}\\[2pt]
\left[
\begin{array}{cccccccccccc}
\dfrac{EA}{L} & & & & & & & & & & & \\[6pt]
0 & \dfrac{12EI_{z'}}{L^3} & & & & & & & & & & \\[6pt]
0 & 0 & \dfrac{12EI_{y'}}{L^3} & & & & & \text{symmetric} & & & & \\[6pt]
0 & 0 & 0 & \dfrac{GJ}{L} & & & & & & & & \\[6pt]
0 & 0 & -\dfrac{6EI_{y'}}{L^2} & 0 & \dfrac{4EI_{y'}}{L} & & & & & & & \\[6pt]
0 & \dfrac{6EI_{z'}}{L^2} & 0 & 0 & 0 & \dfrac{4EI_{z'}}{L} & & & & & & \\[6pt]
-\dfrac{EA}{L} & 0 & 0 & 0 & 0 & 0 & \dfrac{EA}{L} & & & & & \\[6pt]
0 & -\dfrac{12EI_{z'}}{L^3} & 0 & 0 & 0 & -\dfrac{6EI_{z'}}{L^2} & 0 & \dfrac{12EI_{z'}}{L^3} & & & & \\[6pt]
0 & 0 & -\dfrac{12EI_{y'}}{L^3} & 0 & \dfrac{6EI_{y'}}{L^2} & 0 & 0 & 0 & \dfrac{12EI_{y'}}{L^3} & & & \\[6pt]
0 & 0 & 0 & -\dfrac{GJ}{L} & 0 & 0 & 0 & 0 & 0 & \dfrac{GJ}{L} & & \\[6pt]
0 & 0 & -\dfrac{6EI_{y'}}{L^2} & 0 & \dfrac{2EI_{y'}}{L} & 0 & 0 & 0 & \dfrac{6EI_{y'}}{L^2} & 0 & \dfrac{4EI_{y'}}{L} & \\[6pt]
0 & \dfrac{6EI_{z'}}{L^2} & 0 & 0 & 0 & \dfrac{2EI_{z'}}{L} & 0 & -\dfrac{6EI_{z'}}{L^2} & 0 & 0 & 0 & \dfrac{4EI_{z'}}{L}
\end{array}
\right]
\begin{array}{l}
F_{xi}\\[6pt]
F_{yi}\\[6pt]
F_{zi}\\[6pt]
M_{xi}\\[6pt]
M_{yi}\\[6pt]
M_{zi}\\[6pt]
F_{xj}\\[6pt]
F_{yj}\\[6pt]
F_{zj}\\[6pt]
M_{xj}\\[6pt]
M_{yj}\\[6pt]
M_{zj}
\end{array}
\end{array}
$$

$$(12\text{-}44a)$$

$$
[\mathbf{k}'] = \frac{EI_{z'}}{L^3}
\begin{bmatrix}
\frac{AL^2}{I_{z'}} & & & & & & & & & & & \\[4pt]
0 & 12 & & & & & & & & & & \\[4pt]
0 & 0 & 12\frac{I_{y'}}{I_{z'}} & & & & & & & & & \\[4pt]
0 & 0 & 0 & \frac{GJ}{EI_{z'}} & & & & \text{symmetric} & & & & \\[4pt]
0 & 0 & -6\frac{I_{y'}}{I_{z'}} & 0 & 4\frac{I_{y'}}{I_{z'}} & & & & & & & \\[4pt]
0 & 6 & 0 & 0 & 0 & 4 & & & & & & \\[4pt]
\frac{-AL^2}{I_{z'}} & 0 & 0 & 0 & 0 & 0 & \frac{AL^2}{I_{z'}} & & & & & \\[4pt]
0 & -12 & 0 & 0 & 0 & -6 & 0 & 12 & & & & \\[4pt]
0 & 0 & -12\frac{I_{y'}}{I_{z'}} & 0 & 6\frac{I_{y'}}{I_{z'}} & 0 & 0 & 0 & 12\frac{I_{y'}}{I_{z'}} & & & \\[4pt]
0 & 0 & 0 & -\frac{GJ}{EI_{z'}} & 0 & 0 & 0 & 0 & 0 & \frac{GJ}{EI_{z'}} & & \\[4pt]
0 & 0 & -6\frac{I_{y'}}{I_{z'}} & 0 & 2\frac{I_{y'}}{I_{z'}} & 0 & 0 & 0 & 6\frac{I_{y'}}{I_{z'}} & 0 & 4\frac{I_{y'}}{I_{z'}} & \\[4pt]
0 & 6 & 0 & 0 & 0 & 2 & 0 & -6 & 0 & 0 & 0 & 4
\end{bmatrix}
$$

Columns: $u_i' \quad v_i' \quad w_i' \quad \theta_{x'i}L \quad \theta_{y'i}L \quad \theta_{z'i}L \quad u_j' \quad v_j' \quad w_j' \quad \theta_{x'j}L \quad \theta_{y'j}L \quad \theta_{z'j}$

Associated load vector (rows): $F_{x'i},\; F_{y'i},\; F_{z'i},\; M_{x'i}/L,\; M_{y'i}/L,\; M_{z'i}/L,\; F_{x'j},\; F_{y'j},\; F_{z'j},\; M_{x'j}/L,\; M_{y'j}/L,\; M_{z'j}/L$

(12-44b)

or, alternatively

$$
[\mathbf{k}'] = \frac{EI_{z'}}{L^3}
\begin{array}{c}
\begin{array}{cccccc}
u_i' & v_i' & \theta_{z'i}L & u_j' & v_j' & \theta_{z'j}L
\end{array} \\
\begin{bmatrix}
\dfrac{AL^2}{I_{z'}} & & & & & \\
0 & 12 & & \text{symmetric} & & \\
0 & 6 & 4 & & & \\
-\dfrac{AL^2}{I_{z'}} & 0 & 0 & \dfrac{AL^2}{I_{z'}} & & \\
0 & -12 & -6 & 0 & 12 & \\
0 & 6 & 2 & 0 & -6 & 4
\end{bmatrix}
\end{array}
\begin{array}{l}
F_{x'i} \\
F_{y'i} \\
M_{z'i}/L \\
F_{x'j} \\
F_{y'j} \\
M_{z'j}/L
\end{array}
\qquad (12\text{-}45b)
$$

Transformation of $[\mathbf{k}']$ to global coordinates. As described previously in connection with bar elements, the member stiffness matrix generally must be transformed with reference to a global coordinate system (x–y–z shown in Fig. 12-3). That is, we must form the transformed member stiffness matrix $[\mathbf{k}]$ as

$$[\mathbf{k}] = [\mathbf{T}]^T[\mathbf{k}'][\mathbf{T}] \qquad (12\text{-}46)$$

in which, for the three-dimensional beam element, the transformation matrix $[\mathbf{T}]$ is of order 12×12, and is defined as

$$
[\mathbf{T}] =
\begin{bmatrix}
[\Lambda] & & & \\
& [\Lambda] & & \\
& & [\Lambda] & \\
& & & [\Lambda]
\end{bmatrix}
\qquad (12\text{-}47)
$$

where, as before

$$
[\Lambda] =
\begin{bmatrix}
\lambda_{x'} & \mu_{x'} & \nu_{x'} \\
\lambda_{y'} & \mu_{y'} & \nu_{y'} \\
\lambda_{z'} & \mu_{z'} & \nu_{z'}
\end{bmatrix}
\qquad (12\text{-}48)
$$

and where the direction cosines $\lambda_{x'}, \dots, \nu_{z'}$ are defined by Eqs. (12-12).

For two-dimensional problems in which the x'–y' plane is parallel to the x–y-plane (i.e., z' has the same sense as z), then $\nu_{x'} = \nu_{y'} = \lambda_{z'} = \mu_{z'} = 0$ and $\nu_{z'} = 1$. We may also observe that $\lambda_{x'} = \mu_{y'} = \lambda = \cos\theta_{xx'}$ and $\mu_{x'} = -\lambda_{y'} = \mu = \cos\theta_{yx'}$. Then the transformation matrix is reduced to

$$
[\mathbf{T}] =
\begin{bmatrix}
[\Lambda] & \\
& [\Lambda]
\end{bmatrix}
\qquad (12\text{-}49)
$$

where

$$
[\Lambda] =
\begin{bmatrix}
\lambda & \mu & 0 \\
-\mu & \lambda & 0 \\
0 & 0 & 1
\end{bmatrix}
\qquad (12\text{-}50)
$$

It is convenient to express $[\mathbf{k}]$ explicitly for the two-dimensional case as shown in Eq. (12-51). An alternative form, in which all entries of $[\mathbf{k}]$ are dimen-

$$[\mathbf{k}] = \frac{EI_{z'}}{L^3} \begin{array}{cccccc} u_i & v_i & \theta_{zi} & u_j & v_j & \theta_{zj} \\ \end{array}$$

$$[\mathbf{k}] = \frac{EI_{z'}}{L^3}\left[\begin{array}{cccccc}
\dfrac{AL^2}{I_{z'}}\lambda^2 + 12\mu^2 & & & & & \\[2mm]
\left(\dfrac{AL^2}{I_{z'}} - 12\right)\lambda\mu & \dfrac{AL^2}{I_{z'}}\mu^2 + 12\lambda^2 & & & \text{symmetric} & \\[2mm]
-6L\mu & 6L\lambda & 4L^2 & & & \\[2mm]
-\left(\dfrac{AL^2}{I_{z'}}\lambda^2 + 12\mu^2\right) & -\left(\dfrac{AL^2}{I_{z'}} - 12\right)\lambda\mu & 6L\mu & \dfrac{AL^2}{I_{z'}}\lambda^2 + 12\mu^2 & & \\[2mm]
-\left(\dfrac{AL^2}{I_{z'}} - 12\right)\lambda\mu & -\left(\dfrac{AL^2}{I_{z'}}\mu^2 + 12\lambda^2\right) & -6L\lambda & \left(\dfrac{AL^2}{I_{z'}} - 12\right)\lambda\mu & \dfrac{AL^2}{I_{z'}}\mu^2 + 12\lambda^2 & \\[2mm]
-6L\mu & 6L\lambda & 2L^2 & 6L\mu & -6L\lambda & 4L^2
\end{array}\right]
\begin{array}{c} F_{xi} \\[2mm] F_{yi} \\[2mm] M_{zi} \\[2mm] F_{xj} \\[2mm] F_{yj} \\[2mm] M_{zj} \end{array}$$

(12-51)

sionless, may be easily inferred from Eq. (12-51). Note that in the special case where the $x'-y'$ axes coincide with the $x-y$ axes, $\lambda = 1$ and $\mu = 0$; then $[\mathbf{k}]$ is identical to $[\mathbf{k}']$ given by Eq. (12-45a).

12-4 ANALYSIS OF TRUSSES

Trusses may be analyzed by first assembling the structural stiffness matrix $[\mathbf{K}]$ from the set of transformed element stiffness matrices $[\mathbf{k}]$, and then solving the stiffness equations. In Chapter 11, we noted that the stiffness equations may be partitioned to acquire the form

$$\left\{\begin{array}{c} \mathbf{P}_f \\ \hline \mathbf{P}_s \end{array}\right\} = \left[\begin{array}{c:c} \mathbf{K}_{ff} & \mathbf{K}_{fs} \\ \hdashline \mathbf{K}_{sf} & \mathbf{K}_{ss} \end{array}\right] \left\{\begin{array}{c} \mathbf{\Delta}_f \\ \hline \mathbf{\Delta}_s \end{array}\right\} \tag{12-52}$$

in which $\{\mathbf{P}_f\}$ and $\{\mathbf{\Delta}_f\}$ are the vectors comprising known forces and unknown displacements, respectively, at unconstrained nodes; and $\{\mathbf{P}_s\}$ and $\{\mathbf{\Delta}_s\}$ are the vectors of unknown forces (reactions) and known displacements, respectively. The matrix $[\mathbf{K}]$ is partitioned so that $[\mathbf{K}_{ff}]$ and $[\mathbf{K}_{ss}]$ are square matrices having orders equal to the dimensions of $\{\mathbf{\Delta}_f\}$ and $\{\mathbf{\Delta}_s\}$, respectively. As we have noted previously, the unknown quantities in Eq. (12-52) may be solved to obtain

$$\{\mathbf{\Delta}_f\} = [\mathbf{K}_{ff}]^{-1}(\{\mathbf{P}_f\} - [\mathbf{K}_{fs}]\{\mathbf{\Delta}_s\}) \tag{12-53}$$

and

$$\{\mathbf{P}_s\} = [\mathbf{K}_{sf}][\mathbf{K}_{ff}]^{-1}\{\mathbf{P}_f\} - ([\mathbf{K}_{sf}][\mathbf{K}_{ff}]^{-1}[\mathbf{K}_{fs}] - [\mathbf{K}_{ss}])\{\mathbf{\Delta}_s\} \tag{12-54}$$

We shall now apply this procedure to truss analysis.

Example 12-1. Figure 12-6(a) shows a statically determinate planar truss while Fig. 12-6(b) shows a statically indeterminate planar truss. These structures are designated as structures A and B, respectively. Each truss is subjected to a horizontal load acting at node 3. Find the displacements, reactions and internal forces for each case.

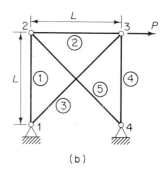

(a)   (b)

Figure 12-6

The Direct Stiffness Method   Chap. 12

We begin with structure A in Fig. 12-6(a) by noting that the stiffness matrix for each bar (the mth element) may be expressed in terms of local coordinates.

$$[\mathbf{k}'^{(m)}] = \left(\frac{EA}{L}\right)_m \begin{bmatrix} 1 & -1 \\ -1 & 1 \end{bmatrix}$$

which then must be transformed with reference in the global x–y coordinate system shown in Fig. 12-7(a). The transformed matrices for each bar may be determined either by employing the relationship

$$[\mathbf{k}] = [\mathbf{T}]^T[\mathbf{k}'][\mathbf{T}] = \begin{bmatrix} \lambda & -\mu & 0 & 0 \\ \mu & \lambda & 0 & 0 \\ 0 & 0 & \lambda & -\mu \\ 0 & 0 & \mu & \lambda \end{bmatrix} \frac{EA}{L} \begin{bmatrix} 1 & 0 & -1 & 0 \\ 0 & 0 & 0 & 0 \\ -1 & 0 & 1 & 0 \\ 0 & 0 & 0 & 0 \end{bmatrix} \begin{bmatrix} \lambda & \mu & 0 & 0 \\ -\mu & \lambda & 0 & 0 \\ 0 & 0 & \lambda & \mu \\ 0 & 0 & -\mu & \lambda \end{bmatrix}$$

or by using the resultant expression directly, i.e.,

$$[\mathbf{k}] = \left(\frac{EA}{L}\right) \begin{bmatrix} \lambda^2 & \lambda\mu & -\lambda^2 & -\lambda\mu \\ \lambda\mu & \mu^2 & -\lambda\mu & -\mu^2 \\ -\lambda^2 & -\lambda\mu & \lambda^2 & \lambda\mu \\ -\lambda\mu & -\mu^2 & \lambda\mu & \mu^2 \end{bmatrix}$$

Therefore, we may write for member 1 ($\lambda = 0$, $\mu = 1$)

$$[\mathbf{k}^{(1)}] = \left(\frac{EA}{L}\right)_1 \begin{matrix} & u_1 & v_1 & u_2 & v_2 \\ & \begin{bmatrix} 0 & 0 & 0 & 0 \\ 0 & 1 & 0 & -1 \\ 0 & 0 & 0 & 0 \\ 0 & -1 & 0 & 1 \end{bmatrix} \end{matrix}$$

for member 2 ($\lambda = 1$, $\mu = 0$)

$$[\mathbf{k}^{(2)}] = \left(\frac{EA}{L}\right)_2 \begin{matrix} & u_2 & v_2 & u_3 & v_3 \\ & \begin{bmatrix} 1 & 0 & -1 & 0 \\ 0 & 0 & 0 & 0 \\ -1 & 0 & 1 & 0 \\ 0 & 0 & 0 & 0 \end{bmatrix} \end{matrix}$$

for member 3 ($\lambda = \mu = \sqrt{2}/2$)

$$[\mathbf{k}^{(3)}] = \left(\frac{EA}{L}\right)_3 \begin{matrix} & u_1 & v_1 & u_3 & v_3 \\ & \begin{bmatrix} \frac{1}{2} & \frac{1}{2} & -\frac{1}{2} & -\frac{1}{2} \\ \frac{1}{2} & \frac{1}{2} & -\frac{1}{2} & -\frac{1}{2} \\ -\frac{1}{2} & -\frac{1}{2} & \frac{1}{2} & \frac{1}{2} \\ -\frac{1}{2} & -\frac{1}{2} & \frac{1}{2} & \frac{1}{2} \end{bmatrix} \end{matrix}$$

and for member 4 ($\lambda = 0$, $\mu = -1$)

$$[\mathbf{k}^{(4)}] = \left(\frac{EA}{L}\right)_4 \begin{matrix} & u_3 & v_3 & u_4 & v_4 \\ & \begin{bmatrix} 0 & 0 & 0 & 0 \\ 0 & 1 & 0 & -1 \\ 0 & 0 & 0 & 0 \\ 0 & -1 & 0 & 1 \end{bmatrix} \end{matrix}$$

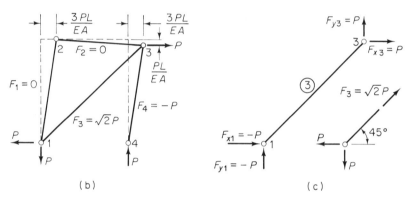

Figure 12-7

We have listed above each column the corresponding degree of freedom, u and v corresponding to horizontal and vertical displacements, respectively, and the subscript corresponding to the node.

Since in this particular case $(EA/L)_1 = (EA/L)_2 = (EA/L)_3 = (EA/L)_4 = EA/L$ is assumed, the combined element stiffness matrices yield

$$[\mathbf{K}] = \frac{EA}{2L}
\begin{array}{c}
\begin{array}{cccccccc} u_1 & v_1 & u_2 & v_2 & u_3 & v_3 & u_4 & v_4 \end{array} \\
\left[
\begin{array}{rrrrrrrr}
1 \\
1 & 3 & & & \text{symmetric} \\
0 & 0 & 2 \\
0 & -2 & 0 & 2 \\
-1 & 1 & -2 & 0 & 3 \\
-1 & -1 & 0 & 0 & 1 & 3 \\
0 & 0 & 0 & 0 & 0 & 0 & 0 \\
0 & 0 & 0 & 0 & 0 & -2 & 0 & 2
\end{array}
\right]
\end{array}$$

To conform with the definitions of $\{P_f\}$ and $\{P_s\}$, we set

$$\{P_f\} = \begin{Bmatrix} P_{x2} \\ P_{y2} \\ P_{x3} \\ P_{y3} \end{Bmatrix} \quad \text{and} \quad \{P_s\} = \begin{Bmatrix} P_{x1} \\ P_{y1} \\ P_{x4} \\ P_{y4} \end{Bmatrix}$$

Corresponding to these force vectors are the displacement vectors

$$\{\Delta_f\} = \begin{Bmatrix} u_2 \\ v_2 \\ u_3 \\ v_3 \end{Bmatrix} \quad \text{and} \quad \{\Delta_s\} = \begin{Bmatrix} u_1 \\ v_1 \\ u_4 \\ v_4 \end{Bmatrix}$$

Accordingly, we must rearrange the system stiffness matrix to the form

$$[K] = \frac{EA}{2L}\begin{array}{c} \\ \begin{array}{cccccccc} u_2 & v_2 & u_3 & v_3 & u_1 & v_1 & u_4 & v_4 \end{array} \\ \left[\begin{array}{cccc|cccc} 2 & & & & & & & \\ 0 & 2 & & & & \text{symmetric} & & \\ -2 & 0 & 3 & & & & & \\ 0 & 0 & 1 & 3 & & & & \\ \hline 0 & 0 & -1 & -1 & 1 & & & \\ 0 & -2 & -1 & -1 & 1 & 3 & & \\ 0 & 0 & 0 & 0 & 0 & 0 & 0 & \\ 0 & 0 & 0 & -2 & 0 & 0 & 0 & 2 \end{array}\right] \end{array}$$

According to Eqs. (12-53) and (12-54),

$$\begin{Bmatrix} u_2 \\ v_2 \\ u_3 \\ v_3 \end{Bmatrix} = \frac{2L}{EA}\begin{bmatrix} 2 & 0 & -2 & 0 \\ 0 & 2 & 0 & 0 \\ -2 & 0 & 3 & 1 \\ 0 & 0 & 1 & 3 \end{bmatrix}^{-1}\left(\begin{Bmatrix} P_{x2} \\ P_{y2} \\ P_{x3} \\ P_{y3} \end{Bmatrix} - \frac{EA}{2L}\begin{bmatrix} 0 & 0 & 0 & 0 \\ 0 & -2 & 0 & 0 \\ -1 & -1 & 0 & 0 \\ -1 & -1 & 0 & -2 \end{bmatrix}\begin{Bmatrix} u_1 \\ v_1 \\ u_4 \\ v_4 \end{Bmatrix}\right)$$

and

$$\begin{Bmatrix} P_{x1} \\ P_{y1} \\ P_{x4} \\ P_{y4} \end{Bmatrix} = \begin{bmatrix} 0 & 0 & -1 & -1 \\ 0 & -2 & -1 & -1 \\ 0 & 0 & 0 & 0 \\ 0 & 0 & 0 & -2 \end{bmatrix}\begin{bmatrix} 2 & 0 & -2 & 0 \\ 0 & 2 & 0 & 0 \\ -2 & 0 & 3 & 1 \\ 0 & 0 & 1 & 3 \end{bmatrix}^{-1}\begin{Bmatrix} P_{x2} \\ P_{y2} \\ P_{x3} \\ P_{y3} \end{Bmatrix}$$

$$-\frac{EA}{2L}\left(\begin{bmatrix} 0 & 0 & -1 & -1 \\ 0 & -2 & -1 & -1 \\ 0 & 0 & 0 & 0 \\ 0 & 0 & 0 & -2 \end{bmatrix}\begin{bmatrix} 2 & 0 & -2 & 0 \\ 0 & 2 & 0 & 0 \\ -2 & 0 & 3 & 1 \\ 0 & 0 & 1 & 3 \end{bmatrix}^{-1}\begin{bmatrix} 0 & 0 & 0 & 0 \\ 0 & -2 & 0 & 0 \\ -1 & -1 & 0 & 0 \\ -1 & -1 & 0 & -2 \end{bmatrix} - \begin{bmatrix} 1 & 1 & 0 & 0 \\ 1 & 3 & 0 & 0 \\ 0 & 0 & 0 & 0 \\ 0 & 0 & 0 & 2 \end{bmatrix}\right)\begin{Bmatrix} u_1 \\ v_1 \\ u_4 \\ v_4 \end{Bmatrix}$$

Thus

$$\begin{Bmatrix} u_2 \\ v_2 \\ u_3 \\ v_3 \end{Bmatrix} = \frac{L}{EA}\begin{bmatrix} 4 & 0 & 3 & -1 \\ 0 & 1 & 0 & 0 \\ 3 & 0 & 3 & -1 \\ -1 & 0 & -1 & 1 \end{bmatrix}\begin{Bmatrix} P_{x2} \\ P_{y2} \\ P_{x3} \\ P_{y3} \end{Bmatrix} + \begin{bmatrix} 1 & 1 & 0 & -1 \\ 0 & 1 & 0 & 0 \\ 1 & 1 & 0 & -1 \\ 0 & 0 & 0 & 1 \end{bmatrix}\begin{Bmatrix} u_1 \\ v_1 \\ u_4 \\ v_4 \end{Bmatrix}$$

and

$$
\begin{Bmatrix} P_{x1} \\ P_{y1} \\ P_{x4} \\ P_{y4} \end{Bmatrix} = \begin{bmatrix} -1 & 0 & -1 & 0 \\ -1 & -1 & -1 & 0 \\ 0 & 0 & 0 & 0 \\ 1 & 0 & 1 & -1 \end{bmatrix} \begin{Bmatrix} P_{x2} \\ P_{y2} \\ P_{x3} \\ P_{y3} \end{Bmatrix} + \frac{EA}{2L} \begin{bmatrix} 0 & 0 & 0 & 0 \\ 0 & 0 & 0 & 0 \\ 0 & 0 & 0 & 0 \\ 0 & 0 & 0 & 0 \end{bmatrix} \begin{Bmatrix} u_1 \\ v_1 \\ u_4 \\ v_4 \end{Bmatrix}
$$

In the present case

$$
\begin{Bmatrix} P_{x2} \\ P_{y2} \\ P_{x3} \\ P_{y3} \end{Bmatrix} = \begin{Bmatrix} 0 \\ 0 \\ P \\ 0 \end{Bmatrix} \quad \text{and} \quad \begin{Bmatrix} u_1 \\ v_1 \\ u_4 \\ v_4 \end{Bmatrix} = \begin{Bmatrix} 0 \\ 0 \\ 0 \\ 0 \end{Bmatrix}
$$

Hence,

$$
\begin{Bmatrix} u_2 \\ v_2 \\ u_3 \\ v_3 \end{Bmatrix} = \frac{L}{EA} \begin{bmatrix} 4 & 0 & 3 & -1 \\ 0 & 1 & 0 & 0 \\ 3 & 0 & 3 & -1 \\ -1 & 0 & -1 & 1 \end{bmatrix} \begin{Bmatrix} 0 \\ 0 \\ P \\ 0 \end{Bmatrix} = \frac{PL}{EA} \begin{Bmatrix} 3 \\ 0 \\ 3 \\ -1 \end{Bmatrix}
$$

and

$$
\begin{Bmatrix} P_{x1} \\ P_{y1} \\ P_{x4} \\ P_{y4} \end{Bmatrix} = \begin{bmatrix} -1 & 0 & -1 & 0 \\ -1 & -1 & -1 & 0 \\ 0 & 0 & 0 & 0 \\ 1 & 0 & 1 & -1 \end{bmatrix} \begin{Bmatrix} 0 \\ 0 \\ P \\ 0 \end{Bmatrix} = P \begin{Bmatrix} -1 \\ -1 \\ 0 \\ 1 \end{Bmatrix}
$$

The foregoing displacements and forces are illustrated in Fig. 12-7(b). Also shown are the internal bar forces which may be determined by computing the internal nodal forces acting on each element. For member 3, for example,

$$
\begin{Bmatrix} F_{x1} \\ F_{y1} \\ F_{x3} \\ F_{y3} \end{Bmatrix} = [\mathbf{k}^{(3)}] \begin{Bmatrix} u_1 \\ v_1 \\ u_3 \\ v_3 \end{Bmatrix}
$$

or

$$
\begin{Bmatrix} F_{x1} \\ F_{y1} \\ F_{x3} \\ F_{y3} \end{Bmatrix} = \frac{EA}{2L} \begin{bmatrix} 1 & 1 & -1 & -1 \\ 1 & 1 & -1 & -1 \\ -1 & -1 & 1 & 1 \\ -1 & -1 & 1 & 1 \end{bmatrix} \begin{Bmatrix} 0 \\ 0 \\ 3PL/EA \\ -PL/EA \end{Bmatrix} = P \begin{Bmatrix} -1 \\ -1 \\ 1 \\ 1 \end{Bmatrix}
$$

From the free-body diagram shown in Fig. 12-7(c), the bar force is

$$
F_3 = \sqrt{2}P
$$

Next consider Structure B in Fig. 12-6(b) which is similar to Structure A, except that a second diagonal member has been added. Structure B is, therefore, statically indeterminate.

We may add to the system stiffness matrix $[\mathbf{K}]$ assembled for Structure A, the transformed member stiffness matrix for member 5, which spans nodes 2 and 4. The latter matrix is obtained from the relationship shown in Fig. 12-8(a).

The Direct Stiffness Method   Chap. 12

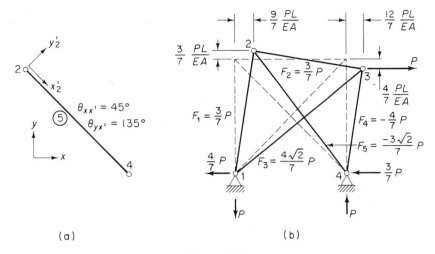

(a)   (b)

Figure 12-8

$$[\mathbf{k}^{(5)}] = \left(\frac{EA}{L}\right)_5 \begin{array}{cccc} u_2 & v_2 & u_4 & v_4 \\ \left[\begin{array}{cccc} \frac{1}{2} & -\frac{1}{2} & -\frac{1}{2} & \frac{1}{2} \\ -\frac{1}{2} & \frac{1}{2} & \frac{1}{2} & -\frac{1}{2} \\ -\frac{1}{2} & \frac{1}{2} & \frac{1}{2} & -\frac{1}{2} \\ \frac{1}{2} & -\frac{1}{2} & -\frac{1}{2} & \frac{1}{2} \end{array} \right] \end{array}$$

and hence the system stiffness matrix for Structure B is

$$[\mathbf{K}] = \frac{EA}{2L} \begin{array}{cccccccc} u_2 & v_2 & u_3 & v_3 & u_1 & v_1 & u_4 & v_4 \\ \left[\begin{array}{cccc|cccc} 3 & & & & & & & \\ -1 & 3 & & & & \text{symmetric} & & \\ -2 & 0 & 3 & & & & & \\ 0 & 0 & 1 & 3 & & & & \\ \hline 0 & 0 & -1 & -1 & 1 & & & \\ 0 & -2 & -1 & -1 & 1 & 3 & & \\ -1 & 1 & 0 & 0 & 0 & 0 & 1 & \\ 1 & -1 & 0 & -2 & 0 & 0 & -1 & 3 \end{array} \right] \end{array}$$

Because $\{\boldsymbol{\Delta}_s\} = \{\mathbf{0}\}$, the displacements $\{\boldsymbol{\Delta}_f\}$ at the unsupported nodes and the reactions $\{\mathbf{P}_s\}$ may be expressed as

$$\{\boldsymbol{\Delta}_f\} = [\mathbf{K}_{ff}]^{-1}\{\mathbf{P}_f\}$$

and

$$\{\mathbf{P}_s\} = [\mathbf{K}_{sf}][\mathbf{K}_{ff}]^{-1}\{\mathbf{P}_f\}$$

where, in view of the foregoing expression for $[\mathbf{K}]$,

$$[\mathbf{K}_{sf}] = \frac{EA}{2L} \begin{bmatrix} 0 & 0 & -1 & -1 \\ 0 & -2 & -1 & -1 \\ -1 & 1 & 0 & 0 \\ 1 & -1 & 0 & -2 \end{bmatrix}$$

and

$$[\mathbf{K}_{ff}] = \frac{EA}{2L} \begin{bmatrix} 3 & -1 & -2 & 0 \\ -1 & 3 & 0 & 0 \\ -2 & 0 & 3 & 1 \\ 0 & 0 & 1 & 3 \end{bmatrix}$$

Hence,

$$[\mathbf{K}_{ff}]^{-1} = \frac{L}{7EA} \begin{bmatrix} 12 & 4 & 9 & -3 \\ 4 & 6 & 3 & -1 \\ 9 & 3 & 12 & -4 \\ -3 & -1 & -4 & 6 \end{bmatrix}$$

$$\{\mathbf{\Delta}_f\} = \begin{Bmatrix} u_2 \\ v_2 \\ u_3 \\ v_3 \end{Bmatrix} = \frac{L}{7EA} \begin{bmatrix} 12 & 4 & 9 & -3 \\ 4 & 6 & 3 & -1 \\ 9 & 3 & 12 & -4 \\ -3 & -1 & -4 & 6 \end{bmatrix} \begin{Bmatrix} 0 \\ 0 \\ P \\ 0 \end{Bmatrix} = \frac{PL}{7EA} \begin{Bmatrix} 9 \\ 3 \\ 12 \\ -4 \end{Bmatrix}$$

and

$$\{\mathbf{P}_s\} = \begin{Bmatrix} P_{x1} \\ P_{y1} \\ P_{x4} \\ P_{y4} \end{Bmatrix} = \frac{1}{7} \begin{bmatrix} -3 & -1 & -4 & -1 \\ -7 & -7 & -7 & 0 \\ -4 & 1 & -3 & 1 \\ 7 & 0 & 7 & -7 \end{bmatrix} \begin{Bmatrix} 0 \\ 0 \\ P \\ 0 \end{Bmatrix} = \frac{P}{7} \begin{Bmatrix} -4 \\ -7 \\ -3 \\ 7 \end{Bmatrix}$$

The computed displacements and reactions are indicated in Fig. 12-8(b). Note that compared to those for the statically determinate truss, structure A, shown in Fig. 12-7(b), the displacements for the statically indeterminate truss, structure B, are smaller due to the increased stiffness provided by member 5. Also, in Fig. 12-8(b), horizontal reactions are provided at both nodes 1 and 4. The internal forces, which may be computed for structure B in the manner described above for structure A, are also indicated.

One of the most distinctive advantages of matrix methods of structural analysis lies with their ability to incorporate multiple loading schemes while incurring very little additional computational effort. If, for example, a vertical downward load P were applied at node 2 while all other loads were set equal to zero, then $\{\mathbf{\Delta}_f\}$ and $\{\mathbf{P}_s\}$ could be computed directly by replacing the load vector appearing in the final two equations above by $\{0, -P, 0, 0\}$. Performing the indicated matrix multiplication in these equations, we would find

$$\{\mathbf{\Delta}_f\} = \begin{Bmatrix} u_2 \\ v_2 \\ u_3 \\ v_3 \end{Bmatrix} = \frac{PL}{7EA} \begin{Bmatrix} -4 \\ -6 \\ -3 \\ 1 \end{Bmatrix} \quad \text{and} \quad \{\mathbf{P}_s\} = \begin{Bmatrix} P_{x1} \\ P_{y1} \\ P_{x4} \\ P_{y4} \end{Bmatrix} = \frac{P}{7} \begin{Bmatrix} 1 \\ 7 \\ -1 \\ 0 \end{Bmatrix}$$

With the direct stiffness method, in contrast with the flexibility method, the computational effort is directly related only to the number of degrees of freedom and not to the degree of statical indeterminacy. Accordingly, except for the need to incorporate an additional member stiffness matrix, structure B is no more difficult to analyze than structure A. In either case, a 4×4 matrix $[\mathbf{K}_{ff}]$ must be inverted.

Example 12-2. Analyze each of the structures of Example 12-1 due to an imposed lateral displacement Δ at node 4, in the absence of applied loads, as shown in Fig. 12-9.

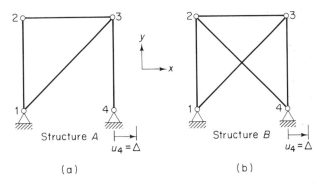

Figure 12-9

We refer again to the Eqs. (12-53) and (12-54) and write for the unloaded structure A in Fig. 12-9(a) (following the development in Example 12-1),

$$
\begin{Bmatrix} u_2 \\ v_2 \\ u_3 \\ v_3 \end{Bmatrix} = \begin{bmatrix} 1 & 1 & 0 & -1 \\ 0 & 1 & 0 & 0 \\ 1 & 1 & 0 & -1 \\ 0 & 0 & 0 & 1 \end{bmatrix} \begin{Bmatrix} u_1 \\ v_1 \\ u_4 \\ v_4 \end{Bmatrix}
$$

and

$$
\begin{Bmatrix} P_{x1} \\ P_{y1} \\ P_{x4} \\ P_{y4} \end{Bmatrix} = \frac{EA}{2L} \begin{bmatrix} 0 & 0 & 0 & 0 \\ 0 & 0 & 0 & 0 \\ 0 & 0 & 0 & 0 \\ 0 & 0 & 0 & 0 \end{bmatrix} \begin{Bmatrix} u_1 \\ v_1 \\ u_4 \\ v_4 \end{Bmatrix}
$$

Setting $\{u_1, v_1, u_4, v_4\} = \{0, 0, \Delta, 0\}$, we find

$$
\begin{Bmatrix} u_2 \\ v_2 \\ u_3 \\ v_3 \end{Bmatrix} = \Delta \begin{Bmatrix} 0 \\ 0 \\ 0 \\ 0 \end{Bmatrix} \quad \text{and} \quad \begin{Bmatrix} P_{x1} \\ P_{y1} \\ P_{x4} \\ P_{y4} \end{Bmatrix} = \frac{EA}{L} \Delta \begin{Bmatrix} 0 \\ 0 \\ 0 \\ 0 \end{Bmatrix}
$$

As shown in Fig. 12-10(a), horizontal translation of the right support leads to a rigid-body rotation of the right column about node 3. Because this structure is statically determinate, all reactions and internal forces are zero; such is the case for any combination of displacements imposed at the supports.

Now we consider structure B in Fig. 12-9(b) subjected only to a support displacement. Using Eqs. (12-53) and (12-54), we may write

$$
\begin{Bmatrix} u_2 \\ v_2 \\ u_3 \\ v_3 \end{Bmatrix} = \frac{1}{7} \begin{bmatrix} 3 & 7 & 4 & -7 \\ 1 & 7 & -1 & 0 \\ 4 & 7 & 3 & -7 \\ 1 & 0 & -1 & 7 \end{bmatrix} \begin{Bmatrix} u_1 \\ v_1 \\ u_4 \\ v_4 \end{Bmatrix}
$$

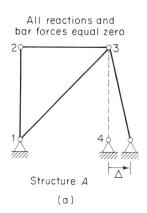

All reactions and
bar forces equal zero

Structure A

(a)

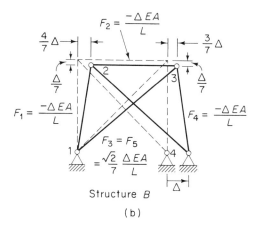

$$F_2 = \frac{-\Delta EA}{L}$$

$\frac{4}{7}\Delta \rightarrow$

$\frac{3}{7}\Delta$

$\frac{\Delta}{7}$

$$F_1 = \frac{-\Delta EA}{L}$$

$$F_4 = \frac{-\Delta EA}{L}$$

$$F_3 = F_5 = \frac{\sqrt{2}}{7}\frac{\Delta EA}{L}$$

$\frac{\Delta}{7}$

Structure B

(b)

Figure 12-10

and

$$\begin{Bmatrix} P_{x1} \\ P_{y1} \\ P_{x4} \\ P_{y4} \end{Bmatrix} = \frac{EA}{2L} \begin{bmatrix} 1 & 0 & -1 & 0 \\ 0 & 0 & 0 & 0 \\ -1 & 0 & 1 & 0 \\ 0 & 0 & 0 & 0 \end{bmatrix} \begin{Bmatrix} u_1 \\ v_1 \\ u_4 \\ v_4 \end{Bmatrix}$$

For the particular case where $\{u_1, v_1, u_4, v_4\} = \{0, 0, \Delta, 0\}$, we obtain

$$\begin{Bmatrix} u_2 \\ v_2 \\ u_3 \\ v_3 \end{Bmatrix} = \frac{\Delta}{7} \begin{Bmatrix} 4 \\ -1 \\ 3 \\ -1 \end{Bmatrix} \quad \text{and} \quad \begin{Bmatrix} P_{x1} \\ P_{y1} \\ P_{x4} \\ P_{y4} \end{Bmatrix} = \frac{EA}{7L}\Delta \begin{Bmatrix} -1 \\ 0 \\ 1 \\ 0 \end{Bmatrix}$$

The deformations, reactions and bar forces in Structure B are shown in Fig. 12-10(b). Because this structure is statically indeterminate, support displacements generally incur more than just rigid body deformations, along with attendant internal forces and reactions. In any case, the analysis of structures subjected to imposed displacements, as well as applied forces, merely requires the direct application of Eqs. (12-53) and (12-54).

Example 12-3. Determine the bar forces and displacements for the truss shown in Fig. 12-11.

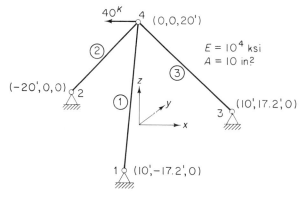

40^K 4 (0,0,20')

②

$E = 10^4$ ksi
$A = 10$ in?

(-20',0,0)

③

z

y

①

x

3 (10',17.2',0)

1 (10',−17.2',0)

Figure 12-11

The Direct Stiffness Method   Chap. 12

Since the displacements at nodes 1, 2 and 3 are constrained in all directions, the truss has only three active degrees of freedom as represented by the generalized coordinates at node 4. Therefore, we need to form only $[\mathbf{K}_{ff}]$ directly without actually partitioning the fully assembled stiffness matrix $[\mathbf{K}]$.

The lengths of the members 1, 2 and 3 of the truss are computed approximately for cases (a), (b), and (c) such that L will be equal for each bar in Fig. 12-12 as follows:

Bar	x	y	z	L
1	$-10'$	$17.2'$	$20'$	$28.21'$
2	$20'$	0	$20'$	$28.21'$
3	$-10'$	$-17.2'$	$20'$	$28.21'$

$$\left(\frac{EA}{L}\right)_1 = \left(\frac{EA}{L}\right)_2 = \left(\frac{EA}{L}\right)_3 = 3544.8^{\,K/ft}$$

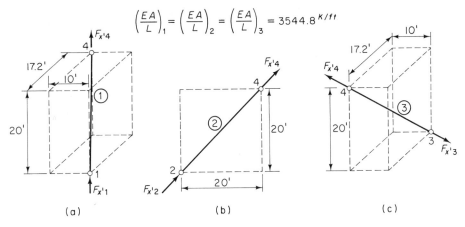

Figure 12-12

With nodes 1, 2 and 3 as the origins of the local coordinates for members 1, 2 and 3, respectively, we obtain the direction cosines from Eqs. (12-12a) as follows:

Bar	$\lambda = x/L$	$\mu = y/L$	$\nu = z/L$
1	-0.3545	0.6097	0.7090
2	0.7090	0	0.7090
3	-0.3545	-0.6097	0.7090

Thus, for member 1, we obtain from Eq. (12-8)

$$[\mathbf{k}'] = 3544.8 \begin{bmatrix} 1 & -1 \\ -1 & 1 \end{bmatrix}$$

and from Eq. (12-15a)

$$[\mathbf{T}] = \begin{bmatrix} -0.3545 & 0.6097 & 0.7090 & 0 & 0 & 0 \\ 0 & 0 & 0 & -0.3545 & 0.6097 & 0.7090 \end{bmatrix}$$

Similarly, for member 2, we also obtain

$$[\mathbf{k'}] = 3544.8 \begin{bmatrix} 1 & -1 \\ -1 & 1 \end{bmatrix}$$

and

$$[\mathbf{T}] = \begin{bmatrix} 0.7090 & 0 & 0.7090 & 0 & 0 & 0 \\ 0 & 0 & 0 & 0.7090 & 0 & 0.7090 \end{bmatrix}$$

For member 3, which is symmetrical with respect to member 1 about the x-z plane, we obtain

$$[\mathbf{k'}] = 3544.8 \begin{bmatrix} 1 & -1 \\ -1 & 1 \end{bmatrix}$$

and

$$[\mathbf{T}] = \begin{bmatrix} -0.3545 & -0.6097 & 0.7090 & 0 & 0 & 0 \\ 0 & 0 & 0 & -0.3545 & -0.6097 & 0.7090 \end{bmatrix}$$

The global stiffness matrices for the members may be obtained according to Eq. (12-12a) and are

$$[\mathbf{k}^{(1)}] = \begin{bmatrix} 445.5 & -766.2 & -891.0 & -445.5 & 766.2 & 891.0 \\ -766.2 & 1317.7 & 1532.3 & 766.2 & -1317.7 & -1532.3 \\ -891.0 & 1532.3 & 1781.9 & 891.0 & -1532.3 & -1781.9 \\ -445.5 & 766.2 & 891.0 & 445.5 & -766.2 & -891.0 \\ 766.2 & -1317.7 & -1532.3 & -766.2 & 1317.7 & 1532.3 \\ 891.0 & -1532.3 & -1781.9 & -891.0 & 1532.3 & 1781.9 \end{bmatrix}$$

$$[\mathbf{k}^{(2)}] = \begin{bmatrix} 1781.9 & 0 & 1781.9 & -1781.9 & 0 & -1781.9 \\ 0 & 0 & 0 & 0 & 0 & 0 \\ 1781.9 & 0 & 1781.9 & -1781.9 & 0 & -1781.9 \\ -1781.9 & 0 & -1781.9 & 1781.9 & 0 & 1781.9 \\ 0 & 0 & 0 & 0 & 0 & 0 \\ -1781.9 & 0 & -1781.9 & 1781.9 & 0 & 1781.9 \end{bmatrix}$$

$$[\mathbf{k}^{(3)}] = \begin{bmatrix} 445.5 & 766.2 & -891.0 & -445.5 & -766.2 & 891.0 \\ 766.2 & 1317.7 & -1532.3 & -766.2 & -1317.7 & 1532.3 \\ -891.0 & -1532.3 & 1781.9 & 891.0 & 1532.3 & -1781.9 \\ -445.5 & -766.2 & 891.0 & 445.5 & 766.2 & -891.0 \\ -766.2 & -1317.7 & 1532.3 & 766.2 & 1317.7 & -1532.3 \\ 891.0 & 1532.3 & -1781.9 & -891.0 & -1532.3 & 1781.9 \end{bmatrix}$$

The reduced system stiffness matrix $[\mathbf{K}_{ff}]$ corresponding to the three degrees of freedom at node 4 is given by

$$[\mathbf{K}_{ff}] = \begin{bmatrix} 2672.9 & 0 & 0 \\ 0 & 2635.4 & 0 \\ 0 & 0 & 5345.7 \end{bmatrix}$$

Using Eq. (12-53) along with $\{\mathbf{P}_f\} = \{40^k, 0, 0\}$, we find the displacements $\{\mathbf{\Delta}_f\}$ at node 4 (in feet):

$$\begin{Bmatrix} u_4 \\ v_4 \\ w_4 \end{Bmatrix} = \begin{Bmatrix} 0.0150 \\ 0 \\ 0 \end{Bmatrix}$$

Finally, the global internal nodal forces for each of the three bars are obtained from Eq. (12-20) with the following results (in kips):

Bar 1	Bar 2	Bar 3
$\begin{Bmatrix} F_{x1} \\ F_{y1} \\ F_{z1} \\ F_{x4} \\ F_{y4} \\ F_{z4} \end{Bmatrix} = \begin{Bmatrix} 6.67 \\ -11.5 \\ -13.3 \\ -6.67 \\ 11.5 \\ 13.3 \end{Bmatrix}$	$\begin{Bmatrix} F_{x2} \\ F_{y2} \\ F_{z2} \\ F_{x4} \\ F_{y4} \\ F_{z4} \end{Bmatrix} = \begin{Bmatrix} 26.7 \\ 0 \\ 26.7 \\ -26.7 \\ 0 \\ -26.7 \end{Bmatrix}$	$\begin{Bmatrix} F_{x3} \\ F_{y3} \\ F_{z3} \\ F_{x4} \\ F_{y4} \\ F_{z4} \end{Bmatrix} = \begin{Bmatrix} 6.67 \\ 11.5 \\ -13.3 \\ -6.67 \\ -11.5 \\ 13.3 \end{Bmatrix}$

The corresponding local internal nodal forces (in kips) are obtained from Eq. (12-13a) as follows:

Bar 1	Bar 2	Bar 3
$F_{x'1} = -18.8$	$F_{x'2} = 37.6$	$F_{x'3} = -18.8$
$F_{x'4} = 18.8$	$F_{x'4} = -37.6$	$F_{x'4} = 18.8$

The resulting bar forces are $F_1 = 18.8^k$ (tension), $F_2 = -37.6^k$ (compression) and $F_3 = 18.8^k$ (tension).

12-5 ANALYSIS OF BEAMS SUBJECTED TO CONCENTRATED LOADS

The simplest class of structures that sustain loading through the development of bending moments and shear forces are beams comprising colinear elements subjected to loading in a single plane. In such cases, we may employ the element stiffness matrix given in Eq. (12-42) for bending in the x–y plane:

$$[\mathbf{k}] = \frac{EI_z}{L^3} \begin{bmatrix} \overset{v_i}{12} & \overset{\theta_i}{6L} & \overset{v_j}{-12} & \overset{\theta_j}{6L} \\ 6L & 4L^2 & -6L & 2L^2 \\ -12 & -6L & 12 & -6L \\ 6L & 2L^2 & -6L & 4L^2 \end{bmatrix} \begin{matrix} F_{yi} \\ M_{zi} \\ F_{yj} \\ M_{zj} \end{matrix} \qquad (12\text{-}55)$$

We have indicated above the columns and next to the rows the transverse and rotational degrees of freedom, v and θ, and corresponding generalized forces F and M at the ends (nodes i and j) as reminders of the meaning of the stiffness coefficients. Because the local and global coordinate systems coincide, the element stiffness matrix is the same when expressed in either coordinate system. To analyze a structure comprising colinear beam elements, the overall stiffness matrix is assembled and the stiffness equations are solved in the manner described in the previous section. While there are advantages to using a stiffness matrix having dimensionless entries, such as Eqs. (12-44b) and (12-45b), in most of the examples that follow we shall employ the 'natural form' as illustrated by Eq. (12-55).

Example 12-4. For the beam shown in Fig. 12-13(a), find the displacements at the point of loading and the reactions and internal forces.

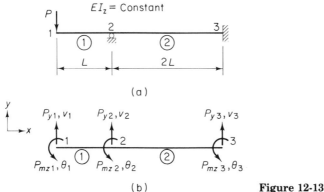

(a)

(b)   **Figure 12-13**

The generalized displacements and forces are indicated in Fig. 12-13(b) and, based on Eq. (12-55), the associated stiffness matrices for beam elements 1 and 2 are

$$[\mathbf{k}^{(1)}] = \frac{EI_z}{L^3} \begin{bmatrix} 12 & 6L & -12 & 6L \\ 6L & 4L^2 & -6L & 2L^2 \\ -12 & -6L & 12 & -6L \\ 6L & 2L^2 & -6L & 4L^2 \end{bmatrix} \begin{matrix} v_1 \\ \theta_1 \\ v_2 \\ \theta_2 \end{matrix}$$

and

$$[\mathbf{k}^{(2)}] = \frac{EI_z}{8L^3} \begin{bmatrix} 12 & 12L & -12 & 12L \\ 12L & 16L^2 & -12L & 8L^2 \\ -12 & -12L & 12 & -12L \\ 12L & 8L^2 & -12L & 16L^2 \end{bmatrix} \begin{matrix} v_2 \\ \theta_2 \\ v_3 \\ \theta_3 \end{matrix}$$

The overall stiffness matrix for the structure is then

$$[\mathbf{K}] = \frac{EI_z}{L^3} \left[\begin{array}{ccc:ccc} 12 & 6L & 6L & -12 & 0 & 0 \\ 6L & 4L^2 & 2L^2 & -6L & 0 & 0 \\ 6L & 2L^2 & 6L^2 & -4.5L & -1.5L & L^2 \\ \hdashline -12 & -6L & -4.5L & 13.5 & -1.5 & 1.5L \\ 0 & 0 & -1.5L & -1.5 & 1.5 & -1.5L \\ 0 & 0 & L^2 & 1.5L & -1.5L & 2L^2 \end{array} \right] \begin{matrix} v_1 \\ \theta_1 \\ \theta_2 \\ v_2 \\ v_3 \\ \theta_3 \end{matrix}$$

This matrix relates the generalized displacements v_1, v_2, v_3, θ_1, θ_2, and θ_3 to the corresponding generalized forces P_{y1}, P_{y2}, P_{y3}, P_{mz1}, P_{mz2}, and P_{mz3} (where the notation P_{mzi} is used to designate the externally applied moment about the z-axis at node i). Note that in assembling $[\mathbf{K}]$ we have interchanged the natural order of v_2 and θ_2 according to the definition of $[\mathbf{K}_{ff}]$.

Thus, according to Eqs. (12-53) and (12-54), the unknown displacements and forces (reactions) may be expressed as

$$
\begin{Bmatrix} v_1 \\ \theta_1 \\ \theta_2 \end{Bmatrix} = \frac{L^3}{EI_z} \begin{bmatrix} 12 & 6L & 6L \\ 6L & 4L^2 & 2L^2 \\ 6L & 2L^2 & 6L^2 \end{bmatrix}^{-1} \left(\begin{Bmatrix} P_{y1} \\ P_{mz1} \\ P_{mz2} \end{Bmatrix} - \frac{EI_z}{L^3} \begin{bmatrix} 12 & 0 & 0 \\ -6L & 0 & 0 \\ -4.5L & -1.5L & L^2 \end{bmatrix} \begin{Bmatrix} v_2 \\ v_3 \\ \theta_3 \end{Bmatrix} \right)
$$

and

$$
\begin{Bmatrix} P_{y2} \\ P_{y3} \\ P_{mz3} \end{Bmatrix} = \begin{bmatrix} -12 & -6L & -4.5L \\ 0 & 0 & -1.5L \\ 0 & 0 & L^2 \end{bmatrix} \begin{bmatrix} 12 & 6L & 6L \\ 6L & 4L^2 & 2L^2 \\ 6L & 2L^2 & 6L^2 \end{bmatrix}^{-1} \begin{Bmatrix} P_{y1} \\ P_{mz1} \\ P_{mz2} \end{Bmatrix}
$$

$$
- \frac{EI_z}{L^3} \left(\begin{bmatrix} -12 & -6L & -4.5L \\ 0 & 0 & -1.5L \\ 0 & 0 & L^2 \end{bmatrix} \begin{bmatrix} 12 & 6L & 6L \\ 6L & 4L^2 & 2L^2 \\ 6L & 2L^2 & 6L^2 \end{bmatrix}^{-1} \begin{bmatrix} -12 & 0 & 0 \\ -6L & 0 & 0 \\ -4.5L & -1.5L & L^2 \end{bmatrix} \right.
$$

$$
\left. - \begin{bmatrix} 13.5 & -1.5 & 1.5L \\ -1.5 & 1.5 & -1.5L \\ 1.5L & -1.5L & 2L^2 \end{bmatrix} \right) \begin{Bmatrix} v_2 \\ v_3 \\ \theta_3 \end{Bmatrix}
$$

or

$$
\begin{Bmatrix} v_1 \\ \theta_1 \\ \theta_2 \end{Bmatrix} = \frac{L}{2EI_z} \begin{bmatrix} \frac{5}{3}L^2 & -2L & -L \\ -2L & 3 & 1 \\ -L & 1 & 1 \end{bmatrix} \begin{Bmatrix} P_{y1} \\ P_{mz1} \\ P_{mz2} \end{Bmatrix} - \frac{1}{4L} \begin{bmatrix} -7L & 3L & -2L^2 \\ 3 & -3 & 2L \\ 3 & -3 & 2L \end{bmatrix} \begin{Bmatrix} v_2 \\ v_3 \\ \theta_3 \end{Bmatrix} \quad \text{(a)}
$$

and

$$
\begin{Bmatrix} P_{y2} \\ P_{y3} \\ P_{mz3} \end{Bmatrix} = \frac{1}{4L} \begin{bmatrix} -7L & 3 & 3 \\ 3L & -3 & -3 \\ -2L^2 & 2L & 2L \end{bmatrix} \begin{Bmatrix} P_{y1} \\ P_{mz1} \\ P_{mz2} \end{Bmatrix} + \frac{3EI_z}{8L^3} \begin{bmatrix} 1 & -1 & 2L \\ -1 & 1 & -2L \\ 2L & -2L & 4L^2 \end{bmatrix} \begin{Bmatrix} v_2 \\ v_3 \\ \theta_3 \end{Bmatrix} \quad \text{(b)}
$$

For the loading condition given, we have

$$
\begin{Bmatrix} P_{y1} \\ P_{mz1} \\ P_{mz2} \end{Bmatrix} = \begin{Bmatrix} -P \\ 0 \\ 0 \end{Bmatrix} \quad \text{and} \quad \begin{Bmatrix} v_2 \\ v_3 \\ \theta_3 \end{Bmatrix} = \begin{Bmatrix} 0 \\ 0 \\ 0 \end{Bmatrix}
$$

Therefore,

$$
\begin{Bmatrix} v_1 \\ \theta_1 \\ \theta_2 \end{Bmatrix} = \frac{PL^3}{2EI_z} \begin{Bmatrix} -5/3 \\ 2/L \\ 1/L \end{Bmatrix} \quad \text{and} \quad \begin{Bmatrix} P_{y2} \\ P_{y3} \\ P_{mz3} \end{Bmatrix} = \frac{P}{4} \begin{Bmatrix} 7 \\ -3 \\ 2L \end{Bmatrix}
$$

We also may determine the internal forces acting at the ends of each member by multiplying the element stiffness matrices by the computed displacements. Thus, for member 1

$$
\begin{Bmatrix} F_{y1} \\ M_{z1} \\ F_{y2} \\ M_{z2} \end{Bmatrix} = \frac{EI_z}{L^3} \frac{PL^3}{2EI_z} \begin{bmatrix} 12 & 6L & -12 & 6L \\ 6L & 4L^2 & -6L & 2L^2 \\ -12 & -6L & 12 & -6L \\ 6L & 2L^2 & -6L & 4L^2 \end{bmatrix} \begin{Bmatrix} -5/3 \\ 2/L \\ 0 \\ 1/L \end{Bmatrix} = P \begin{Bmatrix} -1 \\ 0 \\ 0 \\ -L \end{Bmatrix}
$$

and for member 2,

$$\begin{Bmatrix} F_{y2} \\ M_{z2} \\ F_{y3} \\ M_{z3} \end{Bmatrix} = \frac{EI_z}{8L^3}\frac{PL^3}{2EI_z}\begin{bmatrix} 12 & 12L & -12 & 12L \\ 12L & 16L^2 & -12L & 8L^2 \\ -12 & -12L & 12 & -12L \\ 12L & 8L^2 & -12L & 16L^2 \end{bmatrix}\begin{Bmatrix} 0 \\ 1/L \\ 0 \\ 0 \end{Bmatrix} = \frac{P}{4}\begin{Bmatrix} 3 \\ 4L \\ -3 \\ 2L \end{Bmatrix}$$

These nodal forces (the forces and reactions acting on the joints) and the associated shear forces and bending moments are shown in Fig. 12-14.

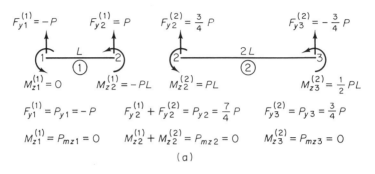

$$F_{y1}^{(1)} = P_{y1} = -P \qquad F_{y2}^{(1)} + F_{y2}^{(2)} = P_{y2} = \frac{7}{4}P \qquad F_{y3}^{(2)} = P_{y3} = \frac{3}{4}P$$

$$M_{z1}^{(1)} = P_{mz1} = 0 \qquad M_{z2}^{(1)} + M_{z2}^{(2)} = P_{mz2} = 0 \qquad M_{z3}^{(2)} = P_{mz3} = 0$$

(a)

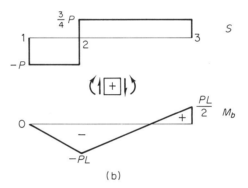

(b)

Figure 12-14

It is worth mentioning again that the structure may be reanalyzed for other loading conditions, including prescribed displacements merely by changing the vectors in Eqs. (a) and (b). If, for example, the structure were given a vertical displacement Δ at node 3 while other applied loads were zero, these equations would yield

$$\begin{Bmatrix} v_1 \\ \theta_1 \\ \theta_2 \end{Bmatrix} = -\frac{1}{4L}\begin{bmatrix} -7L & 3L & -2L^2 \\ 3 & -3 & 2L \\ 3 & -3 & 2L \end{bmatrix}\begin{Bmatrix} 0 \\ \Delta \\ 0 \end{Bmatrix} = \frac{3\Delta}{4}\begin{Bmatrix} -1 \\ 1/L \\ 1/L \end{Bmatrix}$$

and

$$\begin{Bmatrix} P_{y2} \\ P_{y3} \\ P_{mz3} \end{Bmatrix} = \frac{3EI_z}{8L^3}\begin{bmatrix} 3 & -1 & 2L \\ -1 & 1 & -2L \\ -2L & -2L & 4L^2 \end{bmatrix}\begin{Bmatrix} 0 \\ \Delta \\ 0 \end{Bmatrix} = \frac{3EI_z}{8L^3}\Delta\begin{Bmatrix} -1 \\ 1 \\ -2L \end{Bmatrix}$$

Internal member forces may be computed as described above.

Note again that often a statically indeterminate structure is easier to analyze by the direct stiffness method than is a similar statically determinate system. Suppose, for example, node 3 were simply supported rather than clamped. While the corresponding moment at node 3 would necessarily be zero, θ_3 would be an unknown displacement. Accordingly, $[\mathbf{K}_{ff}]$ would increase in size to a 4×4 matrix, and the relatively time consuming part of the computation, i.e., the inversion of $[\mathbf{K}_{ff}]$, would grow considerably. Of course, one might logically prefer to analyze such a structure by an alternative method. But the point to be emphasized is that, as regards the direct stiffness method, the computational effort is related primarily (although not exclusively) to the number of unknown generalized displacements; this number dictates the order of $[\mathbf{K}_{ff}]$.

Finally, recall that just as the element stiffness matrices and the overall stiffness matrix $[\mathbf{K}]$ possess no inverse because rigid-body motion is not restricted, so also will $[\mathbf{K}_{ff}]$ be singular if rigid-body motion of the structure is not prevented. If in the present example the support at node 2 and the moment restraint at node 3 were removed, the beam obviously would be unstable. We would find that the corresponding 5×5 matrix $[\mathbf{K}_{ff}]$ (formed by partitioning out of $[\mathbf{K}]$ the row and column corresponding to v_3) is also singular. Again, the occurrence of a singular matrix $[\mathbf{K}_{ff}]$ is an indication of kinematic instability of the structure.

Example 12-5. The beam shown in Figure 12-15(a) is subjected to a concentrated load P which lies in a plane parallel to a principal bending plane (the x–y plane) but which also incurs a torque Pe due to the eccentricity e. The member is completely restrained at its ends. Find the displacements, reactions and internal forces.

This structure is technically a space frame consisting of three elements 1, 2, and 3. To simplify the problem, however, it is assumed that element 3 is a bracket with a small length e attached to the fixed end beam, at node 2. This bracket transmits the vertical load P and a torque Pe to the beam at that point. Hence, the displacements and forces on element 3 are of no consequence to the problem, and the structure will be treated as a beam with fixed ends at nodes 1 and 3 as shown in Fig. 12-15(b). Although the displacements of the beam normal to the x–y plane will be zero, we must account for the member's twist caused by the torque Pe as well as its in-plane deformation caused by the vertical load P. For members 1 and 2 in Fig. 12-15(c), the element stiffness matrices can be obtained from Eq. (12-44b) by including only the columns and rows pertaining to the relevant degrees of freedom. Since these two elements are colinear, the element stiffness matrix $[\mathbf{k}]$ for each member in global coordinates is identical to the corresponding $[\mathbf{k}']$ in local coordinates and can be expressed in the following form:

$$[\mathbf{k}] = \frac{EI_z}{L^3} \begin{bmatrix} 12 & & & & & \\ 0 & \dfrac{GJ}{EI_z} & & & \text{symmetric} & \\ 6 & 0 & 4 & & & \\ -12 & 0 & -6 & 12 & & \\ 0 & -\dfrac{GJ}{EI_z} & 0 & 0 & \dfrac{GJ}{EI_z} & \\ 6 & 0 & 2 & -6 & 0 & 4 \end{bmatrix} \begin{matrix} F_{yi} \\ M_{xi}/L \\ M_{zi}/L \\ F_{yj} \\ M_{xj}/L \\ M_{zj}/L \end{matrix} \quad \text{(a)}$$

with column labels $v_i \quad \theta_{xi}L \quad \theta_{zi}L \quad v_j \quad \theta_{xj}L \quad \theta_{zj}L$

In order to normalize the rotations and moments with respect to a single length, let $L_1 = L$ and $L_2 = r_2 L$, where r_2 is dimensionless ratio equal to L_2/L_1.

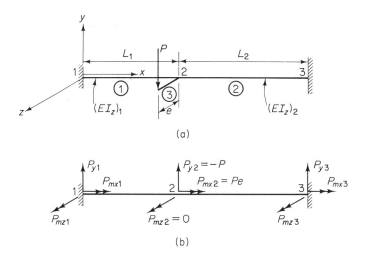

(a)

(b)

$F_{y1}^{(1)} = P_{y1}$ $F_{y2}^{(1)} + F_{y2}^{(2)} = P_{y2} = -P$ $F_{y3}^{(2)} = P_{y3}$

$M_{x1}^{(1)} = P_{mx1}$ $M_{x2}^{(1)} + M_{x2}^{(2)} = P_{mx2} = Pe$ $M_{x3}^{(2)} = P_{mx3}$

$M_{z1}^{(1)} = P_{mz1}$ $M_{z2}^{(1)} + M_{z2}^{(2)} = P_{mz2} = 0$ $M_{z3}^{(2)} = P_{mz3}$

(c)

Figure 12-15

Thus, the internal nodal forces for member 1 can be obtained from the relation $\{F'\} = [k']\{\Delta'\}$, where $[k']$ is identical to $[k]$ in Eq. (a) for $i = 1$ and $j = 2$. Noting that

$$\left(\frac{EI_z}{L^3}\right)_2 = \frac{(EI_z)_2}{r_2^3 L^3} = \frac{(EI_z)_2}{L_2^3} \tag{b}$$

and that

$$\frac{M_{x2}}{L_2} = \left(\frac{L}{L_2}\right)\left(\frac{M_{x2}}{L}\right) \qquad\qquad \theta_{x2} L_2 = \left(\frac{L_2}{L}\right)(\theta_{x2} L)$$

$$\frac{M_{z2}}{L_2} = \left(\frac{L}{L_2}\right)\left(\frac{M_{z2}}{L}\right) \qquad\qquad \theta_{z2} L_2 = \left(\frac{L_2}{L}\right)(\theta_{z2} L) \tag{c}$$

$$\frac{M_{x3}}{L_2} = \left(\frac{L}{L_2}\right)\left(\frac{M_{x3}}{L}\right) \qquad\qquad \theta_{x3}L_2 = \left(\frac{L_2}{L}\right)(\theta_{x3}L)$$

$$\frac{M_{z3}}{L_2} = \left(\frac{L}{L_2}\right)\left(\frac{M_{z3}}{L}\right) \qquad\qquad \theta_{z3}L_2 = \left(\frac{L_2}{L}\right)(\theta_{z3}L)$$

(c)
(cont.)

the stiffness equations for member 2 are given by

$$
\begin{Bmatrix} F_{y2} \\ M_{x2}/L \\ M_{z2}/L \\ F_{y3} \\ M_{x3}/L \\ M_{z3}/L \end{Bmatrix}
= \frac{(EI_z)_2}{L_2^3}
\begin{bmatrix}
12 & 0 & 6\dfrac{L_2}{L} & -12 & 0 & 6\dfrac{L_2}{L} \\[2mm]
0 & \left(\dfrac{GJ}{EI_z}\right)_2 \dfrac{L_2^2}{L^2} & 0 & 0 & -\left(\dfrac{GJ}{EI_z}\right)_2 \dfrac{L_2^2}{L^2} & 0 \\[2mm]
6\dfrac{L_2}{L} & 0 & 4\dfrac{L_2^2}{L^2} & -6\dfrac{L_2}{L} & 0 & 2\dfrac{L_2^2}{L^2} \\[2mm]
-12 & 0 & -6\dfrac{L_2}{L} & 12 & 0 & -6\dfrac{L_2}{L} \\[2mm]
0 & -\left(\dfrac{GJ}{EI_z}\right)_2 \dfrac{L_2^2}{L^2} & 0 & 0 & \left(\dfrac{GJ}{EI_z}\right)_2 \dfrac{L_2^2}{L^2} & 0 \\[2mm]
6\dfrac{L_2}{L} & 0 & 2\dfrac{L_2^2}{L^2} & -6\dfrac{L_2}{L} & 0 & 4\dfrac{L_2^2}{L^2}
\end{bmatrix}
\begin{Bmatrix} v_2 \\ \theta_{x2}L \\ \theta_{z2}L \\ v_3 \\ \theta_{x3}L \\ \theta_{z3}L \end{Bmatrix}
$$

(d)

It is easy to verify that the same internal nodal forces would have been obtained if L_2 instead of L were used to represent the non-dimensional quantities. Since the generalized forces and displacements are now expressed in terms of a single length L, the element stiffness matrices can be expanded to 9×9 to obtain the system stiffness matrix $[\mathbf{K}]$ by direct summation.

Now if alternative boundary conditions are not to be considered and if the present boundary points are completely restrained (i.e., $v_1 = \theta_{x1} = \theta_{z1} = v_3 = \theta_{x3} = \theta_{z3} = 0$), then we would need to form only $[\mathbf{K}_{ff}]$ directly without actually partitioning the fully assembled stiffness matrix $[\mathbf{K}]$. This may be done by working with only the rows and columns corresponding to v_2, $\theta_{x2}L$, and $\theta_{z2}L$ in $[\mathbf{k}^{(1)}]$ and $[\mathbf{k}^{(2)}]$. Thus

$$
[\mathbf{K}_{ff}] = \frac{(EI_z)_1}{L^3}
\begin{matrix} \quad v_2 \quad & \theta_{x2}L & \theta_{z2}L \end{matrix}
\begin{bmatrix}
12 & 0 & -6 \\
0 & \left(\dfrac{GJ}{EI_z}\right)_1 & 0 \\
-6 & 0 & 4
\end{bmatrix}
+ \frac{(EI_z)_2}{L^3}\left(\frac{L^3}{L_2^3}\right)
\begin{matrix} \quad v_2 \quad & \theta_{x2}L & \theta_{z2}L \end{matrix}
\begin{bmatrix}
12 & 0 & 6\dfrac{L_2}{L} \\
0 & \left(\dfrac{GJ}{EI_z}\right)_2\dfrac{L_2^2}{L^2} & 0 \\
6\dfrac{L_2}{L} & 0 & 4\dfrac{L_2^2}{L^2}
\end{bmatrix}
$$

To consider a particular case, suppose $(EI_z)_1 = (EI_z)_2$, $(GJ)_1 = (GJ)_2$ and $L_1 = L_2/2 = L$. Also, for computational convenience, we interchange the order of the rows and columns corresponding to $\theta_{x2}L$ and $\theta_{z2}L$. Then

$$
[\mathbf{K}_{ff}] = \frac{EI_z}{L^3}
\begin{matrix} \quad v_2 \quad & \theta_{z2}L & \theta_{x2}L \end{matrix}
\begin{bmatrix}
13.5 & -4.5 & 0 \\
-4.5 & 6 & 0 \\
0 & 0 & 1.5\dfrac{GJ}{EI_z}
\end{bmatrix}
$$

Note also that because bending in a principal plane is uncoupled from twisting, only the diagonal term in the third row and column is nonzero. We may then write

$$\left\{\begin{array}{c} P_{y2} \\ P_{mz2}/L \\ P_{mx2}/L \end{array}\right\} = \frac{EI_z}{L^3}\begin{bmatrix} 13.5 & -4.5 & 0 \\ -4.5 & 6 & 0 \\ 0 & 0 & 1.5\dfrac{GJ}{EI_z} \end{bmatrix}\left\{\begin{array}{c} v_2 \\ \theta_{z2}L \\ \theta_{x2}L \end{array}\right\}$$

or

$$\left\{\begin{array}{c} v_2 \\ \theta_{z2}L \end{array}\right\} = \frac{L^3}{EI_z}\begin{bmatrix} 13.5 & -4.5 \\ -4.5 & 6 \end{bmatrix}^{-1}\left\{\begin{array}{c} P_{y2} \\ P_{mz2}/L \end{array}\right\}$$

and

$$\theta_{x2}L = \frac{L^3}{1.5GJ}(P_{mx2}/L) = \frac{P_{mx2}L^2}{1.5GJ}$$

Given

$$\left\{\begin{array}{c} P_{y2} \\ P_{mz2}/L \end{array}\right\} = \left\{\begin{array}{c} -P \\ 0 \end{array}\right\} \quad \text{and} \quad P_{mx2}/L = Pe/L$$

we obtain

$$\left\{\begin{array}{c} v_2 \\ \theta_{z2}L \end{array}\right\} = \frac{L^3}{60.75EI_z}\begin{bmatrix} 6 & 4.5 \\ 4.5 & 13.5 \end{bmatrix}\left\{\begin{array}{c} -P \\ 0 \end{array}\right\} = \frac{-PL^3}{20.25EI_z}\left\{\begin{array}{c} 2 \\ 1.5 \end{array}\right\}$$

and

$$\theta_{x2}L = \frac{PeL^2}{1.5GJ} = \frac{13.5}{20.25}\left(\frac{PeL^2}{GJ}\right)$$

Although the reactions cannot be computed directly unless $[\mathbf{K}_{sf}]$ is also developed (see Eq. (12-54)), they always may be obtained from conditions of joint equilibrium once member nodal forces have been determined. The latter may be computed in the usual way by multiplying each element stiffness matrix by the associated displacement vector. Thus, for member 1

$$\left\{\begin{array}{c} F_{y1} \\ M_{x1}/L \\ M_{z1}/L \\ F_{y2} \\ M_{x2}/L \\ M_{z2}/L \end{array}\right\} = \frac{-PL^3}{20.25EI_z}\begin{bmatrix} 12 & & & & & \\ 0 & \dfrac{GJ}{EI_z} & & \text{symmetric} & & \\ 6 & 0 & 4 & & & \\ -12 & 0 & -6 & 12 & & \\ 0 & -\dfrac{GJ}{EI_z} & 0 & 0 & \dfrac{GJ}{EI_z} & \\ 6 & 0 & 2 & -6 & 0 & 4 \end{bmatrix}\left\{\begin{array}{c} 0 \\ 0 \\ 0 \\ 2 \\ -13.5\dfrac{e}{L}\dfrac{EI_z}{GJ} \\ 1.5 \end{array}\right\}$$

A similar relationship for member 2 may be obtained from Eq. (d).

12-6 ANALYSIS OF BEAMS SUBJECTED TO DISTRIBUTED LOADS

In the previous examples concentrated loads were applied at node points of the structure. In cases where only one or two concentrated loads are applied between the ends of a beam, it might be reasonable to define the points of load application as nodes having the requisite generalized displacements. However, this approach generally incurs an unwarranted computational penalty when numerous in-span concentrated loads are applied and an unnecessary approximation to the actual solution if distributed loading is represented by concentrated loads. A fairly simple procedure is now described which involves the replacement of the actual loading with equivalent nodal loading and which leads directly to the complete solution for those parts of the structure that are not subjected to in-span forces. The deformations and internal forces of the loaded members are found by a superposition of this solution and one associated with a fixed-end member subjected to the distributed loading.

By way of explanation, let us return to the beam discussed in Example 12-4 which is now subjected to a uniformly distributed load between nodes 1 and 2 as shown in Fig. 12-16(a). As a general strategy, let us first combine the actual distributed load with a set of generalized forces acting at the nodes of the loaded member, as shown in Fig. 12-16(b). We select these generalized forces such that the combined loading results in deformation only in the loaded member (member 1 in this case). Because there are no translations or rotations at the ends of the member, these generalized forces may be recognized as *fixed-end shears and moments* which we have encountered previously in the context of the moment distribution method; accordingly, we designate them with a superscript F. Also, because in all cases the deformation is confined to

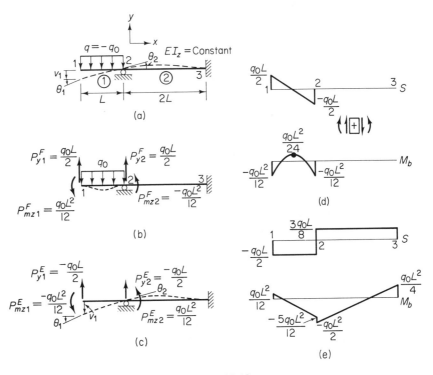

Figure 12-16

the loaded members, the analysis for the combined loading may follow any established approach.

Now consider the structure being subjected to a second set of loads comprising the *negative* of the fixed-end forces and moments as shown in Fig 12-16(c). These loads, acting only at nodal points, generally incur deformations and internal forces throughout the structure which may be analyzed by the direct stiffness method. *Except for the loaded members,* the deformations and internal forces throughout the structure are those that would be produced by the actual loading. Hence the *negative* of the fixed end forces and moments are termed *equivalent nodal loads,* and are designated by a superscript *E*. The complete solution is obtained through the superposition of solutions for the loading conditions illustrated in Figs. 12-16(b) and (c). Through this superposition, one recovers the actual loading condition and the resulting set of deformations and internal forces.

In conducting the matrix analysis, the equivalent nodal forces are to be combined with any other nodal forces that might be applied to the structure. Thus, we solve for the unknown generalized forces and displacements appearing in the stiffness equations

$$\begin{Bmatrix} \mathbf{P}_f \\ \hline \mathbf{P}_s \end{Bmatrix} + \begin{Bmatrix} \mathbf{P}_f^E \\ \hline \mathbf{P}_s^E \end{Bmatrix} = \begin{bmatrix} \mathbf{K}_{ff} & \vdots & \mathbf{K}_{fs} \\ \hline \mathbf{K}_{sf} & \vdots & \mathbf{K}_{ss} \end{bmatrix} \begin{Bmatrix} \mathbf{\Delta}_f \\ \hline \mathbf{\Delta}_s \end{Bmatrix} \qquad (12\text{-}56)$$

where $\{\mathbf{P}_f^E\}$ and $\{\mathbf{P}_s^E\}$ are the vectors of equivalent nodal forces corresponding, respectively, to nodes at which generalized forces and displacements are prescribed.

Example 12-6. Analyze the beam of Example 12-4 subjected to the downward uniformly distributed load q_0 shown in Fig. 12-16(a). Note that a distributed load q is defined as positive in the positive y direction; hence $q = -q_0$ for a uniformly distributed load acting downward.

We begin by computing the fixed-end forces and moments associated with in-span loading. In the present case, only member 1 is so loaded. Thus for member 1, the fixed-end forces and moments are

$$P_{y1}^F = P_{y2}^F = \frac{q_0 L}{2} \qquad \text{and} \qquad P_{mz1}^F = -P_{mz2}^F = \frac{q_0 L^2}{12}$$

These quantities are shown in Fig. 12-16(b) in directions corresponding to those of positive generalized forces. The corresponding shear force and bending moment diagrams are shown in Fig. 12-16(d).

Now the entire structure is analyzed under the action of the equivalent nodal forces along with any other applied nodal forces (which happen to be zero in this case). Recall that

$$\{\mathbf{P}_f\} = \begin{Bmatrix} P_{y1} \\ P_{mz1} \\ P_{mz2} \end{Bmatrix} \qquad \{\mathbf{P}_s\} = \begin{Bmatrix} P_{y2} \\ P_{y3} \\ P_{mz3} \end{Bmatrix}$$

and

$$\{\mathbf{\Delta}_f\} = \begin{Bmatrix} v_1 \\ \theta_1 \\ \theta_2 \end{Bmatrix} \qquad \{\mathbf{\Delta}_s\} = \begin{Bmatrix} v_2 \\ v_3 \\ \theta_3 \end{Bmatrix}$$

Also recognizing that $\{\mathbf{\Delta}_s\} = \{0\}$, we may modify Eqs (a) and (b) of Example 12-4 to acquire the form

$$\begin{Bmatrix} v_1 \\ \theta_1 \\ \theta_2 \end{Bmatrix} = \frac{L}{2EI_z} \begin{bmatrix} \frac{5}{3}L^2 & -2L & -L \\ -2L & 3 & 1 \\ -L & 1 & 1 \end{bmatrix} \left(\begin{Bmatrix} P_{y1} \\ P_{mz1} \\ P_{mz2} \end{Bmatrix} + \begin{Bmatrix} P^E_{y1} \\ P^E_{mz1} \\ P^E_{mz2} \end{Bmatrix} \right)$$

and

$$\left(\begin{Bmatrix} P_{y2} \\ P_{y3} \\ P_{mz3} \end{Bmatrix} + \begin{Bmatrix} P^E_{y2} \\ P^E_{y3} \\ P^E_{mz3} \end{Bmatrix} \right) = \frac{1}{4L} \begin{bmatrix} -7L & 3 & 3 \\ 3L & -3 & -3 \\ -2L^2 & 2L & 2L \end{bmatrix} \left(\begin{Bmatrix} P_{y1} \\ P_{mz1} \\ P_{mz2} \end{Bmatrix} + \begin{Bmatrix} P^E_{y1} \\ P^E_{mz1} \\ P^E_{mz2} \end{Bmatrix} \right)$$

As illustrated in Fig. 12-16(c).

$$\begin{Bmatrix} P^E_{y1} \\ P^E_{mz1} \\ P^E_{mz2} \end{Bmatrix} = \frac{q_0 L}{2} \begin{Bmatrix} -1 \\ -L/6 \\ L/6 \end{Bmatrix} \qquad \begin{Bmatrix} P^E_{y2} \\ P^E_{y3} \\ P^E_{mz3} \end{Bmatrix} = \frac{q_0 L}{2} \begin{Bmatrix} -1 \\ 0 \\ 0 \end{Bmatrix}$$

while, because no other generalized forces are applied,

$$\begin{Bmatrix} P_{y1} \\ P_{mz1} \\ P_{mz2} \end{Bmatrix} = \begin{Bmatrix} 0 \\ 0 \\ 0 \end{Bmatrix}$$

Thus

$$\begin{Bmatrix} v_1 \\ \theta_1 \\ \theta_2 \end{Bmatrix} = \frac{q_0 L^3}{EI_z} \begin{Bmatrix} -3L/8 \\ 5/12 \\ 1/4 \end{Bmatrix}$$

and

$$\begin{Bmatrix} P_{y2} \\ P_{y3} \\ P_{mz3} \end{Bmatrix} = \frac{q_0 L}{2} \begin{Bmatrix} 7/4 \\ -3/4 \\ L/2 \end{Bmatrix} - \frac{q_0 L}{2} \begin{Bmatrix} -1 \\ 0 \\ 0 \end{Bmatrix} = \frac{q_0 L}{2} \begin{Bmatrix} 11/4 \\ -3/4 \\ L/2 \end{Bmatrix}$$

The shear forces and bending moments associated with the application of equivalent nodal forces may be computed in the usual way; these are shown in Fig. 12-16(e). The deformations and the final shear force and bending moment diagrams, obtained by combining those shown in Fig. 12-16, are presented in Fig. 12-17.

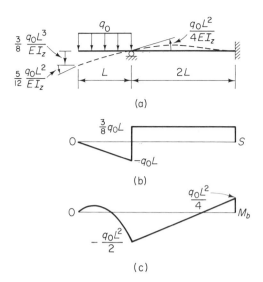

(a)

(b)

(c)

Figure 12-17

12-7 ANALYSIS OF FRAMES

The analysis of frames follows the same procedure as described above for beams. Because the members are not colinear, however, it is necessary to formulate the element stiffness matrices with respect to global coordinates before assembling the overall stiffness matrix. The procedure is illustrated through the following examples.

Example 12-7. Analyze the planar frame shown in Fig. 12-18(a) in which a concentrated vertical load P is applied to node 2 and the horizontal member is subjected to a uniformly varying distributed load.

We wish to use the transformed element stiffness matrix defined by Eq. (12-51). For member 1, $\theta = 60°$; therefore $\lambda = \frac{1}{2}$ and $\mu = \sqrt{3}/2$. Hence, $[\mathbf{k}^{(1)}]$ is shown in Eq. (a). For member 2, $\theta = 0$; thus $\lambda = 1$ and $\mu = 0$, and $[\mathbf{k}^{(2)}]$ is obtained in Eq. (b). Provided the displacements at the supports (nodes 1 and 3) remain equal to zero, we may solve for the displacements by formulating $[\mathbf{K}_{ff}]$ directly (by combining the last three rows and columns of $[\mathbf{k}^{(1)}]$ with the first three of $[\mathbf{k}^{(2)}]$) rather than the entire stiffness matrix $[\mathbf{K}]$. Then $[\mathbf{K}_{ff}]$ results in Eq. (c).

The actual load acting on member 2 must be replaced with the equivalent nodal forces, which are the negative of the fixed-end shears and moments obtained from Table 7-2 in Chapter 7 and shown in Fig. 12-18(b). Thus, the equivalent nodal forces shown in Fig. 12-18(c) are used to determine the displacements at node 2. The resulting deformations and internal forces must be combined with those incurred by the combination of the applied distributed loading and the fixed-end quantities shown in Fig. 12-18(b). The relevant vector of equivalent nodal forces is

$$\begin{Bmatrix} P_{x2}^E \\ P_{y2}^E \\ P_{mz2}^E \end{Bmatrix} = -\frac{q_0 L_2}{10} \begin{Bmatrix} 0 \\ 3/2 \\ L_2/3 \end{Bmatrix}$$

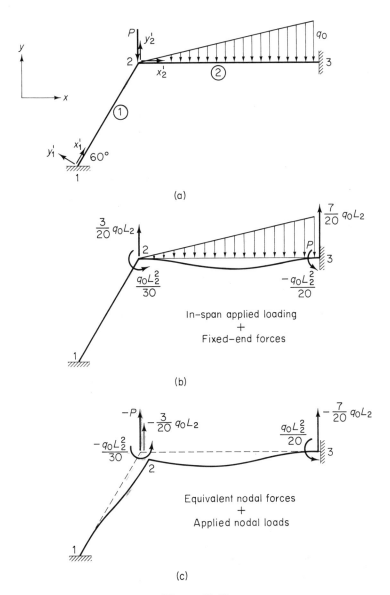

(a)

$\frac{3}{20} q_0 L_2$

$\frac{7}{20} q_0 L_2$

$\frac{q_0 L_2^2}{30}$

$-\frac{q_0 L_2^2}{20}$

In-span applied loading
+
Fixed-end forces

(b)

$-P$

$-\frac{3}{20} q_0 L_2$

$-\frac{7}{20} q_0 L_2$

$-\frac{q_0 L_2^2}{30}$

$\frac{q_0 L_2^2}{20}$

Equivalent nodal forces
+
Applied nodal loads

(c)

Figure 12-18

Sec. 12-7   Analysis of Frames

531

$$[\mathbf{k}^{(1)}] = \left(\frac{EI_z}{L^3}\right)_1
\begin{array}{c}
\begin{array}{cccccc} u_1 & v_1 & \theta_1 & u_2 & v_2 & \theta_2 \end{array} \\
\left[\begin{array}{cccccc}
\frac{1}{4}\left(\frac{AL^2}{I_z}\right)_1+9 & \frac{3}{4}\left(\frac{AL^2}{I_z}\right)_1+3 & & & & \\
\frac{\sqrt{3}}{4}\left(\frac{AL^2}{I_z}\right)_1-3\sqrt{3} & 3L_1 & 4L_1^2 & & \text{symmetric} & \\
-3\sqrt{3}L_1 & -\frac{\sqrt{3}}{4}\left(\frac{AL^2}{I_z}\right)_1+3\sqrt{3} & 3\sqrt{3}L_1 & \frac{1}{4}\left(\frac{AL^2}{I_z}\right)_1+9 & & \\
-\frac{1}{4}\left(\frac{AL^2}{I_z}\right)_1-9 & -\frac{3}{4}\left(\frac{AL^2}{I_z}\right)_1-3 & -3L_1 & \frac{\sqrt{3}}{4}\left(\frac{AL^2}{I_z}\right)_1-3\sqrt{3} & \frac{3}{4}\left(\frac{AL^2}{I_z}\right)_1+3 & \\
-\frac{\sqrt{3}}{4}\left(\frac{AL^2}{I_z}\right)_1+3\sqrt{3} & 3L_1 & 2L_1^2 & 3\sqrt{3}L_1 & -3L_1 & 4L_1^2 \\
-3\sqrt{3}L_1 & & & & &
\end{array}\right]
\end{array}$$

(a)

$$[\mathbf{k}^{(2)}] = \left(\frac{EI_z}{L^3}\right)_2
\begin{array}{c}
\begin{array}{cccccc} u_2 & v_2 & \theta_2 & u_3 & v_3 & \theta_3 \end{array} \\
\left[\begin{array}{cccccc}
\left(\frac{AL^2}{I_z}\right)_2 & 0 & 0 & & & \\
0 & 12 & 6L_2 & & \text{symmetric} & \\
0 & 6L_2 & 4L_2^2 & & & \\
-\left(\frac{AL^2}{I_z}\right)_2 & 0 & 0 & \left(\frac{AL^2}{I_z}\right)_2 & & \\
0 & -12 & -6L_2 & 0 & 12 & \\
0 & 6L_2 & 2L_2^2 & 0 & -6L_2 & 4L_2^2
\end{array}\right]
\end{array}$$

(b)

$$[\mathbf{K}_{ff}] = \left(\frac{EI_z}{L^3}\right)_1
\begin{array}{c}
\begin{array}{ccc} u_2 & v_2 & \theta_2 \end{array} \\
\left[\begin{array}{ccc}
\frac{1}{4}\left(\frac{AL^2}{I_z}\right)_1+9 & \frac{\sqrt{3}}{4}\left(\frac{AL^2}{I_z}\right)_1-3\sqrt{3} & 3\sqrt{3}L_1 \\
\frac{\sqrt{3}}{4}\left(\frac{AL^2}{I_z}\right)_1-3\sqrt{3} & \frac{3}{4}\left(\frac{AL^2}{I_z}\right)_1+3 & -3L_1 \\
3\sqrt{3}L_1 & -3L_1 & 4L_1^2
\end{array}\right]
\end{array}
+ \left(\frac{EI_z}{L^3}\right)_2
\begin{array}{c}
\begin{array}{ccc} u_2 & v_2 & \theta_2 \end{array} \\
\left[\begin{array}{ccc}
\left(\frac{AL^2}{I_z}\right)_2 & 0 & 0 \\
0 & 12 & 6L_2 \\
0 & 6L_2 & 4L_2^2
\end{array}\right]
\end{array}$$

(c)

We must now solve for $\{\Delta_f\} \equiv \{u_2, v_2, \theta_2\}$ from

$$\begin{Bmatrix} u_2 \\ v_2 \\ \theta_2 \end{Bmatrix} = [\mathbf{K}_{ff}]^{-1}\left(\begin{Bmatrix} 0 \\ -P \\ 0 \end{Bmatrix} - \frac{q_0 L_2}{10}\begin{Bmatrix} 0 \\ 3/2 \\ L_2/3 \end{Bmatrix}\right)$$

To carry out the solution, let us suppose $P = 3000$ lbs and $q_0 = 200$ lbs/in. Also, consider the following properties for members 1 and 2:

Member 1 (W 10 × 39)	Member 2 (W 14 × 48)
$E = 30 \times 10^6$ psi	$E = 30 \times 10^6$ psi
$A = 11.48$ in.^{2}	$A = 14.11$ in.^{2}
$I_z = 209.7$ in.^{4}	$I_z = 484.9$ in.^{4}
$L = 120$ in.	$L = 180$ in.

The matrix $[\mathbf{K}_{ff}]$ then becomes

$$[\mathbf{K}_{ff}] = 3640\frac{\text{lb}}{\text{in.}}\begin{array}{c}\begin{array}{ccc} u_2 & v_2 & \theta_2 \end{array}\\ \begin{bmatrix} (197 + 9) & (341 - 5.20) & 624 \text{ in.} \\ (341 - 5.20) & (591 + 3) & -360 \text{ in.} \\ 624 \text{ in.} & -360 \text{ in.} & 57{,}600 \text{ in.}^2 \end{bmatrix}\end{array}$$

$$+\ 2490\frac{\text{lb}}{\text{in.}}\begin{array}{c}\begin{array}{ccc} u_2 & v_2 & \theta_2 \end{array}\\ \begin{bmatrix} 943 & 0 & 0 \\ 0 & 12 & 1080 \text{ in.} \\ 0 & 1080 \text{ in.} & 130{,}000 \text{ in.}^2 \end{bmatrix}\end{array}$$

or

$$[\mathbf{K}_{ff}] = 10^6\frac{\text{lb}}{\text{in.}}\begin{array}{c}\begin{array}{ccc} u_2 & v_2 & \theta_2 \end{array}\\ \begin{bmatrix} 3.10 & 1.22 & 2.27 \text{ in.} \\ 1.22 & 2.18 & 1.38 \text{ in.} \\ 2.27 \text{ in.} & 1.38 \text{ in.} & 533 \text{ in.}^2 \end{bmatrix}\end{array}$$

and hence,

$$[\mathbf{K}_{ff}]^{-1} = \frac{10^{-9}}{\text{lb}}\begin{bmatrix} 414 \text{ in.} & -230 \text{ in.} & -1.17 \\ -230 \text{ in.} & 585 \text{ in.} & -0.536 \\ -1.17 & -0.536 & 1.88 \text{ in.}^{-1} \end{bmatrix}$$

Then the displacements at node 2 are

$$\begin{Bmatrix} u_2 \\ v_2 \\ \theta_2 \end{Bmatrix} = [\mathbf{K}_{ff}]^{-1}\begin{Bmatrix} 0 \\ -8.4 \text{ lb} \\ -216 \text{ lb-in.} \end{Bmatrix} \times 10^3 = \begin{Bmatrix} 2.18 \text{ in.} \\ -4.80 \text{ in.} \\ -0.402 \end{Bmatrix} \times 10^{-3}$$

Premultiplying this displacement vector by the last three columns of $[\mathbf{k}^{(1)}]$ and first three columns of $[\mathbf{k}^{(2)}]$, we obtain the internal nodal forces acting on members 1 and 2. These are

$$\begin{Bmatrix} F_{x1} \\ F_{y1} \\ M_{z1} \\ F_{x2} \\ F_{y2} \\ M_{z2} \end{Bmatrix}^{(1)} = \begin{Bmatrix} 5.15 \text{ lb} \\ 7.19 \text{ lb} \\ -30.9 \text{ lb-in.} \\ -5.15 \text{ lb} \\ -7.19 \text{ lb} \\ -73.0 \text{ lb-in.} \end{Bmatrix} \times 10^3 \quad \text{and} \quad \begin{Bmatrix} F_{x2} \\ F_{y2} \\ M_{z2} \\ F_{x3} \\ F_{y3} \\ M_{z3} \end{Bmatrix}^{(2)} = \begin{Bmatrix} 5.15 \text{ lb} \\ -1.22 \text{ lb} \\ -143 \text{ lb-in.} \\ -5.15 \text{ lb} \\ 1.22 \text{ lb} \\ -78.0 \text{ lb-in.} \end{Bmatrix} \times 10^3$$

Note that at node 2 equilibrium of internal forces and external loads has been satisfied, i.e.,

$$F_{x2}^{(1)} + F_{x2}^{(2)} = 0$$

$$F_{y2}^{(1)} + F_{y2}^{(2)} = -8.4 \times 10^3 \text{ lb.}$$

$$M_{z2}^{(1)} + M_{z2}^{(2)} = -216 \times 10^3 \text{ lb-in.}$$

The shear force and bending moment diagrams corresponding to the foregoing analysis are combined with those for the combination of distributed loading and fixed-end forces to obtain the final set of internal forces. These are shown in Fig. 12-19.

Example 12-8. Analyze the symmetric frame shown in Fig. 12-20(a).

Relative to the global coordinate system, the member stiffness matrices are

$$[\mathbf{k}^{(1)}](= [\mathbf{k}^{(3)}]) = \left(\frac{EI_z}{L^3}\right)_1 \begin{bmatrix} 12 & & & & & \\ 0 & \left(\frac{AL^2}{I_z}\right)_1 & & & \text{symmetric} & \\ -6L_1 & 0 & 4L_1^2 & & & \\ -12 & 0 & 6L_1 & 12 & & \\ 0 & -\left(\frac{AL^2}{I_z}\right)_1 & 0 & 0 & \left(\frac{AL^2}{I_z}\right)_1 & \\ -6L_1 & 0 & 2L_1^2 & 6L_1 & 0 & 4L_1^2 \end{bmatrix} \begin{matrix} u_1(u_4) \\ v_1(v_4) \\ \theta_1(\theta_4) \\ u_2(u_3) \\ v_2(v_3) \\ \theta_2(\theta_3) \end{matrix}$$

$$[\mathbf{k}^{(2)}] = \left(\frac{EI_z}{L^3}\right)_2 \begin{bmatrix} \left(\frac{AL^2}{I_z}\right)_2 & & & & & \\ 0 & 12 & & & \text{symmetric} & \\ 0 & 6L_2 & 4L_2^2 & & & \\ -\left(\frac{AL^2}{I_z}\right)_2 & 0 & 0 & \left(\frac{AL^2}{I_z}\right)_2 & & \\ 0 & -12 & -6L_2 & 0 & 12 & \\ 0 & 6L_2 & 2L_2^2 & 0 & -6L_2 & 4L_2^2 \end{bmatrix} \begin{matrix} u_2 \\ v_2 \\ \theta_2 \\ u_3 \\ v_3 \\ \theta_3 \end{matrix}$$

(a)

Shear force and bending moment due to
distributed loading and fixed–end forces

(b)

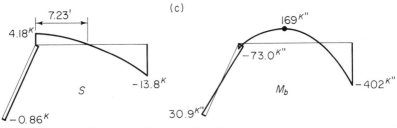

Shear force and bending moment due to
applied nodal loading and equivalent nodal forces

(c)

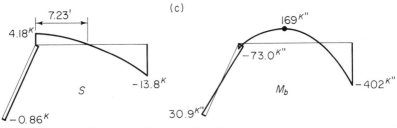

Final shear force and bending moment

(d)

Figure 12-19

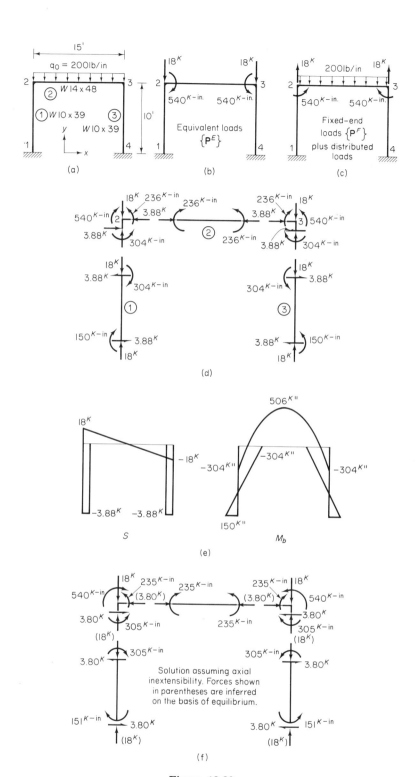

Figure 12-20

The Direct Stiffness Method   Chap. 12

Recognizing that the displacements at nodes 1 and 4 are zero, we may solve the problem by formulating only $[\mathbf{K}_{ff}]$ which, for the specified members, becomes

$$[\mathbf{K}_{ff}] = 10^6 \frac{\text{lb}}{\text{in.}} \begin{array}{c} \\ \end{array} \begin{array}{cccccc} u_2 & v_2 & \theta_2 & u_3 & v_3 & \theta_3 \end{array}$$

$$\begin{bmatrix} 2.39 & & & & & \\ 0 & 2.90 & & \text{symmetric} & & \\ 2.62 \text{ in.} & 2.69 \text{ in.} & 534 \text{ in.}^2 & & & \\ -2.35 & 0 & 0 & 2.39 & & \\ 0 & -0.0299 & -2.69 \text{ in.} & 0 & 2.90 & \\ 0 & 2.69 \text{ in.} & 162 \text{ in.}^2 & 2.62 \text{ in.} & -2.69 \text{ in.} & 534 \text{ in.}^2 \end{bmatrix}$$

Without incurring any further approximation, we may exploit conditions of symmetry to reduce the size of the matrix to be inverted. These conditions are

$$u_2 = -u_3 \qquad v_2 = v_3 \qquad \text{and} \qquad \theta_2 = -\theta_3$$

We shall deal with the general question of symmetry and antisymmetry in greater detail in Section 12-9. For the moment we may use the foregoing conditions to reduce $[\mathbf{K}_{ff}]$ to a 3×3 matrix simply by subtracting column 4 from column 1, adding columns 2 and 5, and subtracting column 6 from column 3. We then retain only the first three rows, and the stiffness matrix is then

$$[\mathbf{K}_{ff}] = \frac{10^6 \text{ lb}}{\text{in.}} \begin{bmatrix} 4.74 & 0 & 2.62 \text{ in.} \\ 0 & 2.87 & 0 \\ 2.62 \text{ in.} & 0 & 372 \text{ in.}^2 \end{bmatrix} \begin{array}{c} u_2 \\ v_2 \\ \theta_2 \end{array}$$

Then

$$[\mathbf{K}_{ff}]^{-1} = 10^{-9}/\text{lb} \begin{bmatrix} 212 \text{ in.} & 0 & -1.49 \\ 0 & 348 \text{ in.} & 0 \\ -1.49 & 0 & 2.70 \text{ in.}^{-1} \end{bmatrix}$$

For the given loading condition the vector of equivalent nodal loads is

$$\begin{Bmatrix} P_{x2}^E \\ P_{y2}^E \\ P_{mz2}^E \end{Bmatrix} = - \begin{Bmatrix} 0 \\ 18 \text{ lb} \\ 540 \text{ lb-in.} \end{Bmatrix} \times 10^3$$

These loads are shown, along with corresponding values at node 3 in Fig. 12-20(b). The corresponding displacements at node 2 are computed as

$$\begin{Bmatrix} u_2 \\ v_2 \\ \theta_2 \end{Bmatrix} = [\mathbf{K}_{ff}]^{-1} \begin{Bmatrix} P_{x2}^E \\ P_{y2}^E \\ P_{mz2}^E \end{Bmatrix} = \begin{Bmatrix} 0.805 \text{ in.} \\ -6.26 \text{ in.} \\ -1.46 \end{Bmatrix} \times 10^{-3}$$

Note that no nodal displacements accrue from the combination of distributed loads and fixed-end forces shown in Fig. 12-20(c).

The member end forces due to equivalent nodal loads may be computed by premultiplying the displacement vector by the appropriate portion of the element stiffness matrices. We then find these forces, expressed here relative to the global coordinate system, for members 1 and 2 to be

$$\begin{Bmatrix} F_{x1} \\ F_{y1} \\ M_{z1} \\ F_{x2} \\ F_{y2} \\ M_{z2} \end{Bmatrix}^{(1)} = \begin{Bmatrix} 3.88 \text{ lb} \\ 18 \text{ lb} \\ -150 \text{ lb-in.} \\ -3.88 \text{ lb} \\ -18 \text{ lb} \\ -304 \text{ lb-in.} \end{Bmatrix} \times 10^3 \quad \text{and} \quad \begin{Bmatrix} F_{x2} \\ F_{y2} \\ M_{z2} \\ F_{x3} \\ F_{y3} \\ M_{z3} \end{Bmatrix}^{(2)} = \begin{Bmatrix} 3.88 \text{ lb} \\ 0 \\ -236 \text{ lb-in.} \\ -3.88 \text{ lb} \\ 0 \\ 236 \text{ lb-in.} \end{Bmatrix} \times 10^3$$

These internal forces are shown in Fig. 12-20(d). For member 2 these internal forces must be combined with the distributed loading and the fixed end forces and moments. The resulting shear and bending moment diagrams are shown in Fig. 12-20(e).

Note that in Fig. 12-20(d) the sums of the internal forces and moments at node 2, for example, are in equilibrium with the externally applied equivalent nodal forces and moments. In addition, the vertical force in the column is *exactly* equal to 18,000 lbs and in the beam it is *exactly* equal to zero, regardless of the axial stiffness of the members. This is evident from the forces being independent of the vertical displacement at node 2. However, a similar statement cannot be made for general support conditions. Suppose, for example, that node 3 were externally supported against vertical displacement. Then the beam would not undergo rigid-body translation and rotation, and the internal forces and moments would depend on the axial deformation of member 1, although not to an appreciable degree in most practical instances.

The analysis of frames comprising only horizontal and vertical members, i.e., members intersecting at right angles, may be simplified by assuming that the members are axially inextensible. Consider, for example, one member being subjected to only an axial load while an identical member is subjected to an equal transverse load. Generally, regardless of the specific support conditions, the axial deformation of the former will be at least an order of magnitude less than the bending displacement of the latter. That is, the axial stiffness of a member typically is much greater than its bending stiffness. We may exploit this fact by analyzing certain structures while assuming that the axial deformations may be neglected. Thus, in the present example the assumption of axial inextensibility of the beam and columns leads to our setting $u_2 = v_2 = 0$. The rows and columns in $[\mathbf{K}_{ff}]$ may then be deleted, and this matrix would then reduce to

$$[\mathbf{K}_{ff}] = 372 \times 10^6 \text{ lb-in.}$$

This would lead to

$$\theta_2 = \frac{-540}{372} \times .10^{-3} = -1.45 \times 10^{-3}$$

which is virtually identical with the value of θ_2 computed above. We may then compute the internal forces associated with equivalent nodal loads by again premultiplying the displacement vector

$$\begin{Bmatrix} u_2 \\ v_2 \\ \theta_2 \end{Bmatrix} = \begin{Bmatrix} 0 \\ 0 \\ -1.45 \end{Bmatrix} \times 10^{-3}$$

by the appropriate portions of the element stiffness matrices. We then obtain

$$
\begin{Bmatrix} F_{x1} \\ F_{y1} \\ M_{z1} \\ F_{x2} \\ F_{y2} \\ M_{z2} \end{Bmatrix}^{(1)} = \begin{Bmatrix} 3.80 \text{ lb} \\ 0 \\ -151 \text{ lb-in.} \\ -3.80 \text{ lb} \\ 0 \\ -305 \text{ lb-in.} \end{Bmatrix} \times 10^3 \quad \text{and} \quad \begin{Bmatrix} F_{x2} \\ F_{y2} \\ M_{z2} \\ F_{x3} \\ F_{y3} \\ M_{z3} \end{Bmatrix}^{(2)} = \begin{Bmatrix} 0 \\ 0 \\ -235 \text{ lb-in.} \\ 0 \\ 0 \\ 235 \text{ lb-in.} \end{Bmatrix} \times 10^3
$$

Although the axial forces are computed to be zero because we have assumed axial inextensibility of the members, we may infer the actual magnitude of these forces by considering equilibrium of forces at the joints as shown in Fig. 12-20(f). Equilibrium at node 2, for example, requires that the axial force in member 1 be $-18,000$ lbs and that in member 2 it be -3.80 lbs. Thus, using the assumption of axial inextensibility, we can still recover virtually the exact solution with minimal computational effort. However, this assumption must be used judiciously.

Two additional points should be mentioned. First, if the frame shown in Fig. 12-20(a) were subjected to asymmetric loading, then we could not have stated that $u_2 = u_3$ due to symmetry, and thus we could not have assumed later that u_2 was equal to zero. We could still employ the assumption of axial inextensibility, however, by designating the horizontal displacement at *both* nodes 2 and 3 as u_2; thus u_3 is removed as an independent degree of freedom. At the same time, we would designate as the generalized force corresponding to u_2 the algebraic sum of the horizontal forces acting at both nodes 2 and 3. In general, therefore, by assuming axial inextensibility, we assign only a single axial displacement to each member.

The other point to be mentioned is that such simplifications are much more difficult to employ in frames such as that shown in Fig. 12-18(a), where some members are inclined. Because not all members intersect at right angles, compatibility at a joint can be maintained only by accounting carefully for the geometry of deformations. While simplified procedures can be developed, the procedures are not straightforward and the analytical results must be carefully interpreted.

Example 12-9. Analyze the three-dimensional frame shown in Fig. 12-21(a), using the assumption of axial inextensibility.

Because nodes 2, 3 and 4 are fully restrained and the members cannot extend or compress, we identify only the rotations θ_x, θ_y, and θ_z at node 1 as generalized displacements. Under more general conditions we would be required to use the 12×12 element stiffness matrix $[\mathbf{k}']$ given by Eq. (12-44a) relative to local coordinates which would be transformed according to Eq. (12-46)

$$[\mathbf{k}] = [\mathbf{T}]^T[\mathbf{k}'][\mathbf{T}] \tag{12-46}$$

where $[\mathbf{T}]$ is defined by Eqs. (12-47) and (12-48).

We must perform this transformation, although for simplicity we are permitted to use only those rows and columns in $[\mathbf{k}']$ and $[\mathbf{T}]$ pertaining to the three active degrees of freedom. Thus we use for each member

Applied loads and fixed-end forces

Equivalent nodal forces

(c)

Figure 12-21

$$[\mathbf{k'}] = \begin{array}{ccc} \theta_{x'1} & \theta_{y'1} & \theta_{z'1} \end{array}$$

$$[\mathbf{k'}] = \begin{bmatrix} \dfrac{GJ}{L} & 0 & 0 \\ 0 & \dfrac{4EI_{y'}}{L} & 0 \\ 0 & 0 & \dfrac{4EI_{z'}}{L} \end{bmatrix}$$

which comprises the fourth, fifth and sixth rows and columns of the general form of $[\mathbf{k'}]$. Also, the requisite transformation matrix becomes

$$[\mathbf{T}] = \begin{bmatrix} \lambda_{x'} & \mu_{x'} & \nu_{x'} \\ \lambda_{y'} & \mu_{y'} & \nu_{y'} \\ \lambda_{z'} & \mu_{z'} & \nu_{z'} \end{bmatrix}$$

The local coordinate systems shown in Fig. 12-21(b) give rise to the following expressions:

$$[\mathbf{T}^{(1)}] = \begin{bmatrix} 0 & -1 & 0 \\ 1 & 0 & 0 \\ 0 & 0 & 1 \end{bmatrix} \qquad [\mathbf{T}^{(2)}] = \begin{bmatrix} 1 & 0 & 0 \\ 0 & 1 & 0 \\ 0 & 0 & 1 \end{bmatrix} \qquad [\mathbf{T}^{(3)}] = \begin{bmatrix} 0 & 0 & 1 \\ 0 & 1 & 0 \\ -1 & 0 & 0 \end{bmatrix}$$

Performing the transformation dictated by Eq. (12-46), we find the transformed element stiffness matrices as shown in Eq. (a) on page 542. These may be combined to provide the reduced system stiffness matrix $[\mathbf{K}_{ff}]$ as shown in Eq. (b) whose inverse is a diagonal matrix comprising the reciprocal of the diagonal terms of $[\mathbf{K}_{ff}]$ itself.

To complete the example, consider the particular loading indicated in Fig. 12-21(c). The relevant vector of equivalent nodal forces is

$$\begin{Bmatrix} P^E_{mx1} \\ P^E_{my1} \\ P^E_{mz1} \end{Bmatrix} = \begin{Bmatrix} \dfrac{q_0 L_3^2}{12} \\ 0 \\ -\dfrac{PL_2}{8} \end{Bmatrix}$$

and the rotations at node 1 are then

$$\begin{Bmatrix} \theta_{x1} \\ \theta_{y1} \\ \theta_{z1} \end{Bmatrix} = [K_{ff}]^{-1} \begin{Bmatrix} P^E_{mx1} \\ P^E_{my1} \\ P^E_{mz1} \end{Bmatrix} = \begin{Bmatrix} \dfrac{q_0 L_3^2}{12}\left[\left(\dfrac{4EI_{y'}}{L}\right)_1 + \left(\dfrac{GJ}{L}\right)_2 + \left(\dfrac{4EI_{z'}}{L}\right)_3 \right]^{-1} \\ 0 \\ -\dfrac{PL_2}{8}\left[\left(\dfrac{4EI_{z'}}{L}\right)_1 + \left(\dfrac{4EI_{z'}}{L}\right)_2 + \left(\dfrac{GJ}{L}\right)_3 \right]^{-1} \end{Bmatrix}$$

These rotations, along with the zero-valued translations, may be included in the nodal displacement vector for each element. This vector may be premultiplied by the element stiffness matrix to determine the member's nodal forces. We may choose to express both the stiffness matrix and force vector for each member with respect to either global or local coordinate systems, but we cannot mix coordinates. That is, we may use either the combination of Eqs. (12-14) and (12-20), or Eq. (12-9) alone. In this instance, the latter approach appears simpler. Note that for member 1,

$$\theta_{x'} = -\theta_y \qquad \theta_{y'} = \theta_x \qquad \theta_{z'} = \theta_z$$

$$[\mathbf{k}^{(1)}] = \begin{bmatrix} \theta_x & \theta_y & \theta_z \\ \left(\dfrac{4EI_{y'}}{L}\right)_1 & 0 & 0 \\ 0 & \left(\dfrac{GJ}{L}\right)_1 & 0 \\ 0 & 0 & \left(\dfrac{4EI_{z'}}{L}\right)_1 \end{bmatrix}$$

$$[\mathbf{k}^{(2)}] = \begin{bmatrix} \theta_x & \theta_y & \theta_z \\ \left(\dfrac{GJ}{L}\right)_2 & 0 & 0 \\ 0 & \left(\dfrac{4EI_{y'}}{L}\right)_2 & 0 \\ 0 & 0 & \left(\dfrac{4EI_{z'}}{L}\right)_2 \end{bmatrix}$$

$$[\mathbf{k}^{(3)}] = \begin{bmatrix} \theta_x & \theta_y & \theta_z \\ \left(\dfrac{4EI_{z'}}{L}\right)_3 & 0 & 0 \\ 0 & \left(\dfrac{4EI_{y'}}{L}\right)_3 & 0 \\ 0 & 0 & \left(\dfrac{GJ}{L}\right)_3 \end{bmatrix}$$

(a)

$$[\mathbf{K}_{ff}] = \begin{bmatrix} \theta_x & \theta_y & \theta_z \\ \left[\left(\dfrac{4EI_{y'}}{L}\right)_1 + \left(\dfrac{GJ}{L}\right)_2 + \left(\dfrac{4EI_{z'}}{L}\right)_3\right] & 0 & 0 \\ 0 & \left[\left(\dfrac{GJ}{L}\right)_1 + \left(\dfrac{4EI_{y'}}{L}\right)_2 + \left(\dfrac{4EI_{y'}}{L}\right)_3\right] & 0 \\ 0 & 0 & \left[\left(\dfrac{4EI_{z'}}{L}\right)_1 + \left(\dfrac{4EI_{z'}}{L}\right)_2 + \left(\dfrac{GJ}{L}\right)_3\right] \end{bmatrix}$$

(b)

for member 2,

$$\theta_{x'} = \theta_x \qquad \theta_{y'} = \theta_y \qquad \theta_{z'} = \theta_z$$

and for member 3,

$$\theta_{x'} = \theta_z \qquad \theta_{y'} = \theta_y \qquad \theta_{z'} = -\theta_x$$

We may then use $[\mathbf{k'}]$, expressed by Eq. (12-44), to find the bending moments, transverse shear forces and torques for each member relative to local coordinates by multiplying this matrix by the appropriate displacement vector. These must be combined with the internal forces associated with in-span loads and fixed-end quantities. Finally, note again that we shall not be able to compute axial forces in this manner. Rather, in the present case, once the shear forces have been computed, we may determine axial forces through equilibrium of forces at the joints. This approach, however, fails when two or more colinear members frame into a joint.

12-8 SELF-STRAINED STRUCTURES

We now consider problems in which a portion of the structure either is improperly fabricated, so as not to fit perfectly with the rest of the structure, or it is subjected to a temperature change which induces axial strain or curvature in some members. The behavior of statically determinate structures may be distinguished from that of statically indeterminate structures. Consider the trusses illustrated in Fig. 12-22 in which, prior to assembling the structure, the diagonal member is incorrectly fabricated to be too long. For the statically determinate truss shown in Fig. 12-22(a), the misfit leads to a departure from the design configuration but the members remain unstressed in the absence of applied loads. For the statically indeterminate truss shown in Fig. 12-22(b), however, the misfit induces a self-equilibrating set of forces in addition to deformation. Further, if any of the members in either of the assembled structures were subjected to a change in temperature, the structure would exhibit behavior similar to that induced by a fabrication error.

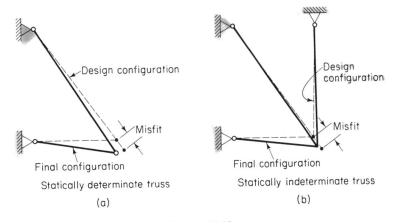

Figure 12-22

If a beam is heated differentially over its depth, a curvature will be induced (in addition possibly to an axial strain). If the beam is statically determinate, such as the simply supported beam shown in Fig. 12-23(a), and subjected to temperatures T_u and T_l along the upper and lower surface, a curvature will be induced in the absence of a bending moment. A statically indeterminate beam, however, such as that shown in Fig. 12-23(b), that is subjected to a similar temperature gradient, will incur bending moment in addition to curvature.

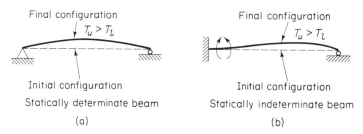

Figure 12-23

We wish to devise an approach for analyzing the foregoing problems under general circumstances. Let us use as an example, however, the statically indeterminate truss shown again in Fig. 12-24(a). Suppose the diagonal member is fabricated to be too long by an amount ΔL_2. Suppose further that prior to placing it in the structure, this member is subjected to a compressive force $P^F = (EA/L_2)\Delta L_2$ in order to negate the misfit. Thus, in this state, which we shall call state 1, all members are unstressed except the diagonal member which is subjected to external loading, and all (compatible) displacements are zero. In contrast with the original structure, however, the truss shown in Fig. 12-24(b) is subjected to nonzero external loading.

Now suppose the fully assembled truss is subjected to forces $\{\mathbf{P}^E\}$ equal and opposite to $\{\mathbf{P}^F\}$ as shown in Fig. 12-24(c). Under the action of $\{\mathbf{P}^E\}$, which we shall call state 2, the structure undergoes compatible deformation while internal bar forces are in equilibrium with the applied forces. Because state 2

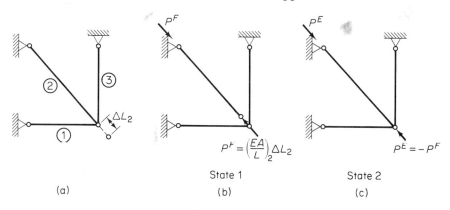

Figure 12-24

The Direct Stiffness Method   Chap. 12

includes externally applied loads, it alone does not represent the situation originally posed. However, the combination of states 1 and 2 does provide an unloaded but internally stressed structure whose deformations are compatible; this combination does, in fact, provide the solution to the original problem.

We already have used this idea in dealing with distributed loads acting on beams. There we first considered the existence of fixed-end forces $\{\mathbf{P}^F\}$ which are in equilibrium with the distributed loading; the resulting nodal displacements are zero. Then to negate the fixed-end forces, equivalent nodal forces $\{\mathbf{P}^E\}$, equal and opposite to $\{\mathbf{P}^F\}$, are applied to the structure. Nodal displacements are generally nonzero and internal forces are in equilibrium with $\{\mathbf{P}^E\}$. The final solution is the combination of these two solutions. Because of the strong similarity between the problem dealing with distributed loading and that of self-strained structures, we have used the same notation, $\{\mathbf{P}^F\}$ and $\{\mathbf{P}^E\}$, in both cases.

Thermal strains. Before looking at some examples, we note that if a bar which is subjected to a change in temperature ΔT (compared with that to which the rest of the structure is subjected) is removed from the structure, the change in length will be

$$\Delta L = (\alpha \Delta T)L \qquad (12\text{-}57)$$

in which α is the coefficient of thermal expansion. The associated fixed-end forces (relative to the local axis extending from node i to node j along the member) are

$$\begin{Bmatrix} P^F_{x'i} \\ P^F_{x'j} \end{Bmatrix} = (\alpha \Delta T)EA \begin{Bmatrix} 1 \\ -1 \end{Bmatrix} \qquad (12\text{-}58)$$

Now if a beam is subjected to temperature changes which vary from ΔT_u at the upper edge to ΔT_l at the lower edge, the member will exhibit a curvature $1/\rho$ equal to

$$\frac{1}{\rho} = \frac{\alpha(\Delta T_l - \Delta T_u)}{h} \qquad (12\text{-}59)$$

in which h is the depth of the member. To negate this curvature it is necessary to apply fixed-end moments

$$\begin{Bmatrix} P^F_{mz'i} \\ P^F_{mz'j} \end{Bmatrix} = \frac{EI_{z'}}{\rho} \begin{Bmatrix} 1 \\ -1 \end{Bmatrix} = \frac{EI_{z'}}{h}\alpha(\Delta T_l - \Delta T_u) \begin{Bmatrix} 1 \\ -1 \end{Bmatrix} \qquad (12\text{-}60)$$

Example 12-10. Consider the planar truss shown in Fig. 12-25(a), which was originally analyzed in Example 12-2. Suppose one diagonal element (member 3) is fabricated to be too short by an amount ΔL_3, but is forced to fit with the rest of the structure. Find the resulting deformation (departure from the intended geometry) and the induced bar forces.

First, the diagonal element alone is subjected to a force P^F which restores the member to the proper length as shown in Fig. 12-25(b). The axial force in member 3 thus equals $P_0 \equiv (EA/L)\Delta L_3$, but the other members are stress-free.

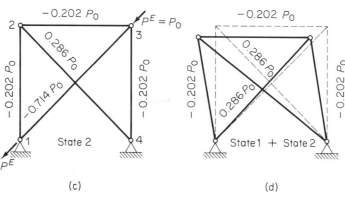

Figure 12-25

This corresponds to state 1 in which all nodal displacements are zero.

Second, P^E (the negative of P^F) is applied to the assembled undeformed truss. The generalized displacements are computed by solving

$$\begin{Bmatrix} u_2 \\ v_2 \\ u_3 \\ v_3 \end{Bmatrix} = [\mathbf{K}_{ff}]^{-1} \begin{Bmatrix} P^E_{x2} \\ P^E_{y2} \\ P^E_{x3} \\ P^E_{y3} \end{Bmatrix}$$

in which, based on Fig. 12-25(c), the vector of equivalent nodal forces expressed in reference to the global coordinate system is

$$\begin{Bmatrix} P^E_{x2} \\ P^E_{y2} \\ P^E_{x3} \\ P^E_{y3} \end{Bmatrix} = \frac{\sqrt{2}}{2} P_0 \begin{Bmatrix} 0 \\ 0 \\ -1 \\ -1 \end{Bmatrix}$$

and, from Example 12-2,

$$[\mathbf{K}_{ff}]^{-1} = \frac{L}{7EA} \begin{bmatrix} 12 & 4 & 9 & -3 \\ 4 & 6 & 3 & -1 \\ 9 & 3 & 12 & -4 \\ -3 & -1 & -4 & 6 \end{bmatrix}$$

The Direct Stiffness Method   Chap. 12

Then,

$$\begin{Bmatrix} u_2 \\ v_2 \\ u_3 \\ v_3 \end{Bmatrix} = -\frac{\sqrt{2}}{7}\frac{L}{EA}P_0 \begin{Bmatrix} 3 \\ 1 \\ 4 \\ 1 \end{Bmatrix} = -\frac{\sqrt{2}}{7}\Delta L_3 \begin{Bmatrix} 3 \\ 1 \\ 4 \\ 1 \end{Bmatrix}$$

Using these displacements in conjunction with the element stiffness matrices, we find the internal bar forces shown in Fig. 12-25(c). The actual state of internal force due to the misfit is the combination of states 1 and 2, as shown in Fig. 12-25(d). We see that in order for the undersized diagonal bar to be force-fit into the structure, both diagonals must stretch while the horizontal and vertical members undergo equal compression.

Example 12-11. Consider the beam originally encountered in Example 12-4. Now we wish to find the states of deformation and stress when the upper, lower and edges are subjected to temperatures ΔT_u and ΔT_l, respectively, as indicated in Fig. 12-26(a).

Recall from Example 12-4 that the unconstrained generalized displacements are related to generalized forces by

$$\begin{Bmatrix} v_1 \\ \theta_1 \\ \theta_2 \end{Bmatrix} = \frac{L}{2EI_z} \begin{bmatrix} \frac{5}{3}L^2 & -2L & -L \\ -2L & . & 3 & 1 \\ -L & 1 & 1 \end{bmatrix} \begin{Bmatrix} P_{y1} \\ P_{mz1} \\ P_{mz2} \end{Bmatrix}$$

where the square matrix is, of course, $[\mathbf{K}_{ff}]^{-1}$. Also the reactions may be expressed as

$$\begin{Bmatrix} P_{y2} \\ P_{y3} \\ P_{mz3} \end{Bmatrix} = \frac{1}{4L} \begin{bmatrix} -7L & 3 & 3 \\ 3L & -3 & -3 \\ -2L^2 & 2L & 2L \end{bmatrix} \begin{Bmatrix} P_{y1} \\ P_{mz1} \\ P_{mz2} \end{Bmatrix}$$

In this instance, we first consider the beam elements to be subjected to fixed-end moments (state 1) $M_T = (EI_z/h)\,\alpha(\Delta T_l - \Delta T_u)$ in order to suppress the curvature that would otherwise occur under the temperature gradient as shown in Fig. 12-26(b). Then, in Fig. 12-26(c), we consider the assembled structure to be subjected to the vector of equivalent nodal forces (state 2) given as

$$\begin{Bmatrix} P^E_{y1} \\ P^E_{mz1} \\ P^E_{mz2} \end{Bmatrix} = M_T \begin{Bmatrix} 0 \\ -1 \\ 0 \end{Bmatrix}$$

The displacements and reactions due to this loading are, from the foregoing equations,

$$\begin{Bmatrix} v_1 \\ \theta_1 \\ \theta_2 \end{Bmatrix} = \frac{M_T L}{2EI_z} \begin{Bmatrix} 2L \\ -3 \\ -1 \end{Bmatrix} = \frac{L}{2h}\alpha(\Delta T_l - \Delta T_u)\begin{Bmatrix} 2L \\ -3 \\ -1 \end{Bmatrix}$$

and

$$\begin{Bmatrix} P_{y2} \\ P_{y3} \\ P_{mz3} \end{Bmatrix} = \frac{M_T}{4L} \begin{Bmatrix} -3 \\ 3 \\ -2L \end{Bmatrix}$$

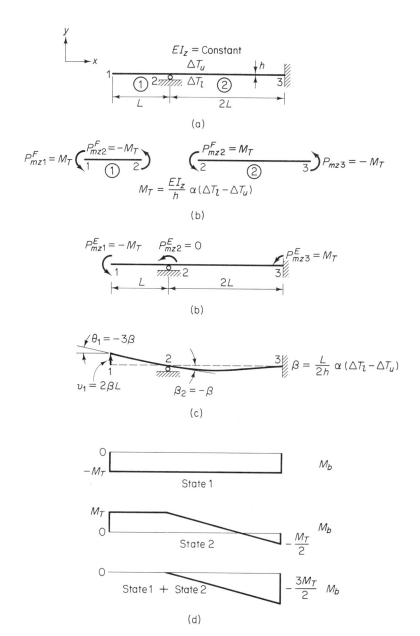

(a)

$$M_T = \frac{EI_z}{h} \alpha (\Delta T_l - \Delta T_u)$$

(b)

(b)

(c)

Figure 12-26

The deformation, which is related to the depth h of the beam (having constant bending rigidity) but not to EI_z, is illustrated in Fig. 12-26(d). The bending moments due to states 1 and 2 are shown in Fig. 12-26(e). Note that although the cantilever member 1 incurs curvature it remains stress-free under the imposition of a temperature gradient. Member 2, however, incurs a linearly varying bending moment.

The Direct Stiffness Method   Chap. 12

A symmetric structure is defined as one possessing a correspondence in size, shape and relative position of parts that exist on opposite sides of a dividing point, line or plane (the point, line or plane of symmetry). We have encountered symmetric structures previously and, in the case of Example 12-8, we have exploited the symmetry property to simplify the analysis. We did this by recognizing that when subjected to symmetric loading, a symmetric structure exhibits symmetric deformation; i.e., the displacements at two corresponding points on either side of the plane of symmetry are mirror images of each other. Accordingly, we were able to reduce the number of unknown displacements by a factor of two. We now wish to formalize a more efficient technique than that employed previously, and expand the methodology to incorporate arbitrary loading conditions.

Symmetric loading. We first note that a planar structure will exhibit symmetric deformation only if its members and boundary conditions are arranged symmetrically with respect to some plane, and if the loading is also symmetric relative to the same plane. Figures 12-27(a) and 12-28(a) illustrate

(a)

(b)

Figure 12-27

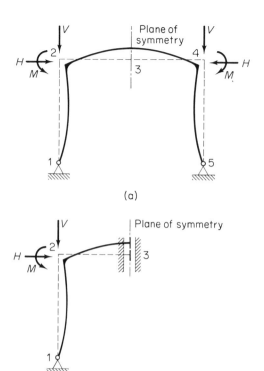

(a)

(b)   **Figure 12-28**

such conditions. For the truss shown in Fig. 12-27(a), equal vertical displacements will occur at nodes 2 and 6; horizontal displacements at these nodes will be equal in magnitude but opposite in sense. Also, horizontal displacements will be zero at nodes 3 and 4, i.e., along the plane of symmetry. The frame shown in Fig. 12-28(a) will exhibit equal vertical displacements at nodes 2 and 4, while horizontal and rotational displacements will be equal and opposite.

According to the approach we took previously, we may ues these conditions of symmetrical displacements to reduce the size of the stiffness matrix. Equivalently, however, we may analyze one half the structure subjected to additional constraints placed along the plane of symmetry to maintain symmetrical deformation. Figure 12-27(b) shows an equivalent analytical model for the truss described above. In order to preserve symmetric deformation with the right half of the truss, the left half is horizontally constrained at nodes 3 and 4. In general, on the plane of symmetry no translations are permitted normal to the plane. Further, both the stiffness of the vertical member lying on the plane of symmetry and the loading in that plane must be taken as one half their actual values. The number of degrees of freedom in the present case is therefore reduced from eight for the entire truss subjected to arbitrary loading to four for the truss subjected to symmetrical loading.

The symmetrically loaded frame shown in Fig. 12-28(a) may be replaced by the frame shown in Fig. 12-28(b). Horizontal and rotational constraints are imposed at a node created on the plane of symmery to preserve the conditions of symmetrical displacements. In general, not only must translations lie in the plane of symmetry, but no rotations are permitted about axes lying in the plane of symmetry. In the present case, the number of degrees of freedom is reduced from eight to five.

Antisymmetric loading. Now let us consider the same symmetric structures subjected to antisymmetric loading. As illustrated in Fig. 12-29(a) and 12-30(a), antisymmetric loading is characterized by the loading on one side of the plane of structural symmetry being the opposite of the mirror image of the loading on the other side of the plane. The structures will exhibit antisymmetric deformation, i.e., deformation that on one side of the plane of structural symmetry is opposite to the mirror image of deformation occurring on the other side of the plane of structural symmetry. Therefore, along the plane of structural symmetry of the truss, the vertical displacements will be zero while the horizontal displacements will be unconstrained, i.e., no translations are permitted in the plane of structural symmetry. Accordingly, only one half the truss need be analyzed subject to constraints at nodes 3 and 4, as shown in Fig. 12-29(b). Note once again that the stiffness of member 3–4 is taken to be one half the actual value, and only one half the actual horizontal loading applied

(a)

(b)

Figure 12-29

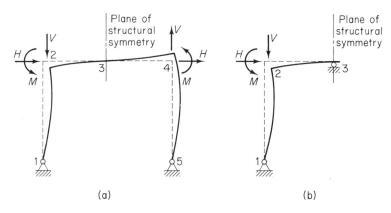

Figure 12-30

to the plane of structural symmetry is considered to act on the one half of the truss analyzed.

If the symmetric frame shown in Fig. 12-30(a) is subjected to anti-symmetric loading, the vertical displacement along the plane of structural symmetry will be zero, while the horizontal displacement will be unconstrained. Further, in order to preserve antisymmetric deformations there will exist a point of contraflexure (i.e., a point at which no bending moment may occur) on the plane of structural symmetry. Accordingly, only a vertical constraint must be furnished to one half the frame along the plane of structural symmetry, as represented by a horizontal roller shown in Fig. 12-30(b). As a general rule, along the plane of structural symmetry, no translations are permitted in the plane and rotations are unrestrained.

General loading. It is important to note that, provided the structure is symmetric about a plane, any loading condition may be represented as a combination of symmetric and antisymmetric loading conditions. Rather than analyze the entire structure subjected to the complete loading, we may instead analyze one half the structure twice: once under symmetric loading (and appropriate constraints along the plane of structural symmetry) and again under antisymmetric loading (with appropriate constraints). As the number of computations increases with at least the square of the number of degrees of freedom, the advantage of solving two relatively small problems instead of one large problem becomes significant in many practical applications. The following examples illustrate the decomposition into analyses of symmetric and antisymmetric problems.

Example 12-12. The symmetric truss shown in Fig. 12-31(a) is subjected to asymmetric (neither symmetric nor antisymmetric) loading, and hence its deformation will be asymmetric. If we were to analyze the entire truss, we would be required to formulate and invert the following 8×8 overall structural stiffness matrix after accounting for the constraints at nodes 1 and 5:

(a)

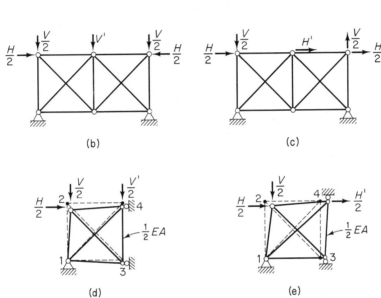

(b)   (c)

(d)   (e)

Figure 12-31

$$[\mathbf{K}_{ff}] = \frac{EA}{L} \begin{bmatrix} \begin{array}{cccccccc} u_2 & v_2 & u_3 & v_3 & u_4 & v_4 & u_6 & v_6 \\ 3 & & & & & \text{symmetric} & & \\ -1 & 3 & & & & & & \\ -1 & 1 & 6 & & & & & \\ 1 & -1 & 0 & 4 & & & & \\ -2 & 0 & 0 & 0 & 6 & & & \\ 0 & 0 & 0 & -2 & 0 & 4 & & \\ 0 & 0 & -1 & -1 & -2 & 0 & 3 & \\ 0 & 0 & -1 & -1 & 0 & 0 & 1 & 3 \end{array} \end{bmatrix}$$

We may represent the actual loading by the combination of symmetric and antisymmetric loadings shown in Figs. 12-31(b) and (c), respectively. Consequently, for each loading condition, we may analyze one half the truss subjected to the appropriate constraints along the plane of structural symmetry. The analytical models and loading conditions for the symmetric and antisymmetric analyses are shown in Figs. 12-31(d) and (e), respectively.

For the symmetric problem, we form the (4×4) structural stiffness matrix and, deleting degrees of freedom that are suppressed, we express the stiffness equations as

$$\frac{EA}{2L}\begin{bmatrix} 3 & -1 & 1 & 0 \\ -1 & 3 & -1 & 0 \\ 1 & -1 & 2 & -1 \\ 0 & 0 & -1 & 2 \end{bmatrix}\begin{Bmatrix} u_2 \\ v_2 \\ v_3 \\ v_4 \end{Bmatrix} = \frac{1}{2}\begin{Bmatrix} H \\ -V \\ 0 \\ -V' \end{Bmatrix}$$

Note that, in the usual way, the negative loads are those acting in directions opposite to the positive global coordinate axes.

Similarly, for the antisymmetric problem, we write

$$\frac{EA}{2L}\begin{bmatrix} 3 & -1 & -1 & -2 \\ -1 & 3 & 1 & 0 \\ -1 & 1 & 3 & 0 \\ -2 & 0 & 0 & 3 \end{bmatrix}\begin{Bmatrix} u_2 \\ v_2 \\ u_3 \\ u_4 \end{Bmatrix} = \frac{1}{2}\begin{Bmatrix} H \\ -V \\ 0 \\ H' \end{Bmatrix}$$

We may invert the stiffness matrices for each problem and solve for the nodal displacements. Once these are found, the nodal displacements associated with that part of the structure which was not analyzed may be inferred by inspection by invoking the conditions of symmetry and antisymmetry. Thus, for example, $u_6 = -u_2$ and $v_6 = v_2$ for the symmetric problem, while $u_6 = u_2$ and $v_6 = -v_2$ for the antisymmetric problem. Accordingly, the entire displacement vector becomes

$$\begin{Bmatrix} u_1 \\ v_1 \\ u_2 \\ v_2 \\ u_3 \\ v_3 \\ u_4 \\ v_4 \\ u_5 \\ v_5 \\ u_6 \\ v_6 \end{Bmatrix} = \frac{L}{16EA}\begin{Bmatrix} 0 \\ 0 \\ 7H - V + 2V' \\ H - 7V - 2V' \\ 0 \\ -4H - 4V - 8V' \\ 0 \\ -2H - 2V - 12V' \\ 0 \\ 0 \\ -7H + V - 2V' \\ H - 7V - 2V' \end{Bmatrix} \quad \text{and} \quad \begin{Bmatrix} u_1 \\ v_1 \\ u_2 \\ v_2 \\ u_3 \\ v_3 \\ u_4 \\ v_4 \\ u_5 \\ v_5 \\ u_6 \\ v_6 \end{Bmatrix} = \frac{L}{14EA}\begin{Bmatrix} 0 \\ 0 \\ 12H - 3V + 8H' \\ 3H - 6V + 2H' \\ 3H + V + 2H' \\ 0 \\ 8H - 2V + 10H' \\ 0 \\ 0 \\ 0 \\ 12H - 3V + 8H' \\ -3H + 6V - 2H' \end{Bmatrix}$$

for the symmetric and antisymmetric problems, respectively. The actual displacements are, of course, the sum of the symmetric and antisymmetric components.

Note that the bar forces may be found for each problem in the usual way, i.e., by multiplying the stiffness matrix for each bar by the displacement vector associated with the nodes of the bar. Once this has been done for one half the structure analyzed, the bar forces in the remaining half of the structure may be found by inspection. Thus the force in the diagonal bar defined by nodes 3 and 6, for example, is equal to that in the bar defined by nodes 3 and 2 under symmetric loading, while the forces in these two bars are of opposite signs under antisymmetric loading. It is permissible, of course, to determine the bar forces for the entire structure from the final superposed nodal displacements, but this involves a greater number of computations than the foregoing approach.

The Direct Stiffness Method Chap. 12

Example 12-13. The four-span continuous beam shown in Fig. 12-32(a) possesses seven degrees of freedom: vertical translations at nodes 1 and 5, and rotations at each of the five nodes. The applied loading may be represented as the super-position of symmetric and antisymmetric cases, as shown in Figs. 12-32(b) and (c).

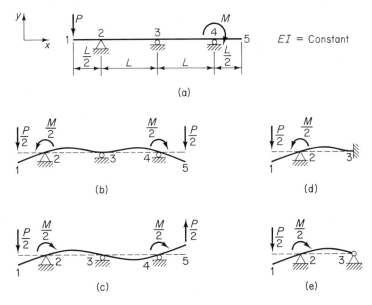

(a)

(b)   (d)

(c)   (e)

Figure 12-32

The symmetric deformation pattern shown in Fig. 12-32(b) requires that no rotation occur at node 3 (i.e., on the plane of structural symmetry). Accordingly, the symmetric problem may be represented by the analytical model shown in Fig. 12-32(d); node 3 is clamped and there exist only three degrees of freedom. The antisymmetric deformation pattern shown in Fig. 12-32(e) requires that no bending moment develop at node 3. Therefore the antisymmetric problem may be solved by analyzing one half the beam having a pin support at node 3; this involves four degrees of freedom.

For the symmetric problem the stiffness equations are

$$\frac{4EI}{L^3}\begin{bmatrix} 24 & 6L & 6L \\ 6L & 2L^2 & L^2 \\ 6L & L^2 & 3L^2 \end{bmatrix}\begin{Bmatrix} v_1 \\ \theta_1 \\ \theta_2 \end{Bmatrix} = \frac{1}{2}\begin{Bmatrix} -P \\ 0 \\ M \end{Bmatrix}$$

and for the antisymmetric problem they are

$$\frac{2EI}{L^3}\begin{bmatrix} 48 & 12L & 12L & 0 \\ 12L & 4L^2 & 2L^2 & 0 \\ 12L & 2L^2 & 6L^2 & L^2 \\ 0 & 0 & L^2 & 2L^2 \end{bmatrix}\begin{Bmatrix} v_1 \\ \theta_1 \\ \theta_2 \\ \theta_3 \end{Bmatrix} = \frac{1}{2}\begin{Bmatrix} -P \\ 0 \\ -M \\ 0 \end{Bmatrix}$$

The foregoing displacements, pertaining to one half the structure, may be found in the usual way after inverting the stiffness matrix, while the remaining displacements for the other half of the structure may be determined by inspection.

For example $v_5 = v_1$, $\theta_4 = -\theta_2$, and $\theta_5 = -\theta_1$ for the symmetric problem, while $v_5 = -v_1$, $\theta_4 = \theta_2$, and $\theta_5 = \theta_1$ for the antisymmetric problem. We then obtain

$$
\begin{Bmatrix} v_1 \\ \theta_1 \\ v_2 \\ \theta_2 \\ v_3 \\ \theta_3 \\ v_4 \\ \theta_4 \\ v_5 \\ \theta_5 \end{Bmatrix} = \frac{L}{384EI} \begin{Bmatrix} -5PL^2 - 6ML \\ 12PL + 12M \\ 0 \\ 6PL + 12M \\ 0 \\ 0 \\ 0 \\ -6PL - 12M \\ -5PL^2 - 6ML \\ -12PL - 12M \end{Bmatrix}
\quad \text{and} \quad
\begin{Bmatrix} v_1 \\ \theta_1 \\ v_2 \\ \theta_2 \\ v_3 \\ \theta_3 \\ v_4 \\ \theta_4 \\ v_5 \\ \theta_5 \end{Bmatrix} = \frac{L}{2304EI} \begin{Bmatrix} -9PL^2 + 12ML \\ 21PL - 24M \\ 0 \\ 12PL - 24M \\ 0 \\ -6PL + 12M \\ 0 \\ 12PL - 24M \\ 9PL^2 - 12M \\ 21PL - 24M \end{Bmatrix}
$$

Internal forces (shear forces and bending moments) may be determined from the displacements most directly by considering the symmetric and antisymmetric problems independently. The results are then combined.

12-10 CONDENSATION

There may exist occasions when the inversion of the stiffness matrix in two or more steps is advantageous, particularly when certain degrees of freedom are of secondary interest and when generalized loads associated with those degrees of freedom are zero. While all degrees of freedom are in fact preserved (i.e., no approximations are made), the behavior of the structure may be described in terms of a set of predetermined *master* degrees of freedom $\{\mathbf{\Delta}_c\}$, which forms a subset of the complete displacement vector $\{\mathbf{\Delta}\}$. The procedure for accomplishing this is termed *condensation*.

Mathematically, we wish to condense the set of stiffness equations from

$$
\begin{bmatrix} \mathbf{K}_{bb} & \vdots & \mathbf{K}_{bc} \\ \cdots & \cdots & \cdots \\ \mathbf{K}_{cb} & \vdots & \mathbf{K}_{cc} \end{bmatrix} \begin{Bmatrix} \mathbf{\Delta}_b \\ \cdots \\ \mathbf{\Delta}_c \end{Bmatrix} = \begin{Bmatrix} \mathbf{P}_b \\ \cdots \\ \mathbf{P}_c \end{Bmatrix}
\tag{12-61}
$$

to the form

$$
[\mathbf{K}_c^*]\{\mathbf{\Delta}_c\} = \{\mathbf{P}_c^*\}
\tag{12-62}
$$

where the entire structural stiffness matrix and load vector appearing in Eq. (12-61) have been partitioned in accordance with the vector of master degrees of freedom $\{\mathbf{\Delta}_c\}$ and the remaining vector of *slave* degrees of freedom $\{\mathbf{\Delta}_b\}$. The *condensed stiffness matrix* $[\mathbf{K}_c^*]$ and associated load vector $\{\mathbf{P}_c^*\}$ are determined by expanding the upper partition in Eq. (12-61) and solving for $\{\mathbf{\Delta}_b\}$; i.e.,

$$
\{\mathbf{\Delta}_b\} = -[\mathbf{K}_{bb}]^{-1}([\mathbf{K}_{bc}]\{\mathbf{\Delta}_c\} - \{\mathbf{P}_b\})
\tag{12-63}
$$

When this expression for $\{\mathbf{\Delta}_b\}$ is substituted into the expansion of the lower partition of Eq. (12-61), the result is

$$
(-[\mathbf{K}_{cb}][\mathbf{K}_{bb}]^{-1}[\mathbf{K}_{bc}] + [\mathbf{K}_{cc}])\{\mathbf{\Delta}_c\} = \{\mathbf{P}_c\} - [\mathbf{K}_{cb}][\mathbf{K}_{bb}]^{-1}\{\mathbf{P}_b\}
\tag{12-64}
$$

This may be written in the form we seek,

$$[\mathbf{K}_c^*]\{\mathbf{\Delta}_c\} = \{\mathbf{P}_c^*\} \tag{12-65}$$

where we define

$$[\mathbf{K}_c^*] = [\mathbf{K}_{cc}] - [\mathbf{K}_{cb}][\mathbf{K}_{bb}]^{-1}[\mathbf{K}_{bc}] \tag{12-66a}$$

and

$$\{\mathbf{P}_c^*\} = \{\mathbf{P}_c\} - [\mathbf{K}_{cb}][\mathbf{K}_{bb}]^{-1}\{\mathbf{P}_b\} \tag{12-66b}$$

The displacement vector $\{\mathbf{\Delta}_c\}$ may be determined by inverting $[\mathbf{K}_c^*]$, which is of the same order as $[\mathbf{K}_{cc}]$. Obviously, however, the formation of $[\mathbf{K}_c^*]$ requires inversion of $[\mathbf{K}_{bb}]$ and additional matrix multiplication. While this procedure generally requires more arithmetic operations than the direct inversion of the original overall stiffness matrix, it does reduce the size of the matrices that must be inverted. This may effect some efficiencies when computer storage is severely limited. Note that although the solution is expressed primarily in terms of $\{\mathbf{\Delta}_c\}$, the values of all degrees of freedom may be recovered by substituting $\{\mathbf{\Delta}_c\}$ into Eq. (12-63). Although one might not always be interested in $\{\mathbf{\Delta}_b\}$, all displacements must be evaluated if all internal forces are to be computed.

Example 12-14. Consider the beam shown in Fig. 12-33, which is step tapered and thus must be represented by three beam elements. If the transverse displacements are of primary importance, then it would be useful to relate directly the loads applied at nodes 2 and 3 to the corresponding displacements.

Using the 4 × 4 stiffness matrix for the beam elements, Eq. (12-55), we may express the overall structural stiffness matrix as

$$[\mathbf{K}] = \frac{6EI}{L^3}
\begin{bmatrix}
6 & & & & & & & \\
3L & 2L^2 & & & & \text{symmetric} & & \\
-6 & -3L & 10 & & & & & \\
3L & L^2 & -L & \dfrac{10}{3}L^2 & & & & \\
0 & 0 & -4 & -2\,L & 6 & & & \\
0 & 0 & 2L & \dfrac{2}{3}L^2 & -\,L & 2L^2 & & \\
0 & 0 & 0 & 0 & -2 & -L & 2 & \\
0 & 0 & 0 & 0 & L & \dfrac{1}{3}L^2 & -L & \dfrac{2}{3}L^2
\end{bmatrix}$$

with column headings $v_1 \quad \theta_1 \quad v_2 \quad \theta_2 \quad v_3 \quad \theta_3 \quad v_4 \quad \theta_4$

Figure 12-33

Owing to the constraints imposed on the ends of the beam, we may, of course, eliminate the rows and columns corresponding to v_1, θ_1, and v_4. Further, recognizing that v_2 and v_3 are to be designated as the master degrees of freedom while θ_2, θ_3, and θ_4 are to be the slaves, we rewrite $[\mathbf{K}]$ in the form

$$
[\mathbf{K}] = \frac{6EI}{L^3}
\begin{array}{c}
\begin{array}{ccccc}
\theta_2 & \theta_3 & \theta_4 & v_2 & v_3
\end{array} \\
\left[
\begin{array}{ccc:cc}
\dfrac{10}{3}L^2 & \dfrac{2}{3}L^2 & 0 & -L & -2L \\[2mm]
\dfrac{2}{3}L^2 & 2\,L^2 & \dfrac{1}{3}L^2 & 2L & -L \\[2mm]
0 & \dfrac{1}{3}L^2 & \dfrac{2}{3}L^2 & 0 & L \\
\hdashline
-L & 2L & 0 & 10 & -4 \\
-2L & -L & L & -4 & 6
\end{array}
\right]
\end{array}
\equiv
\left[
\begin{array}{c:c}
\mathbf{K}_{bb} & \mathbf{K}_{bc} \\
\hdashline
\mathbf{K}_{cb} & \mathbf{K}_{cc}
\end{array}
\right]
$$

The operations indicated by Eqs. (12-66) lead to

$$
[\mathbf{K}_c^*] = \frac{EI}{L^3}
\begin{bmatrix}
41.12 & -19.06 \\
-19.06 & 15.53
\end{bmatrix}
$$

and

$$
\{\mathbf{P}_c^*\} = \{\mathbf{P}_c\} - \{\mathbf{0}\} = -\begin{Bmatrix} 2P \\ P \end{Bmatrix}
$$

Hence,

$$
\begin{Bmatrix} v_2 \\ v_3 \end{Bmatrix} = [\mathbf{K}_c^*]^{-1} \begin{Bmatrix} P_{y2} \\ P_{y3} \end{Bmatrix}
$$

or

$$
\begin{Bmatrix} v_2 \\ v_3 \end{Bmatrix} = \frac{-L^3}{EI}
\begin{bmatrix}
0.0564 & 0.0692 \\
0.0692 & 0.1494
\end{bmatrix}
\begin{Bmatrix} 2P \\ P \end{Bmatrix}
= \frac{-PL^3}{EI}
\begin{Bmatrix} 0.1820 \\ 0.2878 \end{Bmatrix}
$$

The rotations, which constitute $\{\mathbf{\Delta}_b\}$, may be determined by Eq. (12-63). They are

$$
\begin{Bmatrix} \theta_2 \\ \theta_3 \\ \theta_4 \end{Bmatrix} = \frac{PL^2}{EI}
\begin{Bmatrix} -0.2371 \\ 0.0493 \\ 0.4070 \end{Bmatrix}
$$

We may evaluate internal shear forces and bending moments in the conventional way by using the element stiffness matrices.

12-11 SUBSTRUCTURING

The foregoing condensation procedure may be employed in a broader context to develop a *substructure method* for analyzing large-scale structures. As the term implies, substructuring permits us to represent portions of the structure as sort of "super elements", each usually comprising several internal degrees of freedom but interacting with others at relatively few interface nodal points. For any substructure the stiffness matrix associating forces with displacements at these interface nodal points is, of course, directly related to the configuration and stiffnesses of the individual members that constitute the substructure. But this relationship may be established for each substructure alone, without considering the entire structure at once. After the interaction among all substructures, and thus the interface degrees of freedom, have been determined for any specific loading condition, the internal response of each substructure may be established.

Consider the truss shown in Fig. 12-34(a) as an illustrative case. Because there exist 33 unconstrained degrees of freedom, a direct solution involving the entire structure at once would entail our formulating and inverting a 33×33 stiffness matrix. We may, however, view the system as comprising some number of substructures; from the geometry of the present example, the three substructures shown in Fig. 12-34(b) would seem appropriate. We identify nodes 4 and 5 as being interface nodes for substructure 1. Similarly, nodes 6 and 7 are interface nodes for substructure 2, and nodes 4, 5, 6, and 7 are interface nodes for substructure 3. (Note that displacements at the supports, nodes 18 and 19, also would have to be included among the interface nodes if they were not prescribed to be zero.) All other nodes are "internal" to the substructures. If for each substructure we knew the relationship between forces and displacements at the interface nodes, we could view the global problem as illustrated in Fig. 12-34(c). Then our objective would be defined as determining the interface displacements (i.e., the displacements at nodes 4, 5, 6, and 7) due to some equivalent generalized loading applied to the assemblage at these interface nodes. To do this, we note that for the ith substructure, we may write the stiffness equations in the partitioned form

$$
\begin{bmatrix} \mathbf{K}_{bb}^i & \vdots & \mathbf{K}_{bc}^i \\ \cdots & \cdots & \cdots \\ \mathbf{K}_{cb}^i & \vdots & \mathbf{K}_{cc}^i \end{bmatrix} \begin{Bmatrix} \mathbf{\Delta}_b^i \\ \cdots \\ \mathbf{\Delta}_c^i \end{Bmatrix} = \begin{Bmatrix} \mathbf{P}_b^i \\ \cdots \\ \mathbf{P}_c^i \end{Bmatrix} \tag{12-67}
$$

in which the subscript c refers to the nodal points that lie on the interface between the ith substructure and its neighboring substructures, and the subscript b refers to all remaining nodes within the ith substructure. For substructure 1, for example, the vector $\{\mathbf{\Delta}_b^i\}$ would comprise nodal displacements $u_1, v_1, u_2, v_2, u_3,$ and v_3, while the vector $\{\mathbf{\Delta}_c\}$ would comprise $u_4, v_4, u_5,$ and v_5. The vectors $\{\mathbf{P}_b^i\}$ and $\{\mathbf{P}_c^i\}$ would include corresponding force components.

Noting that Eqs. (12-67) and (12-61) have the same form, we may condense Eq. (12-67) to the same form as given by Eq. (12-65), i.e.,

$$
[\tilde{\mathbf{K}}_c^i]\{\mathbf{\Delta}_c^i\} = \{\tilde{\mathbf{P}}_c^i\} \tag{12-68}
$$

where, similar to Eqs. (12-66), we define

$$
[\tilde{\mathbf{K}}_c^i] = [\mathbf{K}_{cc}^i] - [\mathbf{K}_{cb}^i][\mathbf{K}_{bb}^i]^{-1}[\mathbf{K}_{bc}^i] \tag{12-69a}
$$

and

$$
\{\tilde{\mathbf{P}}_c^i\} = \{\mathbf{P}_c^i\} - [\mathbf{K}_{cb}^i][\mathbf{K}_{bb}^i]^{-1}\{\mathbf{P}_b^i\} \tag{12-69b}
$$

(a)

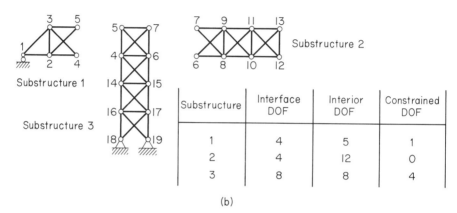

Substructure	Interface DOF	Interior DOF	Constrained DOF
1	4	5	1
2	4	12	0
3	8	8	4

(b)

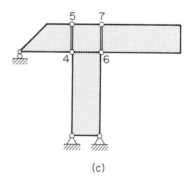

(c)

Figure 12-34

The matrix product in Eq. (12-69b) represents the equivalent forces that must be applied at the interface nodes to represent the forces included in $\{\mathbf{P}_b^i\}$ which are applied to the interior nodes of the substructure. The stiffness matrices $[\tilde{\mathbf{K}}_c^i]$ and force vectors $\{\tilde{\mathbf{P}}_c^i\}$ for all substructures may be combined in the usual way to form the system stiffness matrix $[\tilde{\mathbf{K}}_c]$ and force vector $\{\tilde{\mathbf{P}}_c\}$ associated only with the degrees of freedom at all the interface nodes $\{\boldsymbol{\Delta}_c\}$. Thus we form

$$[\tilde{\mathbf{K}}_c]\{\boldsymbol{\Delta}_c\} = \{\tilde{\mathbf{P}}_c\} \qquad (12\text{-}70)$$

we solve for $\{\mathbf{\Delta}_c\}$, and for each particular substructure we find (following the form of Eq. (12-63)) the displacements at the interior nodes,

$$\{\mathbf{\Delta}_b^i\} = -[\mathbf{K}_{bb}^i]^{-1}([\mathbf{K}_{bc}^i]\{\mathbf{\Delta}_c^i\} - \{\mathbf{P}_b^i\}) \qquad (12\text{-}71)$$

Example 12-15. As a simple example, we consider the truss shown in Fig. 12-35 to comprise two substructures. Because the two substructures happen to be identical, their stiffness matrices would be identical if the degrees of freedom in each were ordered similarly. However, because each stiffness matrix is assembled to accommodate the partitioning prescribed by Eq. (12-67), we have for substructure 1 (see Example 12-2)

$$[\mathbf{K}^1] = \begin{bmatrix} \mathbf{K}_{bb}^1 & \vdots & \mathbf{K}_{bc}^1 \\ \cdots & \vdots & \cdots \\ \mathbf{K}_{cb}^1 & \vdots & \mathbf{K}_{cc}^1 \end{bmatrix} = \frac{EA}{2L} \begin{array}{c} \begin{array}{cccccccc} u_1 & v_1 & u_2 & v_2 & u_3 & v_3 & u_4 & v_4 \end{array} \\ \left[\begin{array}{cccc:cccc} 3 & -1 & -2 & 0 & 0 & 0 & -1 & 1 \\ -1 & 3 & 0 & 0 & 0 & -2 & 1 & -1 \\ -2 & 0 & 3 & 1 & -1 & -1 & 0 & 0 \\ 0 & 0 & 1 & 3 & -1 & -1 & 0 & -2 \\ \hdashline 0 & 0 & -1 & -1 & 1 & 1 & 0 & 0 \\ 0 & -2 & -1 & -1 & 1 & 3 & 0 & 0 \\ -1 & 1 & 0 & 0 & 0 & 0 & 1 & -1 \\ 1 & -1 & 0 & -2 & 0 & 0 & -1 & 3 \end{array} \right] \end{array}$$

and, for substructure 2

$$[\mathbf{K}^2] = [\mathbf{K}_{cc}^2] = \frac{EA}{2L} \begin{array}{c} \begin{array}{cccccccc} u_5 & v_5 & u_6 & v_6 & u_3 & v_3 & u_4 & v_4 \end{array} \\ \left[\begin{array}{cccccccc} 1 & 1 & 0 & 0 & 0 & 0 & -1 & -1 \\ 1 & 3 & 0 & 0 & 0 & -2 & -1 & -1 \\ 0 & 0 & 1 & -1 & -1 & 1 & 0 & 0 \\ 0 & 0 & -1 & 3 & 1 & -1 & 0 & -2 \\ 0 & 0 & -1 & 1 & 3 & -1 & -2 & 0 \\ 0 & -2 & 1 & -1 & -1 & 3 & 0 & 0 \\ -1 & -1 & 0 & 0 & -2 & 0 & 3 & 1 \\ -1 & -1 & 0 & -2 & 0 & 0 & 1 & 3 \end{array} \right] \end{array}$$

Note that $[\mathbf{K}_{bb}^2]$, $[\mathbf{K}_{bc}^2]$, and $[\mathbf{K}_{cb}^2]$ are all null matrices because, formally at least, all nodes associated with substructure 2 must be regarded as interface nodes. Of course, $[\mathbf{K}_{cc}^2]$ may be reduced to a 4×4 matrix by eliminating rows and columns pertaining to the prescribed zero-valued displacements at nodes 5 and 6. Accordingly, the displacement and force vectors for the two substructures are

$$\left\{ \begin{array}{c} \mathbf{\Delta}_b^1 \\ \cdots \\ \mathbf{\Delta}_c^1 \end{array} \right\} = \left\{ \begin{array}{c} u_1 \\ v_1 \\ u_2 \\ v_2 \\ \cdots \\ u_3 \\ v_3 \\ u_4 \\ v_4 \end{array} \right\} \qquad \{\mathbf{\Delta}_c^2\} = \left\{ \begin{array}{c} u_5 \\ v_5 \\ u_6 \\ v_6 \\ u_3 \\ v_3 \\ u_4 \\ v_4 \end{array} \right\} \qquad \left\{ \begin{array}{c} \mathbf{P}_b^1 \\ \cdots \\ \mathbf{P}_c^1 \end{array} \right\} = \left\{ \begin{array}{c} P_{x1} \\ P_{y1} \\ P_{x2} \\ P_{y2} \\ \cdots \\ P_{x3} \\ P_{y3} \\ P_{x4} \\ P_{y4} \end{array} \right\} \qquad \{\mathbf{P}_c^2\} = \left\{ \begin{array}{c} P_{x5} \\ P_{y5} \\ P_{x6} \\ P_{y6} \\ P_{x3} \\ P_{y3} \\ P_{x4} \\ P_{y4} \end{array} \right\}$$

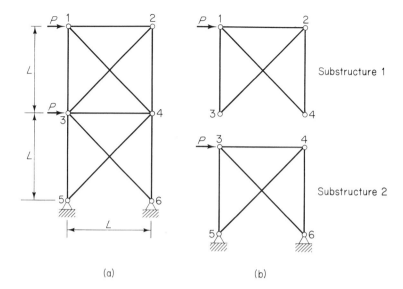

Figure 12-35

The particular loading condition considered here implies that within $\{\mathbf{P}_b^1\}$, $\{\mathbf{P}_c^1\}$, and $\{\mathbf{P}_c^2\}$, only $P_{x1} = P_{x3} = P$ are nonzero. Note, however, that $P_{x3} = P$ may be included in *either* $\{\mathbf{P}_c^1\}$ *or* $\{\mathbf{P}_c^2\}$, but not in both.

Application of Eqs. (12-69) yields

$$
[\tilde{\mathbf{K}}_c^1] = \frac{EA}{7L}
\begin{array}{c}
\begin{array}{cccc} u_3 & v_3 & u_4 & v_4 \end{array} \\
\begin{bmatrix}
1 & 0 & -1 & 0 \\
0 & 0 & 0 & 0 \\
-1 & 0 & 1 & 0 \\
0 & 0 & 0 & 0
\end{bmatrix}
\end{array}
\quad \text{and} \quad
[\tilde{\mathbf{K}}_c^2] = \frac{EA}{2L}
\begin{array}{c}
\begin{array}{cccc} u_3 & v_3 & u_4 & v_4 \end{array} \\
\begin{bmatrix}
3 & -1 & -2 & 0 \\
-1 & 3 & 0 & 0 \\
-2 & 0 & 3 & 1 \\
0 & 0 & 1 & 3
\end{bmatrix}
\end{array}
$$

and

$$
\{\tilde{\mathbf{P}}_c^1\} = \frac{P}{7}
\begin{Bmatrix}
3 \\ 7 \\ 4 \\ -7
\end{Bmatrix}
\quad \text{and} \quad
\{\tilde{\mathbf{P}}_c^2\} = P
\begin{Bmatrix}
1 \\ 0 \\ 0 \\ 0
\end{Bmatrix}
$$

Observe that $[\tilde{\mathbf{K}}_c^2]$ was obtained trivially from $[\mathbf{K}^2]$ by retaining in the latter only those rows and columns corresponding to nonzero displacements. Hence, for the entire structure

$$
[\tilde{\mathbf{K}}_c] = \frac{EA}{14L}
\begin{array}{c}
\begin{array}{cccc} u_3 & v_3 & u_4 & v_4 \end{array} \\
\begin{bmatrix}
23 & -7 & -16 & 0 \\
-7 & 21 & 0 & 0 \\
-16 & 0 & 23 & 7 \\
0 & 0 & 7 & 21
\end{bmatrix}
\end{array}
$$

and

$$\{\tilde{\mathbf{P}}_c\} = \frac{P}{7} \begin{Bmatrix} 10 \\ 7 \\ 4 \\ -7 \end{Bmatrix}$$

Inverting $[\tilde{\mathbf{K}}_c]$, we obtain

$$[\tilde{\mathbf{K}}_c]^{-1} = \frac{L}{EA} \begin{bmatrix} 1.691 & .564 & 1.309 & -.436 \\ .564 & .855 & .436 & -.146 \\ 1.309 & .436 & 1.691 & -.564 \\ -.436 & -.146 & -.564 & .855 \end{bmatrix}$$

We then find

$$\{\mathbf{\Delta}_c\} = \begin{Bmatrix} u_3 \\ v_3 \\ u_4 \\ v_4 \end{Bmatrix} = \frac{PL}{EA} \begin{Bmatrix} 4.16 \\ 2.06 \\ 3.84 \\ -1.95 \end{Bmatrix}$$

and for each substructure we may find $\{\mathbf{\Delta}_b^i\}$ using Eq. (12-71). These displacements for substructure 1 are found to be

$$\{\mathbf{\Delta}_b^1\} = \begin{Bmatrix} u_1 \\ v_1 \\ u_2 \\ v_2 \end{Bmatrix} = \frac{PL}{EA} \begin{Bmatrix} 9.69 \\ 2.67 \\ 9.31 \\ -2.33 \end{Bmatrix}$$

We have already (necessarily) included the condition $u_5 = v_5 = u_6 = v_6 = 0$ in formulating $[\tilde{\mathbf{K}}_c^2]$. The internal bar forces may be computed in the usual way by multiplying the displacement vectors by the member stiffness matrices.

Although, as remarked previously, the total number of computations is not reduced by substructuring, the required amount of computer storage often is reduced significantly. Also, the reduction of the order of matrices that must be inverted, arising from a substructure analysis, permits some problems to be analyzed by hand which would otherwise be intractable. Finally, the substructure analysis may be used to analyze the response under a variety of loading conditions without solving for the displacement at every node and the force in every member until the critical loading condition becomes apparent.

PROBLEMS

12-1. The statically indeterminate truss considered in Example 12-1 is now externally braced, as shown in Fig. P12-1. Demonstrate how the presence of the external brace can be accommodated through appropriate modifications of the system stiffness matrix developed in the example. Compare the displacements and bar forces corresponding to the braced and unbraced frames.

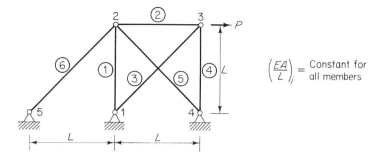

Figure P12-1

12-2. Determine the bar forces in the truss shown in Fig. P12-1 when node 4 undergoes a vertical settlement Δ, but no external force is applied to the truss.

12-3. Using the direct stiffness method, find the displacements and bar forces for the truss shown in Fig. P12-3. Compare the solutions as the cross-sectional area of member 3 varies as 0 in.^{2} (i.e., member disappearing), 5 in.^{2}, and 10 in.^{2}

Figure P12-3

12-4. Determine the displacements and bar forces for the truss shown in Fig. P12-4.

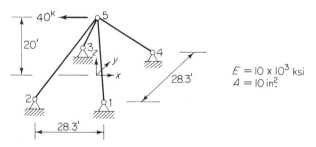

Figure P12-4

12-5. Determine the bar forces and displacements for the truss shown in Fig. P12-3 when node 1 is displaced vertically downward by 2 inches, but no external force is applied to the truss.

The Direct Stiffness Method   Chap. 12

12-6 to **12-11.** Compute the nodal displacements and internal forces and draw the shear force and bending moment diagrams for the beams shown in Figs. P12-6 to P12-11.

Figure P12-6

Figure P12-7

$L = 15'$

$A_1 = 20$

$A_2 = 10$

$E = 30 \times 10^3$

$I = 200$

$P = 20$

Figure P12-8

$L = 25'$

$A = 5$

$I = 240$

$M =$

Figure P12-9

Figure P12-10

Figure P12-11

12-12 to **12-18.** In each of the planar frames shown in Figs. P12-12 to P12-18, the following member properties apply:

$$E = 30 \times 10^3 \text{ ksi}$$

$$A_0 = 10 \text{ in.}^2$$

$$I_0 = 200 \text{ in.}^4$$

$$L = 120 \text{ in.}$$

Determine the nodal displacements and internal member forces due to the prescribed loads or displacements.

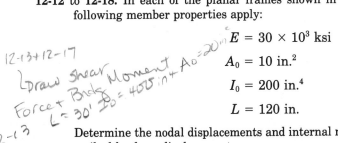

$12-13 + 12-17$

Draw shear Moment

Force + Bndg $A_0 = 20"$

$L = 30'$ $I_0 = 400 \text{ in}^4$

$12-13$

$12-17$ $L = 20'$ $I_0 = 400$ $A_0 = 20$

Figure P12-12

Figure P12-13

Figure P12-14

Figure P12-15

Figure P12-16

Figure P12-17

Figure P12-18

12-19 and **12-20.** Analyze the space frames shown in Figs. P12-19 and P12-20. The properties for all members are those prescribed for Problems 12-12 to 12-18, along with $J_0 = 2I_0$ and $G = 12 \times 10^3$ ksi.

The Direct Stiffness Method   Chap. 12

Figure P12-19

Figure P12-20

12-21. Member 2 of the truss shown in Fig. P12-3 is fabricated 1 in. too short before it is forced into the structure. Find the forces in all three members and the misalignment of node 3 caused by the misfit of member 2.

12-22. In the structure shown in Fig. P12-4, the member spanning nodes 1 and 5 is heated to a temperature of 50°F above the other members. Find the resulting bar forces, assuming the coefficient of thermal expansion is $0.6 \times 10^{-6}/°F$.

12-23. For the structure shown in Fig. P12-7, determine the nodal displacements, shear forces and bending moments due to the top flange being elevated to a temperature ΔT greater than that of the bottom flange for a beam of depth h.

12-24. The left column of the frame shown in Fig. P12-12 is fabricated 0.5 in. too short. Find the nodal displacements, the axial and shear forces and bending moments in the structure due to the misfit of the column.

12-25. The horizontal beam in the frame shown in Fig. P12-16 is subjected to a temperature of 100°F along the top flange and 50°F along the bottom flange; the inclined member has a uniform temperature of 50°F. Assuming the coefficient of thermal expansion is $0.6 \times 10^{-6}/°F$ and the depth of the members is 18 inches, find the displacements, axial and shear forces and bending moments caused by the change in temperature.

12-26. Determine the displacements and internal forces and moments in the frame shown in Fig. P12-26 due to the inclined column being fabricated 0.5 inch too short. Use the dimensions and material properties associated with Problems 12-12 to 12-20.

Figure P12-26

12-27 to 12-29. Exploit the symmetry of the structures presented in Figs. P12-7, P12-15, and P12-20 to analyze them subjected to the loading conditions shown in the figures.

12-30. Exploit the symmetry of the structure in Fig. P12-30 to analyze the problem due to the given loading. Use the dimensions and material properties associated with Problems 12-12 to 12-20.

Figure P12-30

12-31 to 12-34. For the structures shown in Figs. P12-6, P12-12, P12-17, and P12-20, identify nodal translations as master degrees of freedom and rotations as slave degrees of freedom. Use the condensation procedure to find the nodal displacements for the loading shown in the figures.

12-35. The truss shown in Fig. P12-35 consists of eight identical bays, each comprising bars having constant stiffness EA/L. Demonstrate first that the central node in a single bay may be condensed out, leaving only the corner nodes as active degrees of freedom. Then combine two single bays through a substructure analysis to condense out all except the four external nodes of the two-bay system. Finally, using the two-bay system as a substructure, combine two such systems and exploit symmetry to analyze the truss subjected to the loading shown in Fig. P12-35.

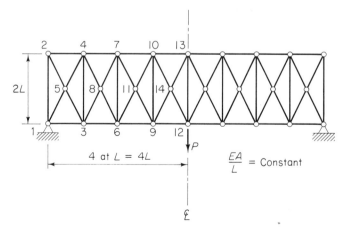

Figure P12-35

12-36. The frame shown in Fig. P12-36 comprises three identical step-tapered columns and a continuous beam. Treat each column as a substructure to condense out all degrees of freedom except those which are common to the beam. Then use the substructure technique to analyze the frame subjected to the loading shown in Fig. P12-36.

Figure P12-36

13

The Flexibility Method

13-1 FORMULATION OF THE FLEXIBILITY EQUATIONS

The flexibility method, which was introduced in Chapter 11, is now employed to analyze trusses and frames. Prior to doing so, however, it is useful to review the solution procedure and the relevant relationships initially presented in Chapter 11.

We begin by identifying the essential variables that describe the behavior of the structure. We define the applied forces and associated displacements pertaining to unrestrained nodes as $\{\mathbf{P}_f\}$ and $\{\mathbf{\Delta}_f\}$, respectively; the internal (member) forces are represented as $\{\mathbf{F}\}$, while the corresponding internal displacements (i.e., the relative displacements of the ends of members) are represented as $\{\boldsymbol{\delta}\}$. For statically indeterminate structures, we identify redundant forces and the corresponding displacements as $\{\mathbf{F}_x\}$ and $\{\boldsymbol{\delta}_x\}$, so that $\{\mathbf{F}\}$ and $\{\boldsymbol{\delta}\}$ may be partitioned as $\{\mathbf{F}\} = \{\mathbf{F}_0 \,\vdots\, \mathbf{F}_x\}$ and $\{\boldsymbol{\delta}\} = \{\boldsymbol{\delta}_0 \,\vdots\, \boldsymbol{\delta}_x\}$.

To determine the member forces and joint displacements, we must involve three essential conditions: equilibrium, compatibility and force-deformation. The first condition, equilibrium, provides the following relationship between unknown internal forces and known applied loads:

$$\{\mathbf{P}_f\} = [\mathbf{B}_0 \,\vdots\, \mathbf{B}_x] \begin{Bmatrix} \mathbf{F}_0 \\ --- \\ \mathbf{F}_x \end{Bmatrix} \tag{13-1}$$

in which the global statics matrix $[\mathbf{B}_0 \,\vdots\, \mathbf{B}_x]$ comprises only geometric parameters related to the structure. Recall that $[\mathbf{B}_0]$ is always a square matrix (having an order equal to the number of elements in $\{\mathbf{F}_0\}$) and $[\mathbf{B}_x]$ is, in general, a rectangular matrix (having as many columns as the number of redundances). Equation (13-1) may be reformulated as

$$\left\{\begin{array}{c} \mathbf{F}_0 \\ \hline \mathbf{F}_x \end{array}\right\} = \left[\begin{array}{c|c} [\mathbf{C}_0] & [\mathbf{C}_x] \\ \hline [\mathbf{0}] & [\mathbf{I}] \end{array}\right] \left\{\begin{array}{c} \mathbf{P}_f \\ \hline \mathbf{F}_x \end{array}\right\} \tag{13-2}$$

where

$$[\mathbf{C}_0] = [\mathbf{B}_0]^{-1} \quad \text{and} \quad [\mathbf{C}_x] = -[\mathbf{B}_0]^{-1}[\mathbf{B}_x] \tag{13-3}$$

The condition of compatibility, relating member deformations and nodal displacements may be expressed as

$$\left\{\begin{array}{c} \boldsymbol{\Delta}_f \\ \hline \mathbf{0} \end{array}\right\} = \left[\begin{array}{c|c} [\mathbf{C}_0]^T & [\mathbf{0}] \\ \hline [\mathbf{C}_x]^T & [\mathbf{I}] \end{array}\right] \left\{\begin{array}{c} \boldsymbol{\delta}_0 \\ \hline \boldsymbol{\delta}_x \end{array}\right\} \tag{13-4}$$

Finally, the relationship between member forces and deformations may be expressed as

$$\left\{\begin{array}{c} \boldsymbol{\delta}_0 \\ \hline \boldsymbol{\delta}_x \end{array}\right\} = \left[\begin{array}{c|c} [\mathbf{f}_{00}] & [\mathbf{f}_{0x}] \\ \hline [\mathbf{f}_{x0}] & [\mathbf{f}_{xx}] \end{array}\right] \left\{\begin{array}{c} \mathbf{F}_0 \\ \hline \mathbf{F}_x \end{array}\right\} \tag{13-5}$$

in which the square symmetric matrix comprises the element flexibility matrices.

As described in Chapter 11, the conditions represented by Eqs. (13-2), (13-4), and (13-5) may be combined into the flexibility equations

$$\left\{\begin{array}{c} \boldsymbol{\Delta}_f \\ \hline \mathbf{0} \end{array}\right\} = \left[\begin{array}{c|c} [\mathscr{F}_{pp}] & [\mathscr{F}_{px}] \\ \hline [\mathscr{F}_{xp}] & [\mathscr{F}_{xx}] \end{array}\right] \left\{\begin{array}{c} \mathbf{P}_f \\ \hline \mathbf{F}_x \end{array}\right\} \tag{13-6}$$

where
$$[\mathscr{F}_{pp}] = [\mathbf{C}_0]^T[\mathbf{f}_{00}][\mathbf{C}_0] \tag{13-7a}$$

$$[\mathscr{F}_{px}] = [\mathscr{F}_{xp}]^T = [\mathbf{C}_0]^T[\mathbf{f}_{00}][\mathbf{C}_x] + [\mathbf{C}_0]^T[\mathbf{f}_{0x}] \tag{13-7b}$$

$$[\mathscr{F}_{xx}] = [\mathbf{C}_x]^T[\mathbf{f}_{00}][\mathbf{C}_x] + [\mathbf{C}_x]^T[\mathbf{f}_{0x}] + [\mathbf{f}_{x0}][\mathbf{C}_x] + [\mathbf{f}_{xx}] \tag{13-7c}$$

The lower partition of Eq. (13-6) may be solved directly for $\{\mathbf{F}_x\}$, which then may be substituted into Eq. (13-2) to find $\{\mathbf{F}_0\}$. These operations lead to

$$\{\mathbf{F}_x\} = -[\mathscr{F}_{xx}]^{-1}[\mathscr{F}_{xp}]\{\mathbf{P}_f\} \tag{13-8a}$$

$$\{\mathbf{F}_0\} = ([\mathbf{C}_0] - [\mathbf{C}_x][\mathscr{F}_{xx}]^{-1}[\mathscr{F}_{xp}])\{\mathbf{P}_f\} \tag{13-8b}$$

It is not necessary to compute the joint displacements in order to determine internal forces. If, however, displacements are desired, they may be computed as

$$\boldsymbol{\Delta}_f = [\mathscr{F}]\{\mathbf{P}_f\} \tag{13-9a}$$

where the system flexibility matrix is

$$[\mathcal{F}] = [\mathcal{F}_{pp}] - [\mathcal{F}_{px}][\mathcal{F}_{xx}]^{-1}[\mathcal{F}_{xp}] \qquad (13\text{-}9\text{b})$$

In the sequel, we investigate in detail the formulation and solution of the flexibility equation for trusses and frames. We begin by expressing equilibrium equations for these structures in the form of Eq. (13-1), which establishes the matrices $[\mathbf{B}_0]$ and $[\mathbf{B}_x]$. We then form the member flexibility matrices which constitute the matrices $[\mathbf{f}_{00}]$, $[\mathbf{f}_{0x}] = [\mathbf{f}_{x0}]^T$, and $[\mathbf{f}_{xx}]$. The final equations, Eqs. (13-8) and (13-9), may then be formulated and solved, as will be demonstrated later in examples.

13-2 EQUILIBRIUM EQUATIONS
FOR STATICALLY DETERMINATE STRUCTURES

Because internal forces in statically determinate structures may be determined solely by considering conditions of joint and member equilibrium, it is convenient to treat such cases first. For statically determinate systems, the equilibrium equations, Eq. (13-1), reduce to

$$\{\mathbf{P}_f\} = [\mathbf{B}_0]\{\mathbf{F}_0\} \qquad (13\text{-}10)$$

The global statics matrix $[\mathbf{B}_0]$ is square, and it may be inverted if the structure is kinematically stable. Hence, we seek a solution to Eq. (13-10) in the form

$$\{\mathbf{F}_0\} = [\mathbf{C}_0]\{\mathbf{P}_f\} \qquad (13\text{-}11\text{a})$$

where

$$[\mathbf{C}_0] = [\mathbf{B}_0]^{-1} \qquad (13\text{-}11\text{b})$$

Our primary objective therefore is to determine $[\mathbf{B}_0]$ and its inverse by expressing the equations of equilibrium at each unrestrained joint, i.e., an equilibrium equation corresponding to each degree of freedom.

Because trusses comprise bar elements, for which there exist only axial forces, the formulation of truss analysis follows directly that developed in Chapter 11 for systems composed of uniaxial springs. Each member of the truss is represented by its axial force which, for loads acting solely at the joints of the truss, is uniform throughout the member. Force equilibrium of the member is implied by our considering the same axial force to act at each node defining the end points of the bar. In a flexural member, however, the internal forces comprise, in addition to an axial force, shear force and bending moment, which generally vary along the length of the member. Although the shear force and bending moment at either end of the member may differ, they are related through conditions of equilibrium for the member. The equilibrium equations of the joints must be expressed in terms of independent internal forces, and thus we must invoke the equilibrium equations of each member to eliminate linearly dependent forces and moments. As will be demonstrated, we choose to express equilibrium of each joint that defines a member's end point in terms of the shear force and bending moment that act at only one of the two end points.

Example 13-1.   Consider the truss shown in Fig. 13-1(a), which originally was considered in Example 12-1. We wish to determine the bar forces and reactions due to the horizontal load applied at node 3.

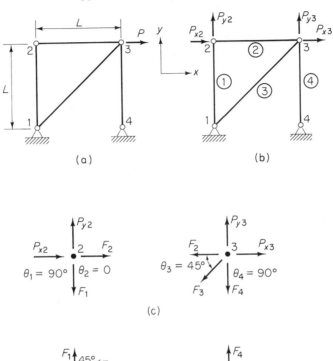

Figure 13-1

For generality, we consider horizontal and vertical forces to be applied in the positive x- and y-directions at all unconstrained nodes, as shown in Fig. 13-1(b). As usual, we also consider internal bar forces to be positive in tension, and we write the equations of equilibrium for the nodes corresponding to each unrestrained degree of freedom, as shown in Fig. 13-1(c). Equilibrium at node 2 dictates that

$$\sum F_x = 0 \qquad \text{or} \quad P_{x2} = -F_2$$

$$\sum F_y = 0 \qquad \text{or} \quad P_{y2} = F_1$$

Similarly, at node 3

$$\sum F_x = 0 \qquad \text{or} \quad P_{x3} = F_2 + F_3 \cos \theta_3$$

$$\sum F_y = 0 \qquad \text{or} \quad P_{y3} = F_3 \sin \theta_3 + F_4$$

Expressed in matrix form, these equilibrium equations are

$$\begin{Bmatrix} P_{x2} \\ P_{y2} \\ P_{x3} \\ P_{y3} \end{Bmatrix} \equiv \begin{Bmatrix} 0 \\ 0 \\ P \\ 0 \end{Bmatrix} = \begin{bmatrix} 0 & -1 & 0 & 0 \\ 1 & 0 & 0 & 0 \\ 0 & 1 & \lambda_3 & 0 \\ 0 & 0 & \mu_3 & 1 \end{bmatrix} \begin{Bmatrix} F_1 \\ F_2 \\ F_3 \\ F_4 \end{Bmatrix}$$

in which $\lambda_m = \cos \theta_m$ and $\mu_m = \sin \theta_m$. Here, $\lambda_3 = \mu_3 = \sqrt{2}/2$.

The square matrix of coefficients may be identified as $[\mathbf{B}_0]$. Its inverse is found to be

$$[\mathbf{C}_0] = \begin{bmatrix} 0 & 1 & 0 & 0 \\ -1 & 0 & 0 & 0 \\ 1/\lambda_3 & 0 & 1/\lambda_3 & 0 \\ -\mu_3/\lambda_3 & 0 & -\mu_3/\lambda_3 & 1 \end{bmatrix}$$

Hence, for the particular loading considered here, Eq. (13-11a) yields

$$\begin{Bmatrix} F_1 \\ F_2 \\ F_3 \\ F_4 \end{Bmatrix} = P \begin{Bmatrix} 0 \\ 0 \\ 1/\lambda_3 \\ -\mu_3/\lambda_3 \end{Bmatrix} = P \begin{Bmatrix} 0 \\ 0 \\ \sqrt{2} \\ -1 \end{Bmatrix}$$

Once the internal forces have been determined, the reactions may be found by expressing equilibrium conditions at the supports, as illustrated in Fig. 13-1(d). (Here reactions are chosen positive in the negative x- and y-directions; this choice is arbitrary, but is made to conform with the sign convention established later in Section 13-8.) Hence,

$$\begin{Bmatrix} R_{x1} \\ R_{y1} \\ R_{x4} \\ R_{y4} \end{Bmatrix} = P \begin{Bmatrix} 1 \\ \mu_3/\lambda_3 \\ 0 \\ -\mu_3/\lambda_3 \end{Bmatrix} = P \begin{Bmatrix} 1 \\ 1 \\ 0 \\ -1 \end{Bmatrix}$$

Obviously, inverting $[\mathbf{B}_0]$ is computationally intensive, and it can be argued that for this case the foregoing procedure is unduly complicated and time consuming. The inversion process is, however, equivalent to solving the four equilibrium equations for general loading conditions. In fact, $[\mathbf{C}_0]$ was obtained here by considering general loading conditions and solving the equilibrium equations in a traditional manner, rather than through the formal inversion of $[\mathbf{B}_0]$. Once $[\mathbf{C}_0]$ has been determined, the analysis of the truss subjected to multiple loading conditions is very efficiently performed.

Example 13-2. Analyze the beam shown in Fig. 13-2(a). For generality, we consider the loading shown in Fig. 13-2(b).

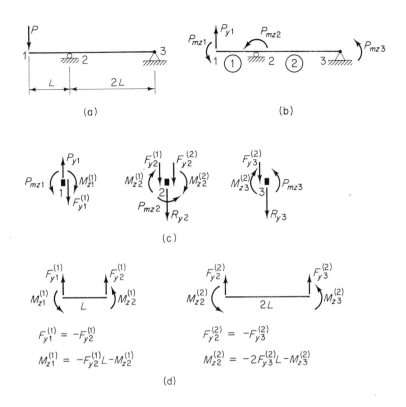

Figure 13-2

Because no horizontal loads are applied, we must express only vertical force and moment equilibrium conditions at those joints where corresponding vertical and rotational degrees of freedom are unrestrained. According to previously defined sign conventions adopted for matrix formulation, we consider positive axial forces and shear forces at the end points of a member to be positive in the positive x'- and y'-directions and positive bending moments acting at the end points of a member to be counterclockwise (i.e., in the positive z-direction). Note that in this case the positive y'-(local) direction also corresponds to the positive y-(global) direction. Thus, positive shear forces and bending moments act on the joints in the negative y- and z-directions, as shown in Fig. 13-2(c). Equilibrium conditions are expressed at each joint in a direction corresponding to an unrestrained degree of freedom. At node 1,

$$\sum F_y = 0 \qquad \text{or} \qquad -F_{y1}^{(1)} + P_{y1} = 0$$

$$\sum M_z = 0 \qquad \text{or} \qquad -M_{z1}^{(1)} + P_{mz1} = 0 \qquad \text{(a)}$$

at node 2,

$$\sum M_z = 0 \qquad \text{or} \qquad -M_{z2}^{(1)} - M_{z2}^{(2)} + P_{mz2} = 0 \qquad \text{(b)}$$

and, at node 3,

$$\sum M_z = 0 \qquad \text{or} \qquad -M_{z3}^{(2)} + P_{mz3} = 0 \qquad \text{(c)}$$

As noted above, the shear forces and bending moments acting at the ends of a member are not all independent. As shown in Fig. 13-2(d), equilibrium of member 1, for example, requires that

$$F_{y1}^{(1)} = -F_{y2}^{(1)}$$

and

$$M_{z1}^{(1)} = -F_{y2}^{(1)}L - M_{z2}^{(1)}$$

(d)

Similar relationships exist for member 2, as indicated in Fig. 13-2(d).

We choose to express the equilibrium conditions of each joint in terms of the shear force and bending moment acting at the right end of each member. (This choice is arbitrary, as shown by Example 13-3). Then, by substituting Eqs. (d) into Eq. (a), we may express equilibrium of node 1 as

$$F_{y2}^{(1)} + P_{y1} = 0$$

$$F_{y2}^{(1)} L + M_{z2}^{(1)} + P_{mz1} = 0$$

(e)

The moment equilibrium equation is similarly modified by accounting for the equilibrium conditions of member 2, to yield

$$-M_{z2}^{(1)} + 2F_{y3}^{(2)}L + M_{z3}^{(2)} + P_{mz2} = 0 \qquad \text{(f)}$$

The independent shear forces and bending moments acting on the three nodes of the structure are shown in Fig. 13-2(e). The relevant nodal equilibrium equations, Eqs. (e), (f), and (c), may then be expressed in matrix form as

$$\begin{Bmatrix} P_{y1} \\ P_{mz1} \\ P_{mz2} \\ P_{mz3} \end{Bmatrix} = \begin{bmatrix} -1 & 0 & 0 & 0 \\ -L & -1 & 0 & 0 \\ 0 & 1 & -2L & -1 \\ 0 & 0 & 0 & 1 \end{bmatrix} \begin{Bmatrix} F_{y2}^{(1)} \\ M_{z2}^{(1)} \\ F_{y3}^{(2)} \\ M_{z3}^{(2)} \end{Bmatrix} \qquad \text{(g)}$$

where, for the present case,

$$\begin{Bmatrix} P_{y1} \\ P_{mz1} \\ P_{mz2} \\ P_{mz3} \end{Bmatrix} = \begin{Bmatrix} -P \\ 0 \\ 0 \\ 0 \end{Bmatrix}$$

Recognizing Eq. (g) to have the form

$${\mathbf{P}_f} = [\mathbf{B}_0]{\mathbf{F}_0}$$

we may either invert $[\mathbf{B}_0]$ formally or solve the equations in a traditional manner to obtain

$${\mathbf{F}_0} = [\mathbf{C}_0]{\mathbf{P}_f}$$

or

$$\begin{Bmatrix} F_{y2}^{(1)} \\ M_{z2}^{(1)} \\ F_{y3}^{(2)} \\ M_{z3}^{(2)} \end{Bmatrix} = \begin{bmatrix} -1 & 0 & 0 & 0 \\ L & -1 & 0 & 0 \\ 1/2 & -1/2L & -1/2L & -1/2L \\ 0 & 0 & 0 & 1 \end{bmatrix} \begin{Bmatrix} P_{y1} \\ P_{mz1} \\ P_{mz2} \\ P_{mz3} \end{Bmatrix}$$

For the particular loading considered in Fig. 13-2(a),

$$\begin{Bmatrix} F_{y2}^{(1)} \\ M_{z2}^{(1)} \\ F_{y3}^{(2)} \\ M_{z3}^{(2)} \end{Bmatrix} = -P \begin{Bmatrix} -1 \\ L \\ 1/2 \\ 0 \end{Bmatrix}$$

The remaining internal forces and reactions may be determined from the equilibrium conditions of the members and joints described in Figs. 13-2(c), (d), and (e), and shear force and bending moment diagrams may be constructed by employing the sign convention normally used for that purpose.

Example 13-3. Analyze the framework subjected to the loading shown in Fig. 13-3(a). In addition to generalized loads, of which only P_{x2} is nonzero, we must accommodate the distributed transverse load acting upward on the beam. The complete set of applied loads is shown in Fig. 13-3(b).

Internal forces acting at the end points of the two members are referred to the local member coordinates, as shown in Fig. 13-3(b). These forces then act in the reverse directions on the nodes, as illustrated in Fig. 13-3(c). As noted in the preceding example, not all the nodal forces are linearly independent. Rather, as shown in Fig. 13-3(d), in order to satisfy equilibrium, only three independent generalized forces exist for each member. We previously chose to retain all the forces at one end of each member and eliminate those at the other through satisfaction of equilibrium for the member. Here, somewhat arbitrarily, we choose to formulate the problem in terms of the axial force acting at one end of each member and the bending moments at both ends. We thus eliminate the six forces appearing on the left side of the equilibrium equations presented in Fig. 13-3(d). Note that these equations also incorporate the distributed loading acting on the beam.

The equilibrium equations for the system are

$$\begin{Bmatrix} P_{x1} \\ P_{y1} \\ P_{mz1} \\ P_{x2} \\ P_{y2} \\ P_{mz2} \end{Bmatrix} = \begin{bmatrix} -1 & 0 & 0 & 0 & 0 & 0 \\ 0 & 1/L & 1/L & 0 & 0 & 0 \\ 0 & 1 & 0 & 0 & 0 & 0 \\ 1 & 0 & 0 & 0 & 1/2L & 1/2L \\ 0 & -1/L & -1/L & 1 & 0 & 0 \\ 0 & 0 & 0 & 0 & 1 & 0 \end{bmatrix} \begin{Bmatrix} F_{x2}^{(1)} \\ M_{z1}^{(1)} \\ M_{z2}^{(1)} \\ F_{y3}^{(2)} \\ M_{z2}^{(2)} \\ M_{z3}^{(2)} \end{Bmatrix} + \begin{Bmatrix} 0 \\ -qL/2 \\ 0 \\ 0 \\ -qL/2 \\ 0 \end{Bmatrix}$$

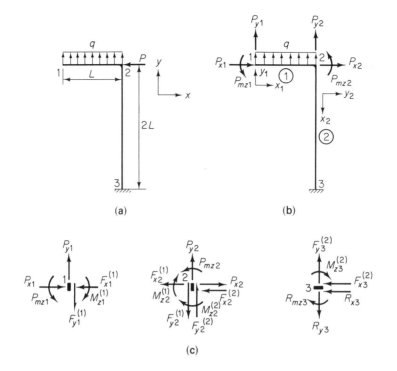

(a)

(b)

(c)

$F_{y2}^{(2)} = -F_{y3}^{(2)}$

$F_{x2}^{(2)} = \dfrac{1}{2L}(M_{z2}^{(2)} + M_{z3}^{(2)})$

$F_{x3}^{(2)} = -\dfrac{1}{2L}(M_{z2}^{(2)} + M_{z3}^{(2)})$

$F_{x1}^{(1)} = -F_{x2}^{(1)}$

$F_{y1}^{(1)} = \dfrac{1}{L}(M_{z1}^{(1)} + M_{z2}^{(1)}) - \dfrac{qL}{2}$

$F_{y2}^{(1)} = -\dfrac{1}{L}(M_{z1}^{(1)} + M_{z2}^{(1)}) - \dfrac{qL}{2}$

(d)

Figure 13-3

The internal forces are then found to be

$$
\begin{Bmatrix} F_{x2}^{(1)} \\ M_{z1}^{(1)} \\ M_{z2}^{(1)} \\ F_{y3}^{(2)} \\ M_{z2}^{(2)} \\ M_{z3}^{(2)} \end{Bmatrix}
=
\begin{bmatrix}
-1 & 0 & 0 & 0 & 0 & 0 \\
0 & 0 & 1 & 0 & 0 & 0 \\
0 & L & -1 & 0 & 0 & 0 \\
0 & 1 & 0 & 0 & 1 & 0 \\
0 & -L & 1 & 0 & 0 & 1 \\
2L & L & -1 & 2L & 0 & -1
\end{bmatrix}
\begin{Bmatrix} P_{x1} \\ P_{y1} \\ P_{mz1} \\ P_{x2} \\ P_{y2} \\ P_{mz2} \end{Bmatrix}
+
\begin{Bmatrix} 0 \\ 0 \\ qL^2/2 \\ qL \\ -qL^2/2 \\ qL^2/2 \end{Bmatrix}
$$

For the particular loading given,

$$
\begin{Bmatrix} P_{x1} \\ P_{y1} \\ P_{mz1} \\ P_{x2} \\ P_{y2} \\ P_{mz2} \end{Bmatrix} = \begin{Bmatrix} 0 \\ 0 \\ 0 \\ -P \\ 0 \\ 0 \end{Bmatrix} \quad \text{and hence} \quad \begin{Bmatrix} F_{x2}^{(1)} \\ M_{z1}^{(1)} \\ M_{z2}^{(1)} \\ F_{y3}^{(2)} \\ M_{z2}^{(2)} \\ M_{z3}^{(2)} \end{Bmatrix} = \begin{Bmatrix} 0 \\ 0 \\ qL^2/2 \\ qL \\ -qL^2/2 \\ -2PL + qL^2/2 \end{Bmatrix}
$$

The remaining internal nodal forces may be recovered from the equilibrium conditions expressed in Fig. 13-3(d). Also, reactions may be evaluated from the equilibrium conditions of the supports. In this case, equilibrium of node 3 requires that

$$
R_{x3} = -F_{x3}^{(2)} = \frac{1}{2L}(M_{z2}^{(2)} + M_{z3}^{(2)})
$$

$$
R_{y3} = F_{y3}^{(2)}
$$

$$
R_{mz3} = -M_{z3}^{(2)}
$$

or, for the particular loading considered in Fig. 13-3(a),

$$
R_{x3} = -P
$$

$$
R_{y3} = qL
$$

$$
P_{mz3} = 2PL - \frac{qL^2}{2}
$$

13-3 FLEXIBILITY MATRICES FOR BAR AND BEAM ELEMENTS

The determination of nodal displacements and, more importantly, the solution of statically indeterminate structures, require that force-deformation relationships of the members enter the formulation. After we have done this, we may deploy Eqs. (13-8) and (13-9) which incorporate [**f**], the matrix of member flexibilities.

   Bar element.   The flexibility matrix for a bar element relates the (constant) axial force to the relative axial displacements of the two ends of the member. In general, we may write this relationship as

$$
\{\boldsymbol{\delta}_m\} = [\mathbf{f}_m]\{\mathbf{F}_m\} \tag{13-12}
$$

where, for the bar shown in Fig. 13-4, $\{\boldsymbol{\delta}_m\}$ represents the relative axial displacement between nodes j and i, or $\{\boldsymbol{\delta}_m\} = \{u'_j - u'_i\}$ (the prime being a re-

Figure 13-4

minder that the displacements are referred to local coordinates); $\{\mathbf{F}_m\}$ is the bar force, i.e., $\{\mathbf{F}_m\} = F_j = -F_i$; and $[\mathbf{f}_m] = [(L/EA)_m]$ is the member flexibility matrix (of order one). Then

$$\{\boldsymbol{\delta}_m\} = [(L/EA)_m]\{\mathbf{F}_m\} \qquad (13\text{-}13)$$

Clearly, this flexibility equation is identical to that described in Chapter 11 for a spring element when the spring constant k_m is set equal to $(EA/L)_m$.

The matrix of member flexibilities $[\mathbf{f}]$ relates all M bar forces in the structure to the axial deformation of each bar, i.e.,

$$\{\boldsymbol{\delta}\} = [\mathbf{f}]\{\mathbf{F}\} \qquad (13\text{-}14)$$

where

$$\{\boldsymbol{\delta}\} = \begin{Bmatrix} \delta_1 \\ \delta_2 \\ \cdot \\ \cdot \\ \cdot \\ \delta_M \end{Bmatrix} \qquad \text{and} \quad \{\mathbf{F}\} = \begin{Bmatrix} F_1 \\ F_2 \\ \cdot \\ \cdot \\ \cdot \\ F_M \end{Bmatrix} \qquad (13\text{-}15a,b)$$

and $[\mathbf{f}]$ is a diagonal matrix of the form

$$[\mathbf{f}] = \begin{bmatrix} [\mathbf{f}_1] & & & \\ & [\mathbf{f}_2] & & \\ & & \ddots & \\ & & & [\mathbf{f}_M] \end{bmatrix} \equiv \begin{bmatrix} \left(\dfrac{L}{EA}\right)_1 & & & \\ & \left(\dfrac{L}{EA}\right)_2 & & \\ & & \ddots & \\ & & & \left(\dfrac{L}{EA}\right)_M \end{bmatrix} \qquad (13\text{-}15c)$$

Planar beam element. The flexibility relationship for a beam element undergoing deformation in a single principal plane also may be expressed in the form of Eq. (13-12). Because three nodal degrees of freedom and corresponding forces are required to characterize a beam element, however, the matrix $[\mathbf{f}_m]$ must be of order 3×3. Referring to Fig. 13-5(a), in which one end (node j) of the beam element m is free and the other (node i) is fully restrained (to prevent rigid-body motion), we have

$$\begin{Bmatrix} u'_j \\ v'_j \\ \theta'_{z'j} \end{Bmatrix}_m = \begin{bmatrix} \dfrac{L}{EA} & 0 & 0 \\ 0 & \dfrac{L^3}{3EI_{z'}} & \dfrac{L^2}{2EI_{z'}} \\ 0 & \dfrac{L^{2'}}{2EI_{z'}} & \dfrac{L'}{EI_{z'}} \end{bmatrix}_m \begin{Bmatrix} F^{(m)}_{x'j} \\ F^{(m)}_{y'j} \\ M^{(m)}_{z'j} \end{Bmatrix} \qquad (13\text{-}16)$$

Thus we identify

$$[\boldsymbol{\delta}_m] = \left\{\begin{matrix} u'_j \\ v'_j \\ \theta_{z'j} \end{matrix}\right\}_m \qquad \{\mathbf{F}_m\} = \left\{\begin{matrix} F^{(m)}_{x'j} \\ F^{(m)}_{y'j} \\ M^{(m)}_{z'j} \end{matrix}\right\} \qquad \text{(13-17a, b)}$$

and the symmetric member flexibility matrix

$$[\mathbf{f}_m] = \begin{bmatrix} \dfrac{L}{EA} & 0 & 0 \\ 0 & \dfrac{L^3}{3EI_{z'}} & \dfrac{L^2}{2EI_{z'}} \\ 0 & \dfrac{L^2}{2EI_{z'}} & \dfrac{L'}{EI_{z'}} \end{bmatrix}_m = \dfrac{L^3}{EI_{z'}}\begin{bmatrix} \dfrac{I_{z'}}{AL^2} & 0 & 0 \\ 0 & \dfrac{1}{3} & \dfrac{1}{2L} \\ 0 & \dfrac{1}{2L} & \dfrac{1}{L^2} \end{bmatrix}_m \qquad \text{(13-17c)}$$

Equation (13-16) was derived by solving the two uncoupled governing differential equations for a beam, namely

$$\frac{d^2 u'}{dx'^2} = 0 \qquad \text{(13-18a)}$$

and

$$\frac{d^4 v'}{dx'^4} = 0 \qquad \text{(13-18b)}$$

subject to the respective boundary conditions

$$u'(0) = 0 \qquad \frac{du'(L)}{dx'} = \frac{F^{(m)}_{x'j}}{EA} \qquad \text{(13-19a, b)}$$

$$v'(0) = 0 \qquad \frac{d^2 v'(L)}{dx^2} = \frac{M^{(m)}_{z'j}}{EI_{z'}} \qquad \text{(13-19c, d)}$$

$$\frac{dv'(0)}{dx'} = 0 \qquad \frac{d^3 v'(L)}{dx'^3} = -\frac{F^{(m)}_{y'j}}{EI_{z'}} \qquad \text{(13-19e, f)}$$

The member flexibility matrix also could have been determined by inverting the member stiffness matrix, subject to the constraints shown in Fig. 13-5(a).

An alternative form of the member flexibility matrix may be developed in conjunction with the support conditions shown in Fig. 13-5(b). Here rigid-body

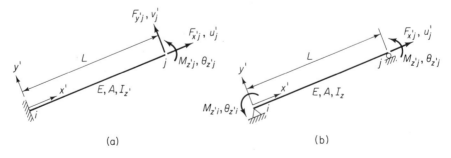

(a)   (b)

Figure 13-5

motion is still prevented while permitting both ends of the member to rotate. We then may define the member displacement and force vectors as

$$\{\boldsymbol{\delta}_m\} = \begin{Bmatrix} u'_j \\ \theta_{z'i} \\ \theta_{z'j} \end{Bmatrix}_m \qquad \{\mathbf{F}_m\} = \begin{Bmatrix} F^{(m)}_{x'j} \\ M^{(m)}_{z'i} \\ M^{(m)}_{z'j} \end{Bmatrix} \qquad \text{(13-20a,b)}$$

and the member flexibility matrix as

$$[\mathbf{f}_m] = \begin{bmatrix} \dfrac{L}{AE} & 0 & 0 \\ 0 & \dfrac{L}{3EI_{z'}} & -\dfrac{L}{6EI_{z'}} \\ 0 & -\dfrac{L}{6EI_{z'}} & \dfrac{L}{3EI_{z'}} \end{bmatrix}_m = \dfrac{L}{6EI_{z'}} \begin{bmatrix} \dfrac{6I_{z'}}{A} & 0 & 0 \\ 0 & 2 & -1 \\ 0 & -1 & 2 \end{bmatrix}_m \qquad \text{(13-20c)}$$

This alternative form of $[\mathbf{f}_m]$ offers some advantage when the axial force is ignored, as in the case of continuous beams, for example; then all remaining coefficients in $[\mathbf{f}_m]$ possess the common factor $L/6EI_{z'}$.

Three-dimensional beam element. Analysis of bending of members comprising space frames requires the use of a member flexibility matrix which relates six independent generalized forces to the corresponding generalized displacements. In a manner analogous to the preceding derivation, we could derive the relationship between the forces and displacements shown in Fig. 13-6. The vectors $\{\boldsymbol{\delta}_m\}$ and $\{\mathbf{F}_m\}$ associated with this configuration are

$$\{\boldsymbol{\delta}_m\} = \begin{Bmatrix} u'_j \\ v'_j \\ w'_j \\ \theta_{x'j} \\ \theta_{y'j} \\ \theta_{z'j} \end{Bmatrix}_m \qquad \text{and} \quad \{\mathbf{F}_m\} = \begin{Bmatrix} F^{(m)}_{x'j} \\ F^{(m)}_{y'j} \\ F^{(m)}_{z'j} \\ M^{(m)}_{x'j} \\ M^{(m)}_{y'j} \\ M^{(m)}_{z'j} \end{Bmatrix} \qquad \text{(13-21a, b)}$$

We then find $[\mathbf{f}_m]$ to have the form

$$[\mathbf{f}_m] = \begin{bmatrix} \dfrac{L}{EA} & 0 & 0 & 0 & 0 & 0 \\ 0 & \dfrac{L^3}{3EI_{z'}} & 0 & 0 & 0 & \dfrac{L^2}{2EI_{z'}} \\ 0 & 0 & \dfrac{L^3}{3EI_{y'}} & 0 & -\dfrac{L^2}{2EI_{y'}} & 0 \\ 0 & 0 & 0 & \dfrac{L}{GJ} & 0 & 0 \\ 0 & 0 & -\dfrac{L^2}{2EI_{y'}} & 0 & \dfrac{L}{EI_{y'}} & 0 \\ 0 & \dfrac{L^2}{2EI_{z'}} & 0 & 0 & 0 & \dfrac{L}{EI_{z'}} \end{bmatrix} \qquad \text{(13-21c)}$$

The Flexibility Method   Chap. 13

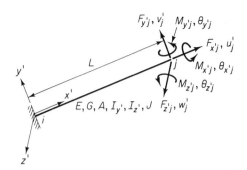

Figure 13-6

Regardless whether the member flexibility matrix possesses the form provided by Eq. (13-17c), Eq. (13-20c), or Eq. (13-21c), the matrix of member flexibilities $[\mathbf{f}]$ for the structure acquires the form

$$[\mathbf{f}] = \begin{bmatrix} [\mathbf{f}_1] & & & \\ & [\mathbf{f}_2] & & \\ & & \ddots & \\ & & & [\mathbf{f}_M] \end{bmatrix} \tag{13-22}$$

where, in contrast with the truss element, the matrices $[\mathbf{f}_m]$ are not diagonal; hence $[\mathbf{f}]$ is not diagonal, but it is symmetric, of course. Finally, note that in deriving the member flexibilities, we have assumed that no loading is applied between the ends of the member. We shall consider the case of distributed loading in Section 13-6.

13-4 ANALYSIS OF STATICALLY INDETERMINATE STRUCTURES SUBJECTED TO GENERALIZED LOADS

The analysis of statically indeterminate structures requires the solution of Eqs. (13-8) and, if displacements are desired, the solution of Eq. (11-9), i.e.,

$$\{\mathbf{F}_x\} = -[\mathscr{F}_{xx}]^{-1}[\mathscr{F}_{xp}]\{\mathbf{P}_f\} \tag{13-8a}$$

$$\{\mathbf{F}_0\} = ([\mathbf{C}_0] - [\mathbf{C}_x][\mathscr{F}_{xx}]^{-1}[\mathscr{F}_{xp}])\{\mathbf{P}_f\} \tag{13-8b}$$

$$\{\mathbf{\Delta}_f\} = [\mathscr{F}]\{\mathbf{P}_f\} \tag{13-9a}$$

where

$$[\mathscr{F}] = [\mathscr{F}_{pp}] - [\mathscr{F}_{px}][\mathscr{F}_{xx}]^{-1}[\mathscr{F}_{xp}] \tag{13-9b}$$

The matrices that appear in these equations have been defined previously in Chapter 11 and Section 13-1. As noted previously, the derivation of the equations incorporates not only conditions of equilibrium but also of compatibility and force deformation (reflected by the matrix of member flexibilities).

In the sequel, we analyze a truss and a beam subjected to generalized forces, i.e., forces applied to nodal points.

Example 13-4. Analyze the truss shown in Fig. 13-7(a). This truss, which was considered in Example 12-1, is statically indeterminate to one degree. Because in Example 13-1 we have solved the statically determinate truss in which one of the diagonals, member 5, was absent, it is convenient for us now to designate the force in this member as the redundance.

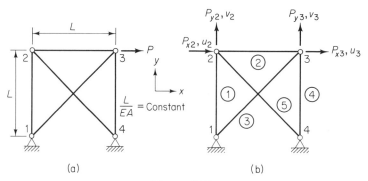

(a)   (b)

Figure 13-7

The equations of equilibrium for the unrestrained nodes, joints 2 and 3, are expressed as

$$\{P_f\} = [B]\{F\} \tag{a}$$

where the generalized forces comprising $\{P_f\}$ and the member designations are shown in Fig. 13-7(b). Because F_5, the force in the redundant member, is now included, Eq. (a) is

$$\begin{Bmatrix} P_{x2} \\ P_{y2} \\ P_{x3} \\ P_{y3} \end{Bmatrix} = \begin{bmatrix} 0 & -1 & 0 & 0 & \vdots & -\lambda_5 \\ 1 & 0 & 0 & 0 & \vdots & \mu_5 \\ 0 & 1 & \lambda_3 & 0 & \vdots & 0 \\ 0 & 0 & \mu_3 & 1 & \vdots & 0 \end{bmatrix} \begin{Bmatrix} F_1 \\ F_2 \\ F_3 \\ F_4 \\ \hdashline F_5 \end{Bmatrix} \tag{b}$$

where λ_m and μ_m are the cosine and sine of the angle that member m makes with the x-axis (here $\mu_3 = \lambda_3 = \lambda_5 = \mu_5 = 1/\sqrt{2}$).

We have partitioned the internal force vector and the global statics matrix to acquire the forms

$$\{F\} = \{F_0 \vdots F_x\}$$

$$[B] = [B_0 \vdots B_x]$$

in which $[B_0]$ may be recognized as the global statics matrix developed for the statically determinate truss in Example 13-1. We may now form

$$[C_0] = [B_0]^{-1} = \begin{bmatrix} 0 & 1 & 0 & 0 \\ -1 & 0 & 0 & 0 \\ 1/\lambda_3 & 0 & 1/\lambda_3 & 0 \\ -\mu_3/\lambda_3 & 0 & -\mu_3/\lambda_3 & 1 \end{bmatrix} = \begin{bmatrix} 0 & 1 & 0 & 0 \\ -1 & 0 & 0 & 0 \\ \sqrt{2} & 0 & \sqrt{2} & 0 \\ -1 & 0 & -1 & 1 \end{bmatrix}$$

and

$$(c)$$

$$[\mathbf{C}_x] = -[\mathbf{B}_0]^{-1}[\mathbf{B}_x] = \begin{bmatrix} -\mu_5 \\ -\lambda_5 \\ \lambda_5/\lambda_3 \\ -\lambda_5\mu_3/\lambda_3 \end{bmatrix} = \begin{bmatrix} -1/\sqrt{2} \\ -1/\sqrt{2} \\ 1 \\ -1/\sqrt{2} \end{bmatrix}$$

The flexibility matrix for each member is

$$[\mathbf{f}_m] = \left[\left(\frac{L}{EA} \right)_m \right]$$

and the matrix of member flexibilities is

$$[\mathbf{f}] = \begin{bmatrix} [\mathbf{f}_1] & & & & \\ & [\mathbf{f}_2] & & & \\ & & [\mathbf{f}_3] & & \\ & & & [\mathbf{f}_4] & \\ & & & & [\mathbf{f}_5] \end{bmatrix}$$

where the flexibilities for all members are equal in this particular case. We write $[\mathbf{f}]$ in partitioned form in accord with the partitioning of $\{\mathbf{F}\}$ and $[\mathbf{B}]$. Hence,

$$[\mathbf{f}] = \begin{bmatrix} [\mathbf{f}_{00}] & \vdots & [\mathbf{f}_{0x}] \\ \cdots & + & \cdots \\ [\mathbf{f}_{x0}] & \vdots & [\mathbf{f}_{xx}] \end{bmatrix} = \frac{L}{EA} \begin{bmatrix} 1 & & & \vdots \\ & 1 & & \vdots \\ & & 1 & \vdots \\ \cdots & \cdots & \cdots & + \cdots \\ & & & \vdots & 1 \end{bmatrix} \qquad \text{(d)}$$

It is to be understood that all coefficients that are not explicitly designated in $[\mathbf{f}]$ are zero. Thus, for all problems involving only bar elements,

$$[\mathbf{f}_{0x}] = [\mathbf{f}_{x0}]^T = [\mathbf{0}]$$

Now we may form

$$[\mathscr{F}_{pp}] = [\mathbf{C}_0]^T[\mathbf{f}_{00}][\mathbf{C}_0] = \begin{bmatrix} 4 & 0 & 3 & -1 \\ 0 & 1 & 0 & 0 \\ 3 & 0 & 3 & -1 \\ -1 & 0 & -1 & 0 \end{bmatrix}$$

$$[\mathscr{F}_{px}] = [\mathscr{F}_{xp}]^T = [\mathbf{C}_0]^T[\mathbf{f}_{00}][\mathbf{C}_x] + [\mathbf{C}_0]^T[\mathbf{f}_{0x}] = \frac{L}{\sqrt{2}EA} \begin{bmatrix} 4 \\ -1 \\ 3 \\ -1 \end{bmatrix}$$

$$[\mathscr{F}_{xx}] = [\mathbf{C}_x]^T[\mathbf{f}_{00}][\mathbf{C}_x] + [\mathbf{C}_x]^T[\mathbf{f}_{0x}] + [\mathbf{f}_{x0}][\mathbf{C}_x] + [\mathbf{f}_{xx}] = \frac{7L}{2EA}$$

Finally, Eqs. (13-8) may be employed to obtain the member forces.

$$\{\mathbf{F}_x\} \equiv F_5 = -[\mathscr{F}_{xx}]^{-1}[\mathscr{F}_{xp}]\{\mathbf{P}_f\} = \frac{\sqrt{2}}{7}(-4P_{x2} + P_{y2} - 3P_{x3} + P_{y3})$$

$$\{\mathbf{F}_0\} \equiv \begin{Bmatrix} F_1 \\ F_2 \\ F_3 \\ F_4 \end{Bmatrix} = ([\mathbf{C}_0] - [\mathbf{C}_x][\mathscr{F}_{xx}]^{-1}[\mathscr{F}_{xp}])\{\mathbf{P}_f\} = \frac{1}{7} \begin{bmatrix} 4 & 6 & 3 & -1 \\ -3 & -1 & 3 & -1 \\ 3\sqrt{2} & \sqrt{2} & 4\sqrt{2} & \sqrt{2} \\ -3 & -1 & -4 & 6 \end{bmatrix} \begin{Bmatrix} P_{x2} \\ P_{y2} \\ P_{x3} \\ P_{y3} \end{Bmatrix}$$

In this case the applied loads are

$$\begin{Bmatrix} P_{x2} \\ P_{y2} \\ P_{x3} \\ P_{y3} \end{Bmatrix} = \begin{Bmatrix} 0 \\ 0 \\ P \\ 0 \end{Bmatrix}$$

Therefore,

$$F_5 = -\frac{3\sqrt{2}}{7}P \quad \text{and} \quad \begin{Bmatrix} F_1 \\ F_2 \\ F_3 \\ F_4 \end{Bmatrix} = \frac{P}{7} \begin{Bmatrix} 3 \\ 3 \\ 4\sqrt{2} \\ -4 \end{Bmatrix}$$

If displacements are desired, they may be obtained from Eqs. (13-9). Hence,

$$\{\mathbf{\Delta}_f\} \equiv \begin{Bmatrix} u_2 \\ v_2 \\ u_3 \\ v_3 \end{Bmatrix} = [\mathcal{F}]\{\mathbf{P}_f\} \tag{e}$$

where

$$[\mathcal{F}] = [\mathcal{F}_{pp}] - [\mathcal{F}_{px}][\mathcal{F}_{xx}]^{-1}[\mathcal{F}_{xp}] = \frac{L}{7EA} \begin{bmatrix} 12 & 4 & 9 & -3 \\ 4 & 6 & 3 & -1 \\ 9 & 3 & 12 & -4 \\ -3 & -1 & -4 & -1 \end{bmatrix} \tag{f}$$

For the particular loading in Fig. 13-7(a), Eqs. (e) and (f) yield

$$\begin{Bmatrix} u_2 \\ v_2 \\ u_3 \\ v_3 \end{Bmatrix} = \frac{PL}{7EA} \begin{Bmatrix} 9 \\ 3 \\ 12 \\ -4 \end{Bmatrix}$$

The foregoing results were previously obtained by the direct stiffness method in Example 12-1. If we would invert the system flexibility matrix $[\mathcal{F}]$ determined above, we would find the inverted matrix to be equal to $[\mathbf{K}_{ff}]$ calculated in Example 12-1.

Example 13-5. We now consider the statically indeterminate beam shown in Figure 13-8(a). The beam is similar to that analyzed in Example 13-2, except that here the right support is clamped rather than hinged, thus rendering the structure statically indeterminate to one degree.

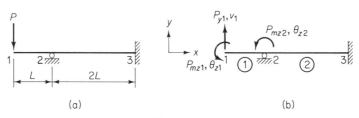

(a)   (b)

Figure 13-8

The equilibrium equations relating internal shear forces and bending moments to the generalized forces shown in Fig. (13-8b) may be written as

$$\begin{Bmatrix} P_{y1} \\ P_{mz1} \\ P_{mz2} \end{Bmatrix} = \begin{bmatrix} -1 & 0 & 0 & \vdots & 0 \\ -L & -1 & 0 & \vdots & 0 \\ 0 & 1 & -2L & \vdots & -1 \end{bmatrix} \begin{Bmatrix} F_{y2}^{(1)} \\ M_{z2}^{(1)} \\ F_{y3}^{(2)} \\ \text{----} \\ M_{z3}^{(2)} \end{Bmatrix} \tag{g}$$

These equations are identical to the first three equilibrium equations derived previously in Example 13-2. Now, because the right support is clamped, the fourth equilibrium equation previously obtained is no longer applicable.

We may cast Eq. (g) in the form

$$\{\mathbf{P}_f\} = [\mathbf{B}_0 \mathrel{\vdots} \mathbf{B}_x] \begin{Bmatrix} \mathbf{F}_0 \\ \text{---} \\ \mathbf{F}_x \end{Bmatrix}$$

by defining

$$\{\mathbf{P}_f\} = \begin{Bmatrix} P_{y1} \\ P_{mz1} \\ P_{mz2} \end{Bmatrix} \qquad \begin{Bmatrix} \mathbf{F}_0 \\ \text{---} \\ \mathbf{F}_x \end{Bmatrix} = \begin{Bmatrix} F_{y2}^{(1)} \\ M_{z2}^{(1)} \\ F_{y3}^{(2)} \\ \text{----} \\ M_{z3}^{(2)} \end{Bmatrix}$$

and

$$[\mathbf{B}_0 \mathrel{\vdots} \mathbf{B}_x] = \begin{bmatrix} -1 & 0 & 0 & 0 \\ -L & -1 & 0 & 0 \\ 0 & 1 & -2L & -1 \end{bmatrix}$$

Therefore,

$$[\mathbf{C}_0] = \begin{bmatrix} -1 & 0 & 0 \\ L & -1 & 0 \\ 1/2 & -1/2L & -1/2L \end{bmatrix}$$

and

$$[\mathbf{C}_x] = \begin{bmatrix} 0 \\ 0 \\ -1/2L \end{bmatrix}$$

We have selected $M_{z3}^{(2)}$ as the redundant force, a convenient choice because in Example 13-2 we have already solved the problem for which $M_{z3}^{(2)} = 0$. Alternatively, we could have chosen the redundant force to be $F_{y3}^{(2)}$. However, neither $F_{y2}^{(1)}$ nor $M_{z2}^{(1)}$ would be acceptable choices for the redundant, because the released structure (in which the redundant forces have been removed) would be kinematically unstable; in such a case $[\mathbf{B}_0]$ would be singular.

The member flexibility matrix may be expressed as

$$[\mathbf{f}]_m = \left(\frac{L}{EI_z'}\right)_m \begin{bmatrix} \dfrac{L_m^2}{3} & \dfrac{L_m}{2} \\ \dfrac{L_m}{2} & 1 \end{bmatrix}$$

where we have reduced the matrix to order 2 by deleting the first row and column in Eq. (13-16c), due to the absence of axial deformation in the present case. We may now write

$$[\mathbf{f}] = \begin{bmatrix} [\mathbf{f}_{00}] & \vdots & [\mathbf{f}_{0x}] \\ \text{-----} & + & \text{-----} \\ [\mathbf{f}_{x0}] & \vdots & [\mathbf{f}_{xx}] \end{bmatrix} = \frac{L}{EI_z} \begin{bmatrix} L^2/3 & L/2 & 0 & \vdots & 0 \\ L/2 & 1 & 0 & \vdots & 0 \\ 0 & 0 & 8L^2/3 & \vdots & 2L \\ \text{-----} & & & + & \text{--} \\ 0 & 0 & 2L & \vdots & 2 \end{bmatrix}$$

Note that, in contrast with the matrix of member flexibilities for a truss, for beams $[\mathbf{f}]$ is not diagonal and $[\mathbf{f}_{0x}] = [\mathbf{f}_{x0}]^T$ are not null matrices.

Following the procedure described in the preceding example, we obtain

$$[\mathscr{F}_{pp}] = \frac{L}{6EI_z} \begin{bmatrix} 6L^2 & -7L & -4L \\ -7L & 10 & 4 \\ -4L & 4 & 4 \end{bmatrix}$$

$$[\mathscr{F}_{px}] = [\mathscr{F}_{xp}]^T = \frac{L}{3EI_z} \begin{bmatrix} L \\ -1 \\ -1 \end{bmatrix}$$

$$[\mathscr{F}_{xx}] = \frac{2}{3} \frac{L}{EI_z}$$

and

$$[\mathscr{F}] = \frac{L}{6EI_z} \begin{bmatrix} 5L^2 & -6L & -3L \\ -6L & 9 & 3 \\ -3L & 3 & 3 \end{bmatrix}$$

We then obtain

$$\{\mathbf{F}_x\} \equiv M_{z3}^{(2)} = -\frac{1}{2}P_{y1}L + \frac{1}{2}P_{mz1} + \frac{1}{2}P_{mz2}$$

$$\{\mathbf{F}_0\} \equiv \begin{Bmatrix} F_{y2}^{(1)} \\ M_{z2}^{(1)} \\ F_{y3}^{(2)} \end{Bmatrix} = \begin{bmatrix} -1 & 0 & 0 \\ L & -1 & 0 \\ \frac{3}{4} & -\frac{3}{4L} & -\frac{3}{4L} \end{bmatrix} \begin{Bmatrix} P_{y1} \\ P_{mz1} \\ P_{mz2} \end{Bmatrix}$$

and

$$\{\mathbf{\Delta}_f\} \equiv \begin{Bmatrix} v_1 \\ \theta_{z1} \\ \theta_{z2} \end{Bmatrix} = \frac{L}{6EI_z} \begin{bmatrix} 5L^2 & -6L & -3L \\ -6L & 9 & 3 \\ -3L & 3 & 3 \end{bmatrix} \begin{Bmatrix} P_{y1} \\ P_{mz1} \\ P_{mz2} \end{Bmatrix}$$

For the particular loading given in Fig. 13-8(a),

$$\begin{Bmatrix} P_{y1} \\ P_{mz1} \\ P_{mz2} \end{Bmatrix} = \begin{Bmatrix} -P \\ 0 \\ 0 \end{Bmatrix}$$

$$M_{z3}^{(2)} = \frac{1}{2}PL \qquad \begin{Bmatrix} F_{y2}^{(1)} \\ M_{z2}^{(1)} \\ F_{y3}^{(2)} \end{Bmatrix} = P \begin{Bmatrix} 1 \\ -L \\ -\frac{3}{4} \end{Bmatrix} \qquad \text{and} \qquad \begin{Bmatrix} v_1 \\ \theta_{z1} \\ \theta_{z2} \end{Bmatrix} = \frac{PL^2}{6EI_z} \begin{Bmatrix} -5L \\ 6 \\ 3 \end{Bmatrix}$$

Additional internal forces and reactions may, of course, be determined from equilibrium of members and joints.

Example 13-6. Analyze the beam of the preceding example by using the alternative form of the member flexibility matrix, Eq. (13-20c).

First, the equilibrium equations must be expressed in terms of bending moments acting at the ends of each member. For the beam shown in Fig. 13-8(b), the equilibrium equations are

$$\begin{Bmatrix} P_{y1} \\ P_{mz1} \\ P_{mz2} \end{Bmatrix} = \begin{bmatrix} 1/L & 1/L & 0 & \vdots & 0 \\ 1 & 0 & 0 & \vdots & 0 \\ 0 & 1 & 1 & \vdots & 0 \end{bmatrix} \begin{Bmatrix} M_{z1}^{(1)} \\ M_{z2}^{(1)} \\ M_{z2}^{(2)} \\ \text{----} \\ M_{z3}^{(2)} \end{Bmatrix}$$

Among the bending moments comprising the internal force vector, the redundant force must be chosen as $M_{z3}^{(2)}$ if the released structure is to be kinematically stable as well as statically determinate. Accordingly, we identify

$$\{\mathbf{F}_0\} = \begin{Bmatrix} M_{z1}^{(1)} \\ M_{z2}^{(1)} \\ M_{z2}^{(2)} \end{Bmatrix} \qquad\qquad \{\mathbf{F}_x\} = M_{z3}^{(2)}$$

$$[\mathbf{B}_0] = \begin{bmatrix} 1/L & 1/L & 0 \\ 1 & 0 & 0 \\ 0 & 1 & 1 \end{bmatrix} \qquad [\mathbf{B}_x] = \begin{bmatrix} 0 \\ 0 \\ 0 \end{bmatrix}$$

Thus

$$[\mathbf{C}_0] = \begin{bmatrix} 0 & 1 & 0 \\ L & -1 & 0 \\ -L & 1 & 1 \end{bmatrix} \qquad [\mathbf{C}_x] = \begin{bmatrix} 0 \\ 0 \\ 0 \end{bmatrix}$$

If axial deformation is ignored, the member flexibility matrix defined by Eq. (13-20c) relates the bending moments at the ends of a beam to the corresponding rotations. Then,

$$[\mathbf{f}_m] = \left(\frac{L}{6EI_z}\right)_m \begin{bmatrix} 2 & -1 \\ -1 & 2 \end{bmatrix}$$

and, therefore,

$$[\mathbf{f}] = \begin{bmatrix} [\mathbf{f}_{00}] & \vdots & [\mathbf{f}_{0x}] \\ \text{----} & \text{+} & \text{----} \\ [\mathbf{f}_{x0}] & \vdots & [\mathbf{f}_{xx}] \end{bmatrix} = \frac{L}{6EI_z} \begin{bmatrix} 2 & -1 & 0 & \vdots & 0 \\ -1 & 2 & 0 & \vdots & 0 \\ 0 & 0 & 4 & \vdots & -2 \\ \text{----} & & & \text{+} & \text{---} \\ 0 & 0 & -2 & \vdots & 4 \end{bmatrix}$$

One advantage to using this form of $[\mathbf{f}]$ is that the term L/EI_z factors out of all terms, leaving the elements within the matrix dimensionless.

If we would proceed in the usual way, we would find that $[\mathscr{F}_{pp}]$, $[\mathscr{F}_{px}] = [\mathscr{F}_{xp}]^T$, $[\mathscr{F}_{xx}]$ have precisely the same form as those determined in the preceding example. This is to be expected, as these matrices constitute $[\mathscr{F}]$, which is independent of the set of internal forces used to characterize the structure. While $\{\mathbf{F}_x\}$ and $\{\boldsymbol{\Delta}_f\}$ are identical to those obtained previously, the vector $\{\mathbf{F}_0\}$ is different, as it currently comprises entirely bending moments. Recall that

$$\{\mathbf{F}_0\} = ([\mathbf{C}_0] - [\mathbf{C}_x][\mathcal{F}_{xx}]^{-1}[\mathcal{F}_{xp}])\{\mathbf{P}_f\} \qquad (13\text{-}8\text{b})$$

Because $[\mathbf{C}_0]$ and $[\mathbf{C}_x]$ are different from the corresponding matrices obtained in Example 13-5, we obtain

$$\{\mathbf{F}_0\} = \begin{Bmatrix} M_{z1}^{(1)} \\ M_{z2}^{(1)} \\ M_{z2}^{(2)} \end{Bmatrix} = \begin{bmatrix} 0 & 1 & 0 \\ L & -1 & 0 \\ -L & 1 & 1 \end{bmatrix} \begin{Bmatrix} P_{y1} \\ P_{mz1} \\ P_{mz2} \end{Bmatrix} = PL \begin{Bmatrix} 0 \\ -1 \\ 1 \end{Bmatrix}$$

13-5 SELF-STRAINED STRUCTURES

We have previously treated problems involving self-strained structures by the direct stiffness method. With that approach, initial deformations associated with either misfit of members or thermal gradients were represented in terms of equivalent generalized loading that was then imposed on the structure. With the flexibility method, the initial deformations are incorporated into the force-deformation relationship which, after entering the formulation, leads to a modification of the resulting expressions for $\{\mathbf{F}_0\}$, $\{\mathbf{F}_x\}$, and $\{\mathbf{\Delta}_f\}$.

Let us begin by examining the modification of the force-deformation relationship due to the presence of initial deformations of a member.

Bar Elements. In the absence of initial member deformations, the force-deformation relationship for a bar was previously found to be

$$\{\boldsymbol{\delta}_m\} = \left[\left(\frac{L}{EA} \right)_m \right] \{\mathbf{F}_m\} \qquad (13\text{-}13)$$

in which $\{\boldsymbol{\delta}_m\}$ is a single-row vector equal to the relative axial displacement of the two ends of the member, $\{\mathbf{F}_m\}$ is the axial force, and $[(L/EA)_m]$ is the element flexibility matrix $[\mathbf{f}_m]$. If the bar is endowed with some initial elongation, ΔL, then the total deformation in the presence of both ΔL and the axial force becomes

$$\{\boldsymbol{\delta}_m\} = \left[\left(\frac{L}{EA} \right)_m \right] \{\mathbf{F}_m\} + \{\Delta L\} \qquad (13\text{-}23)$$

Recall that an initial axial deformation arising from a change in temperature, ΔT, may be expressed as

$$\Delta L = (\alpha \, \Delta T) L \qquad (13\text{-}24)$$

in which α is the coefficient of thermal expansion.

Beam Elements. The force-deformation relationship for a beam, fixed at one end and free at the other as shown in Fig. 13-5(a), was previously derived as

$$
\left\{ \begin{array}{c} u_j' \\ v_j' \\ \theta_{z'j} \end{array} \right\}_m = \begin{bmatrix} \dfrac{L}{EA} & 0 & 0 \\[2mm] 0 & \dfrac{L^3}{3EI_{z'}} & \dfrac{L^2}{2EI_{z'}} \\[2mm] 0 & \dfrac{L^2}{2EI_{z'}} & \dfrac{L}{EI_{z'}} \end{bmatrix}_m \left\{ \begin{array}{c} F_{x'j}^{(m)} \\ F_{y'j}^{(m)} \\ M_{z'j}^{(m)} \end{array} \right\}
\tag{13-16c}
$$

If the beam is initially endowed with an initial positive curvature

$$
\frac{d^2 v^i}{dx'^2} = \frac{1}{\rho}
\tag{13-25}
$$

then the initial angle $\theta_{z'j}^i$ and transverse displacement v_j^i at the free end of the beam (relative to the fixed end) may be obtained by successive integration of Eq. (13-25). In the case of a *constant* radius of curvature we obtain

$$
\theta_{z'j}^i = \frac{dv^i}{dx'} \bigg|_j = \frac{L}{\rho}
\tag{13-26a}
$$

and

$$
v_j^i = \frac{L^2}{2\rho}
\tag{13-26b}
$$

If the initial curvature is produced by a temperature gradient across the height of the beam, from ΔT_u at the upper edge to ΔT_l at the lower edge, then the associated curvature is

$$
\frac{1}{\rho} = \frac{\alpha}{h} (\Delta T_l - \Delta T_u)
\tag{13-27}
$$

Therefore, accounting also for the axial deformation associated with the *average* temperature change of the beam, we may modify Eq. (13-16c) to acquire the form

$$
\left\{ \begin{array}{c} u_j' \\ v_j' \\ \theta_{z'j} \end{array} \right\}_m = \begin{bmatrix} \dfrac{L}{EA} & 0 & 0 \\[2mm] 0 & \dfrac{L^3}{3EI_{z'}} & \dfrac{L^2}{2EI_{z'}} \\[2mm] 0 & \dfrac{L^2}{2EI_{z'}} & \dfrac{L}{EI_{z'}} \end{bmatrix}_m \left\{ \begin{array}{c} F_{x'j}^{(m)} \\ F_{y'j}^{(m)} \\ M_{z'j}^{(m)} \end{array} \right\} + \alpha \left\{ \begin{array}{c} (\Delta T_l + \Delta T_u)L/2 \\ (\Delta T_l - \Delta T_u)L^2/2h \\ (\Delta T_l - \Delta T_u)L/h \end{array} \right\}_m
\tag{13-28}
$$

Alternatively, we may modify the force-deformation relationship, Eq. (13-21c), which corresponds to a simply supported beam, as shown in Fig. 13-5(b). For a uniform initial curvature, the initial rotations at the ends of the beam are

$$
\theta_{z'i}^i = -\frac{L}{2\rho} \qquad \theta_{z'j}^i = \frac{L}{2\rho}
\tag{13-29a, b}
$$

Thus, accounting for Eq. (13-27), the modified force-deformation relationship becomes

$$
\begin{Bmatrix} u'_j \\ \theta_{z'i} \\ \theta_{z'j} \end{Bmatrix} = \left(\frac{L}{6EI_{z'}}\right)_m \begin{bmatrix} \dfrac{6I_{z'}}{A} & 0 & 0 \\ 0 & 2 & -1 \\ 0 & -1 & 2 \end{bmatrix}_m \begin{Bmatrix} F^{(m)}_{x'j} \\ M^{(m)}_{z'i} \\ M^{(m)}_{z'j} \end{Bmatrix} + \alpha \begin{Bmatrix} (\Delta T_l + \Delta T_u)L/2 \\ -(\Delta T_l - \Delta T_u)L/2h \\ (\Delta T_l - \Delta T_u)L/2h \end{Bmatrix}_m \quad (13\text{-}30)
$$

Whether initial deformations are related to changes in temperature or to misfit, the modified force-deformation relationships given by Eqs. (13-23), (13-28), and (13-30) may be generalized to the form

$$
\{\boldsymbol{\delta}_m\} = [\mathbf{f}_m]\{\mathbf{F}_m\} + \{\boldsymbol{\delta}^i_m\} \quad (13\text{-}31)
$$

where $\{\boldsymbol{\delta}^i_m\}$ represents the vector of initial deformations. When Eq. (13-31) is used to assemble the force-deformation relationships for the entire system, the result may be expressed as

$$
\begin{Bmatrix} \boldsymbol{\delta}_0 \\ \hline \boldsymbol{\delta}_x \end{Bmatrix} = \begin{bmatrix} [\mathbf{f}_{00}] & \vdots & [\mathbf{f}_{0x}] \\ \hline [\mathbf{f}_{x0}] & \vdots & [\mathbf{f}_{xx}] \end{bmatrix} \begin{Bmatrix} \mathbf{F}_0 \\ \hline \mathbf{F}_x \end{Bmatrix} + \begin{Bmatrix} \boldsymbol{\delta}^i_0 \\ \hline \boldsymbol{\delta}^i_x \end{Bmatrix} \quad (13\text{-}32)
$$

in which $\{\boldsymbol{\delta}^i_0\}$ and $\{\boldsymbol{\delta}^i_x\}$ are the combined vectors of initial displacements for the nonredundant and redundant structural elements, respectively; these vectors must, of course, be ordered identically to $\{\boldsymbol{\delta}_0\}$ and $\{\boldsymbol{\delta}_x\}$.

Recall that the equilibrium and compatibility conditions, specified by Eqs. (13-2) and (13-4), have the form

$$
\begin{Bmatrix} \mathbf{F}_0 \\ \hline \mathbf{F}_x \end{Bmatrix} = \begin{bmatrix} [\mathbf{C}_0] & \vdots & [\mathbf{C}_x] \\ \hline [\mathbf{0}] & \vdots & [\mathbf{I}] \end{bmatrix} \begin{Bmatrix} \mathbf{P}_f \\ \hline \mathbf{F}_x \end{Bmatrix} \quad (13\text{-}2)
$$

and

$$
\begin{Bmatrix} \boldsymbol{\Delta}_f \\ \hline \mathbf{0} \end{Bmatrix} = \begin{bmatrix} [\mathbf{C}_0]^T & \vdots & [\mathbf{0}] \\ \hline [\mathbf{C}_x]^T & \vdots & [\mathbf{I}] \end{bmatrix} \begin{Bmatrix} \boldsymbol{\delta}_0 \\ \hline \boldsymbol{\delta}_x \end{Bmatrix} \quad (13\text{-}4)
$$

Substituting Eq. (13-2) into Eq. (13-32), and the resulting expression into Eq. (13-4), we obtain

$$
\begin{Bmatrix} \boldsymbol{\Delta}_f \\ \hline \mathbf{0} \end{Bmatrix} = \begin{bmatrix} [\mathscr{F}_{pp}] & \vdots & [\mathscr{F}_{px}] \\ \hline [\mathscr{F}_{xp}] & \vdots & [\mathscr{F}_{xx}] \end{bmatrix} \begin{Bmatrix} \mathbf{P}_f \\ \hline \mathbf{F}_x \end{Bmatrix} + \begin{Bmatrix} \boldsymbol{\Delta}^i_f \\ \hline \boldsymbol{\Delta}^i_x \end{Bmatrix} \quad (13\text{-}33)
$$

in which

$$
\{\boldsymbol{\Delta}^i_f\} = [\mathbf{C}_0]^T\{\boldsymbol{\delta}^i_0\} \quad (13\text{-}34\text{a})
$$

and

$$
\{\boldsymbol{\Delta}^i_x\} = [\mathbf{C}_x]^T\{\boldsymbol{\delta}^i_0\} + [\mathbf{I}]\{\boldsymbol{\delta}^i_x\} \quad (13\text{-}34\text{b})
$$

We may interpret $\{\boldsymbol{\Delta}^i_f\}$ as the nodal displacements (corresponding to the generalized forces $\{\mathbf{P}_f\}$) of the released structure due to the initial member deformations $\{\delta_0^i\}$; because redundant members are, by definition, independent of the released structure, $\{\delta_x^i\}$ plays no role in determining $\{\Delta_f^i\}$. The vector $\{\Delta_x^i\}$ represents the set of relative displacements between the redundant members and the released structure, at each point where a redundant member has been severed from the released structure, due to initial deformations of members of the released structure and of the redundant members themselves.

Proceeding as we did previously in the absence of initial deformations, we may solve the lower partition of Eq. (13-33) for $\{F_x\}$. The resulting expression may be substituted into the upper partition of Eq. (13-2) to find $\{F_0\}$ and into the upper partition of Eq. (13-33) to determine $\{\Delta_f\}$. Hence,

$$\{F_x\} = -[\mathscr{F}_{xx}]^{-1}[\mathscr{F}_{xp}]\{P_f\} - [\mathscr{F}_{xx}]^{-1}\{\Delta_x^i\} \tag{13-35a}$$

$$\{F_0\} = ([C_0] - [C_x][\mathscr{F}_{xx}]^{-1}[\mathscr{F}_{xp}])\{P_f\} - [C_x][\mathscr{F}_{xx}]^{-1}\{\Delta_x^i\} \tag{13-35b}$$

$$\{\Delta_f\} = [\mathscr{F}]\{P_f\} + \{\Delta_f^i\} - [\mathscr{F}_{px}][\mathscr{F}_{xx}]^{-1}\{\Delta_x^i\} \tag{13-35c}$$

Equations (13-35) are then the final governing equations which account for both applied loads and initial member deformations.

Example 13-7. Compute the member forces and nodal displacements for the truss shown in Fig. 13-9(a), due to an initial misfit of diagonal member 3. (This problem was treated in Example 12-10 by the direct stiffness method.)

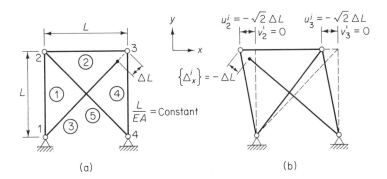

Figure 13-9

From Example 13-4, in which we analyzed the same truss subjected to applied loads, we have

$$[C_0] = \begin{bmatrix} 0 & 1 & 0 & 0 \\ -1 & 0 & 0 & 0 \\ \sqrt{2} & 0 & \sqrt{2} & 0 \\ -1 & 0 & -1 & 1 \end{bmatrix} \qquad [C_x] = -\frac{1}{\sqrt{2}} \begin{bmatrix} 1 \\ 1 \\ -\sqrt{2} \\ 1 \end{bmatrix}$$

$$[\mathscr{F}_{pp}] = \frac{L}{EA} \begin{bmatrix} 4 & 0 & 3 & -1 \\ 0 & 1 & 0 & 0 \\ 3 & 0 & 3 & -1 \\ -1 & 0 & -1 & 0 \end{bmatrix} \qquad [\mathscr{F}_{px}] = [\mathscr{F}_{xp}]^T = \frac{L}{\sqrt{2}EA} \begin{bmatrix} 4 \\ -1 \\ 3 \\ -1 \end{bmatrix}$$

and

$$[\mathcal{F}_{xx}] = \frac{7}{2}\frac{L}{EA}$$

Recall that member 5 had been chosen as the redundant bar; thus, in computing displacements of the released structure due to initial deformations, we consider member 5 to be severed from the rest of the structure. Because only member 3 possesses initial deformation, we have

$$\{\boldsymbol{\delta}_0^i\} = \Delta L \begin{Bmatrix} 0 \\ 0 \\ -1 \\ 0 \end{Bmatrix} \qquad \text{and} \quad \{\boldsymbol{\delta}_x^i\} = \{0\}$$

Thus, from Eqs. (13-34), we obtain

$$\{\boldsymbol{\Delta}_f^i\} = \begin{Bmatrix} u_2^i \\ v_2^i \\ u_3^i \\ v_3^i \end{Bmatrix} = \Delta L \begin{bmatrix} 0 & -1 & \sqrt{2} & -1 \\ 1 & 0 & 0 & 0 \\ 0 & 0 & \sqrt{2} & -1 \\ 0 & 0 & 0 & 1 \end{bmatrix} \begin{Bmatrix} 0 \\ 0 \\ -1 \\ 0 \end{Bmatrix} = \Delta L \begin{Bmatrix} -\sqrt{2} \\ 0 \\ -\sqrt{2} \\ 0 \end{Bmatrix} = \frac{-\sqrt{2}}{7}\Delta L \begin{Bmatrix} 7 \\ 0 \\ 7 \\ 0 \end{Bmatrix}$$

and

$$\{\boldsymbol{\Delta}_x^i\} = \Delta L \begin{bmatrix} -\dfrac{1}{\sqrt{2}}, & -\dfrac{1}{\sqrt{2}}, & 1, & -\dfrac{1}{\sqrt{2}} \end{bmatrix} \begin{Bmatrix} 0 \\ 0 \\ -1 \\ 0 \end{Bmatrix} = -\Delta L$$

These displacements, resulting from initial deformations that occur in the released (and hence unstrained) structure, are shown in Fig. 13-9(b). To maintain compatibility (i.e., requiring that members 1, 2, 3, and 4 all fit together) due to member 3 being too short by an amount ΔL, the released structure must sway to the left by an amount $\sqrt{2}\,\Delta L$. This means, however, that a gap will exist between node 2 of the released structure and the end of member 5 which must eventually be joined to node 2. This gap is $\{\boldsymbol{\Delta}_x^i\} = -\Delta L$, while the displacement of the released structure is defined by $\{\boldsymbol{\Delta}_f^i\}$.

In the absence of applied loads ($\{\mathbf{P}_f\} = \{\mathbf{0}\}$), Eqs. (13-35) reduce to

$$\{\mathbf{F}_x\} \equiv F_5 = -[\mathcal{F}_{xx}]^{-1}\{\boldsymbol{\Delta}_x^i\} = \frac{2}{7}\frac{EA\,\Delta L}{L}$$

$$\{\mathbf{F}_0\} \equiv \begin{Bmatrix} F_1 \\ F_2 \\ F_3 \\ F_4 \end{Bmatrix} = -[\mathbf{C}_x][\mathcal{F}_{xx}]^{-1}\{\boldsymbol{\Delta}_x^i\} = -\frac{\sqrt{2}}{7}\frac{EA}{L}\Delta L \begin{Bmatrix} 1 \\ 1 \\ -\sqrt{2} \\ 1 \end{Bmatrix}$$

$$\{\boldsymbol{\Delta}_f\} \equiv \begin{Bmatrix} u_2 \\ v_2 \\ u_3 \\ v_3 \end{Bmatrix} = \{\boldsymbol{\Delta}_f^i\} - [\mathcal{F}_{px}][\mathcal{F}_{xx}]^{-1}\{\boldsymbol{\Delta}_x^i\}$$

$$= \frac{-\sqrt{2}}{7}\Delta L \left(\begin{Bmatrix} 7 \\ 0 \\ 7 \\ 0 \end{Bmatrix} - \begin{Bmatrix} 4 \\ -1 \\ 3 \\ -1 \end{Bmatrix} \right) = \frac{-\sqrt{2}}{7}\Delta L \begin{Bmatrix} 3 \\ 1 \\ 4 \\ 1 \end{Bmatrix}$$

These results are, of course, in agreement with those we obtained previously using the direct stiffness method.

Example 13-8. Determine the internal shear forces and bending moments in the beam shown in Fig. 13-10(a), which is subjected to a temperature gradient across its height. This problem was treated previously in Example 12-11 by the direct stiffness method.

(a)

(b)   **Figure 13-10**

The changes in temperature (relative to the ambient temperature) are ΔT_u and ΔT_l at the upper and lower edges, respectively. We may use the matrices developed in either Example 13-5 or Example 13-6; choosing the latter, in which the redundant force is the bending moment $M_{z3}^{(2)}$ at the fixed end of the beam, we recall that

$$[\mathbf{C}_0] = \begin{bmatrix} 0 & 1 & 0 \\ L & -1 & 0 \\ -L & 1 & 1 \end{bmatrix} \qquad [\mathbf{C}_x] = \begin{bmatrix} 0 \\ 0 \\ 0 \end{bmatrix}$$

$$[\mathscr{F}_{pp}] = \frac{L}{6EI_z}\begin{bmatrix} 6L^2 & -7L & -4L \\ -7L & 10 & 4 \\ -4L & 4 & 4 \end{bmatrix}$$

$$[\mathscr{F}_{px}] = [\mathscr{F}_{xp}]^T = \frac{L}{3EI_z}\begin{bmatrix} L \\ -1 \\ -1 \end{bmatrix} \qquad [\mathscr{F}_{xx}] = \frac{2}{3}\frac{L}{EI_z}$$

In this problem, the initial deformation for both members is the initial curvature; we shall ignore the axial deformation, as the roller support permits such deformation without the beam's incurring axial force. The initial rotations at the ends of member 1 are then, from Eqs. (13-29)

$$\theta_{z1}^{(1)i} = \frac{-L}{2\rho} \qquad \text{and} \qquad \theta_{z2}^{(1)i} = \frac{L}{2\rho}$$

Similarly, the initial rotations at the ends of member 2 are

$$\theta_{z2}^{(2)i} = -\frac{2L}{2\rho} \qquad \text{and} \qquad \theta_{z3}^{(2)i} = \frac{2L}{2\rho}$$

where, according to Eq. (13-27)

$$\frac{1}{\rho} = \frac{\alpha}{h}(\Delta T_l - \Delta T_u)$$

According to the composition of $\{\delta_0\}$ and $\{\delta_x\}$ established in Example 13-6, we must define the initial deformation vectors as

$$\{\delta_0^i\} = \begin{Bmatrix} \theta_{z1}^{(1)i} \\ \theta_{z2}^{(1)i} \\ \theta_{z2}^{(2)i} \end{Bmatrix} = \frac{L}{\rho}\begin{Bmatrix} -1/2 \\ 1/2 \\ -1 \end{Bmatrix} \qquad \text{and} \qquad \{\delta_x^i\} = \{\theta_{z3}^{(2)i}\} = \{L/\rho\}$$

Therefore, from Eqs. (13-34), we obtain

$$\{\mathbf{\Delta}_f^i\} = \begin{Bmatrix} v_1^i \\ \theta_{z1}^i \\ \theta_{z2}^i \end{Bmatrix} = \frac{L}{\rho}\begin{bmatrix} 0 & L & -L \\ 1 & -1 & 1 \\ 0 & 0 & 1 \end{bmatrix}\begin{Bmatrix} -1/2 \\ 1/2 \\ -1 \end{Bmatrix} = \frac{L}{\rho}\begin{Bmatrix} 3L/2 \\ -2 \\ -1 \end{Bmatrix}$$

$$\{\mathbf{\Delta}_x^i\} = \{\theta_{z3}^i\} = \frac{L}{\rho}\begin{bmatrix} 0 \\ 0 \\ 0 \end{bmatrix}^T\begin{Bmatrix} -1/2 \\ 1/2 \\ -1 \end{Bmatrix} + [1]\{L/\rho\} = \frac{L}{\rho}$$

These initial deformations of the released structure are shown in Fig. 13-10(b).

We find internal forces and, if we desire, nodal displacements from Eqs. (13-35). Then

$$\{\mathbf{F}_x\} \equiv M_{z3}^{(2)} = -[\mathscr{F}_{xx}]^{-1}\{\mathbf{\Delta}_x^i\} = -\frac{3}{2}\frac{EI_z}{\rho}$$

$$\{\mathbf{F}_0\} \equiv \begin{Bmatrix} M_{z1}^{(1)} \\ M_{z2}^{(1)} \\ M_{z2}^{(2)} \end{Bmatrix} = -[\mathbf{C}_x][\mathscr{F}_{xx}]^{-1}\{\mathbf{\Delta}_x^i\} = \begin{Bmatrix} 0 \\ 0 \\ 0 \end{Bmatrix}$$

$$\{\mathbf{\Delta}_f\} \equiv \begin{Bmatrix} v_1 \\ \theta_{z1}^i \\ \theta_{z2}^i \end{Bmatrix} = \{\mathbf{\Delta}_f^i\} - [\mathscr{F}_{px}][\mathscr{F}_{xx}]^{-1}\{\mathbf{\Delta}_x^i\} = \frac{L}{\rho}\left(\begin{Bmatrix} 3L/2 \\ -2 \\ -1 \end{Bmatrix} - \begin{Bmatrix} L/2 \\ -1/2 \\ -1/2 \end{Bmatrix}\right) = \frac{L}{\rho}\begin{Bmatrix} L \\ -3/2 \\ -1/2 \end{Bmatrix}$$

It was to be expected that the bending moments which comprise $\{\mathbf{F}_0\}$ would be zero, because they pertain to that part of the structure which is statically determinate (member 1). As shown in Example 12-11, the bending moment varies linearly in member 2 from zero at node 2 to $-3EI_z/2\rho$ at node 3.

13-6 BEAMS AND FRAMES SUBJECTED TO DISTRIBUTED LOADING

Thus far, we have treated statically indeterminate beams subjected only to generalized forces, i.e., forces and moments applied at nodal points in the directions of generalized displacements. We have also solved statically determinate problems in which applied loading was distributed between nodal points. Distributed loading, like generalized loads, were found to enter the formulation through the governing equations of equilibrium. To accommodate distributed loading applied to statically indeterminate systems, we must recognize that distributed loading not only enters the equilibrium conditions, but also creates deformation of the members for which the force-deformation relationships have been established. Thus, in-span loading requires that the member force-deformation relations be modified to account for the initial deformations caused by the loading.

As in the case of initial axial deformation or curvature due to a change in temperature, the initial deformation caused by in-span loading of a member is represented by the initial displacements at one or both ends of the member. The load-deformation relationships are then modified accordingly, once again acquiring the form of Eq. (13-31); i.e.,

$$\{\boldsymbol{\delta}_m\} = [\mathbf{f}_m]\{\mathbf{F}_m\} + \{\boldsymbol{\delta}_m^i\} \tag{13-31}$$

where now the initial deformation vector $\{\boldsymbol{\delta}_m^i\}$ is associated with the loading distributed between the ends of the member. The analysis then proceeds as described in Section 13-5.

Let us take as an example the case of a concentrated transverse load P applied at some point a distance a from one end of the prismatic member shown in Fig. 13-11(a). Because we wish to form the load-deformation relationship for a member that is fixed at one end and free at the other, for such a case $\{\boldsymbol{\delta}_m^i\}$ corresponds to the initial translations and rotation at the free end. A convenient way of computing these quantities is by the moment-area method. The moment diagram for the concentrated load is shown in Fig. 13-11(b). Therefore, the initial rotation at $x' = L$ (or at any point $a \le x' \le L$) is

$$\theta_{z'j}^i = \int_0^a \frac{M_b}{EI_{z'}} dx' = \frac{a}{2}\left(\frac{Pa}{EI_{z'}}\right) = \frac{Pa^2}{2EI_{z'}} \tag{13-36a}$$

(a)

(b)

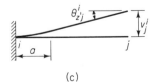

(c)   **Figure 13-11**

Similarly, the initial transverse displacement at $x = L$ is

$$v_j^i = \int_0^a \frac{M_b}{EI_{z'}} x' dx' = \frac{a}{2}\left(\frac{Pa}{EI_{z'}}\right)\left(L - \frac{a}{3}\right) = \frac{Pa^2}{2EI_{z'}}\left(L - \frac{a}{3}\right) \qquad \text{(13-36b)}$$

These quantities are shown in Fig. 13-11(c).

The modified force-determination relationship for the fixed-free member subjected to an in-span concentrated load is then

$$\left\{\begin{array}{c} u_j' \\ v_j' \\ \theta_j \end{array}\right\}_m = \begin{bmatrix} \dfrac{L}{EA} & 0 & 0 \\ 0 & \dfrac{L^3}{3EI_{z'}} & \dfrac{L^2}{2EI_{z'}} \\ 0 & \dfrac{L^2}{2EI_{z'}} & \dfrac{L}{EI_{z'}} \end{bmatrix}_m \left\{\begin{array}{c} F_{x'j}^{(m)} \\ F_{y'j}^{(m)} \\ M_{z'j}^{(m)} \end{array}\right\} + \left(\frac{Pa^2}{2EI_{z'}}\right)_m \left\{\begin{array}{c} 0 \\ \left(L_m - \dfrac{a}{3}\right) \\ 1 \end{array}\right\} \qquad \text{(13-37)}$$

Note that, because we have considered only a transverse load to act on the beam, the initial axial displacement is zero. This would not be the case, of course, if P possessed an axial component $P_{x'}$; then we would find that $u_j^i = P_{x'}a/EA$.

Table 13-1 summarizes the initial deformation for beams subjected to a few simple loading cases. Because we have previously developed force-deformation relationships for both cantilever and simply supported members,

Table 13-1 INITIAL DISPLACEMENTS DUE TO IN-SPAN LOADING

Loading Condition		
P (upward at distance a)	$v_j^i = \dfrac{Pa^2}{2EI}\left(L - \dfrac{a}{3}\right)$ $\theta_j^i = \dfrac{Pa^2}{2EI}$	$\theta_i^i = \dfrac{P}{6EI}\dfrac{a}{L}(L-a)(2L-a)$ $\theta_j^i = \dfrac{-P}{6EI}\dfrac{a}{L}(L^2-a^2)$
M (at distance a)	$v_j^i = \dfrac{Ma}{EI}\left(L - \dfrac{a}{2}\right)$ $\theta_j^i = \dfrac{Ma}{EI}$	$\theta_i^i = \dfrac{M}{6EIL}(2L^2 - 6aL + 3a^2)$ $\theta_j^i = \dfrac{M}{6EIL}(3a^2 - L^2)$
q (uniform)	$v_j^i = \dfrac{qL^4}{8EI}$ $\theta_j^i = \dfrac{qL^3}{6EI}$	$\theta_i^i = \dfrac{qL^3}{24EI}$ $\theta_j^i = \dfrac{-qL^3}{24EI}$
q (triangular)	$v_j^i = \dfrac{qL^4}{30EI}$ $\theta_j^i = \dfrac{qL^3}{24EI}$	$\theta_i^i = \dfrac{8qL^3}{360EI}$ $\theta_j^i = \dfrac{-7qL^3}{360EI}$

the components of the initial deformation vector are listed for both systems. The transverse displacements and rotations may, of course, be derived by various procedures, such as the moment-area method used above, the principle of virtual work, and direct integration of the governing equation for beam bending.

The following example illustrates the manner in which distributed loading is accommodated by the flexibility method.

Example 13-9. Find the internal forces and the nodal displacements of the frame, shown in Fig. 13-12(a), which was analyzed previously in Example 12-8 by the direct stiffness method. Before beginning the analysis we note that, because both the structure and the loading are symmetric, we may choose to analyze only one half the structure, as shown in Fig. 13-12(b). In the process, we reduce the number of redundant forces from three to two.

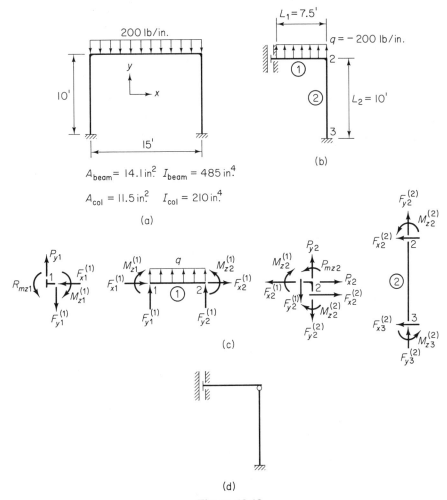

$A_{beam} = 14.1\,in.^2 \quad I_{beam} = 485\,in.^4$

$A_{col} = 11.5\,in.^2 \quad I_{col} = 210\,in.^4$

(a)

(b)

(c)

(d)

Figure 13-12

Having in view the application of Eqs. (13-35), we note that the matrices appearing in those equations are developed from the systems statics matrix $[\mathbf{B}]$ and the matrix of element flexibilities $[\mathbf{f}]$. Accordingly, we begin with the equations of equilibrium at each node in the directions of unrestrained displacement. At node 1, only the transverse displacement in the y-direction is unrestrained; at node 2, both translations and the rotation are unrestrained; and at node 3, no displacement is unrestrained. We consider, therefore, generalized forces to be applied only in the directions of unrestrained generalized displacements, and we write the equilibrium equations associated with each generalized force. Free body diagrams of the nodes and members are shown in Fig. 13-12(c).

Thus, for node 1,

$$P_{y1} - F_{y1}^{(1)} = 0 \tag{a}$$

and, for node 2,

$$P_{x2} - F_{x2}^{(1)} + F_{x2}^{(2)} = 0$$

$$P_{y2} - F_{y2}^{(1)} - F_{y2}^{(2)} = 0 \tag{b}$$

$$P_{mz2} - M_{z2}^{(1)} - M_{z2}^{(2)} = 0$$

Recall that only three independent forces exist for each member. Therefore, we use the equilibrium conditions for member 1 to relate $F_{y1}^{(1)}$ to $F_{y2}^{(1)}$, i.e.,

$$F_{y1}^{(1)} = -F_{y2}^{(1)} - qL \tag{c}$$

where, as shown in Fig. 13-12(c), the distributed load q has been chosen as positive in the positive y-direction. When Eq. (c) is substituted into Eq. (a), and the result is combined with Eq. (b) in matrix form, we obtain

$$
\begin{Bmatrix} P_{y1} \\ P_{x2} \\ P_{y2} \\ P_{mz2} \end{Bmatrix} + \begin{Bmatrix} qL \\ 0 \\ 0 \\ 0 \end{Bmatrix} = \begin{bmatrix} 0 & -1 & 0 & 0 & \vdots & 0 & 0 \\ 1 & 0 & 0 & 0 & \vdots & -1 & 0 \\ 0 & 1 & 0 & 1 & \vdots & 0 & 0 \\ 0 & 0 & 1 & 0 & \vdots & 0 & 1 \end{bmatrix} \begin{Bmatrix} F_{x2}^{(1)} \\ F_{y2}^{(1)} \\ M_{z2}^{(1)} \\ F_{y2}^{(2)} \\ \text{----} \\ F_{x2}^{(2)} \\ M_{z2}^{(2)} \end{Bmatrix} \tag{d}
$$

or

$$\{\mathbf{P}_f\} + \{\mathbf{P}_f^E\} = [\mathbf{B}_0 \mid \mathbf{B}_x]\{\mathbf{F}\} \tag{e}$$

The loads appearing on the left side of Eqs. (d) and (e) include both the vector of applied nodal forces (which happens to be zero in this problem, i.e., $\{\mathbf{P}_f\} = \{\mathbf{0}\}$) and a vector of equivalent nodal loads $\{\mathbf{P}_f^E\}$ that are related to the distributed loading. Note that these equivalent loads are *not* the same as those defined in Chapter 12 with regard to the direct stiffness method; there, equivalent nodal loads were those that produced the same nodal displacements as the actual distributed loading. Here, the equivalent loads are simply the equilibrium equivalents of the applied loads for each member.

The matrix $[\mathbf{B}]$ on the right side of (d) has been partitioned to furnish a square matrix $[\mathbf{B}_0]$, which is the system statics matrix for the released structure, i.e., the structure that emerges when the redundant forces are set to zero. Here we have chosen the redundant forces to be $F_{x2}^{(2)}$ and $M_{z2}^{(2)}$, the shear force and bending moment in member 2 at node 2. The released structure is shown in Fig. 13-12(d). Note that it would *not* be permissible to substitute $F_{y2}^{(2)}$ for one of the redundant forces, as the released structure then would be kinematically unstable and $[\mathbf{B}_0]$ would be singular. For the chosen system of redundant forces, we obtain

$$[\mathbf{C}_0] = [\mathbf{B}_0]^{-1} = \begin{bmatrix} 0 & 1 & 0 & 0 \\ -1 & 0 & 0 & 0 \\ 0 & 0 & 0 & 1 \\ 1 & 0 & 1 & 0 \end{bmatrix} \quad \text{and} \quad [\mathbf{C}_x] = -[\mathbf{C}_0][\mathbf{B}_x] = \begin{bmatrix} 0 & 0 \\ 1 & 0 \\ 0 & -1 \\ 0 & -1 \end{bmatrix} \quad \text{(f)}$$

The member flexibility equations relate the relative displacements between two ends of a member to the corresponding forces; i.e., for member 1,

$$\begin{Bmatrix} u_2 \\ v_2 \\ \theta_{z2} \end{Bmatrix}_1 = \begin{bmatrix} \dfrac{L}{EA} & 0 & 0 \\ 0 & \dfrac{L^3}{3EI_z} & \dfrac{L^2}{2EI_z} \\ 0 & \dfrac{L^2}{2EI_z} & \dfrac{L}{EI_z} \end{bmatrix}_1 \begin{Bmatrix} F_{x2}^{(1)} \\ F_{y2}^{(1)} \\ M_{z2}^{(1)} \end{Bmatrix} + \begin{Bmatrix} u_2^i \\ v_2^i \\ \theta_{z2}^i \end{Bmatrix}_1$$

and for member 2,

$$\begin{Bmatrix} v_2 \\ u_2 \\ \theta_{z2} \end{Bmatrix}_2 = \begin{bmatrix} \dfrac{L}{EA} & 0 & 0 \\ 0 & \dfrac{L^3}{3EI_z} & \dfrac{L^2}{2EI_z} \\ 0 & \dfrac{L^2}{2EI_z} & \dfrac{L}{EI_z} \end{bmatrix}_2 \begin{Bmatrix} F_{y2}^{(2)} \\ F_{x2}^{(2)} \\ M_{z2}^{(2)} \end{Bmatrix} + \begin{Bmatrix} v_2^i \\ u_2^i \\ \theta_{z2}^i \end{Bmatrix}_2$$

Note that in forming the flexibility relations, we have referred the relative displacements to the global x-and y-axes. We may form the matrix of element flexibilities, which is

$$[\mathbf{f}] = \begin{bmatrix} [\mathbf{f}_{oo}] & [\mathbf{f}_{ox}] \\ [\mathbf{f}_{xo}] & [\mathbf{f}_{xx}] \end{bmatrix} = \begin{bmatrix} \left(\dfrac{L}{EA}\right)_1 & 0 & 0 & 0 & 0 & 0 \\ 0 & \left(\dfrac{L^3}{3EI_z}\right)_1 & \left(\dfrac{L^2}{2EI_z}\right)_1 & 0 & 0 & 0 \\ 0 & \left(\dfrac{L^2}{2EI_z}\right)_1 & \left(\dfrac{L}{EI_z}\right)_1 & 0 & 0 & 0 \\ 0 & 0 & 0 & \left(\dfrac{L}{EA}\right)_2 & 0 & 0 \\ 0 & 0 & 0 & 0 & \left(\dfrac{L^3}{3EI_z}\right)_2 & \left(\dfrac{L^2}{2EI_z}\right)_2 \\ 0 & 0 & 0 & 0 & \left(\dfrac{L^2}{2EI_z}\right)_2 & \left(\dfrac{L}{EI_z}\right)_2 \end{bmatrix} \begin{matrix} F_{x2}^{(1)} \\ F_{y2}^{(1)} \\ M_{z2}^{(1)} \\ F_{y2}^{(2)} \\ F_{x2}^{(2)} \\ M_{z2}^{(2)} \end{matrix} \quad \text{(g)}$$

with column headers $u_2^{(1)}\quad v_2^{(1)}\quad \theta_{z2}^{(1)}\quad v_2^{(2)}\quad u_2^{(2)}\quad \theta_{z2}^{(2)}$

where we have listed the relative displacements and member forces as a reminder of the meaning of $[\mathbf{f}]$. Using the member properties indicated in Fig. 13-12(a), we may express the submatrices of $[\mathbf{f}]$ numerically as

$$[\mathbf{f}_{00}] = \frac{1}{E} \begin{bmatrix} 6.38 \text{ in.}^{-1} & 0 & 0 & 0 \\ 0 & 501 \text{ in.}^{-1} & 8.35 \text{ in.}^{-2} & 0 \\ 0 & 8.35 \text{ in.}^{-2} & 0.186 \text{ in.}^{-3} & 0 \\ 0 & 0 & 0 & 10.43 \text{ in.}^{-1} \end{bmatrix}$$

$$[\mathbf{f}_{0x}] = [\mathbf{f}_{x0}]^T = \begin{bmatrix} 0 & 0 \\ 0 & 0 \\ 0 & 0 \\ 0 & 0 \end{bmatrix} \tag{h}$$

$$[\mathbf{f}_{xx}] = \frac{1}{E} \begin{bmatrix} 2760 \text{ in.}^{-1} & 34.5 \text{ in.}^{-2} \\ 34.5 \text{ in.}^{-2} & 0.574 \text{ in.}^{-3} \end{bmatrix}$$

The initial element displacements for member 1, due to the uniformly distributed load, $q = -200$ lb/in., may be determined from Table 13-1. We obtain

$$\begin{Bmatrix} u_2^i \\ v_2^i \\ \theta_{z2}^i \end{Bmatrix} = \left(\frac{qL^3}{EI_z} \right)_1 \begin{Bmatrix} 0 \\ L_1/8 \\ 1/6 \end{Bmatrix}$$

The initial displacements are zero for member 2, as it is subjected to no in-span loading. We may now form

$$\{\boldsymbol{\delta}_0^i\} = \left(\frac{qL^3}{EI_z} \right)_1 \begin{Bmatrix} 0 \\ L_1/8 \\ 1/6 \\ 0 \end{Bmatrix} \qquad \text{and} \qquad \{\boldsymbol{\delta}_x^i\} = \begin{Bmatrix} 0 \\ 0 \end{Bmatrix} \tag{i}$$

These vectors may be transformed to provide the vector of initial nodal displacements. Then

$$\{\boldsymbol{\Delta}_f^i\} = [\mathbf{C}_0]^T \{\boldsymbol{\delta}_0^i\} = \left(\frac{qL^3}{EI_z} \right)_1 \begin{Bmatrix} -L_1/8 \\ 0 \\ 0 \\ 1/6 \end{Bmatrix}$$

and

$$\{\boldsymbol{\Delta}_x^i\} = [\mathbf{C}_x]^T \{\boldsymbol{\delta}_0^i\} + [\mathbf{I}]\{\boldsymbol{\delta}_x^i\} = \left(\frac{qL^3}{EI_z} \right)_1 \begin{Bmatrix} 0 \\ -1/6 \end{Bmatrix} \tag{j}$$

We may employ Eqs. (13-7) and (13-9b) to obtain

$$[\mathscr{F}_{pp}] = [\mathbf{C}_0]^T [\mathbf{f}_{00}][\mathbf{C}_0] = \frac{1}{E} \begin{bmatrix} 511 & 0 & 10.4 & -8.35 \\ 0 & 6.38 & 0 & 0 \\ 10.4 & 0 & 10.4 & 0 \\ -8.35 & 0 & 0 & 0.186 \end{bmatrix}$$

$$[\mathscr{F}_{px}] = [\mathscr{F}_{xp}]^T = [\mathbf{C}_0]^T [\mathbf{f}_{00}][\mathbf{C}_x] + [\mathbf{C}_0]^T [\mathbf{f}_{0x}] = \frac{1}{E} \begin{bmatrix} 0 & 8.35 \\ -6.38 & 0 \\ 0 & 0 \\ 0 & -0.186 \end{bmatrix} \tag{k}$$

$$[\mathscr{F}_{xx}] = [\mathbf{C}_x]^T [\mathbf{f}_{00}][\mathbf{C}_x] + [\mathbf{C}_x]^T [\mathbf{f}_{0x}] + [\mathbf{f}_{x0}][\mathbf{C}_x] + [\mathbf{f}_{xx}] = \frac{1}{E} \begin{bmatrix} 2760 & 34.5 \\ 34.5 & 0.760 \end{bmatrix}$$

$$[\mathscr{F}] = [\mathscr{F}_{pp}] - [\mathscr{F}_{px}][\mathscr{F}_{xx}]^{-1}[\mathscr{F}_{xp}] = \frac{1}{E}\begin{bmatrix} 300 & -2.01 & 10.4 & -3.65 \\ -2.01 & 6.80 & 0 & 0.045 \\ 10.4 & 0 & 10.4 & 0 \\ -3.65 & 0.045 & 0 & 0.291 \end{bmatrix}$$

For simplicity, we have not indicated the dimensions pertaining to the coefficients indicated in Eqs. (k), but the dimensions become apparent when Eqs. (k) are compared with Eqs. (h).

Finally, replacing $\{\mathbf{P}_f\}$ with $\{\mathbf{P}_f\} + \{\mathbf{P}_f^E\}$, we find from Eqs. (13-35)

$$[\mathbf{F}_x] \equiv \begin{Bmatrix} F_{x2}^{(2)} \\ M_{z2}^{(2)} \end{Bmatrix} = -[\mathscr{F}_{xx}]^{-1}[\mathscr{F}_{xp}]\{\mathbf{P}_f\} - [\mathscr{F}_{xx}]^{-1}\{\boldsymbol{\Delta}_x^i\} = \begin{Bmatrix} 3.79^k \\ 304^{k\text{-in.}} \end{Bmatrix}$$

$$\{\mathbf{F}_0\} \equiv \begin{Bmatrix} F_{x2}^{(1)} \\ F_{y2}^{(1)} \\ M_{z2}^{(1)} \\ F_{y2}^{(2)} \end{Bmatrix} = ([\mathbf{C}_0] - [\mathbf{C}_x][\mathscr{F}_{xx}]^{-1}[\mathscr{F}_{xp}])\{\mathbf{P}_f\} - [\mathbf{C}_x][\mathscr{F}_{xx}]^{-1}\{\boldsymbol{\Delta}_x^i\} = \begin{Bmatrix} 3.79^k \\ 18^k \\ -304^{k\text{-in.}} \\ -18^k \end{Bmatrix}$$

$$\{\boldsymbol{\Delta}_f\} \equiv \begin{Bmatrix} v_1 \\ u_2 \\ v_2 \\ \theta_{z2} \end{Bmatrix} = [\mathscr{F}]\{\mathbf{P}_f\} + \{\boldsymbol{\Delta}_f^i\} - [\mathscr{F}_{px}][\mathscr{F}_{xx}]^{-1}\{\boldsymbol{\Delta}_x^i\} = \begin{Bmatrix} -1100 \text{ in.} \\ 0.805 \text{ in.} \\ -6.26 \text{ in.} \\ 1.46 \end{Bmatrix} \times 10^{-3}$$

Additional internal forces may be determined from the equilibrium conditions for the members and, if desired, the shear and bending moment diagrams, as shown in Fig. 12-20, may be developed.

13-7 SELECTION OF REDUNDANT FORCES*

We have previously observed, in Examples 13-5 and 13-9 for example, that generally not all internal forces may be considered as candidates for the redundant forces. Some internal forces, if selected as the redundant forces, leave us with a released structure that is kinematically unstable. In mathematical terms, this situation corresponds to $[\mathbf{B}_0]$ being singular, i.e., it possesses no inverse. Although, for the relatively simple examples we considered, an admissible selection of redundant forces was fairly easy to make, it is desirable to devise a method that automatically identifies an admissible set of redundant forces, particularly for complicated structures. The *Gauss-Jordan elimination* method, described below, does precisely that, while computing $[\mathbf{C}_0]$ and $[\mathbf{C}_x]$ in the process. In addition, if a structure is kinematically unstable, this method will identify it as such.

We work solely with the equilibrium equations

$$\{\mathbf{P}_f\} = [\mathbf{B}]\{\mathbf{F}\} \tag{13-38}$$

which may be rewritten as

$$[\mathbf{B}]\{\mathbf{F}\} - [\mathbf{I}]\{\mathbf{P}_f\} = \{\mathbf{0}\} \tag{13-39a}$$

*The topics covered in this and the following section are treated in greater detail by W. McGuire and R.H. Gallagher, *Matrix Structural Analysis*, (New York: John Wiley, 1979).

or

$$[\mathbf{B} \mid - \mathbf{I}]\left\{\begin{array}{c}\mathbf{F} \\ \text{---} \\ \mathbf{P}_f\end{array}\right\} = \{\mathbf{0}\} \qquad (13\text{-}39b)$$

in which the rectangular matrix $[\mathbf{B} \mid - \mathbf{I}]$ is termed the *augmented matrix*. We wish to operate on Eq. (13-39b) until it acquires the form

$$[\mathbf{I} \mid -\mathbf{C}_x \mid -\mathbf{C}_0]\left\{\begin{array}{c}\mathbf{F}_0 \\ \text{---} \\ \mathbf{F}_x \\ \text{---} \\ \mathbf{P}_f\end{array}\right\} = \{\mathbf{0}\} \qquad (13\text{-}40)$$

where the order of the square matrices $[\mathbf{I}]$ and $[\mathbf{C}_0]$ is, of course, equal to the number of equilbrium equations. Equation (13-40) may be expressed in the form

$$\{\mathbf{F}_0\} = [\mathbf{C}_0]\{\mathbf{P}_f\} + [\mathbf{C}_x]\{\mathbf{F}_x\} \qquad (13\text{-}41)$$

Thus, not only does an admissible combination of redundant forces $\{\mathbf{F}_x\}$ emerge from this process, but also the necessary computation of $[\mathbf{C}_0]$ and $[\mathbf{C}_x]$ is conducted.

The Gauss-Jordan elimination procedure, applied to the augmented matrix, leads to the matrix in Eq. (13-40) in the following way:

1. Begin with the first row of the augmented matrix, assuring that the coefficient in the first column is nonzero, by rearranging columns if necessary. Divide all coefficients in the row by the value of the coefficient in the first column, thus rendering the first coefficient equal to unity.
2. Multiply the modified first row by the coefficient in the second row/first column, and subtract the result from the second row. This renders the coefficient in the second row/first column equal to zero. Proceed similarly with other rows to render all coefficients zero in the first column.
3. Now return to the second row, and divide all coefficients in that row by the coefficient in the second column. Then produce zero coefficients in the second column of all other rows by successively subtracting a properly scaled second row from all other rows, as described in step 2.
4. Continue this procedure for all rows, always producing values of unity for the diagonal coefficients and zeros elsewhere. When the process has been conducted for every row, the augmented matrix will have acquired the form indicated in Eq. (13-40).

Example 13-10. Conduct the Gauss-Jordan elimination procedure for the structure analyzed in Example 13-9.

Recall that the equations of equilibrium are

$$\begin{Bmatrix} P_{y1} \\ P_{x2} \\ P_{y2} \\ P_{mz2} \end{Bmatrix} + \begin{Bmatrix} qL \\ 0 \\ 0 \\ 0 \end{Bmatrix} = \begin{bmatrix} 0 & -1 & 0 & 0 & 0 & 0 \\ 1 & 0 & 0 & -1 & 0 & 0 \\ 0 & 1 & 0 & 0 & 1 & 0 \\ 0 & 0 & 1 & 0 & 0 & 1 \end{bmatrix} \begin{Bmatrix} F_{x2}^{(1)} \\ F_{y2}^{(1)} \\ M_{z2}^{(1)} \\ F_{x2}^{(2)} \\ F_{y2}^{(2)} \\ M_{z2}^{(2)} \end{Bmatrix} \qquad (a)$$

which may be identified as

$$\{\overline{\mathbf{P}}_f\} = [\mathbf{B}]\{\mathbf{F}\} \qquad (b)$$

In Eq. (b), $\{\overline{\mathbf{P}}_f\} = \{\mathbf{P}_f\} + \{\mathbf{P}_f^E\}$, i.e., $\{\overline{\mathbf{P}}_f\}$ includes both generalized forces and equivalent forces due to distributed loading. Note that the matrix $[\mathbf{B}]$ differs slightly from its counterpart in Eq. (d) of Example 13-9. Here, in forming Eq. (a), we have listed the member forces in a "natural" way by ordering them as F_x, F_y, and M_z at successive joints. We are not required to know that $F_{y2}^{(2)}$ is inadmissible as a redundant force; the procedure will prevent it from being chosen as one.

The augmented matrix is

$$\begin{array}{cccccccccc} F_{x2}^{(1)} & F_{y2}^{(1)} & M_{z2}^{(1)} & F_{x2}^{(2)} & F_{y2}^{(2)} & M_{z2}^{(2)} & \overline{P}_{y1} & \overline{P}_{x2} & \overline{P}_{y2} & \overline{P}_{mz2} \end{array}$$
$$\left[\begin{array}{cccccc:cccc} 0 & -1 & 0 & 0 & 0 & 0 & -1 & 0 & 0 & 0 \\ 1 & 0 & 0 & -1 & 0 & 0 & 0 & -1 & 0 & 0 \\ 0 & 1 & 0 & 0 & 1 & 0 & 0 & 0 & -1 & 0 \\ 0 & 0 & 1 & 0 & 0 & 1 & 0 & 0 & 0 & -1 \end{array}\right]$$

We have listed the internal and external forces above the matrix because, as columns are rearranged, we must keep track of the associated change in the vector of internal forces.

Step 1. Interchange columns 1 and 2 to provide a non-zero coefficient in the first row first column. Then divide the first row by -1 to make the coefficient in the first column equal to 1. The result is

$$\begin{array}{cccccccccc} F_{y2}^{(1)} & F_{x2}^{(1)} & M_{z2}^{(1)} & F_{x2}^{(2)} & F_{y2}^{(2)} & M_{z2}^{(2)} & \overline{P}_{y1} & \overline{P}_{x2} & \overline{P}_{y2} & \overline{P}_{mz2} \end{array}$$
$$\left[\begin{array}{cccccc:cccc} 1 & 0 & 0 & 0 & 0 & 0 & 1 & 0 & 0 & 0 \\ 0 & 1 & 0 & -1 & 0 & 0 & 0 & -1 & 0 & 0 \\ 1 & 0 & 0 & 0 & 1 & 0 & 0 & 0 & -1 & 0 \\ 0 & 0 & 1 & 0 & 0 & 1 & 0 & 0 & 0 & -1 \end{array}\right]$$

Step 2. Now multiply the first row by the first coefficient in the third row (this coefficient happens to be unity) and subtract the result from the third row. Note that the first element in the second row (and in the fourth row) is already zero, and hence this row need not be modified in this step. The result is

$$\begin{array}{cccccccccc} F_{y2}^{(1)} & F_{x2}^{(1)} & M_{z2}^{(1)} & F_{x2}^{(2)} & F_{y2}^{(2)} & M_{z2}^{(2)} & \overline{P}_{y1} & \overline{P}_{x2} & \overline{P}_{y2} & \overline{P}_{mz2} \end{array}$$
$$\left[\begin{array}{cccccc:cccc} 1 & 0 & 0 & 0 & 0 & 0 & 1 & 0 & 0 & 0 \\ 0 & 1 & 0 & -1 & 0 & 0 & 0 & -1 & 0 & 0 \\ 0 & 0 & 0 & 0 & 1 & 0 & -1 & 0 & -1 & 0 \\ 0 & 0 & 1 & 0 & 0 & 1 & 0 & 0 & 0 & -1 \end{array}\right]$$

Step 3. Normally, the second row would now be modified but the diagonal coefficient (i.e., the coefficient in the second column on this row) already is unity. Moreover, all other coefficients in the second column are zero. We therefore proceed to the third row, but to furnish a nonzero diagonal coefficient in this row we must interchange the third and fifth columns. We then obtain

$$
\begin{array}{cccccc}
F_{y2}^{(1)} & F_{x2}^{(1)} & F_{y2}^{(2)} & F_{x2}^{(2)} & M_{z2}^{(1)} & M_{z2}^{(2)} \\
\end{array}
\qquad
\begin{array}{cccc}
\bar{P}_{y1} & \bar{P}_{x2} & \bar{P}_{y2} & \bar{P}_{mz2}
\end{array}
$$

$$
\left[
\begin{array}{cccccc|cccc}
1 & 0 & 0 & 0 & 0 & 0 & 1 & 0 & 0 & 0 \\
0 & 1 & 0 & -1 & 0 & 0 & 0 & -1 & 0 & 0 \\
0 & 0 & 1 & 0 & 0 & 0 & -1 & 0 & -1 & 0 \\
0 & 0 & 0 & 0 & 1 & 1 & 0 & 0 & 0 & -1
\end{array}
\right]
$$

Observing that the third column contains all zeros, except for unity in the third row, we proceed now to the fourth row. The fourth column must be exchanged for either the fifth or sixth column. We choose the former, and see that the diagonal coefficient in the fourth row happens to be unity and all other coefficients in the fourth column already are zero. We obtain

$$
\begin{array}{cccc}
F_{y2}^{(1)} & F_{x2}^{(1)} & F_{y2}^{(2)} & M_{z2}^{(1)} \\
\end{array}
\qquad
\begin{array}{cc}
F_{x2}^{(2)} & M_{z2}^{(2)}
\end{array}
\qquad
\begin{array}{cccc}
\bar{P}_{y1} & \bar{P}_{x2} & \bar{P}_{y2} & \bar{P}_{mz2}
\end{array}
$$

$$
\left[
\begin{array}{cccc|cc|cccc}
1 & 0 & 0 & 0 & 0 & 0 & 1 & 0 & 0 & 0 \\
0 & 1 & 0 & 0 & -1 & 0 & 0 & -1 & 0 & 0 \\
0 & 0 & 1 & 0 & 0 & 0 & -1 & 0 & -1 & 0 \\
0 & 0 & 0 & 1 & 0 & 1 & 0 & 0 & 0 & -1
\end{array}
\right]
$$

We have added the partition between the fourth and fifth columns to identify the 4×4 identity matrix as well as the matrices $-[C_x]$ and $-[C_0]$. We thus have obtained the transformed equilibrium equations

$$
\begin{Bmatrix} F_{y2}^{(1)} \\ F_{x2}^{(1)} \\ F_{y2}^{(2)} \\ M_{z2}^{(1)} \end{Bmatrix}
=
\begin{bmatrix} -1 & 0 & 0 & 0 \\ 0 & 1 & 0 & 0 \\ 1 & 0 & 1 & 0 \\ 0 & 0 & 0 & 1 \end{bmatrix}
\left(
\begin{Bmatrix} P_{y1} \\ P_{x2} \\ P_{y2} \\ P_{mz2} \end{Bmatrix}
+
\begin{Bmatrix} qL \\ 0 \\ 0 \\ 0 \end{Bmatrix}
\right)
+
\begin{bmatrix} 0 & 0 \\ 1 & 0 \\ 0 & 0 \\ 0 & -1 \end{bmatrix}
\begin{Bmatrix} F_{x2}^{(2)} \\ M_{z2}^{(2)} \end{Bmatrix}
\qquad (c)
$$

which has the desired form

$$
\{F_0\} = [C_0]\{\bar{P}_f\} + [C_x]\{F_x\}
$$

Note that the form of $[C_0]$ in Eq. (c) is slightly different from that indicated in Eq. (f) of Example 13-9 simply because of the reordering of $\{F_0\}$ that emerged during the Gauss-Jordan elimination. The previous form is readily obtained by interchanging the first two rows in $[C_0]$ above.

It should be mentioned that in cases where more than one combination of redundant forces is admissible, the combination that emerges from the elimination process will be determined strictly by the choices that the analyst makes in reordering columns. Thus, the sets of components comprising $\{F_0\}$ and $\{F_x\}$ often are not unique, and hence the matrices $[C_0]$ and $[C_x]$ might not be unique. Finally, we reiterate that if for some structure it is impossible to form an identity matrix from the Gauss-Jordan elimination, then that structure is kinematically unstable.

13-8 DIRECT COMPUTATION OF REACTIONS

In the foregoing flexibility formulation, we have chosen to solve for the internal member forces directly, while computing reactions from equilibrium once internal forces have been determined. Although such a procedure is computationally efficient, it is not as readily amenable to automatic computation as the alternative approach of including the reactions in the formulation from the outset. While it is computationally more intensive, the alternative approach permits supports to be treated in the same manner as unrestrained nodes; it also allows us to solve problems in which the supports undergo prescribed displacements.

We may express the equations of equilibrium of all nodes in the form

$$\{\mathbf{P}\} = [\mathbf{B}]\{\overline{\mathbf{F}}\} \qquad (13\text{-}42)$$

where the load vector $\{\mathbf{P}\}$ incorporates forces applied to *all* nodes, including supports; and the force vector $\{\overline{\mathbf{F}}\}$ includes unknown reactions $\{\mathbf{R}\}$ as well as unknown member forces, $\{\mathbf{F}\}$, i.e.,

$$\{\overline{\mathbf{F}}\} = \left\{ \begin{array}{c} \mathbf{F} \\ \text{---} \\ \mathbf{R} \end{array} \right\} \qquad (13\text{-}43)$$

If the structure is statically determinate, then $[\mathbf{B}]$ is square and the equilibrium equations may be solved for $\{\mathbf{F}\}$ and $\{\mathbf{R}\}$.

If the structure is statically indeterminate, conditions of compatibility and force-deformation must be included in the formulation. Then, as in the previous formulation, the force vector $\{\overline{\mathbf{F}}\}$ must be partitioned into redundant and nonredundant parts, i.e.,

$$\{\overline{\mathbf{F}}\} = \left\{ \begin{array}{c} \mathbf{F}_0 \\ \text{---} \\ \mathbf{F}_x \end{array} \right\} \qquad (13\text{-}44)$$

Note that some reactions will be included in $\{\mathbf{F}_0\}$ (i.e., they are present in the released system), while others might be included in $\{\mathbf{F}_x\}$ (i.e., they are redundant forces).

It is useful to think of the reactions as being provided through reaction members, as for the truss shown in Figs. 13-13(a) and (b). As many reaction members are provided as there are reactions. For the truss shown, each of four reactions may be visualized as acting through translational springs. If a beam were fixed at a support, then the reactive moment could be considered to be furnished by a rotational spring element, as shown in Fig. 13-13(c) and (d). The motivation for devising reaction members is to incorporate degrees of freedom corresponding to the reactions. By doing this, we preserve the relationship between the system kinematics matrix $[\mathbf{A}]$ and the system statics matrix $[\mathbf{B}]$, i.e.,

$$[\mathbf{A}]^T = [\mathbf{B}] \qquad (13\text{-}45)$$

We ascribe to each reaction member a flexibility matrix $[\mathbf{f}_r]$. In most cases, for which the supports are fully restrained, the flexibilities of the reaction members are zero. Nevertheless, these flexibilities are included in the force-

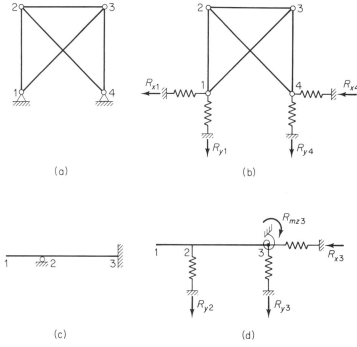

(a)

(b)

(c)

(d)

Figure 13-13

deformation relationships for the system

$$\left\{ \frac{\delta_0}{\delta_x} \right\} = \left[\begin{array}{c|c} [\mathbf{f}_{00}] & [\mathbf{f}_{0x}] \\ \hline [\mathbf{f}_{x0}] & [\mathbf{f}_{xx}] \end{array} \right] \left\{ \frac{\mathbf{F}_0}{\mathbf{F}_x} \right\} \tag{13-46}$$

where now, just as $\{\mathbf{F}_0 \mid \mathbf{F}_x\}$ includes reactions as well as member forces, $\{\delta_0 \mid \delta_x\}$ includes support deformations and the matrix of member flexibilities includes the flexibilities of reaction members.

The following examples illustrate the computational procedure.

Example 13-11. Analyze the truss shown in Fig. 13-14(a), incorporating the reactions directly into the formulation.

This structure, which was previously analyzed in Example 13-4, is now considered to bear on reaction members, as shown in Fig. 13-14(b). These members are, as remarked previously, a convenient analytical construct; their flexibilities are zero (i.e., the members are infinitely stiff) when the supports are immovable.

Equilibrium equations may be expressed for free-body diagrams of each of the four nodes, as shown in Fig. 13-14(c). Then, in accordance with Eq. (13-39), we may write

$$\begin{Bmatrix} P_{x1} \\ P_{y1} \\ P_{x2} \\ P_{y2} \\ P_{x3} \\ P_{y3} \\ P_{x4} \\ P_{y4} \end{Bmatrix} = \begin{bmatrix} 0 & 0 & -\lambda_3 & 0 & 0 & 1 & 0 & 0 & 0 \\ -1 & 0 & -\mu_3 & 0 & 0 & 0 & 1 & 0 & 0 \\ 0 & -1 & 0 & 0 & -\lambda_5 & 0 & 0 & 0 & 0 \\ 1 & 0 & 0 & 0 & \mu_5 & 0 & 0 & 0 & 0 \\ 0 & 1 & \lambda_3 & 0 & 0 & 0 & 0 & 0 & 0 \\ 0 & 0 & \mu_3 & 1 & 0 & 0 & 0 & 0 & 0 \\ 0 & 0 & 0 & 0 & \lambda_5 & 0 & 0 & 1 & 0 \\ 0 & 0 & 0 & -1 & -\mu_5 & 0 & 0 & 0 & 1 \end{bmatrix} \begin{Bmatrix} F_1 \\ F_2 \\ F_3 \\ F_4 \\ F_5 \\ R_{x1} \\ R_{y1} \\ R_{x4} \\ R_{y4} \end{Bmatrix} \qquad \text{(a)}$$

The system statics matrix $[\mathbf{B}]$ appearing on the right side of Eq. (a) has eight rows

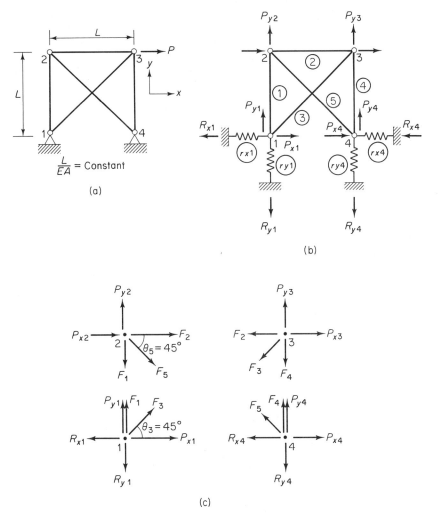

(a)

(b)

(c)

Figure 13-14

and nine columns, indicating that the structure is statically indeterminate. The enclosed portion of $[\mathbf{B}]$ was the entire system statics matrix developed with our former approach, where we related the four forces at nodes 2 and 3 to the five bar forces. Although significantly more effort is now required to compute $[\mathbf{C}_0] = [\mathbf{B}_0]^{-1}$ and $[\mathbf{C}_x] = -[\mathbf{C}_0][\mathbf{B}_x]$, the present formulation is more amenable to machine computation and, of course, it directly provides the reactions.

We may partition $[\mathbf{B}] = [\mathbf{B}_0 \mid \mathbf{B}_x]$ by selecting any one of the bar forces or either of the horizontal reactions as redundant forces. Alternatively, we may use the Gauss-Jordan elimination to identify an admissible redundant force and, at the same time, furnish $[\mathbf{C}_0]$ and $[\mathbf{C}_x]$. Employing this procedure, we obtain

$$\{\mathbf{F}_0\} = \begin{Bmatrix} F_1 \\ F_2 \\ F_3 \\ F_4 \\ R_{x1} \\ R_{y1} \\ R_{x4} \\ R_{y4} \end{Bmatrix} \quad \text{and} \quad \{\mathbf{F}_x\} = \{F_5\} \tag{b}$$

which, incidentally, correspond to member deformations

$$\{\boldsymbol{\delta}_0\} = \begin{Bmatrix} \delta_1 \\ \delta_2 \\ \delta_3 \\ \delta_4 \\ \delta_{rx1} \\ \delta_{ry1} \\ \delta_{rx4} \\ \delta_{ry4} \end{Bmatrix} \quad \text{and} \quad \{\boldsymbol{\delta}_x\} = \{\delta_5\} \tag{c}$$

In addition,

$$[\mathbf{C}_0] = \begin{bmatrix} 0 & 0 & 0 & 1 & 0 & 0 & 0 & 0 \\ 0 & 0 & -1 & 0 & 0 & 0 & 0 & 0 \\ 0 & 0 & \sqrt{2} & 0 & \sqrt{2} & 0 & 0 & 0 \\ 0 & 0 & -1 & 0 & -1 & 1 & 0 & 0 \\ 1 & 0 & 1 & 0 & 1 & 0 & 0 & 0 \\ 0 & 1 & 1 & 1 & 1 & 0 & 0 & 0 \\ 0 & 0 & 0 & 0 & 0 & 0 & 1 & 0 \\ 0 & 0 & -1 & 0 & -1 & 1 & 0 & 1 \end{bmatrix} \qquad [\mathbf{C}_x] = \frac{1}{\sqrt{2}} \begin{bmatrix} -1 \\ -1 \\ \sqrt{2} \\ -1 \\ 1 \\ 0 \\ -1 \\ 0 \end{bmatrix} \tag{d}$$

where we have used $\lambda_3 = \mu_3 = \lambda_5 = \mu_5 = 1/\sqrt{2}$.

Now we express the matrix of member flexibilities as

$$[\mathbf{f}] = \begin{bmatrix} [\mathbf{f}_{oo}] & \vdots & [\mathbf{f}_{ox}] \\ \cdots & \cdots & \cdots \\ [\mathbf{f}_{xo}] & \vdots & [\mathbf{f}_{xx}] \end{bmatrix} = \begin{bmatrix} f_1 \\ & f_2 \\ & & f_3 \\ & & & f_4 \\ & & & & f_{rx1} \\ & & & & & f_{ry1} \\ & & & & & & f_{rx4} \\ & & & & & & & f_{ry4} \\ \cdots & \cdots & \cdots & \cdots & \cdots & \cdots & \cdots & \cdots & \vdots & \cdots \\ & & & & & & & & \vdots & f_5 \end{bmatrix} \tag{e}$$

The member flexibilities appear in $[\mathbf{f}]$ in a sequence associated with the vectors $\{\mathbf{F}_o\}$ and $\{\mathbf{F}_x\}$. In the present case, we set $f_1 = \ldots = f_5 = L/EA$ and $f_{rx1} = \ldots = f_{ry4} = 0$. We may then form

$$[\mathscr{F}_{pp}] = [\mathbf{C}_o]^T[\mathbf{f}_{oo}][\mathbf{C}_o] = \frac{L}{EA} \begin{bmatrix} 0 & 0 & 0 & 0 & 0 & 0 & 0 & 0 \\ 0 & 0 & 0 & 0 & 0 & 0 & 0 & 0 \\ 0 & 0 & 4 & 0 & 3 & -1 & 0 & 0 \\ 0 & 0 & 0 & 1 & 0 & 0 & 0 & 0 \\ 0 & 0 & 3 & 0 & 3 & -1 & 0 & 0 \\ 0 & 0 & -1 & 0 & -1 & 1 & 0 & 0 \\ 0 & 0 & 0 & 0 & 0 & 0 & 0 & 0 \\ 0 & 0 & 0 & 0 & 0 & 0 & 0 & 0 \end{bmatrix}$$

$$[\mathscr{F}_{px}] = [\mathbf{C}_o]^T[\mathbf{f}_{oo}][\mathbf{C}_x] + [\mathbf{C}_o]^T[\mathbf{f}_{ox}] = \frac{L}{\sqrt{2}\,EA} \begin{bmatrix} 0 \\ 0 \\ 4 \\ -1 \\ 3 \\ -1 \\ 0 \\ 0 \end{bmatrix}$$

$$[\mathscr{F}_{xx}] = [\mathbf{C}_x]^T[\mathbf{f}_{oo}][\mathbf{C}_x] + [\mathbf{C}_x]^T[\mathbf{f}_{ox}] + [\mathbf{f}_{xo}][\mathbf{C}_x] + [\mathbf{f}_{xx}] = \frac{7}{2}\frac{L}{EA}$$

We then obtain

$$\{\mathbf{F}_x\} = -[\mathscr{F}_{xx}]^{-1}[\mathscr{F}_{xp}]\{\mathbf{P}_f\} = \frac{\sqrt{2}}{7}(-4P_{x2} + P_{y2} - 3P_{x3} + P_{y3}) \tag{f}$$

$$\{\mathbf{F}_o\} = ([\mathbf{C}_o] - [\mathbf{C}_x][\mathscr{F}_{xx}]^{-1}[\mathscr{F}_{xp}])\{\mathbf{P}\} = \begin{bmatrix} 0 & 0 & 4 & 6 & 3 & -1 & 0 & 0 \\ 0 & 0 & -3 & -1 & 3 & -1 & 0 & 0 \\ 0 & 0 & 3\sqrt{2} & \sqrt{2} & 4\sqrt{2} & \sqrt{2} & 0 & 0 \\ 0 & 0 & -3 & -1 & -4 & 6 & 0 & 0 \\ 7 & 0 & 3 & 1 & 4 & 1 & 0 & 0 \\ 0 & 7 & 7 & 7 & 7 & 0 & 0 & 0 \\ 0 & 0 & 4 & -1 & 3 & -1 & 7 & 0 \\ 0 & 0 & -7 & 0 & -7 & 7 & 0 & 7 \end{bmatrix} \begin{Bmatrix} P_{x1} \\ P_{y1} \\ P_{x2} \\ P_{y2} \\ P_{x3} \\ P_{y3} \\ P_{x4} \\ P_{y4} \end{Bmatrix} \tag{g}$$

We may also compute displacements from

$$\{\boldsymbol{\Delta}\} = [\mathcal{F}]\{\mathbf{P}\}$$

where

$$[\mathcal{F}] = [\mathcal{F}_{pp}] - [\mathcal{F}_{px}][\mathcal{F}_{xx}]^{-1}[\mathcal{F}_{xp}]$$

Hence,

$$
\begin{Bmatrix} u_1 \\ v_1 \\ u_2 \\ v_2 \\ u_3 \\ v_3 \\ u_4 \\ v_4 \end{Bmatrix}
= \frac{L}{7EA}
\begin{bmatrix}
0 & 0 & 0 & 0 & 0 & 0 & 0 & 0 \\
0 & 0 & 0 & 0 & 0 & 0 & 0 & 0 \\
0 & 0 & 12 & 4 & 9 & -3 & 0 & 0 \\
0 & 0 & 4 & 6 & 3 & -1 & 0 & 0 \\
0 & 0 & 9 & 3 & 12 & -4 & 0 & 0 \\
0 & 0 & -3 & -1 & -4 & 6 & 0 & 0 \\
0 & 0 & 0 & 0 & 0 & 0 & 0 & 0 \\
0 & 0 & 0 & 0 & 0 & 0 & 0 & 0
\end{bmatrix}
\begin{Bmatrix} P_{x1} \\ P_{y1} \\ P_{x2} \\ P_{y2} \\ P_{x3} \\ P_{y3} \\ P_{x4} \\ P_{y4} \end{Bmatrix}
\qquad \text{(h)}
$$

For the particular case in which only $P_{x3} = P$ is nonzero, Eqs. (f), (g), and (h) yield

$$
\{\mathbf{F}_x\} \equiv F_5 = \frac{-3\sqrt{2}}{7}P
\qquad
\{\mathbf{F}_0\} \equiv
\begin{Bmatrix} F_1 \\ F_2 \\ F_3 \\ F_4 \\ R_{x1} \\ R_{y1} \\ R_{x4} \\ R_{y4} \end{Bmatrix}
= P
\begin{Bmatrix} 3 \\ 3 \\ 4\sqrt{2} \\ -4 \\ 4 \\ 7 \\ 3 \\ -7 \end{Bmatrix}
$$

and

$$
\{\boldsymbol{\Delta}\} \equiv
\begin{Bmatrix} u_1 \\ v_1 \\ u_2 \\ v_2 \\ u_3 \\ v_3 \\ u_4 \\ v_4 \end{Bmatrix}
= \frac{PL}{7EA}
\begin{Bmatrix} 0 \\ 0 \\ 9 \\ 3 \\ 12 \\ -4 \\ 0 \\ 0 \end{Bmatrix}
$$

Example 13-12. Compute member forces, reactions and displacements that occur due to a horizontal displacement Δ imposed at the support node 4, as shown in Fig. 13-15(a). We have treated this problem in Example 12-2 by the direct stiffness method.

With the flexibility method, we consider an appropriate reaction member to undergo an initial deformation equal to the prescribed support displacement, and we may proceed in the manner described in Section 13-5. In the present case, we have $u_4 = \Delta$; hence the initial deformation of the horizontal reaction member is $\delta_{rx4}^i = \Delta$, as illustrated in Fig. 13-15(b). In general, the deformation of reaction members may be distributed between $\{\boldsymbol{\delta}_0\}$ and $\{\boldsymbol{\delta}_x\}$. In this particular case, according to the analysis in Example 13-11, δ_{rx4} is included in $\{\boldsymbol{\delta}_0\}$. Therefore, the initial

The Flexibility Method   Chap. 13

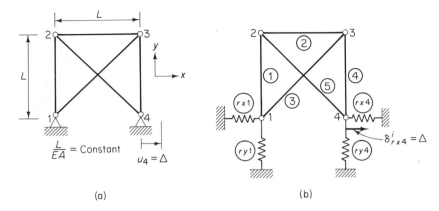

(a)   (b)

Figure 13-15

deformation vectors are

$$\{\boldsymbol{\delta}_0^i\} = \begin{Bmatrix} 0 \\ 0 \\ 0 \\ 0 \\ 0 \\ 0 \\ \Delta \\ 0 \end{Bmatrix} \qquad \{\boldsymbol{\delta}_x^i\} = \{0\} \qquad \text{(a)}$$

We may use Eqs. (13-34) and matrices developed in the previous example to compute the initial nodal displacements, i.e.,

$$\{\boldsymbol{\Delta}_0^i\} = [\mathbf{C}_0]^T\{\boldsymbol{\delta}_0^i\} = \begin{Bmatrix} 0 \\ 0 \\ 0 \\ 0 \\ 0 \\ 0 \\ \Delta \\ 0 \end{Bmatrix} \qquad \text{and} \qquad \{\boldsymbol{\Delta}_x^i\} = [\mathbf{C}_x]^T\{\boldsymbol{\delta}_0^i\} + [\mathbf{I}]\{\boldsymbol{\delta}_x^i\} = -\frac{\Delta}{\sqrt{2}} \qquad \text{(b)}$$

Accordingly, recognizing that all applied loads are zero, i.e., $\{\mathbf{P}_f\} = \{0\}$, we employ Eqs. (13-35) to obtain

$$\{\mathbf{F}_x\} \equiv F_5 = -[\mathscr{F}_{xx}]^{-1}\{\boldsymbol{\Delta}_x^i\} = \frac{\sqrt{2}}{7}\frac{EA\,\Delta}{L}$$

$$\{\mathbf{F}_0\} \equiv \begin{Bmatrix} F_1 \\ F_2 \\ F_3 \\ F_4 \\ R_{x1} \\ R_{y1} \\ R_{x4} \\ R_{y4} \end{Bmatrix} = -[\mathbf{C}_x][\mathscr{F}_{xx}]^{-1}\{\boldsymbol{\Delta}_x^i\} = \frac{EA\,\Delta}{7L} \begin{Bmatrix} -1 \\ -1 \\ \sqrt{2} \\ -1 \\ 1 \\ 0 \\ -1 \\ 0 \end{Bmatrix}$$

and

$$\{\boldsymbol{\Delta}\} \equiv \left\{\begin{array}{c} u_1 \\ v_1 \\ u_2 \\ v_2 \\ u_3 \\ v_3 \\ u_4 \\ v_4 \end{array}\right\} = \{\boldsymbol{\Delta}_0^i\} - [\mathscr{F}_{px}][\mathscr{F}_{xx}]^{-1}\{\boldsymbol{\Delta}_x^i\} = \frac{\Delta}{7} \left\{\begin{array}{c} 0 \\ 0 \\ 4 \\ -1 \\ 3 \\ -1 \\ 7 \\ 0 \end{array}\right\}$$

PROBLEMS

13-1 to **13-4.** Establish the global statics matrix for each of the statically determinate structures shown in Figs. P13-1 to P13-4, and solve for the member forces.

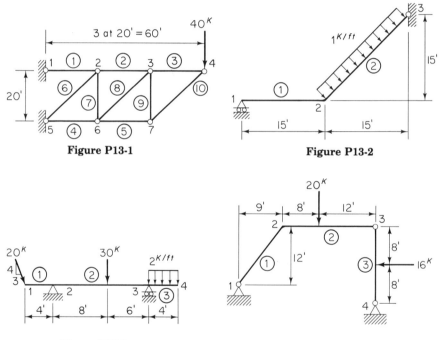

Figure P13-1

Figure P13-2

Figure P13-3

Figure P13-4

13-5. Derive the member flexibility matrix given by Eq. (13-17c) by solving the governing differential equations, Eqs. (13-18a, b), subject to the boundary conditions, Eq. (13-19a–f).

13-6. Derive the member flexibility matrix given by Eq. (13-17c) by first establishing the member stiffness matrix subject to the constraints shown in Fig. 13-5(a) and then inverting that stiffness matrix.

13-7. Derive the member flexibility matrix given by Eq. (13-20c).

13-8 to 13-11. Use the flexibility method to determine the bar forces in the trusses shown in Figs. P13-8 to P13-11.

Figure P13-8

Figure P13-9   **Figure P13-10**

Figure P13-11

13-12 to 13-14. Find the internal member forces for the systems shown in Figs. P13-12 to P13-14.

Figure P13-12   **Figure P13-13**

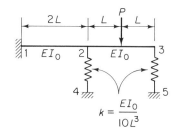

Figure P13-14

13-15 to 13-18. In each of the planar frames shown in Figs. P13-15 to P13-18, the following properties apply:

$$E = 30 \times 10^3 \text{ ksi} \qquad G = 12 \times 10^3 \text{ ksi}$$

$$A_0 = 10 \text{ in.}^2$$

$$I_0 = 200 \text{ in.}^4 \qquad J_0 = 400 \text{ in.}^4$$

Determine the member forces and nodal displacements due to the prescribed loads.

Figure P13-15

Figure P13-16

Figure P13-17

Figure P13-18

13-19. In the structure shown in Fig. P13-11, the member spanning nodes 1 and 5 is heated to a temperature of 50°F above the other members. Find the resulting bar forces, assuming the coefficient of thermal expansion is 0.6×10^{-6}/°F.

13-20 and **13-21.** In each of the structures shown in Figs. P13-15 and P13-16, the member spanning nodes 1 and 2 is subjected to a temperature of 100°F along the top flange and 50°F along the bottom flange. The other members have a uniform temperature of 50°F. Assuming the coefficient of thermal expansion is 0.6×10^{-6}/°F and the depth of the members is 18 inches, determine the internal forces in the structures.

13-22. The left column of the frame shown in Fig. P13-17 is fabricated 0.5 inch too short. Find the nodal displacements and the internal forces due to the misfit of the column.

13-23. Using the Gauss-Jordan method determine whether the trusses shown in Fig. P13-23 are kinematically stable and, if they are stable, establish the degree of static indeterminacy.

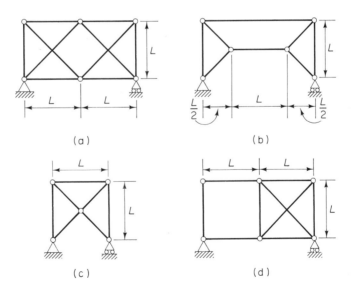

Figure P13-23

13-24 to 13-26. Use the Gauss-Jordan method to determine $[C_0]$ and $[C_x]$ for the structures shown in Figs. P13-2, P13-9, and P13-17.

13-27. Introduce reaction elements in the structure shown in Fig. P13-15 and compute reactions and member forces directly using the flexibility method.

13-28. Using the concept of reaction elements, determine the reactions and member forces when the frame shown in Fig. P13-16 is subjected to a vertical settlement of 1 inch at node 4.

14

Introduction to the Finite Element Method

Preceding chapters have been devoted to the analysis of structures composed of discrete members such as bars, beams, and columns. Although each of these members comprises an infinite number of material points in three dimensions, they may be idealized as one-dimensional elements, because their lengths are much greater than their cross-sectional dimensions. For example, the axial stress and displacement are considered to be uniform over the cross section of a bar and to vary linearly over the depth of a beam. Accordingly, the behavior of either member may be described by one or more ordinary differential equations in which only the distance along the axis of the member appears as the independent variable. For members possessing constant cross-sectional properties, i.e., prismatic members, the coefficients in the governing differential equations are constants, and the solutions to those equations have elementary forms. On the basis of such solutions, we have been able to describe the behavior of any point in the member in terms of the behavior of the end points, i.e., in terms of generalized displacements and forces. Regardless of the length of a beam, for example, or the complexity of loading over its span, its deformation may always be described in terms of the translations and rotations of cross sections at the ends of the beam. Thus, the behavior of structures composed of such one-dimensional members may be described in terms of generalized displacements associated with joints that are defined by the terminal points of the members.

A structure such as a plate or shell cannot be idealized as a one-dimensional element, and the partial differential equations that describe its behavior often become intractable. Thus, deformations and stresses at arbitrary points in the structure cannot usually be described in terms of the behavior of points along its boundaries, because the latter cannot be determined analytically. It may be intuitively appealing, however, to imagine a structure such as a thin plate to be nearly equivalent to a gridwork of bar elements as shown in Fig. 14-1. The thin sheet shown in Fig. 14-1(a) is subjected to in-plane forces, and thus in-plane stresses σ_x, σ_y, and τ_{xy} and displacements u and v occur in the body; these stresses and displacements generally vary spatially, i.e., they are functions of x and y. If we were to replace the continuum by a trusswork comprising many small bars, as shown in Fig. 14-1(b), the computed forces in the bars could be used in some manner to infer the stresses in the continuum. For example, the normal stress σ_x at a generic point P in the continuum could be approximated by dividing the x-components of bar forces near the equivalent point (the shaded zone) in the trusswork by the distance spanned by those bars in the y-direction. Similarly, the normal stress σ_y could be related to the y-components of bar forces, while the shear stress τ_{xy} could be related to the forces in nearby diagonal bars. Also, provided the combined cross-sectional area of the bars were equal to the area across a section of the continuum, the displacements of the trusswork would approximate those of the continuum.

A similar argument may be developed for the flexural response of a plate subjected to transverse loads, as shown in Fig. 14-2(a). The gridwork shown in Fig. 14-2(b) comprises beam elements that sustain shear forces and bending and twisting moments which may be related to the shear forces Q_x and $Q_{y'}$, the

(a)   (b)

Figure 14-1

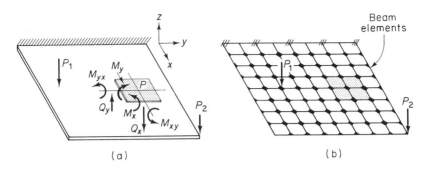

Figure 14-2

bending moments M_x and M_y, and the twisting moments M_{xy} and M_{yx} that occur within the plate. One would expect the responses of both gridworks shown in Figs. 14-1 and 14-2 to represent more accurately those of the continua as the number of bar elements and beam elements increases, i.e., as the spacing of the elements becomes small relative the distance over which their internal forces are averaged.

This discretization procedure, which was advanced in the 1940's by Hrennikoff,[*] McHenry,[†] Newmark,[‡] and others, was the precursor of the so-called finite element method that was introduced some fifteen years later. The initial approach, however, suffered from two drawbacks: first, the specification of a sufficiently representative discrete system of bars or beams was neither obvious nor particularly appealing from a formal analytical viewpoint; second, the number of joint displacements that must be computed via a stiffness approach was prohibitively large at the time, when electronic computation was yet nonexistent.

The 1956 publication by Turner, et al .[§] is generally regarded as having introduced the finite element method as we consider it today. Exploiting the rapid developments in matrix methods of structural analysis and especially in electronic computation, these investigators formulated and applied the relationships pertaining to the triangular finite element used for plane stress and plane strain analyses. The development of an element of triangular form enabled a continuum subjected to in-plane forces to be represented by an assemblage of these two-dimensional elements, as shown in Fig. 14-3. The physical contiguity that exists between any two elements obviates many of the approximations associated with gridworks of bars and affords more accurate solutions for a given computational effort.

[*]Hrennikoff, A., "Solution of Problems of Elasticity by the Framework Method," *Journal of Applied Mechanics*, Vol. A8, (1941), pp. 169–175.

[†]McHenry, D., "A Lattice Analogy for the Solution of Plane Stress Problems," *Journal of the Institution for Civil Engineers*, Vol. 21, (1943), pp. 59–82.

[‡]Newmark, N. W., "Numerical Methods of Analysis in Bars, Plates and Elastic Bodies," in *Numerical Methods in Analysis in Engineering*, ed. L. E. Grinter, (New York: Macmillan, 1949).

[§]Turner, M. J., R. W. Clough, H. C. Martin and L. J. Topp, "Stiffness and Deflection Analysis of Complex Structures," *Journal of Aeronautical Sciences*, Vol. 23, No. 9, (1956), pp. 805–824.

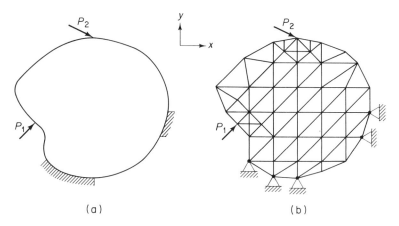

Figure 14-3

The finite elements shown in Fig. 14-3(b) are considered to be interconnected only at the vertices of the triangles. The essence of the finite element method lies in developing the relationships between the nodal forces and displacements, i.e., the stiffness matrix, for a generic element. The system stiffness matrix for the entire assemblage may be constructed in the usual manner from the element stiffness matrices. In addition, a relationship must be developed between computed nodal displacements and internal stresses within each element. Just as we have been able to solve truss problems by formulating the system stiffness matrix that relates applied nodal forces to nodal displacements, we also may analyze an assemblage of triangular elements. Once nodal displacements of a truss have been computed, we may find internal forces in the bars by employing the element stiffness matrices. For a triangular element, the process of determining internal stresses is somewhat more involved, as is the development of the element stiffness matrix. However, the basic approach is the same in solving all finite element problems. Indeed, it should be emphasized that the finite element method includes a great variety of element types and applications in addition to those described above.

This chapter is intended to provide a brief introduction to the theory and application of the finite element method to problems in structural mechanics. Literally thousands of research papers and scores of texts have been written on the subject, including excellent discourses by Zienkiewicz[*] and by Cook,[†] among others. In the sequel, we first provide the groundwork for developing the requisite finite element relationships. This is followed by the derivation of these relationships for several types of elements, along with numerical examples that illustrate the applicability of the method.

*Zienkiewicz, O. C., *The Finite Element Method*, 3rd ed., (New York: McGraw-Hill, 1977).
†Cook, R. D., *Concepts and Applications of Finite Element Analysis*, 2nd ed., (New York: John Wiley, 1981).

We wish to develop, independently of specific applications, guidelines for idealizing problems in structural mechanics by the finite element method, and to derive the general relationships that enter finite element formulations. Although in this discussion it may be useful to envision a mesh of triangular elements covering a thin plate subjected to in-plane forces, as shown in Fig. 14-3(b), we should bear in mind that the same general formulation applies to problems of plates in flexure, shells, three-dimensional solids, and others.

As illustrated by Fig. 14-3, the continuum is imagined to comprise numerous elements that are interconnected at a discrete number of nodal points, such as the vertices of the triangular elements. Within the context of a stiffness approach, the displacements of these nodal points constitute the primary unknowns to be determined.

The governing stiffness equations may be assembled and solved once the element stiffness matrices have been obtained. When we derived the element stiffness matrices for bar and beam elements before, we did so by directly integrating the differential equations that govern the behavior of the element. The solutions of these differential equations permit displacements at points along the bar or beam to be expressed in terms of those at the end points. We found that the axial displacements of a bar or beam of length L varied linearly with the distance x measured from one end (node i) of the member, i.e.,

$$u(x) = u_i\left(1 - \frac{x}{L}\right) + u_j\frac{x}{L} \tag{14-1}$$

in which u_i and u_j are the axial displacements of nodes i and j defining the ends of the member. We also found that the transverse displacement of a beam loaded only at its ends varies as a cubic function of x, i.e.,

$$v(x) = v_i\left[1 - 3\left(\frac{x}{L}\right)^2 + 2\left(\frac{x}{L}\right)^3\right] + v_j\left(\frac{x}{L}\right)^2\left[3 - 2\left(\frac{x}{L}\right)\right]$$
$$+ \theta_{zi}L\left(\frac{x}{L}\right)\left[\left(\frac{x}{L}\right)^2 - 2\left(\frac{x}{L}\right) + 1\right] + \theta_{zj}L\left(\frac{x}{L}\right)^2\left[\left(\frac{x}{L}\right) - 1\right] \tag{14-2}$$

in which v_i and v_j are the transverse displacements and θ_{zi} and θ_{zj} are the rotations at the ends of the beam. Once we found the nodal displacements, we were able to determine displacements and stress resultants at any other point x.

The essential difference between the foregoing approach and that which must be employed for a two-dimensional element, such as the plane stress triangle, lies with our inability to solve the governing differential equation of equilibrium for the latter. Rather than *derive* a relationship between displacements at an interior point of the element and those at the nodal boundary points, we must *assume* such a relationship. Proceeding in this way makes the problem tractable but introduces an approximation to the solution for most problems. The chosen displacement functions must satisfy continuity conditions (i.e., no holes or overlaps are permitted to exist) within the element. Specification of the nodal displacements therefore establishes the displacements, and hence the stresses and strains at interior points. What is not yet clear is precisely how the specification of an assumed displacement function leads to the development of the stiffness equations; the remainder of this section is devoted to that task. While the derivation will be general, we shall refer at times to a triangular element, such as the one shown in Fig. 14-4, in order to clarify ideas.

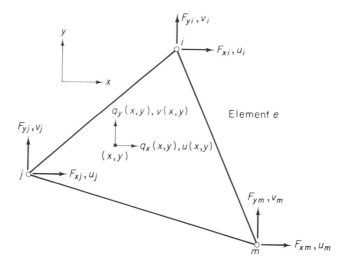

Figure 14-4

Forces and displacements.   We begin by defining for a generic element the set of nodal displacements as

$$\{\mathbf{\Delta}\} = \begin{Bmatrix} \mathbf{\Delta}_i \\ \mathbf{\Delta}_j \\ \vdots \\ \mathbf{\Delta}_m \end{Bmatrix} \qquad (14\text{-}3\text{a})$$

For the triangular element shown in Fig. 14-4, therefore,

$$\{\mathbf{\Delta}_i\} = \begin{Bmatrix} u_i \\ v_i \end{Bmatrix} \qquad (14\text{-}3\text{b})$$

and thus

$$\{\mathbf{\Delta}\} = \begin{Bmatrix} u_i \\ v_i \\ \vdots \\ v_m \end{Bmatrix} \qquad (14\text{-}3\text{c})$$

Corresponding to these nodal displacements are nodal forces, exerted on the element by adjacent elements, which we designate as

$$\{\mathbf{F}\} = \begin{Bmatrix} \mathbf{F}_i \\ \mathbf{F}_j \\ \vdots \\ \mathbf{F}_m \end{Bmatrix} \qquad (14\text{-}4a)$$

For the triangular element,

$$\{\mathbf{F}_i\} = \begin{Bmatrix} F_{xi} \\ F_{yi} \end{Bmatrix} \qquad (14\text{-}4b)$$

and thus,

$$\{\mathbf{F}\} = \begin{Bmatrix} F_{xi} \\ F_{yi} \\ \vdots \\ F_{ym} \end{Bmatrix} \qquad (14\text{-}4c)$$

We also may identify the displacements of any point in the element by the *vector of displacement functions* $\{\mathbf{\Phi}\}$. For the triangular element in the x–y plane, the displacements at some point (x, y) are $u(x, y)$ and $v(x, y)$. Thus

$$\{\mathbf{\Phi}(x, y)\} = \begin{Bmatrix} u(x, y) \\ v(x, y) \end{Bmatrix} \qquad (14\text{-}5)$$

Corresponding to the vector of displacement functions $\{\mathbf{\Phi}\}$, there may exist a distributed force vector $\{\mathbf{q}\}$. For the triangular element, this vector has the form

$$\{\mathbf{q}\} = \begin{Bmatrix} q_x(x, y) \\ q_y(x, y) \end{Bmatrix} \qquad (14\text{-}6)$$

where the components of $\{\mathbf{q}\}$ may be thought of as body forces per unit volume in the x- and y-directions.

Shape functions. Now we define a *connectivity matrix* $[\mathbf{N}(x, y)]$ which relates the internal displacements $\{\mathbf{\Phi}\}$ to the nodal displacements $\{\mathbf{\Delta}\}$, i.e.,

$$\{\mathbf{\Phi}\} = [\mathbf{N}]\{\mathbf{\Delta}\} \qquad (14\text{-}7)$$

The functions that appear in $[\mathbf{N}]$ are termed the *shape functions*. Also, the matrix $[\mathbf{N}]$ may be formed to comprise several submatrices $[\mathbf{N}_i]$, $[\mathbf{N}_j]$, ... ; thus, for the triangular element, Eq. (14-7) may be written as

$$\begin{Bmatrix} u(x, y) \\ v(x, y) \end{Bmatrix} = \begin{bmatrix} [\mathbf{N}_i], [\mathbf{N}_j], [\mathbf{N}_m] \end{bmatrix} \begin{Bmatrix} u_i \\ v_i \\ \vdots \\ v_m \end{Bmatrix} \qquad (14\text{-}8)$$

where the order of the submatrices is 2×2. Note that when (x, y) coincides ith (x_i, y_i), it is necessary that $u(x_i, y_i) = u_i$ and $v(x_i, y_i) = v_i$. This implies that in general

$$[\mathbf{N}_i(x_i, y_i)] = [\mathbf{I}] \qquad (14\text{-}9a)$$

while

$$[\mathbf{N}_j(x_i, y_i)] = [\mathbf{N}_m(x_i, y_i)] = [\mathbf{0}] \qquad (14\text{-}9b)$$

Similar arguments apply when $(x, y) = (x_j, y_j)$ and when $(x, y) = (x_m, y_m)$.

The crucial issue involves the form of the functions beyond those requirements, such as Eqs. (14-9), imposed at the nodal points. In the case of a bar element for which the displacement $u(x)$ varies linearly with x, in view of Eq. (14-1), $[\mathbf{N}]$ would take the form

$$[\mathbf{N}] = [\mathbf{N}_i(x), \mathbf{N}_j(x)] = [(1 - x/L), x/L] \qquad (14\text{-}10)$$

These shape functions are shown in Fig. 14-5. Similarly, if we were to assume that within a triangular element both $u(x, y)$ and $v(x, y)$ vary linearly with x and y, then we would conclude that $[\mathbf{N}_i]$ must have the form

$$[\mathbf{N}_i] = \frac{1}{2A_e}(a_i + b_i x + c_i y)[\mathbf{I}] \qquad (14\text{-}11)$$

in which A_e is the plan area of the element and a_i, b_i and c_i are constants that depend on the geometry of the element. Similar forms apply to $[\mathbf{N}_j]$ and $[\mathbf{N}_m]$. Equation (14-11) will be derived in Section 14-4.

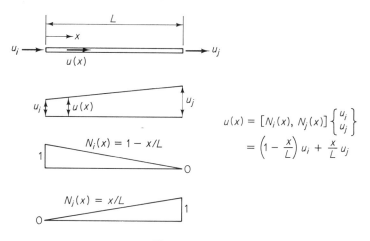

Figure 14-5

Strain-displacement relationships. Strains may be determined for the element by differentiating displacements. In the case of either plane stress or plane strain, the components of strain in the x–y plane may be expressed as

$$\epsilon_x = \frac{\partial u}{\partial x}$$

$$\epsilon_y = \frac{\partial v}{\partial y} \qquad (14\text{-}12)$$

$$\gamma_{xy} = \frac{\partial u}{\partial y} + \frac{\partial v}{\partial x}$$

By defining the *strain vector* as

$$\{\boldsymbol{\epsilon}\} = \begin{Bmatrix} \epsilon_x \\ \epsilon_y \\ \gamma_{xy} \end{Bmatrix} \qquad (14\text{-}13)$$

we may write

$$\{\boldsymbol{\epsilon}\} = \begin{bmatrix} \dfrac{\partial}{\partial x} & 0 \\[2mm] 0 & \dfrac{\partial}{\partial y} \\[2mm] \dfrac{\partial}{\partial y} & \dfrac{\partial}{\partial x} \end{bmatrix} \begin{Bmatrix} u\,(x,\, y) \\ v\,(x,\, y) \end{Bmatrix} \qquad (14\text{-}14)$$

Then, in view of Eqs. (14-3) and (14-7), we may rewrite Eq. (14-14) as

$$\{\boldsymbol{\epsilon}\} = \begin{bmatrix} \dfrac{\partial}{\partial x} & 0 \\[2mm] 0 & \dfrac{\partial}{\partial y} \\[2mm] \dfrac{\partial}{\partial y} & \dfrac{\partial}{\partial x} \end{bmatrix} [\mathbf{N}]\{\boldsymbol{\Delta}\} \qquad (14\text{-}15)$$

This expression, relating the strain at a generic point $(x,\, y)$ within the element to the nodal displacements, applies to any plane stress or plane strain problem, regardless of the specific finite element that is employed. In general terms, the relationship between a strain vector and a nodal displacement vector may be written as

$$\{\boldsymbol{\epsilon}\} = [\mathbf{b}]\{\boldsymbol{\Delta}\} \qquad (14\text{-}16)$$

where $[\mathbf{b}]$ is obtained by the appropriate differentiation of $[\mathbf{N}]$.

Stress-strain relationships. We may define the *stress vector* as $\{\boldsymbol{\sigma}\}$. In the case of plane stress, $\{\boldsymbol{\sigma}\}$ is defined as

$$\{\boldsymbol{\sigma}\} = \begin{Bmatrix} \sigma_x \\ \sigma_y \\ \tau_{xy} \end{Bmatrix} \qquad (14\text{-}17)$$

in a form analogous to the strain vector $\{\boldsymbol{\epsilon}\}$. We may, of course, relate the stress and strain vectors through a constitutive law, such as Hooke's law for a linear material, i.e.,

$$\{\boldsymbol{\sigma}\} = [\mathbf{D}]\{\boldsymbol{\epsilon}\} \tag{14-18}$$

in which $[\mathbf{D}]$ is called the *elasticity matrix*. If the material is isotropic, as well as linearly elastic, then under conditions of plane stress,

$$[\mathbf{D}] = \frac{E}{1 - \nu^2} \begin{bmatrix} 1 & \nu & 0 \\ \nu & 1 & 0 \\ 0 & 0 & (1 - \nu)/2 \end{bmatrix} \tag{14-19}$$

Occasionally, initial strains exist due to changes in temperature or due to geometric misfit. The stresses $\{\boldsymbol{\sigma}\}$ are then proportional to the difference between the final strains $\{\boldsymbol{\epsilon}\}$ and the initial strains, designated as $\{\boldsymbol{\epsilon}_0\}$. In addition, it is useful to account for any initial stresses that might exist, before loads are applied. Both initial strains and initial stresses may be incorporated into the stress-strain relationship. Thus, Eq. (14-18) may be generalized for a linear material to the form

$$\{\boldsymbol{\sigma}\} = [\mathbf{D}](\{\boldsymbol{\epsilon}\} - \{\boldsymbol{\epsilon}_0\}) + \{\boldsymbol{\sigma}_0\} \tag{14-20}$$

Element stiffness equations. We now use the principle of virtual work to determine the relationship between the external forces acting at the nodes of a single element and nodal displacements, initial stresses, initial strains and distributed forces. We define virtual nodal displacements for the element as $\{\delta\boldsymbol{\Delta}\}$. Then compatible virtual displacements and virtual strains within the element may be expressed as

$$\{\delta\boldsymbol{\Phi}\} = [\mathbf{N}]\{\delta\boldsymbol{\Delta}\} \tag{14-21a}$$

and

$$\{\delta\boldsymbol{\epsilon}\} = [\mathbf{b}]\{\delta\boldsymbol{\Delta}\} \tag{14-21b}$$

The principle of virtual work states that, in order for a body to be in equilibrium, the sum of the external virtual work and the internal virtual work must equal zero. In the present case, the external virtual work is related to the actual nodal forces and the distributed forces by

$$\delta W_{\text{ext}} = \{\delta\boldsymbol{\Delta}\}^T\{\mathbf{F}\} + \int_{V_e} \{\delta\boldsymbol{\Phi}\}^T\{\mathbf{q}\}dV_e \tag{14-22}$$

where, because the distributed forces are defined per unit volume, the second term indicates integration over the volume of the element V_e.

The internal virtual work is associated with actual stresses acting through virtual strains. Thus

$$\delta W_{\text{int}} = -\int_{V_e} \{\delta\boldsymbol{\epsilon}\}^T\{\boldsymbol{\sigma}\}dV_e \tag{14-23}$$

We may use Eqs. (14-21) to express the virtual distributed displacement $\{\delta\Phi\}$ and the virtual strain $\{\delta\epsilon\}$ in terms of the virtual nodal displacements. Then, setting the sum of Eqs. (14-22) and (14-23) equal to zero, we obtain

$$\{\delta\Delta\}^T\{\mathbf{F}\} + \{\delta\Delta\}^T \int_{V_e} [\mathbf{N}]^T\{\mathbf{q}\}dV_e - \{\delta\Delta\}^T \int_{V_e} [\mathbf{b}]^T\{\boldsymbol\sigma\}dV_e = 0 \qquad (14\text{-}24a)$$

or,

$$\{\delta\Delta\}^T\{\mathbf{F}\} = \{\delta\Delta\}^T\left(\int_{V_e} [\mathbf{b}]^T\{\boldsymbol\sigma\}dV_e - \int_{V_e} [\mathbf{N}]^T\{\mathbf{q}\}dV_e\right) \qquad (14\text{-}24b)$$

As the virtual displacements must be arbitrary, we conclude that

$$\{\mathbf{F}\} = \int_{V_e} [\mathbf{b}]^T\{\boldsymbol\sigma\}dV_e - \int_{V_e} [\mathbf{N}]^T\{\mathbf{q}\}dV_e \qquad (14\text{-}25)$$

This relationship is valid for any stress-strain relationship. Substitution of Eq. (14-20) into Eq. (14-25) leads to

$$\{\mathbf{F}\} = \int_{V_e} [\mathbf{b}]^T[\mathbf{D}]\{\boldsymbol\epsilon\}dV_e - \int_{V_e} [\mathbf{b}]^T[\mathbf{D}]\{\boldsymbol\epsilon_0\}dV_e + \int_{V_e} [\mathbf{b}]^T\{\boldsymbol\sigma_0\}dV_e - \int_{V_e} [\mathbf{N}]^T\{\mathbf{q}\}dV_e$$
$$(14\text{-}26)$$

Because virtual displacements must be completely arbitrary, provided they satisfy the compatibility conditions, Eq. (14-26) incurs no approximation. Thus, the nodal forces $\{\mathbf{F}\}$ are precisely in equilibrium with the combination of stresses associated with elastic strains and prescribed initial strains $\{\boldsymbol\epsilon_0\}$, with initial stresses $\{\boldsymbol\sigma_0\}$, and with distributed forces $\{\mathbf{q}\}$. Note, however, that the real strain vector $\{\boldsymbol\epsilon\}$, which is related to the unknown real nodal displacements, is unknown and cannot be computed until the nodal displacements have been determined. Suppose, however, that we *assume* the *real* strains to be related to the *real* nodal displacements in the same way as *virtual* strains have been related to *virtual* displacements, i.e., according to Eq. (14-16)

$$\{\boldsymbol\epsilon\} = [\mathbf{b}]\{\Delta\} \qquad (14\text{-}16)$$

Substituting this *approximation* into Eq. (14-26), we obtain

$$\{\mathbf{F}\} = \left(\int_{V_e} [\mathbf{b}]^T[\mathbf{D}][\mathbf{b}]dV_e\right)\{\Delta\} - \int_{V_e} [\mathbf{b}]^T[\mathbf{D}]\{\boldsymbol\epsilon_0\}dV_e$$
$$+ \int_{V_e} [\mathbf{b}]^T\{\boldsymbol\sigma_0\}dV_e - \int_{V_e} [\mathbf{N}]^T\{\mathbf{q}\}dV_e \qquad (14\text{-}27)$$

or

$$\{\mathbf{F}\} = [\mathbf{k}]\{\Delta\} - \{\mathbf{F}_{\epsilon_0}^E\} - \{\mathbf{F}_{\sigma_0}^E\} - \{\mathbf{F}_q^E\} \qquad (14\text{-}28)$$

in which the element stiffness matrix is identified as

$$[\mathbf{k}] = \int_{V_e} [\mathbf{b}]^T[\mathbf{D}][\mathbf{b}]dV_e \qquad (14\text{-}29a)$$

and the vectors of equivalent forces related to initial strains, initial stresses and distributed forces are, respectively,

$$\{\mathbf{F}^E_{\boldsymbol{\epsilon}_0}\} = \int_{V_e} [\mathbf{b}]^T [\mathbf{D}]\{\boldsymbol{\epsilon}_0\} dV_e \qquad (14\text{-}29\text{b})$$

$$\{\mathbf{F}^E_{\boldsymbol{\sigma}_0}\} = -\int_{V_e} [\mathbf{b}]^T \{\boldsymbol{\sigma}_0\} dV_e \qquad (14\text{-}29\text{c})$$

and

$$\{\mathbf{F}^E_q\} = \int_{V_e} [\mathbf{N}]^T \{\mathbf{q}\} dV_e \qquad (14\text{-}29\text{d})$$

These equivalent forces have the same meaning as those introduced in Chapter 12; they are generalized forces which are equivalent to the initial stresses, strains, and distributed loading.

The expression for $[\mathbf{k}]$ given by Eq. (14-29a) is approximate unless the actual displacements and strains are exactly satisfied by Eq. (14-16). As we shall see in an example, an exact stiffness matrix is in fact obtained in the case of a prismatic bar, for which $[\mathbf{b}]$ is related to the exact connectivity matrix $[\mathbf{N}]$ given by Eq. (14-10). Nor are any approximations incurred in the analysis of prismatic beams when the displacement function defined by Eq. (14-2) is used to establish $[\mathbf{N}]$ and $[\mathbf{b}]$. For other elements, however, Eq. (14-29a) is usually approximate.

System stiffness equations. In the same manner used for the direct stiffness analysis of trusses and frames, we identify the vector of nodal displacements for the system as $\{\boldsymbol{\Delta}\}$. Accordingly, we also may formulate the system matrix by properly combining the element stiffness matrices for the M elements comprising the system, i.e.,

$$[\mathbf{K}] = \sum_{m=1}^{M} [\mathbf{k}^{(m)}] \qquad (14\text{-}30)$$

Similarly, the vector of forces for the system is constructed by combining the forces defined by Eqs. (14-29b) through (14-29d) for all elements, i.e.,

$$\{\mathbf{P}^E_{\boldsymbol{\epsilon}_0}\} = \sum_{m=1}^{M} \{\mathbf{F}^E_{\boldsymbol{\epsilon}_0}\}^{(m)} \qquad (14\text{-}31\text{a})$$

$$\{\mathbf{P}^E_{\boldsymbol{\sigma}_0}\} = \sum_{m=1}^{M} \{\mathbf{F}^E_{\boldsymbol{\sigma}_0}\}^{(m)} \qquad (14\text{-}31\text{b})$$

$$\{\mathbf{P}^E_q\} = \sum_{m=1}^{M} \{\mathbf{F}^E_q\}^{(m)} \qquad (14\text{-}31\text{c})$$

Finally, note that the set of equivalent nodal forces must be added to the vector of any external nodal forces $\{\mathbf{P}\}$ applied to the system. Thus the system stiffness equations are

$$\{\mathbf{P}\} + \{\mathbf{P}^E_{\epsilon_0}\} + \{\mathbf{P}^E_{\sigma_0}\} + \{\mathbf{P}^E_q\} = [\mathbf{K}]\{\mathbf{\Delta}\} \qquad (14\text{-}32)$$

The stiffness equations are solved for unknown nodal displacements in the manner described in Chapters 11 and 12. We then may compute stresses in the elements by employing Eqs. (14-16) and (14-20). Hence, for any element

$$\{\boldsymbol{\sigma}\} = [\mathbf{D}][\mathbf{b}]\{\mathbf{\Delta}\} - [\mathbf{D}]\{\boldsymbol{\epsilon}_0\} + \{\boldsymbol{\sigma}_0\} \qquad (14\text{-}33)$$

Example 14-1. A prismatic bar, shown in Fig. 14-6, is subjected to initial axial stress σ_{x0} and strain, ϵ_{x0}, and to an axially distributed body force q_x. Derive the element stiffness matrix $[\mathbf{k}]$ and the equivalent forces defined by Eqs. (14-29).

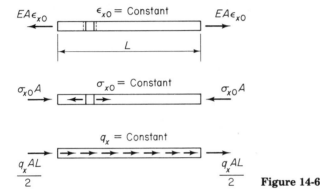

Figure 14-6

To determine the stiffness matrix, the matrices $[\mathbf{b}]$ and $[\mathbf{D}]$ first must be prescribed. Let us assume that the connectivity matrix is given by Eq. (14-10). Then, because only one relevant strain component ϵ_x exists, Eq. (14-15) reduces to

$$\epsilon_x = \frac{d}{dx}[(1 - x/L), \quad x/L]\begin{Bmatrix} u_i \\ u_j \end{Bmatrix}$$

or

$$\{\boldsymbol{\epsilon}\} = [\mathbf{b}]\{\mathbf{\Delta}\}$$

in which

$$\{\boldsymbol{\epsilon}\} = \epsilon_x$$

$$\{\mathbf{\Delta}\} = \begin{Bmatrix} u_i \\ u_j \end{Bmatrix}$$

and

$$[\mathbf{b}] = \frac{1}{L}[-1, \quad 1]$$

Also, because $\{\boldsymbol{\sigma}\}$ reduces to σ_x in this case, the elasticity matrix becomes

$$[\mathbf{D}] = E$$

The element stiffness matrix, relating $\{u_i, u_j\}$ to the corresponding nodal forces, is then obtained from Eq. (14-29a), i.e.,

$$[\mathbf{k}] = \int_{V_e} [\mathbf{b}]^T [\mathbf{D}][\mathbf{b}] dV_e = (1/L^2) \int_{V_e} [-1, \quad 1]^T E[-1, \quad 1] dV_e$$

Because the cross-sectional area A is constant, we may represent dV_e as $A dx$ and integrate over the length of the bar. Hence

$$[\mathbf{k}] = \frac{EA}{L^2} \int_0^L [-1, \quad 1]^T [-1, \quad 1] dx = \frac{EA}{L} \begin{bmatrix} 1 & -1 \\ -1 & 1 \end{bmatrix}$$

This is the stiffness matrix that we derived in Chapter 12 through the solution of the differential equation governing the axial displacement of the bar. The preceding computations incurred no approximation because the connectivity matrix $[\mathbf{N}]$, from which $[\mathbf{b}]$ was derived, incorporated the exact shape functions.

The equivalent forces are defined by Eqs. (14-29b) through (14-29d), for which we may prescribe initial axial strain, initial axial stress and the axial distributed load

$$\{\boldsymbol{\epsilon}_0\} = \epsilon_{x0}$$

$$\{\boldsymbol{\sigma}_0\} = \sigma_{x0}$$

and

$$\{\mathbf{q}\} = q_x$$

For simplicity we consider here ϵ_{x0}, σ_{x0}, and q_x all to be constant in x. Then

$$\{\mathbf{F}^E_{\epsilon_0}\} = \int_0^L \frac{1}{L}[-1, \quad 1]^T E\epsilon_{x0}(A dx) = E\epsilon_{x0}A \begin{Bmatrix} -1 \\ 1 \end{Bmatrix}$$

$$\{\mathbf{F}^E_{\sigma_0}\} = -\int_0^L \frac{1}{L}[-1, \quad 1]^T \sigma_{x0}(A dx) = \sigma_{x0}A \begin{Bmatrix} 1 \\ -1 \end{Bmatrix}$$

$$\{\mathbf{F}^E_q\} = \int_0^L [(1 - x/L), \quad x/L]^T q_x(A dx) = \frac{1}{2}ALq_x \begin{Bmatrix} 1 \\ 1 \end{Bmatrix}$$

Note that the initial strain and initial stress lead to equal and opposite nodal forces of magnitude $(E\epsilon_{x0})A$ and $\sigma_{x0}A$, respectively. The applied distributed force per unit volume q_x is replaced by equivalent nodal forces (both directed in the same sense as q_x) of magnitude $(AL)q_x/2$. These forces are illustrated in Fig. 14-6.

14-3 CONVERGENCE CRITERIA

The implementation of the finite element method first requires that a physical system be idealized through the specification of the type, number and pattern of elements to be used. The element stiffness matrices are then generated and combined to produce the system stiffness matrix. The product of this stiffness matrix and the vector of nodal displacements is combined with the vector of nodal forces to provide the stiffness equations, Eq. (14-32), from which unknown nodal displacements and forces may be computed. The element stresses may then be computed by Eq. (14-33).

The type, number and pattern of elements to be used depend on the nature of the problem to be solved. However, it is important to identify general criteria that must be satisfied to assure convergence, i.e., that the exact solution will be approached as the element mesh is refined by increasing the number of elements. Consider, for example, the case of a tapered bar subjected to an axial force at one end and fixed at the other end, as shown in Fig. 14-7. Because the cross-sectional area varies exponentially along the length of the bar, one would expect that rather poor results would emerge from an analysis in which the actual bar was approximated by a single prismatic bar element. As more numerous prismatic elements are used to represent the tapered bar, however, one would expect the numerical results to approach the exact solution. We shall demonstrate that indeed this is the case. Before doing so, however, we identify the criteria that the assumed element displacement functions must satisfy to assure convergence. While the criteria listed below are generally applicable, to solidify the ideas we shall focus on the displacement function

$$u(x) = u_i(1 - x/L) + u_j x/L \qquad (14\text{-}34)$$

which pertains to the axial deformation in a bar element.

Figure 14-7

The convergence criteria may be stated as follows:*

1. The displacement function within an element must be continuous. In Eq. (14-34), for example, $u(x)$ is finite and single-valued for every value of x. Thus, the displacement function is continuous.

2. When prescribed nodal displacements correspond to a state of constant strain, the displacement function must produce that state of constant strain throughout the element. Because the displacement function described by Eq. (14-34) varies linearly with x, this criterion is automatically satisfied for all combinations of nodal displacements. Note, however, that this would not be the case if the terms x/L were replaced by $(x/L)^2$. Also, in certain two-dimensional elements, this criterion is not easily satisfied.

3. When the element is subjected to rigid-body displacement, the displacement function should produce zero strains and hence zero nodal forces. If u_i is set equal to u_j in Eq. (14-34), then $u(x) = u_i$ (constant); hence,

*See, for example, Cook, *Concepts and Applications of Finite Element Analysis*, pp. 87–91, for further discussion.

$\epsilon_x = du/dx = 0$. If this criterion is violated, the stiffness equations will be altered by the erroneous creation of nonzero nodal forces.

4. Compatibility should exist between adjacent elements. This criterion is automatically satisfied by one-dimensional elements. However, two- or three-dimensional adjacent elements might exhibit gaps or overlaps along an edge that spans nodes common to both elements. Although satisfaction of this criterion is desirable, many elements violate it, but still lead to acceptable results.

5. The element should have no preferred direction; i.e., the behavior of the element must be independent of its orientation with respect to the coordinate system. This criterion has no bearing on one-dimensional elements. For two-dimensional elements, this criterion would be violated if the displacement functions were not "complete" with respect to x and y. If, for example, the function

$$w(x, y) = \alpha_1 + \alpha_2 x + \alpha_3 y + \alpha_4 x^2 + \alpha_5 xy + \alpha_6 y^2 + \alpha_7 x^3 + \alpha_8 x^2 y + \alpha_9 y^3$$

were used to represent the bending displacement of a plate (as has been attempted), the results would be incorrect because the term xy^2 is absent; i.e., a lack of symmetry exists with regard to x and y.

We shall refer to these convergence criteria as we develop formulations for various two-dimensional elements in subsequent sections. At this point, however, we consider two examples that demonstrate convergence using one-dimensional elements.

Example 14-2. The bar shown in Fig. 14-7 has a cross-sectional area that varies exponentially with x; i.e., $A(x) = A_0 e^{-\beta x}$, where $\beta \geq 0$ and A_0 is the area at $x = 0$. Assess the convergence of the numerical solution as the number of prismatic bar elements increases.*

First, we may find the exact solution for this problem by integrating the governing differential equation pertaining to a nonprismatic bar

$$\frac{d}{dx}\left(EA\,\frac{du}{dx}\right) = 0$$

The general solution is

$$u(x) = C_1 \frac{e^{\beta x}}{EA_0} + C_2$$

which, for the problem at hand, must satisfy the boundary conditions

$$u(0) = 0$$

and

$$\left(EA\,\frac{du}{dx}\right)_{x=L} = P$$

---

*This example is also treated by H. C. Martin and G. F. Carey, *Introduction to Finite Element Analysis*, (New York: McGraw-Hill, 1973), pp. 46–62.

These boundary conditions permit the constants of integration C_1 and C_2 to be evaluated. The resulting solution for displacement is then

$$u(x) = \frac{P}{EA_0} \frac{1}{\beta}(e^{\beta x} - 1)$$

and the axial stress is

$$\sigma(x) = E \frac{du(x)}{dx} = \frac{P}{A_0} e^{\beta x}$$

We now consider the bar to comprise two prismatic elements as shown in Fig. 14-8(a), each element having a length equal to $L/2$ and a cross-sectional area equal to the mean of the areas corresponding to their end points. The parameter β is set equal to $1/L$. Thus, for element 1 ($0 \le x \le 0.5L$),

$$A_1 = \frac{A_0}{2}(1 + 0.607) = 0.804A_0 \quad \text{and} \quad [\mathbf{k}^{(1)}] = \frac{0.804EA_0}{L/2}\begin{bmatrix} 1 & -1 \\ -1 & 1 \end{bmatrix}$$

For element 2 ($0.5L \le x \le L$),

$$A_2 = \frac{A_0}{2}(0.607 + 0.368) = 0.488A_0 \quad \text{and} \quad [\mathbf{k}^{(2)}] = \frac{0.488EA_0}{L/2}\begin{bmatrix} 1 & -1 \\ -1 & 1 \end{bmatrix}$$

(a)

(b)

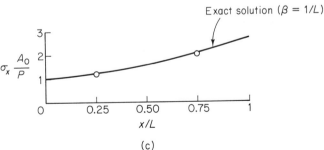

(c)

Figure 14-8

The resulting stiffness equation is

$$\frac{EA_0}{L/2}\begin{bmatrix} 0.804 & -0.804 & 0 \\ -0.804 & 1.292 & -0.488 \\ 0 & -0.488 & 0.488 \end{bmatrix}\begin{Bmatrix} u_1 \\ u_2 \\ u_3 \end{Bmatrix} = \begin{Bmatrix} P_1 \\ P_2 \\ P_3 \end{Bmatrix}$$

where the boundary and loading conditions imply that

$$u_1 = 0, \quad P_2 = 0, \quad \text{and} \quad P_3 = P$$

Solving for the unknown nodal displacements, we obtain

$$\begin{Bmatrix} u_2 \\ u_3 \end{Bmatrix} = \frac{PL}{EA_0}\begin{Bmatrix} 0.622 \\ 1.643 \end{Bmatrix}$$

The axial stress, which we assign to the midpoint for each element, may be determined in the usual way from the element stiffness matrices. For element 1

$$\sigma_x^{(1)} = \frac{F_x^{(1)}}{A_1} = \frac{1}{0.804A_0}\left(\frac{0.804EA_0}{L/2}[-1, \ 1]\right)\left(\frac{PL}{EA_0}\begin{Bmatrix} 0 \\ 0.622 \end{Bmatrix}\right) = 1.244\frac{P}{A_0}$$

Similarly for element 2

$$\sigma_x^{(2)} = \frac{F_x^{(2)}}{A_2} = \frac{1}{0.488A_0}\left(\frac{0.488EA_0}{L/2}[-1, \ 1]\right)\left(\frac{PL}{EA_0}\begin{Bmatrix} 0.622 \\ 1.643 \end{Bmatrix}\right) = 2.042\frac{P}{A_0}$$

The foregoing displacements and stresses are plotted in Fig. 14-8(b) and (c) for comparison with exact values. The two-element model underestimates displacements at mid-span and at the free end by slightly more than 4 percent. Stresses at $x = 0.25$ and $x = 0.75$ are underestimated by 3 to 4 percent. The good accuracy achieved in this case by such a crude finite element model is remarkable; it stems, however, from the fairly small coefficient of taper, $\beta = 1/L$. (Of course, when $\beta = 0$, the bar has uniform cross section A_0, and even a one-element model provides the exact solution.)

To illustrate further the dependence of accuracy (i.e., convergence) on the coefficient of taper, consider the case shown in Fig. 14-9, in which $\beta = 2/L$. The results for a two-element model and for a four-element model are compared with the exact solution. The two-element model underestimates nodal displacements by approximately 17 percent and underestimates element stresses by approximately 11 percent. The four-element model underestimates nodal displacements by approximately 5 percent and underestimates element stresses by less than 3 percent.

In general, a finite element representation will overestimate the stiffness of the actual structure, because using an assumed displacement function is equivalent to constraining the structure from acquiring its true deformation pattern. Accordingly, on average, nodal displacements will be underestimated; however, not necessarily will every displacement be underestimated as in the foregoing examples. These examples are unusual in another way. Usually, stresses are predicted less accurately than are displacements, because stresses are related to the spatial derivatives of the displacement functions; the derivatives, of course, vary less smoothly with respect to the coordinates than do the displacement functions themselves. The relatively good accuracy associated with computed stresses is an idiosyncracy of this particular example.

Refining the finite element mesh by increasing the number of elements always will improve the overall solution. In general, additional elements will do

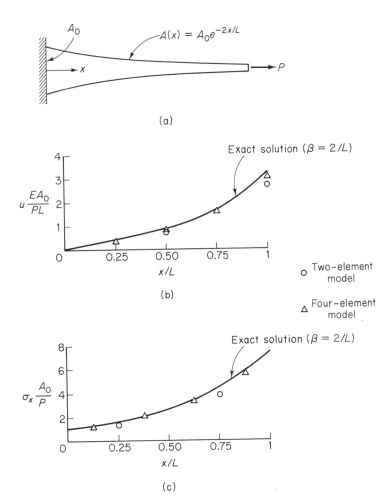

Figure 14-9

the most good in regions where the strain (or stress) gradient is largest. While in the present example, we realized an increased accuracy by increasing the number of equal-length elements from two to four, additional accuracy could have been gained, still using four elements, by making the elements near the free end somewhat shorter than $L/4$ and those nearer the fixed end somewhat longer. Although this strategy probably is not worth the trouble in the present case, for most problems, it is essential to refine the mesh in regions of high strain gradient. Such a strategy, of course, requires the analyst to have some notion of the strain distribution at the outset.

Example 14-3. A circular ring of uniform thickness bears on a smooth, rigid surface and is subjected to only its own weight, as shown in Fig. 14-10(a). The radius R of the ring equals 1.0 and the width w and the thickness h both equal 0.10. The weight per unit length $W/2\pi R$ also equals 1.0, and Young's modulus is $E = 10^6$. All units are assumed to be consistent. Determine the displacement, bending

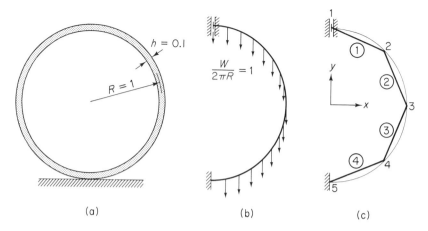

Figure 14-10

moment, and axial force in the ring by representing it as a set of rectilinear beam elements.

By accounting for symmetry, only one-half the ring need be modeled, as shown in Fig. 14-10(b). Horizontal displacement and rotation at both top ($\theta = 0$) and bottom ($\theta = \pi$) and vertical displacement at the bottom are zero. The finite element model shown in Fig. 14-10(c) comprises four planar beam-column elements, each possessing, in general, two translations and a rotation at each end. Accordingly, the system stiffness matrix, which may be formed by combining the element stiffness matrices, will be of order 15. Because five degrees of freedom are constrained, the reduced system stiffness matrix will be of order 10.

The analysis follows that described in Chapter 12. Consider element 1, for example, as shown in Fig. 14-11(a). The generalized displacements are referred to the global x–y coordinate system. The length of the element is $L = 0.765R$ and its angle of inclination relative to the x-axis is $\theta = -22.5°$; hence, the components of the transformation matrix are $\lambda = \cos\theta = 0.924$ and $\mu = \sin\theta = -0.383$. Noting that the cross-sectional area is $A = 0.01$ and the moment of inertia is $I = 8.333 \times 10^{-6}$, we obtain from Eq. (12-51)

$$[\mathbf{k}^{(1)}] = \begin{array}{c} \\ \\ \\ \\ \\ \\ \end{array}
\begin{array}{cccccc}
u_1 & v_1 & \theta_1 & u_2 & v_2 & \theta_2
\end{array}$$

$$[\mathbf{k}^{(1)}] = \begin{bmatrix}
11200 & 4550 & 32.7 & -11200 & -4550 & 32.7 \\
4550 & 2100 & -60.4 & -4550 & -2100 & -60.4 \\
32.7 & -60.4 & 43.5 & -32.7 & 60.4 & 21.8 \\
-11200 & -4550 & -32.7 & 11200 & 4550 & -32.7 \\
-4550 & -2100 & 60.4 & 4550 & 2100 & 60.4 \\
32.7 & -60.4 & 21.8 & -32.7 & 60.4 & 43.5
\end{bmatrix}$$

The stiffness matrices for the remaining elements may be similarly determined and combined with $[\mathbf{k}^{(1)}]$ to form the system stiffness matrix $[\mathbf{K}]$. The reduced stiffness matrix $[\mathbf{K}_{ff}]$ may be obtained directly by deleting from $[\mathbf{K}]$ the rows and columns corresponding to u_1, θ_1, u_5, v_5, and θ_5, i.e., those generalized displacements prescribed as zero.

The equivalent nodal forces to be applied to the nodes may be computed in

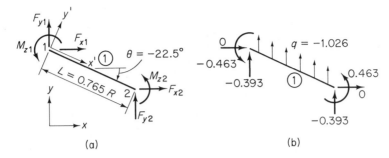

Figure 14-11

the manner described in Chapter 12; they are equal and opposite to the fixed-end forces and bending moments. Thus, for element 1

$$\{\mathbf{P}^E\}^{(1)} = \begin{Bmatrix} P_{x1}^E \\ P_{y1}^E \\ P_{mz1}^E \\ P_{x2}^E \\ P_{y2}^E \\ P_{mz2}^E \end{Bmatrix}^{(1)} = \frac{qL}{12} \begin{Bmatrix} 0 \\ 6 \\ L \\ 0 \\ 6 \\ -L \end{Bmatrix}^{(1)} = \begin{Bmatrix} 0 \\ -0.393 \\ -0.0463 \\ 0 \\ -0.393 \\ 0.0463 \end{Bmatrix}^{(1)}$$

where we have used $q = -1.026$ as the uniformly distributed vertical load and $L = 0.765$ as the length of the element. The equivalent nodal forces are shown in Fig. 14-11(b). Equivalent nodal forces for the remaining elements may be found in a similar manner and combined with $\{\mathbf{P}^E\}^{(1)}$ to form the equivalent nodal force vector for the systems.

Note that while we have chosen to determine the element stiffness matrices and force vectors according to the method described in Chapter 12, we would have attained the same results by employing Eq. (14-29a) to compute $[\mathbf{k}]$ and Eq. (14-29d) to compute $\{\mathbf{F}_q^E\}$ (which, in the notation adopted in this chapter, is identical to $\{\mathbf{P}^E\}$). To do this we would have to develop the matrices $[\mathbf{b}]$ and $[\mathbf{N}]$ based on the displacement function expressed by Eq. (14-2).

The finite element solutions for the four-element model, as well as for a refined eight-element model, are compared with the exact solutions in Fig. 14-12. Deflections and bending moments are accurately predicted by both finite element models. The exact value of the maximum radial displacement equals 0.0561 at the top of the ring; the four- and eight-element models underestimate this displacement by 9.3 percent and 1.7 percent, respectively. At the base of the ring, where the exact value of bending moment equals -1.5, the four- and eight-element models predict bending moments equal to -1.564 and -1.463; the corresponding errors are therefore 4.3 percent and -2.5 percent.

14-4 PLANE STRESS AND PLANE STRAIN

We now consider two-dimensional problems in which either all nonzero stress components or all nonzero strain components lie in a plane. The stretching of a thin plate is an example of the former case (plane stress); the behavior of a

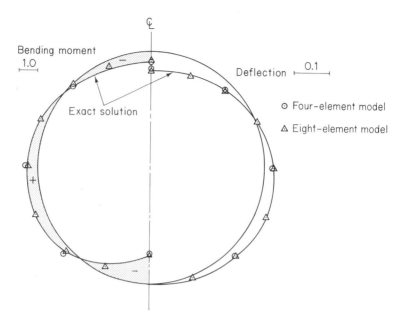

Bending moment
├─1.0─┤

Deflection ├─0.1─┤

Exact solution

○ Four-element model

△ Eight-element model

Figure 14-12

cross-section of a long retaining wall subjected to lateral loading is an example of the latter case (plane strain). In either case, an analysis may be formulated by representing the plane as an assemblage of finite elements, such as the set of triangular elements shown in Fig. 14-3(b). Although numerous choices of elements exist, we shall limit our discussion to the simplest two-dimensional element, the constant-strain triangle.

We consider the triangles that constitute an assemblage to be interconnected only at their vertices (nodes). Therefore, as described in Section 14-2, our first objective is to compute the system stiffness matrix that relates nodal forces to nodal displacements. The nodal force vectors comprise applied nodal loads plus those related to initial strains, initial stresses, and distributed loading. The general expressions that enable us to make these computations have already been derived, i.e.,

$$[\mathbf{k}] = \int_{V_e} [\mathbf{b}]^T[\mathbf{D}][\mathbf{b}]dV_e \tag{14-29a}$$

$$\{\mathbf{F}_{\epsilon_0}^E\} = \int_{V_e} [\mathbf{b}]^T[\mathbf{D}]\{\boldsymbol{\epsilon}_0\}dV_e \tag{14-29b}$$

$$\{\mathbf{F}_{\sigma_0}^E\} = -\int_{V_e} [\mathbf{b}]^T\{\boldsymbol{\sigma}_0\}dV_e \tag{14-29c}$$

$$\{\mathbf{F}_q^E\} = \int_{V_e} [\mathbf{N}]^T\{\mathbf{q}\}dV_e \tag{14-29d}$$

Ultimately, of course, we wish to solve the stiffness equations for the unknown displacements, which lead to the element stresses.

Displacement functions. The key to obtaining the element stiffness matrix and force vectors for a particular choice of element lies with an appropriate selection of the shape functions that constitute the matrix [N] and its derivative [b].

Considering a triangular element to lie in the x–y plane, as shown in Fig. 14-13, we may assume the displacements $u(x, y)$ and $v(x, y)$ within the element to be linear functions of x and y, i.e.,

$$u(x, y) = \alpha_1 + \alpha_2 x + \alpha_3 y \tag{14-35a}$$

$$v(x, y) = \alpha_4 + \alpha_5 x + \alpha_6 y \tag{14-35b}$$

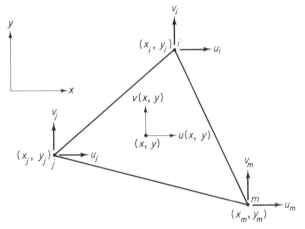

Figure 14-13

This is the simplest possible assumption for the displacement functions, which are analogous to that employed for a bar element. The constants $\alpha_1, \ldots, \alpha_6$ must be chosen such that the functions $u(x, y)$ and $v(x, y)$ yield the displacements at nodes i, j, and m (having counterclockwise order) when the coordinates x, y coincide with x_i, y_i, x_j, y_j, and x_m, y_m, i.e.,

$$
\begin{Bmatrix} u(x_i, y_i) \\ u(x_j, y_j) \\ u(x_m, y_m) \\ v(x_i, y_i) \\ v(x_j, y_j) \\ v(x_m, y_m) \end{Bmatrix}
\equiv
\begin{Bmatrix} u_i \\ u_j \\ u_m \\ v_i \\ v_j \\ v_m \end{Bmatrix}
=
\begin{bmatrix}
1 & x_i & y_i & 0 & 0 & 0 \\
1 & x_j & y_j & 0 & 0 & 0 \\
1 & x_m & y_m & 0 & 0 & 0 \\
0 & 0 & 0 & 1 & x_i & y_i \\
0 & 0 & 0 & 1 & x_j & y_j \\
0 & 0 & 0 & 1 & x_m & y_m
\end{bmatrix}
\begin{Bmatrix} \alpha_1 \\ \alpha_2 \\ \alpha_3 \\ \alpha_4 \\ \alpha_5 \\ \alpha_6 \end{Bmatrix}
\tag{14-36}
$$

By inverting the matrix in Eq. (14-36), we may find $\alpha_1, \ldots, \alpha_6$ in terms of the nodal displacements $u_i, \ldots, v_m$ and the nodal coordinates $x_i, \ldots, y_m$. The expressions for $\alpha_1, \ldots, \alpha_6$ then may be substituted into Eqs. (14-35) which, after some manipulation, lead to

$$u(x, y) = \frac{1}{2A_e}[(a_i + b_i x + c_i y)u_i + (a_j + b_j x + c_j y)u_j$$

$$+ (a_m + b_m x + c_m y)u_m] \quad (14\text{-}37\text{a})$$

and

$$v(x, y) = \frac{1}{2A_e}[(a_i + b_i x + c_i y)v_i + (a_j + b_j x + c_j y)v_j$$

$$+ (a_m + b_m x + c_m y)v_m] \quad (14\text{-}37\text{b})$$

where

$$a_i = x_j y_m - x_m y_j \quad (14\text{-}38\text{a})$$

$$b_i = y_j - y_m \quad (14\text{-}38\text{b})$$

$$c_i = x_m - x_j \quad (14\text{-}38\text{c})$$

and

$$2A_e = \begin{vmatrix} 1 & x_i & y_i \\ 1 & x_j & y_j \\ 1 & x_m & y_m \end{vmatrix} = 2(\text{Plan area of triangle } i, j, m) \quad (14\text{-}38\text{d})$$

Similar expressions may be written for $a_j, \ldots, c_m$ through a cyclic permutation of the subscripts i, j, m in a counterclockwise order. If we define the shape function N_i as

$$N_i = \frac{1}{2A_e}(a_i + b_i x + c_i y) \quad (14\text{-}39)$$

and similar expressions for N_j and N_m, then Eqs. (14-37) may be written in the form

$$\{\mathbf{\Phi}\} \equiv \begin{Bmatrix} u(x, y) \\ v(x, y) \end{Bmatrix} = [N_i[\mathbf{I}], N_j[\mathbf{I}], N_m[\mathbf{I}]] \begin{Bmatrix} u_i \\ v_i \\ u_j \\ v_j \\ u_m \\ v_m \end{Bmatrix} \equiv [\mathbf{N}]\{\mathbf{\Delta}\} \quad (14\text{-}40)$$

Note that the displacement functions, Eqs. (14-37) or Eq. (14-40) satisfy the first and fifth convergence criteria; i.e., N_i, N_j, and N_m are continuous functions of x and y, and they are "complete" linear functions of the spatial variables. Figure 14-14 provides a geometric interpretation for the shape functions N_i, N_j, and N_m, which may be viewed as weighting functions applied to the nodal displacements to determine the displacements throughout the element. N_i, for example, varies linearly with x and y from unity at node i to zero at nodes j and m. Thus, at a point (x, y) nearer to (x_i, y_i) than to either (x_j, y_j) or (x_m, y_m),

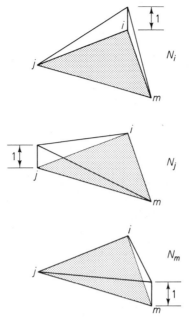

Figure 14-14

the displacements $u(x, y)$ and $v(x, y)$ are more strongly influenced by u_i and v_i, than by the displacements at nodes j and m. Note also that because the displacements along an edge of the element vary linearly with x and y, two adjacent elements (which have identical displacements at their two common nodes) will have compatible displacements along their common edge. Hence the fourth convergence criterion is satisfied.

Strain-displacement relation. As noted in Section 14-2, the total strains occurring in the (x, y) plane of the element are defined in terms of derivatives of the displacements, i.e.,

$$\{\boldsymbol{\epsilon}\} = \begin{Bmatrix} \epsilon_x \\ \epsilon_y \\ \gamma_{xy} \end{Bmatrix} = \begin{bmatrix} \dfrac{\partial}{\partial x} & 0 \\ 0 & \dfrac{\partial}{\partial y} \\ \dfrac{\partial}{\partial y} & \dfrac{\partial}{\partial x} \end{bmatrix} \begin{Bmatrix} u(x, y) \\ v(x, y) \end{Bmatrix} \tag{14-41}$$

in view of Eq. (14-40), we may express the total strain vector $\{\boldsymbol{\epsilon}\}$ as

$$\{\boldsymbol{\epsilon}\} = [\mathbf{b}]\{\boldsymbol{\Delta}\} \tag{14-42a}$$

in which

$$[\mathbf{b}] = [[\mathbf{b}_i], [\mathbf{b}_j], [\mathbf{b}_m]] \tag{14-42b}$$

where

$$[\mathbf{b}_i] = \begin{bmatrix} \dfrac{\partial N_i}{\partial x} & 0 \\[2mm] 0 & \dfrac{\partial N_i}{\partial y} \\[2mm] \dfrac{\partial N_i}{\partial y} & \dfrac{\partial N_i}{\partial x} \end{bmatrix} = \frac{1}{2A_e}\begin{bmatrix} b_i & 0 \\ 0 & c_i \\ c_i & b_i \end{bmatrix} \tag{14-42c}$$

with similar expressions holding for $[\mathbf{b}_j]$ and $[\mathbf{b}_m]$.

Because b_i and c_i, etc., are constants, Eqs. (14-42) imply that the strain is constant throughout the element for any arbitrary set of nodal displacements. Hence, the element is not merely capable of exhibiting constant strain, as required to satisfy the second convergence criterion; it is limited to do so under all combinations of nodal displacement. While leading to a relatively simple formulation, this limitation leads to reduced accuracy, compared with that attainable by an element which is capable of exhibiting, for instance, linearly varying strain. Also, when an assemblage of constant-strain elements is subjected to a spatially varying strain field, discontinuities in stress must necessarily exist between any one element and its neighboring elements. This implies that an increased number of elements (i.e., a finer mesh) must be placed in regions of high strain gradient to attain acceptable accuracy. It also should be mentioned that when all three nodes of an element experience displacements corresponding to rigid-body translation and rotation, the strains are zero, i.e., $[\mathbf{b}] = [\mathbf{0}]$; this satisfies the third convergence criteria.

Stress-strain relation. We noted previously that, in general, the relationship between stresses and strains may be expressed as

$$\{\boldsymbol{\sigma}\} = [\mathbf{D}](\{\boldsymbol{\epsilon}\} - \{\boldsymbol{\epsilon}_0\}) + \{\boldsymbol{\sigma}_0\} \tag{14-43}$$

where $\{\boldsymbol{\sigma}\}$ and $\{\boldsymbol{\epsilon}\}$ are, respectively, the vectors of *total* stresses and strains, $\{\boldsymbol{\sigma}_0\}$ and $\{\boldsymbol{\epsilon}_0\}$ are the vectors of *initial* stresses and strains, and $[\mathbf{D}]$ is the elasticity matrix. In the case of either plane stress or plane strain (in the x–y plane),

$$\{\boldsymbol{\sigma}\} = \begin{Bmatrix} \sigma_x \\ \sigma_y \\ \tau_{xy} \end{Bmatrix} \quad \text{and} \quad \{\boldsymbol{\epsilon}\} = \begin{Bmatrix} \epsilon_x \\ \epsilon_y \\ \gamma_{xy} \end{Bmatrix} \tag{14-44}$$

The vectors $\{\boldsymbol{\sigma}_0\}$ and $\{\boldsymbol{\epsilon}_0\}$ have analogous forms.

If the material is isotropic and is in a state of *plane stress*, then the elasticity matrix is

$$[\mathbf{D}] = \frac{E}{1 - \nu^2}\begin{bmatrix} 1 & \nu & 0 \\ \nu & 1 & 0 \\ 0 & 0 & (1 - \nu)/2 \end{bmatrix} \tag{14-45a}$$

If an isotropic material is in a state of *plane strain*, then the elasticity matrix is

$$[\mathbf{D}] = \frac{E(1-\nu)}{(1+\nu)(1-2\nu)} \begin{bmatrix} 1 & \dfrac{\nu}{(1-\nu)} & 0 \\ \dfrac{\nu}{(1-\nu)} & 1 & 0 \\ 0 & 0 & \dfrac{(1-2\nu)}{2(1-\nu)} \end{bmatrix} \qquad (14\text{-}45\text{b})$$

Note that the plane strain case cannot be treated in this manner when the material is incompressible, i.e., when $\nu = 1/2$, as the elements of $[\mathbf{D}]$ then become infinitely large.

Element stiffness matrix. The 6×6 element stiffness matrix relating nodal forces to nodal displacements is given by

$$[\mathbf{k}] = \int_{V_e} [\mathbf{b}]^T [\mathbf{D}][\mathbf{b}] dV_e \qquad (14\text{-}46\text{a})$$

For both the case of plane stress and plane strain, the matrices $[\mathbf{b}]$ and $[\mathbf{D}]$ comprise only constant terms (i.e., they are independent of x and y). Hence, considering the element to have a thickness (normal to the x–y plane) equal to t, we may write

$$[\mathbf{k}] = [\mathbf{b}]^T [\mathbf{D}][\mathbf{b}] \int_{V_e} dV_e = [\mathbf{b}]^T [\mathbf{D}][\mathbf{b}](tA_e) \qquad (14\text{-}46\text{b})$$

Recognizing the partitioned form of $[\mathbf{b}]$, as indicated by Eq. (14-42b), we may express the element stiffness matrix as

$$[\mathbf{k}] = \begin{bmatrix} [\mathbf{k}_{ii}] & [\mathbf{k}_{ij}] & [\mathbf{k}_{im}] \\ [\mathbf{k}_{ji}] & [\mathbf{k}_{jj}] & [\mathbf{k}_{jm}] \\ [\mathbf{k}_{mi}] & [\mathbf{k}_{mj}] & [\mathbf{k}_{mm}] \end{bmatrix} \qquad (14\text{-}47)$$

in which, in general,

$$[\mathbf{k}_{ij}] = [\mathbf{b}_i]^T [\mathbf{D}][\mathbf{b}_j](tA_e) \qquad (14\text{-}48)$$

Hence, for the case of plane stress,

$$[\mathbf{k}_{ij}] = \left(\frac{1}{2A_e} \begin{bmatrix} b_i & 0 & c_i \\ 0 & c_i & b_i \end{bmatrix} \right) \left(\frac{E}{(1-\nu^2)} \begin{bmatrix} 1 & \nu & 0 \\ \nu & 1 & 0 \\ 0 & 0 & \dfrac{(1-\nu)}{2} \end{bmatrix} \right) \left(\frac{1}{2A_e} \begin{bmatrix} b_j & 0 \\ 0 & c_j \\ c_j & b_j \end{bmatrix} \right) (tA_e)$$

$$(14\text{-}49\text{a})$$

or

$$[\mathbf{k}_{ij}] = \frac{tE}{4A_e(1-\nu^2)} \left(\begin{bmatrix} b_i b_j & \nu b_i c_j \\ \nu c_i b_j & c_i c_j \end{bmatrix} + \frac{(1-\nu)}{2} \begin{bmatrix} c_i c_j & c_i b_j \\ b_i c_j & b_i b_j \end{bmatrix} \right) \qquad (14\text{-}49\text{b})$$

where the first matrix in Eq. (14-49b) represents the contribution of the normal stresses to the stiffness and the second matrix the contribution of the shear stresses. Similarly, for the case of plane strain,

$$[\mathbf{k}_{ij}] = \frac{tE(1-\nu)}{4A_e(1+\nu)(1-2\nu)} \begin{bmatrix} b_i b_j & \dfrac{\nu}{1-\nu}b_i c_j \\ \dfrac{\nu}{1-\nu}c_i b_j & c_i c_j \end{bmatrix} + \frac{(1-2\nu)}{2(1-\nu)}\begin{bmatrix} c_i c_j & c_i b_j \\ b_i c_j & b_i b_j \end{bmatrix}$$

(14-50)

Equation (14-49b) may be rewritten in terms of the shear modulus G and Poisson's ratio ν. Hence,

$$[\mathbf{k}_{ij}] = \frac{Gt}{2A_e(1-\nu)}\left(\begin{bmatrix} b_i b_j & \nu b_i c_j \\ \nu c_i b_j & c_i c_j \end{bmatrix} + \frac{(1-\nu)}{2}\begin{bmatrix} c_i c_j & c_i b_j \\ b_i c_j & b_i b_j \end{bmatrix}\right)$$

(14-51)

This expression is valid for conditions of plane stress. It is useful to recognize, however, that the same expression holds for conditions of plane strain if the numerical value of ν is replaced by the numerical value of $\nu/(1-\nu)$. Equation (14-51) will be used subsequently in an example to assemble the element stiffness matrix. The system stiffness matrix is then assembled from the element stiffness matrices in the standard way.

Equivalent element force vectors. The equivalent nodal force vectors associated with initial strains, initial stresses and distributed loads, may be derived for the constant strain triangular element by specializing Eq. (14-29b), (14-29c), and (14-29d).

Thus, for an initial strain vector $\{\boldsymbol{\epsilon}_0\}$, the two forces at node i are

$$\{\mathbf{F}^E_{i\epsilon_0}\} = [\mathbf{b}_i]^T[\mathbf{D}]\{\boldsymbol{\epsilon}_0\}(tA_e)$$

(14-52a)

For the case of plane stress,

$$\{\mathbf{F}^E_{i\epsilon_0}\} = \left\{ \begin{matrix} F^E_{xi} \\ F^E_{yi} \end{matrix} \right\}_{\epsilon_0} = \frac{Gt}{(1-\nu)}\left\{ \begin{matrix} b_i(\epsilon_{x0}+\nu\epsilon_{y0}) + c_i(1-\nu)\gamma_{xy0}/2 \\ c_i(\nu\epsilon_{x0}+\epsilon_{y0}) + b_i(1-\nu)\gamma_{xy0}/2 \end{matrix} \right\}$$

(14-52b)

For plane strain, the force vector may be obtained from Eq. (14-52b) by replacing ν by $\nu/(1-\nu)$. Forces at nodes j and m may be computed analogously.

For both plane stress and plane strain conditions, the forces at node i that are associated with an initial stress vector $\{\boldsymbol{\sigma}_0\}$ are

$$\{\mathbf{F}^E_{i\sigma_0}\} = \left\{ \begin{matrix} F^E_{xi} \\ F^E_{yi} \end{matrix} \right\}_{\sigma_0} = -[\mathbf{b}_i]^T\{\boldsymbol{\sigma}_0\}(tA_e) = -t\left\{ \begin{matrix} b_i\sigma_{x0}+c_i\tau_{xy0} \\ c_i\sigma_{y0}+b_i\tau_{xy0} \end{matrix} \right\}$$

(14-53)

Finally, the forces at node i that are related to distributed loading, $q(x, y)$ per unit volume, are

$$\{\mathbf{F}^E_{iq}\} = \left\{ \begin{matrix} F^E_{xi} \\ F^E_{yi} \end{matrix} \right\}_q = \int_{V_e} N_i[\mathbf{I}]\{\mathbf{q}(x, y)\}\, dV_e = \int_{V_e} N_i\left\{ \begin{matrix} q_x \\ q_y \end{matrix} \right\}\, dV_e$$

(14-54)

In general, both N_i and $\{q_x, q_y\}$ vary with x and y, and thus they cannot be taken outside the integral. If, however, $\{q_x, q_y\}$ is constant, such as in the case of a uniform body force, then we find that

$$\int_{V_e} N_i \, dV_e = \frac{tA_e}{3} \tag{14-55}$$

and hence,

$$\begin{Bmatrix} F_{xi}^E \\ F_{yi}^E \end{Bmatrix}_q = \frac{tA_e}{3} \begin{Bmatrix} q_x \\ q_y \end{Bmatrix} \tag{14-56}$$

This implies that one-third the body force of the element is imposed as an equivalent force at each node.

Another special case of interest corresponds to loading distributed along an edge of the element, as when a pressure is applied to a boundary of a finite element mesh. Consider $\{\mathbf{q}(x, y)\}$ now to represent constant force per unit *area* acting on an element along the side defined by nodes i and j. Recognizing that the volume integral in Eq. (14-54) may be replaced by a line integral between nodes i and j (the only region where $\{\mathbf{q}\}$ is nonzero), after some algebraic manipulation we find

$$\begin{Bmatrix} F_{xi}^E \\ F_{yi}^E \end{Bmatrix}_q = \frac{1}{2} \sqrt{(x_j - x_i)^2 + (y_j - y_i)^2} \begin{Bmatrix} q_x \\ q_y \end{Bmatrix} \tag{14-57}$$

where it must be remembered that $\{q_x, q_y\}$ is constant between nodes i and j. Note that Eq. (14-57) means that one-half the total force (in both the x- and y-directions) applied to side ij may be concentrated at node i. The equivalent force vector $\{F_{xj}^E, F_{yj}^E\}$ pertaining to node j also is defined by Eq. (14-57), while the equivalent force vector at node m is zero. Of course, if a traction is applied to another side, say side im, then an equivalent force will exist at node m and an additional contribution will act at node i.

Example 14-4. Use a two-element model to determine the state of stress in the thin plate, shown in Fig. 14-15(a), which is subjected to a uniform traction on its upper horizontal boundary and is confined against lateral displacement.

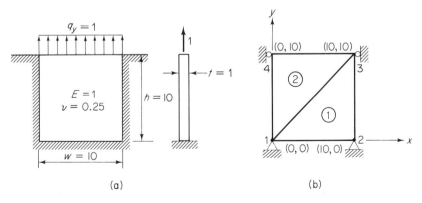

(a)   (b)

Figure 14-15

As in all cases, first we must establish the system stiffness matrix and force vector by combining the element stiffness matrices and force vectors. After solving the stiffness equations (subject to imposed displacement constraints) for nodal displacements, we may determine element stresses. We assume in this example that all quantities have consistent units. Thus, for the model shown in Fig. 14-15(b), the width and height of each element are $h = w = 10$ and the thickness is $t = 1$ in any consistent units. Also, the uniformly distributed traction along the top of the plate $q_y = 1$ and Young's modulus $E = 1$ have units that are consistent and which also are consistent with the units of h and t. The unit values for q_y and E are chosen for convenience. Both displacements and stresses are proportional to q_y; also, displacements are inversely proportional to E, while stresses are independent of E. Since Poisson's ratio is $\nu = 0.25$, the shear modulus is $G = 0.40$.

We begin by establishing the stiffness matrix $[\mathbf{k}^{(1)}]$ for element 1. According to Eq. (14-47), this matrix has the form

$$[\mathbf{k}^{(1)}] = \begin{bmatrix} [\mathbf{k}_{1,1}] & [\mathbf{k}_{1,2}] & [\mathbf{k}_{1,3}] \\ [\mathbf{k}_{2,1}] & [\mathbf{k}_{2,2}] & [\mathbf{k}_{2,3}] \\ [\mathbf{k}_{3,1}] & [\mathbf{k}_{3,2}] & [\mathbf{k}_{3,3}] \end{bmatrix}$$

with $[\mathbf{k}_{ij}]$ having dimension 2×2. The first two rows of the element stiffness matrix represent the forces that must be applied to nodes 1, 2 and 3 in both the x- and y-directions to maintain unit displacements $u_1 = 1$ and $v_1 = 1$ imposed in turn at node 1 while all other nodal displacements are zero. Similarly, the third and fourth rows relate nodal forces to $u_2 = 1$ and $v_2 = 1$, and the fifth and sixth rows relate forces to $u_3 = 1$ and $v_3 = 1$. To form $[\mathbf{k}^{(1)}]$, use Eq. (14-51) along with

$$b_1 = y_2 - y_3 = -10 \qquad b_2 = y_3 - y_1 = 10 \qquad b_3 = y_1 - y_2 = 0$$

$$c_1 = x_3 - x_2 = 0 \qquad c_2 = x_1 - x_3 = -10 \qquad c_3 = x_2 - x_1 = 10$$

Then,

$$[\mathbf{k}_{1,1}] = \frac{(0.40)(1)}{(2)(50)(0.75)}\left(\begin{bmatrix} 100 & 0 \\ 0 & 0 \end{bmatrix} + \frac{(0.75)}{2}\begin{bmatrix} 0 & 0 \\ 0 & 100 \end{bmatrix}\right) = \frac{1}{15}\begin{bmatrix} 8 & 0 \\ 0 & 3 \end{bmatrix}$$

$$[\mathbf{k}_{1,2}] = \frac{(0.40)(1)}{(2)(50)(0.75)}\left(\begin{bmatrix} -100 & 25 \\ 0 & 0 \end{bmatrix} + \frac{(0.75)}{2}\begin{bmatrix} 0 & 0 \\ 100 & -100 \end{bmatrix}\right) = \frac{1}{15}\begin{bmatrix} -8 & 2 \\ 3 & -3 \end{bmatrix}$$

$$[\mathbf{k}_{1,3}] = \frac{(0.40)(1)}{(2)(50)(0.75)}\left(\begin{bmatrix} 0 & -25 \\ 0 & 0 \end{bmatrix} + \frac{(0.75)}{2}\begin{bmatrix} 0 & 0 \\ -100 & 0 \end{bmatrix}\right) = \frac{1}{15}\begin{bmatrix} 0 & -2 \\ -3 & 0 \end{bmatrix}$$

These matrices constitute the first two rows of $[\mathbf{k}^{(1)}]$. The interpretation is illustrated in Fig. 14-16 in which the nodal forces indicated are those required to hold all displacements equal to zero except, in turn, $u_1 = 1$ and $v_1 = 1$. The remaining submatrices may be determined in a similar manner. Thus, for element 1

$$[\mathbf{k}^{(1)}] = \frac{1}{15}\begin{bmatrix} 8 & 0 & -8 & 2 & 0 & -2 \\ 0 & 3 & 3 & -3 & -3 & 0 \\ -8 & 3 & 11 & -5 & -3 & 2 \\ 2 & -3 & -5 & 11 & 3 & -8 \\ 0 & -3 & -3 & 3 & 3 & 0 \\ -2 & 0 & 2 & -8 & 0 & 8 \end{bmatrix} \begin{matrix} u_1 \\ v_1 \\ u_2 \\ v_2 \\ u_3 \\ v_3 \end{matrix}$$

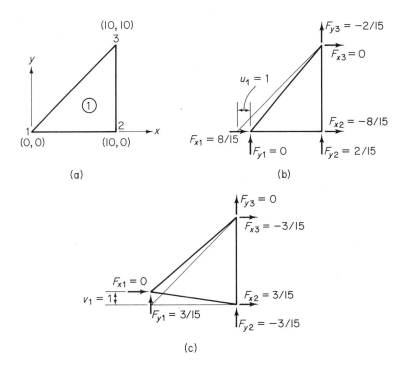

Figure 14-16

Similarly, Eq. (14-51) may be used to establish the stiffness matrix $[\mathbf{k}^{(2)}]$ for element 2. Note, however, that elements 1 and 2 are congruent; only their orientations are different. Therefore, we may formally find $[\mathbf{k}^{(2)}]$ through a transformation of $[\mathbf{k}^{(1)}]$, i.e., by considering element 1 to be rotated by $\theta = 180°$ to acquire the orientation of element 2. Hence

$$[\mathbf{k}^{(2)}] = [\mathbf{T}]^{T}[\mathbf{k}^{(1)}][\mathbf{T}]$$

where

$$[\mathbf{T}] = \begin{bmatrix} \lambda & \mu & & & & \\ -\mu & \lambda & & & & \\ & & \lambda & \mu & & \\ & & -\mu & \lambda & & \\ & & & & \lambda & \mu \\ & & & & -\mu & \lambda \end{bmatrix}$$

and $\lambda = \cos \theta = -1$ and $\mu = \sin \theta = 0$. Because, for $\theta = 180°$, $[\mathbf{T}] = -[\mathbf{I}]$, the form of $[\mathbf{k}^{(2)}]$ is identical to that of $[\mathbf{k}^{(1)}]$; i.e.,

$$[\mathbf{k}^{(2)}] = \frac{1}{15} \begin{matrix} & \begin{matrix} u_3 & \; v_3 & \; u_4 & \; v_4 & \; u_1 & \; v_1 \end{matrix} \\ \begin{matrix} \\ \\ \\ \\ \\ \\ \end{matrix} & \begin{bmatrix} 8 & 0 & -8 & 2 & 0 & -2 \\ 0 & 3 & 3 & -3 & -3 & 0 \\ -8 & 3 & 11 & -5 & -3 & 2 \\ 2 & -3 & -5 & 11 & 3 & -8 \\ 0 & -3 & -3 & 3 & 3 & 0 \\ -2 & 0 & 2 & -8 & 0 & 8 \end{bmatrix} \end{matrix}$$

The combination of element stiffness matrices provides the system stiffness matrix

$$
[\mathbf{K}] = \frac{1}{15}
\begin{array}{c c c c c c c c}
u_1 & v_1 & u_2 & v_2 & u_3 & v_3 & u_4 & v_4 \\
\end{array}
$$

$$
[\mathbf{K}] = \frac{1}{15}
\begin{bmatrix}
11 & 0 & -8 & 2 & 0 & -5 & -3 & 3 \\
0 & 11 & 3 & -3 & -5 & 0 & 2 & -8 \\
-8 & 3 & 11 & -5 & -3 & 2 & 0 & 0 \\
2 & -3 & -5 & 11 & 3 & -8 & 0 & 0 \\
0 & -5 & -3 & 3 & 11 & 0 & -8 & 2 \\
-5 & 0 & 2 & -8 & 0 & 11 & 3 & -3 \\
-3 & 2 & 0 & 0 & -8 & 3 & 11 & -5 \\
3 & -8 & 0 & 0 & 2 & -3 & -5 & 11
\end{bmatrix}
$$

The reduced system stiffness matrix $[\mathbf{K}_{ff}]$ may be extracted from $[\mathbf{K}]$ by deleting rows and columns of $[\mathbf{K}]$ corresponding to the displacements that are prescribed as zero, namely u_1, v_1, u_2, v_2, u_3, and u_4.

Hence

$$
[\mathbf{K}_{ff}] = \frac{1}{15}
\begin{bmatrix}
11 & -3 \\
-3 & 11
\end{bmatrix}
$$

and

$$
[\mathbf{K}_{ff}]^{-1} = \frac{15}{112}
\begin{bmatrix}
11 & 3 \\
3 & 11
\end{bmatrix}
$$

The nodal displacements may be found by multiplying $[\mathbf{K}_{ff}]$ by the nodal force vector. In the present case, no concentrated nodal forces are prescribed, nor are initial strains or stresses present. Hence, we must determine only

$$
\{\mathbf{F}_q^E\} = \int_{V_e} [\mathbf{N}]^T \{\mathbf{q}\} \, dV_e \tag{14-29d}
$$

which is related to the traction applied to the top edge of the plate. Because the vector $\{\mathbf{q}\} = \{q_x, q_y\} = \{0, 1\}$ is constant, we may employ Eq. (14-57) to find the equivalent nodal forces applied to element 2. Hence, the expression

$$
\begin{Bmatrix} F_{xi}^E \\ F_{yi}^E \end{Bmatrix} = \frac{1}{2} \sqrt{(x_j - x_i)^2 + (y_j - y_i)^2} \begin{Bmatrix} q_x \\ q_y \end{Bmatrix} \tag{14-57}
$$

is employed first with $i = 3$ and $j = 4$, then with $i = 4$ and $j = 3$. We then obtain

$$
\begin{Bmatrix} F_{x3}^E \\ F_{y3}^E \end{Bmatrix}^{(2)} = \frac{1}{2} \sqrt{(10 - 0)^2 + (10 - 10)^2} \begin{Bmatrix} 0 \\ 1 \end{Bmatrix} = \begin{Bmatrix} 0 \\ 5 \end{Bmatrix}
$$

and

$$
\begin{Bmatrix} F_{x4}^E \\ F_{y4}^E \end{Bmatrix}^{(2)} = \frac{1}{2} \sqrt{(0 - 10)^2 + (10 - 10)^2} \begin{Bmatrix} 0 \\ 1 \end{Bmatrix} = \begin{Bmatrix} 0 \\ 5 \end{Bmatrix}
$$

Necessarily, the sum of these two force vectors must be equal to the total applied vertical force. We then solve

$$
[\mathbf{K}_{ff}]\{\Delta_f\} = \{\mathbf{P}_f^E\} \equiv \{\mathbf{F}_q^E\}^{(2)}
$$

or

$$\frac{1}{15}\begin{bmatrix} 11 & -3 \\ -3 & 11 \end{bmatrix}\begin{Bmatrix} v_3 \\ v_4 \end{Bmatrix} = \begin{Bmatrix} 5 \\ 5 \end{Bmatrix}$$

Thus,

$$\begin{Bmatrix} v_3 \\ v_4 \end{Bmatrix} = \frac{15}{112}\begin{bmatrix} 11 & 3 \\ 3 & 11 \end{bmatrix}\begin{Bmatrix} 5 \\ 5 \end{Bmatrix} = 9.375\begin{Bmatrix} 1 \\ 1 \end{Bmatrix}$$

The element stresses may be expressed as

$$\{\boldsymbol{\sigma}\} = [\mathbf{D}](\{\boldsymbol{\epsilon}\} - \{\boldsymbol{\epsilon}_0\}) + \{\boldsymbol{\sigma}_0\} \qquad (14\text{-}43)$$

in which the vector of total strains is related to the nodal displacements through Eqs. (14-42); i.e.,

$$\{\boldsymbol{\epsilon}\} \equiv \begin{Bmatrix} \epsilon_x \\ \epsilon_y \\ \gamma_{xy} \end{Bmatrix} = \frac{1}{2A_e}\begin{bmatrix} b_i & 0 & \vdots & b_j & 0 & \vdots & b_m & 0 \\ 0 & c_i & \vdots & 0 & c_j & \vdots & 0 & c_m \\ c_i & b_i & \vdots & c_j & b_j & \vdots & c_m & b_m \end{bmatrix}\begin{Bmatrix} \Delta_i \\ \Delta_j \\ \Delta_m \end{Bmatrix}$$

Then, if we set $i, j, m = 1, 2, 3$ for element 1, we obtain

$$\begin{Bmatrix} \epsilon_x \\ \epsilon_y \\ \gamma_{xy} \end{Bmatrix} = \frac{1}{2(50)}\begin{bmatrix} -10 & 0 & \vdots & 10 & 0 & \vdots & 0 & 0 \\ 0 & 0 & \vdots & 0 & -10 & \vdots & 0 & 10 \\ 0 & -10 & \vdots & -10 & 10 & \vdots & 10 & 0 \end{bmatrix}\begin{Bmatrix} 0 \\ 0 \\ 0 \\ 0 \\ 0 \\ 0 \\ 0 \\ 9.375 \end{Bmatrix}$$

or

$$\begin{Bmatrix} \epsilon_x \\ \epsilon_y \\ \gamma_{xy} \end{Bmatrix} = \begin{Bmatrix} 0 \\ 0.9375 \\ 0 \end{Bmatrix}$$

In the present case, no initial strains or stresses are specified, i.e., $\{\boldsymbol{\epsilon}_0\} = \{\boldsymbol{\sigma}_0\} = \{0\}$. Because this is a case of plane stress, the elasticity matrix is

$$[\mathbf{D}] = \frac{E}{1-\nu^2}\begin{bmatrix} 1 & \nu & 0 \\ \nu & 1 & 0 \\ 0 & 0 & (1-\nu)/2 \end{bmatrix} = \frac{1}{0.9375}\begin{bmatrix} 1 & 0.25 & 0 \\ 0.25 & 1 & 0 \\ 0 & 0 & 0.375 \end{bmatrix}$$

Hence, the stresses in element 1 are

$$\begin{Bmatrix} \sigma_x \\ \sigma_y \\ \tau_{xy} \end{Bmatrix} = \frac{1}{0.9375}\begin{bmatrix} 1 & 0.25 & 0 \\ 0.25 & 1 & 0 \\ 0 & 0 & 0.375 \end{bmatrix}\begin{Bmatrix} 0 \\ 0.9375 \\ 0 \end{Bmatrix} = \begin{Bmatrix} 0.25 \\ 1 \\ 0 \end{Bmatrix}$$

These stresses are shown in Fig. 14-17.

$v_3 = 9.375$

$\sigma_x = 0.25$

$\sigma_y = 1$

$\tau_{xy} = 0$

Figure 14-17

The same procedure may be employed to find the stresses in element 2; these stresses are identical to those in element 1. Note that the computed displacements and stresses are exactly equal to those associated with a two-dimensional elasticity solution. This was to be expected, as the actual stress and strain fields are constant, and thus, they must be predicted by the finite element methods regardless of the coarseness of the mesh.

Example 14-5. Find the displacements and stresses in the uniformly loaded deep beam shown in Fig. 14-18(a). Because the length of the beam equals only twice its depth, classical beam theory is not applicable, and hence the beam is represented by an assemblage of triangular elements under conditions of plane stress. As shown in Fig. 14-18(b), we exploit conditions of symmetry by analyzing only one-half the beam. The end conditions on displacement at first may appear somewhat unrealistic, but they are chosen to permit comparison between our numerical solution and the exact elasticity solution.*

The length $L = 16$, the depth $h = 8$, and the thickness $t = 1$ are in any consistent units. Also, the uniformly distributed loading along the top of the beam $q_y = 1$ and Young's modulus $E = 1$ have consistent units. Since Poisson's ratio is $\nu = 0.25$, the shear modulus is $G = 0.40$.

We first compute element stiffness matrices which then may be combined to form the system stiffness matrix. Because two degrees of freedom exist at each of the 25 nodes, [**K**] will be of order 50; the 10 constraints along the end and centerline of the beam then result in [$\mathbf{K}_{ff}$] being of order 40. Clearly, machine computation is necessary. Because all elements are congruent and, in fact, are geometrically similar to the elements employed in Example 14-3, the element stiffness matrices are identical to those computed in that example. It might at first be surprising to note that the stiffness of two similar elements having the same material properties are independent of the relative size of the elements. One would perhaps expect the smaller element to be stiffer. The independence of stiffness with size is, however, a direct consequence of the assumption that the stress is constant within an element. Hence, the stiffness matrix for element 1, for example, is

---

*Timoshenko, S. and J. N. Goodier, *Theory of Elasticity,* 2nd ed. (New York: McGraw-Hill, 1951), pp. 35–44.

(a)

(b)

Figure 14-18

$$[\mathbf{k}^{(1)}] = \frac{1}{15}\begin{array}{c}\begin{array}{cccccc}u_1 & v_1 & u_2 & v_2 & u_7 & v_7\end{array}\\\begin{bmatrix}8 & 0 & -8 & 2 & 0 & -2\\0 & 3 & 3 & -3 & -3 & 0\\-8 & 3 & 11 & -5 & -3 & 2\\2 & -3 & -5 & 11 & 3 & -8\\0 & -3 & -3 & 3 & 3 & 0\\-2 & 0 & 2 & -8 & 0 & 8\end{bmatrix}\end{array}$$

The stiffness matrices for all other elements will contain the same coefficients as $[\mathbf{k}^{(1)}]$. The positions of the coefficients may, of course, differ among the elements, depending on the sequence of nodal numbering. In practice, the element stiffness matrices usually are not computed. Rather, each row or column of the system stiffness matrix is computed by having the computer call each node in turn and, for each element which incorporates that node, calculate the stiffness coefficients for that node. These coefficients then are placed in the system stiffness matrix.

For the present example, the force vector is related only to the uniform load $\{q_x, q_y\} = \{0, -1\}$ applied along the top of the beam. Thus, Eq. (14-57), which is a special case of Eq. (14-29d), again may be invoked to compute the force vectors applied to nodes 21, . . . , 25; because self-weight is neglected, all other forces are zero. Consider element 29, which includes nodes 21 and 22 along the top boundary. According to Eq. (14-57), the equivalent force vectors acting at nodes 21 and 22 of element 29 are

$$\begin{Bmatrix} F^E_{x21} \\ F^E_{y21} \end{Bmatrix}^{(29)}_q = \frac{1}{2}\sqrt{(2-0)^2 + (8-8)^2} \begin{Bmatrix} 0 \\ -1 \end{Bmatrix} = \begin{Bmatrix} 0 \\ -1 \end{Bmatrix}$$

$$\begin{Bmatrix} F^E_{x22} \\ F^E_{y22} \end{Bmatrix}^{(29)}_q = \frac{1}{2}\sqrt{(2-0)^2 + (8-8)^2} \begin{Bmatrix} 0 \\ -1 \end{Bmatrix} = \begin{Bmatrix} 0 \\ -1 \end{Bmatrix}$$

Note that node 22 also is common to element 30. Hence, the total equivalent force vector associated with node 22 is

$$\begin{Bmatrix} P^E_{x22} \\ P^E_{y22} \end{Bmatrix}_q = \begin{Bmatrix} F^E_{x22} \\ F^E_{y22} \end{Bmatrix}^{(29)}_q + \begin{Bmatrix} F^E_{x22} \\ F^E_{y22} \end{Bmatrix}^{(30)}_q = \begin{Bmatrix} 0 \\ -2 \end{Bmatrix}$$

Similar combinations must be employed at nodes 23 and 24. The sum of the forces acting at nodes 21, . . . , 25 must, and does, equal the total applied load, as indicated in Fig. 14-18(b).

Once the system stiffness matrix and force vector have been formulated, the stiffness equations, Eq. (14-32) may be solved in the usual way. In so doing, we first must account for prescribed displacements. In the present example, horizontal displacements at nodes 1, 6, 11, 16 and 21 and the vertical displacement at nodes 5, 10, 15, 20 and 25 are prescribed to be zero. We may, therefore, eliminate the rows and columns in $[\mathbf{K}]$ corresponding to these degrees of freedom; this leads to $[\mathbf{K}_{ff}]$. Of course, the prescription of nonzero displacements would require that we partition $[\mathbf{K}]$ and solve the stiffness equations in the manner described in Chapter 11.

The computed displacement pattern is shown in Fig. 14-19(a), in which the diagonal lines of the mesh have been deleted for clarity. The maximum vertical displacements occur along the centerline ($x = 0$), and the rotations of the cross sections are evident. The shear deformation also is apparent as, except for the vertical centerline ($x = 0$), none of the originally plane cross sections remains plane; this is particularly evident at the end of the beam ($x = 8$). In Fig. 14-19(b) displacements associated with the finite element model at middepth ($y = 4$) are compared with the two-dimensional elasticity solution and with the solution corresponding to elementary beam bending. Because beam theory ignores shear deformation, the displacements are underestimated by approximately 35 percent. Moreover, as the finite element model incorporates assumed displacement functions and is therefore stiffer than the elasticity model, it also underestimates the displacements, but only by approximately 15 percent. A second finite element analysis, corresponding to a model possessing twice as many elements (64 elements) with the same pattern as the first model, predicts more accurate displacements, the error being approximately 5 percent.

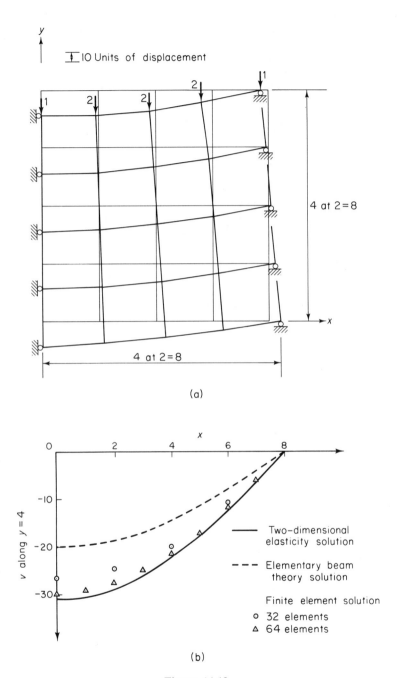

(a)

(b)

Figure 14-19

Figure 14-20 shows the stresses in the elements near midspan. In Fig. 14-20(a) are plotted the horizontal and vertical normal stresses, σ_x and σ_y, respectively along the centerline ($x = 0$). The two-dimensional elasticity solution for σ_x indicates that, due to shear deformation, the bending stress does not vary linearly across the depth of the beam, as elementary beam theory would predict. The finite element stresses are, of course, constant within any element. However, they are considered to be most representative of the actual stresses near the centroid of the element. Therefore, stresses are plotted at values of y corresponding to the locations of the centroids of the elements. Generally, the finite element values for σ_x straddle the exact solution; the average error is 28 percent. Given the coarseness of the mesh and the horizontal distance between the centerline and the element's centroid, the accuracy is good. For the vertical normal stress, σ_y, which is ignored in elementary beam theory, even better agreement exists between the finite element and exact solutions.

The stresses acting along the cross section $x = 2$ are shown in Fig. 14-20(b). The exact solution is compared with the stresses in elements having one side congruent with the line $x = 2$. The accuracy of the finite element solution is similar to that described above. Note, however, that accuracy for a stress component is improved at interior nodes by plotting the average values for all elements having a common node. Estimates of stresses at boundary nodes, however, usually are not improved by using this procedure. Various weighting methods exist for acquiring improved estimates of nodal stresses, but significant refinement usually can be achieved only by increasing the number of elements. A refined mesh comprising 64 triangular elements reduces the average error by approximately one-half.

Example 14-6. Find the displacements and stresses in a plate having a finite depth but infinite plan dimensions and subjected to infinitely long line loads along its top and bottom edges, as shown in Fig. 14-21(a).

In this case we represent a finite portion of the plate under conditions of plane strain with 64 triangular elements, as shown in Fig. 14-21(b). Because we expect the stresses to diminish rapidly with increasing values of x, we set boundaries at a horizontal distance from the loads equal to the depth of the plate. Also, we exploit both vertical and horizontal symmetry by analyzing only the first quadrant of the plate.

To derive element stiffness matrices, we may use either Eq. (14-50) or Eq. (14-51); if we choose the latter, we must substitute $\nu/(1 - \nu)$ for ν (i.e., 0.333 for 0.25) to account for conditions of plane strain. For convenience we have chosen Young's modulus to be $E = 1$ (hence $G = 0.40$) and $P = 1$ as the load per unit length normal to the x–y plane. We also assume the elements to have unit thickness, i.e., $t = 1$. Thus the stiffness matrix for element 1 may be found by first evaluating

$$b_1 = y_6 - y_7 = -1 \qquad b_6 = y_7 - y_1 = 1 \qquad b_7 = y_1 - y_6 = 0$$

$$c_1 = x_7 - x_6 = 0 \qquad c_6 = x_1 - x_7 = -1 \qquad c_1 = x_6 - x_1 = 1$$

Then, for example,

$$[\mathbf{k}_{1,1}] = \frac{(0.40)(1)}{2(0.5)(0.667)}\left(\begin{bmatrix} 1 & 0 \\ 0 & 0 \end{bmatrix} + \frac{(0.667)}{2}\begin{bmatrix} 0 & 0 \\ 0 & 1 \end{bmatrix}\right) = \frac{1}{5}\begin{bmatrix} 3 & 0 \\ 0 & 1 \end{bmatrix}$$

(a)

(b)

Figure 14-20

(a)

(b)

Figure 14-21

Other submatrices may be similarly formulated and combined to provide

$$[\mathbf{k}^{(1)}] = \frac{1}{5}\begin{array}{cccccc} u_1 & v_1 & u_6 & v_6 & u_7 & v_7 \end{array}\\\begin{bmatrix} 3 & 0 & -3 & 1 & 0 & -1 \\ 0 & 1 & 1 & -1 & -1 & 0 \\ -3 & 1 & 4 & -2 & 1 & 1 \\ 1 & -1 & -2 & 4 & 1 & -3 \\ 0 & -1 & -1 & 1 & 1 & 0 \\ -1 & 0 & 1 & -3 & 0 & 3 \end{bmatrix}$$

Because all elements are congruent, their stiffness matrices contain the same coefficients.

Introduction to the Finite Element Method   Chap. 14

The force vector comprises only one nonzero term, the vertical concentrated force (equal to -0.5) applied at node 5. The 90×90 system stiffness may be modified by eliminating the rows and columns corresponding to the 14 degrees of freedom that are prescribed as zero; this yields the reduced system stiffness matrix $[\mathbf{K}_{ff}]$, which thus is of order 76. The displacements may be solved directly by inverting $[\mathbf{K}_{ff}]$, and the stresses may then be evaluated for each element by using Eqs. (14-42), (14-43), and (14-45b).

The displacement pattern of the mesh is shown, at an exaggerated scale, in Fig. 14-22(a). (For clarity, the diagonal lines are not shown.) Note that the vertical displacement is largest directly under the applied load, and diminishes with increasing distance, both along the vertical centerline ($x = 0$) and along a horizontal line ($y = $ constant). Due to the presence of the rollers along $y = 0$, a lateral expansion occurs through most of the mesh. In Fig. 14-22(b) are plotted the vertical displacements along the vertical centerline. The displacements for the 64-element mesh are compared with those for a 128-element mesh formed by dividing the original mesh (shown in Fig. 14-21(b)) by an orthogonal set of diagonal lines. The displacements are nearly the same for both meshes, except near the load, where the finer mesh predicts a greater vertical displacement. Note that

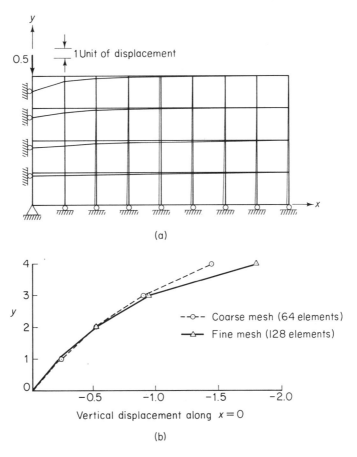

(a)

(b)

Vertical displacement along $x = 0$

--o-- Coarse mesh (64 elements)
—△— Fine mesh (128 elements)

Figure 14-22

theoretically the displacement is infinite directly beneath the load, due to the stress singularity that actually exists at that point. If an increasingly refined mesh were employed, increasingly large displacements would occur under the load. All other displacements, however, would be finite, and would be in reasonably good agreement with those shown.

The distribution of vertical normal stress σ_y along the horizontal centerline is shown in Fig. 14-23(a). While the curve represents the theoretical distribution along the line $y = 0$, the stresses in the bottom row of elements (elements 1 through 8) are considered to apply to the centroids of the elements. It may be seen that the computed stresses, represented by the open circles significantly underestimate the exact values for approximately $x < 2$. If the stress in the first and second rows of elements along the bottom are averaged, then a more accurate estimate of σ_y is obtained, as shown by the closed circles. These values are in fairly good agreement with those corresponding to the bottom row of elements in the 128-element refined mesh. The component of vertical stress for these three schemes is shown in Fig. 14-23(b) for the set of elements nearest the origin of the coordinate system. The stresses shown in Fig. 14-23(b) correspond to those en-

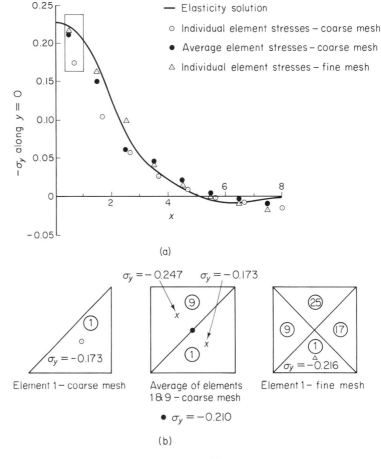

Figure 14-23

closed by the box in Fig. 14-23(a). Of course, additional accuracy could be gained by averaging the stresses in the refined mesh as well.

14-5 AXISYMMETRIC SOLIDS

When axisymmetric bodies (bodies that are symmetric about an axis of revolution) are subjected to axisymmetric loads, such as illustrated in Fig. 14-24(a), the deformations and the stresses may be determined through a two-dimensional analysis of a radial $(r-z)$ cross section. This approach is possible because all radial planes deform only in their planes and in an identical way. Accordingly, the body may be represented as an assemblage of rings, the cross sections of which might be triangular, for example, as shown in Fig. 14-24(b). The analytical problem, therefore, is similar to that associated with the plane stress or plane stress problem: to find first the two components of nodal displacements (u, v) in the cross-sectional plane and then, using those displacements, compute the stresses in each element. The components of stress and strain in cylindrical coordinates are shown in Fig. 14-25.

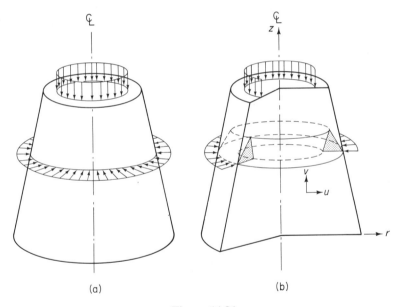

(a)   (b)

Figure 14-24

The element stiffness matrix and equivalent nodal forces are derived, of course, from the same general expressions that were applied in the cases of plane stress and plane strain, i.e.,

$$[\mathbf{k}] = \int_{V_e} [\mathbf{b}]^T[\mathbf{D}][\mathbf{b}]dV_e \tag{14-29a}$$

$$\{\mathbf{F}_q^E\} = \int_{V_z} [\mathbf{N}]^T\{\mathbf{q}\}dV_e \tag{14-29d}$$

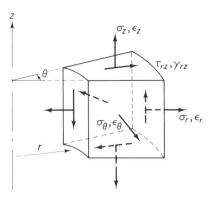

Figure 14-25

etc. It is important to recognize that the volume V_e over which the integration must be performed is now a ring having a triangular cross section.

Displacement functions.   Although the volume of integration differs from that associated with plane stress and plane strain problems, the displacements within the radial cross section may acquire the same form as those encountered previously. Thus, once again we may write expressions for the displacement functions for a typical element, shown in Fig. 14-26, as

$$\{\boldsymbol{\Phi}\} \equiv \begin{Bmatrix} u(r, z) \\ v(r, z) \end{Bmatrix} = [N_i[\mathbf{I}],\ N_j[\mathbf{I}],\ N_m[\mathbf{I}]] \begin{Bmatrix} u_i \\ v_i \\ u_j \\ v_j \\ u_m \\ v_m \end{Bmatrix} = [\mathbf{N}]\{\boldsymbol{\Delta}\} \qquad (14\text{-}58)$$

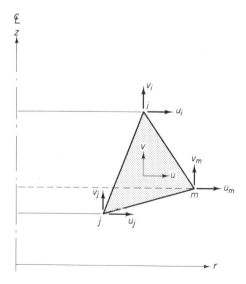

Figure 14-26

where again $[\mathbf{I}]$ is a 2×2 identity matrix while

$$N_i = \frac{1}{2A_e}(a_i + b_i r + c_i z) \tag{14-59}$$

and

$$a_i = r_j z_m - r_m z_j \tag{14-60a}$$

$$b_i = z_j - z_m \tag{14-60b}$$

$$c_i = r_m - r_j \tag{14-60c}$$

with N_j and N_m, etc., having similar forms.

Strain-displacement relation.   Although the displacement functions have the same form in the axisymmetric problem as those in plane stress and plane strain problems, the relationships between element displacements and axisymmetric strains are different from their plane stress and plane strain counterparts. While circumferential displacements are zero, the circumferential strain ϵ_θ generally is nonzero owing to the radial displacement u. Thus,

$$\{\boldsymbol{\epsilon}\} \equiv \begin{Bmatrix} \epsilon_z \\ \epsilon_r \\ \epsilon_\theta \\ \gamma_{rz} \end{Bmatrix} = \begin{bmatrix} 0 & \partial/\partial z \\ \partial/\partial r & 0 \\ 1/r & 0 \\ \partial/\partial z & \partial/\partial r \end{bmatrix} \begin{Bmatrix} u(r, z) \\ v(r, z) \end{Bmatrix} \tag{14-61}$$

In view of Eq. (14-58), we may express the element strain components in terms of nodal displacements, i.e.,

$$\{\boldsymbol{\epsilon}\} = [\mathbf{b}]\{\boldsymbol{\Delta}\} = [[\mathbf{b}_i], [\mathbf{b}_j], [\mathbf{b}_m]]\{\boldsymbol{\Delta}\} \tag{14-62}$$

where, for example,

$$[\mathbf{b}_i] = \begin{bmatrix} 0 & \partial N_i/\partial z \\ \partial N_i/\partial r & 0 \\ N_i/r & 0 \\ \partial N_i/\partial z & \partial N_i/\partial r \end{bmatrix} = \frac{1}{2A_e} \begin{bmatrix} 0 & c_i \\ b_i & 0 \\ (a_i/r + b_i + c_i z/r) & 0 \\ c_i & b_i \end{bmatrix} \tag{14-63}$$

Note that $[\mathbf{b}_i]$ no longer contains only constant terms as it does in the cases of plane stress and plane strain; it now comprises one term, associated with ϵ_θ, which is a function of r and z. Hence the integration required to evaluate the element stiffness matrix and the equivalent force vectors is more difficult than that required in the case of plane stress or plane strain.

Stress-strain relation.   The stress-strain relation also is similar to that encountered previously, except now the circumferential normal stress and strain must be accounted for. Thus, as before, we have

$$\{\boldsymbol{\sigma}\} = [\mathbf{D}](\{\boldsymbol{\epsilon}\} - \{\boldsymbol{\epsilon}_0\}) + \{\boldsymbol{\sigma}_0\} \tag{14-64}$$

where now

$$\{\boldsymbol{\sigma}\} = \begin{Bmatrix} \sigma_z \\ \sigma_r \\ \sigma_\theta \\ \tau_{rz} \end{Bmatrix} \quad \text{and} \quad \{\boldsymbol{\epsilon}\} = \begin{Bmatrix} \epsilon_z \\ \epsilon_r \\ \epsilon_\theta \\ \gamma_{rz} \end{Bmatrix} \qquad (14\text{-}65)$$

The vectors of initial stress $\{\boldsymbol{\sigma}_0\}$ and initial strain $\{\boldsymbol{\epsilon}_0\}$ have analogous forms. For an isotropic linearly elastic material, the elasticity matrix is

$$[\mathbf{D}] = \frac{E(1-\nu)}{(1+\nu)(1-2\nu)} \begin{bmatrix} 1 & \nu/(1-\nu) & \nu/(1-\nu) & 0 \\ \nu/(1-\nu) & 1 & \nu/(1-\nu) & 0 \\ \nu/(1-\nu) & \nu/(1-\nu) & 1 & 0 \\ 0 & 0 & 0 & (1-2\nu)/2(1-\nu) \end{bmatrix}$$

$$(14\text{-}66)$$

Element stiffness matrix.   The expression for the element stiffness matrix may be expressed in polar coordinates as

$$[\mathbf{k}] = \int_{V_e} [\mathbf{b}]^T[\mathbf{D}][\mathbf{b}] dV_e = \int_z \int_r \int_0^{2\pi} [\mathbf{b}]^T[\mathbf{D}][\mathbf{b}](r d\theta)\, dr\, dz \qquad (14\text{-}67)$$

The first integration is over the circumference of the element, while the second and third are over the radius r and height z within the cross section of the element. Because the integrand is independent of θ, we may write

$$[\mathbf{k}] = 2\pi \int_z \int_r [\mathbf{b}]^T[\mathbf{D}][\mathbf{b}] r\, dr\, dz \qquad (14\text{-}68)$$

Rather than attempt to evaluate this integral exactly by accounting for the dependence of $[\mathbf{b}]$ on r and z, we may choose to evaluate $[\mathbf{b}]$ at some prescribed values of the coordinates $\bar{r}$ and $\bar{z}$ within the confines of the element and then regard $[\mathbf{b}]$ as a matrix comprising constant coefficients. In fact, there will exist values of $\bar{r}$ and $\bar{z}$ that lead to the exact determination of $[\mathbf{k}]$, but these values are unknown. It is logical to choose $\bar{r}$ and $\bar{z}$ as the centroidal coordinates of the triangular cross section, i.e.,

$$\bar{r} = \frac{1}{3}(r_i + r_j + r_m) \qquad (14\text{-}69\text{a})$$

and

$$\bar{z} = \frac{1}{3}(z_i + z_j + z_m) \qquad (14\text{-}69\text{b})$$

Denoting as $[\bar{\mathbf{b}}]$ the value of $[\mathbf{b}]$ corresponding to $\bar{r}$ and $\bar{z}$ and recognizing the double integral in Eq. (14-68) as applying to the cross-sectional area, we may write

$$[\mathbf{k}] = 2\pi(\bar{r}A_e)[\bar{\mathbf{b}}]^T[\mathbf{D}][\bar{\mathbf{b}}] \qquad (14\text{-}70)$$

It is to be noted that any term in $[\mathbf{k}]$ is a stiffness coefficient relating a nodal displacement in the r–z plane to a nodal ring force, i.e., the total force acting over the ring defined by a node of the element. This is a consequence of our having integrated over the volume of the element, and not over merely a "slice" of the ring.

Element nodal forces. We designate the total nodal ring forces in the r and z directions at a typical node i as F_{ri} and F_{zi}. Thus, if forces f_{ri} and f_{zi} are specified per unit length along a ring having radius r_i, then

$$F_{ri} = 2\pi r_i f_{ri} \tag{14-71a}$$

and

$$F_{zi} = 2\pi r_i f_{zi} \tag{14-71b}$$

If forces per unit volume $\{q_r, q_z\}$ are distributed over an element, then the equivalent ring forces at node i, for example, are

$$\{F_{iq}^E\} = \begin{Bmatrix} F_{ri}^E \\ F_{zi}^E \end{Bmatrix}_q = 2\pi \int_{A_e} N_i [\mathbf{I}] \begin{Bmatrix} q_r \\ q_z \end{Bmatrix} r \, dr \, dz \tag{14-72a}$$

If the forces are uniformly distributed over the volume, a good approximation to this integral is*

$$\begin{Bmatrix} F_{ri}^E \\ F_{zi}^E \end{Bmatrix}_q = 2\pi \frac{\bar{r} A_e}{3} \begin{Bmatrix} q_r \\ q_z \end{Bmatrix} \tag{14-72b}$$

where again $\bar{r}$ is the radial coordinate of the centroid of the element's cross section. If constant forces are distributed over a surface of the element, i.e., $\{\mathbf{q}\}$ is prescribed as constant force per unit area, say, between nodes i and j, then the equivalent nodal forces at node i are approximately,

$$\begin{Bmatrix} F_{ri}^E \\ F_{zi}^E \end{Bmatrix}_q = \pi r_i \sqrt{(r_i - r_j)^2 + (z_i - z_j)^2} \begin{Bmatrix} q_r \\ q_z \end{Bmatrix} \tag{14-72c}$$

Using similar arguments to simplify integrals for equivalent forces related to initial strains $\{\boldsymbol{\epsilon}_0\}$ and initial stresses $\{\boldsymbol{\sigma}_0\}$, we would obtain, for example,

$$\begin{Bmatrix} F_{ri}^E \\ F_{zi}^E \end{Bmatrix}_{\epsilon_0} = 2\pi \, \bar{r} A_e [\bar{\mathbf{b}}_i]^T [\mathbf{D}] \{\boldsymbol{\epsilon}_o\} \tag{14-73}$$

and

$$\begin{Bmatrix} F_{ri}^E \\ F_{zi}^E \end{Bmatrix}_{\sigma_0} = -2\pi \, \bar{r} A_e [\bar{\mathbf{b}}_i]^T \{\boldsymbol{\sigma}_o\} \tag{14-74}$$

*Zienkiewicz, O.C., *The Finite Element Method*, p. 127.

Similar expressions may be written for the equivalent forces acting at nodes j and m.

Example 14-7. Use a two-element model to estimate the state of stress in a ring which is subjected to a uniform axisymmetric external pressure and is restrained in the axial direction by two perfectly smooth, rigid plates. A cross section of the ring is shown in Fig. 14-27(a).

The finite element model shown in Fig. 14-27(b) comprises two ring elements having identical triangular cross sections. In cross section, these elements are identical to those of Example 14-4, as shown in Fig. 14-15(b). The nodes are restrained against axial displacement but they are free in the horizontal direction to represent the presence of smooth plates acting on the horizontal boundaries. Note that rigid-body translation is prevented in the horizontal direction because axisymmetric horizontal movement can occur only by stretching or compressing the ring circumferentially.

(a)

(b)

Figure 14-27

The element stiffness matrices are computed from Eq. (14-70). For both elements, $A_e = 50$, $E = 1$ and $\nu = 0.25$. Hence the elasticity matrix given by Eq. (14-66) is

$$[\mathbf{D}] = 1.2 \begin{bmatrix} 1 & 1/3 & 1/3 & 0 \\ 1/3 & 1 & 1/3 & 0 \\ 1/3 & 1/3 & 1 & 0 \\ 0 & 0 & 0 & 1/3 \end{bmatrix}$$

For element 1, we may compute the components of $[\bar{\mathbf{b}}]$ from Eq. (14-63) by substituting for (r, z) the centroidal coordinates $\bar{r} = 56.67$ and $\bar{z} = 3.33$, and using

$$a_1 = r_2 z_3 - r_3 z_2 = 600 \qquad a_2 = r_3 z_1 - r_1 z_3 = -500 \qquad a_3 = r_1 z_2 - r_2 z_1 = 0$$

$$b_1 = z_2 - z_3 = -10 \qquad b_2 = z_3 - z_1 = 10 \qquad b_3 = z_1 - z_2 = 0$$

$$c_1 = r_3 - r_2 = 0 \qquad c_2 = r_1 - r_3 = -10 \qquad c_3 = r_2 - r_1 = 10$$

Thus,

$$[\bar{\mathbf{b}}_1^{(1)}] = \frac{1}{100}\begin{bmatrix} 0 & 0 \\ -10 & 0 \\ 0.588 & 0 \\ 0 & -10 \end{bmatrix} \quad [\bar{\mathbf{b}}_2^{(1)}] = \frac{1}{100}\begin{bmatrix} 0 & -10 \\ 10 & 0 \\ 0.588 & 0 \\ -10 & 10 \end{bmatrix} \quad [\bar{\mathbf{b}}_3^{(1)}] = \frac{1}{100}\begin{bmatrix} 0 & 10 \\ 0 & 0 \\ 0.588 & 0 \\ 10 & 0 \end{bmatrix}$$

and, therefore, from Eq. (14-70)

$$[\mathbf{k}^{(1)}] = \begin{array}{c} \begin{array}{cccccc} u_1 & v_1 & u_2 & v_2 & u_3 & v_3 \end{array} \\ \begin{bmatrix} 206.0 & 0 & -212.8 & 67.0 & -3.45 & -67.0 \\ 0 & 71.2 & 71.2 & -71.2 & -71.2 & 0 \\ -212.8 & 71.2 & 294.0 & -146.6 & -66.3 & 75.4 \\ 67.0 & -71.2 & -146.6 & 284.8 & 67.0 & -213.6 \\ -3.45 & -71.2 & -66.3 & 67.0 & 71.9 & 4.19 \\ -67.0 & 0 & 75.4 & -213.6 & 4.19 & 213.6 \end{bmatrix} \end{array}$$

The same approach may be used to compute the stiffness matrix for element 2. Then

$$[\mathbf{k}^{(2)}] = \begin{array}{c} \begin{array}{cccccc} u_1 & v_1 & u_3 & v_3 & u_4 & v_4 \end{array} \\ \begin{bmatrix} 67.8 & -4.19 & 4.97 & -67.0 & -70.4 & 71.2 \\ -4.19 & 201.1 & -71.2 & 0 & 62.8 & -201.1 \\ 4.97 & -71.2 & 210.0 & 0 & -200.3 & 71.2 \\ -67.0 & 0 & 0 & 67.0 & 67.0 & -67.0 \\ -70.4 & 62.8 & -200.3 & 67.0 & 263.5 & -129.9 \\ 71.2 & -201.1 & 71.2 & -67.0 & -129.9 & 268.1 \end{bmatrix} \end{array}$$

Note that the coefficients of $[\mathbf{k}^{(2)}]$ are not identical to those of $[\mathbf{k}^{(1)}]$, even though the cross sections of the two elements are congruent. The differences, which are significant, arise from the differences in $\bar{r}$ and $\bar{z}$ between the two elements.

Noting that the vertical displacements of all nodes equal zero, we may directly form the reduced system stiffness matrix. Hence,

$$[\mathbf{K}_{ff}] = \begin{array}{c} \begin{array}{cccc} u_1 & u_2 & u_3 & u_4 \end{array} \\ \begin{bmatrix} 273.8 & -212.8 & 1.52 & -70.4 \\ -212.8 & 294.0 & -66.3 & 0 \\ 1.52 & -66.3 & 281.9 & -200.3 \\ -70.4 & 0 & -200.3 & 263.5 \end{bmatrix} \end{array}$$

and its inverse is

$$[\mathbf{K}_{ff}]^{-1} = 10^{-3} \begin{bmatrix} 72.41 & 66.65 & 63.13 & 67.33 \\ 66.65 & 65.19 & 60.07 & 63.47 \\ 63.13 & 60.07 & 63.75 & 65.32 \\ 67.33 & 63.47 & 65.32 & 71.44 \end{bmatrix}$$

The equivalent nodal forces due to the uniform external pressure $\{q_r, q_z\} = \{-1, 0\}$ applied between nodes 2 and 3 are computed from Eq. (14-72c) as

$$\left\{ \begin{matrix} F^E_{r2} \\ F^E_{z2} \end{matrix} \right\}^{(1)}_q = \left\{ \begin{matrix} F^E_{r3} \\ F^E_{z3} \end{matrix} \right\}^{(1)}_q = \pi(60)\sqrt{(60-60)^2+(10-0)^2}\left\{ \begin{matrix} -1 \\ 0 \end{matrix} \right\} = 600\pi\left\{ \begin{matrix} -1 \\ 0 \end{matrix} \right\}$$

The equivalent external load vector $\{\mathbf{P}^E\}$ is, of course, the combination of $\{\mathbf{F}^E\}^{(1)}$ and $\{\mathbf{F}^E\}^{(2)}$.

The nodal displacements may be determined from

$$\left\{ \begin{matrix} u_1 \\ u_2 \\ u_3 \\ u_4 \end{matrix} \right\} = [\mathbf{K}_{ff}]^{-1}\left\{ \begin{matrix} P^E_{r1} \\ P^E_{r2} \\ P^E_{r3} \\ P^E_{r4} \end{matrix} \right\}$$

or

$$\left\{ \begin{matrix} u_1 \\ u_2 \\ u_3 \\ u_4 \end{matrix} \right\} = 0.6\pi\begin{bmatrix} 72.41 & 66.65 & 63.13 & 67.33 \\ 66.65 & 65.19 & 60.07 & 63.47 \\ 63.13 & 60.07 & 63.75 & 65.32 \\ 67.33 & 63.47 & 65.32 & 71.44 \end{bmatrix}\left\{ \begin{matrix} 0 \\ 0 \\ -1 \\ -1 \end{matrix} \right\} = \left\{ \begin{matrix} -246 \\ -233 \\ -243 \\ -258 \end{matrix} \right\}$$

The displacements are, of course, directed inward due to the externally applied pressure, the internal nodes (1 and 4) translating slightly more than the external nodes (2 and 3). While this trend is correct, displacements are underestimated by approximately 18 percent. Note also that because the finite element mesh is asymmetric about the horizontal centroidal axis of the cross section, the nodal displacements also are slightly asymmetric.

The element stresses may be computed by employing Eqs. (14-62) and (14-64). For element 1, the strain vector is

$$\left\{ \begin{matrix} \epsilon_z \\ \epsilon_r \\ \epsilon_\theta \\ \gamma_{rz} \end{matrix} \right\}^{(1)} = 10^{-2}\begin{bmatrix} 0 & 0 & \vdots & 0 & -10 & \vdots & 0 & 10 \\ -10 & 0 & \vdots & 10 & 0 & \vdots & 0 & 0 \\ 0.588 & 0 & \vdots & 0.588 & 0 & \vdots & 0.588 & 0 \\ 0 & -10 & \vdots & -10 & 10 & \vdots & 10 & 0 \end{bmatrix}\left\{ \begin{matrix} -246 \\ 0 \\ -233 \\ 0 \\ -243 \\ 0 \end{matrix} \right\} = \left\{ \begin{matrix} 0 \\ 1.30 \\ -4.25 \\ -1.00 \end{matrix} \right\}$$

Accordingly, the stress vector is

$$\left\{ \begin{matrix} \sigma_z \\ \sigma_r \\ \sigma_\theta \\ \tau_{rz} \end{matrix} \right\}^{(1)} = 1.2\begin{bmatrix} 1 & 1/3 & 1/3 & 0 \\ 1/3 & 1 & 1/3 & 0 \\ 1/3 & 1/3 & 1 & 0 \\ 0 & 0 & 0 & 1/3 \end{bmatrix}\left\{ \begin{matrix} 0 \\ 1.30 \\ -4.25 \\ -1.00 \end{matrix} \right\} = \left\{ \begin{matrix} -1.18 \\ -0.14 \\ -4.58 \\ -0.40 \end{matrix} \right\}$$

Similarly, for element 2, the stress vector is

$$\left\{ \begin{matrix} \sigma_z \\ \sigma_r \\ \sigma_\theta \\ \tau_{rz} \end{matrix} \right\}^{(2)} = \left\{ \begin{matrix} -1.27 \\ -0.07 \\ -5.00 \\ -0.48 \end{matrix} \right\}$$

It may be seen that the maximum compressive stress is the circumferential normal stress σ_θ. The exact elasticity solution* yields $\sigma_\theta = -6.55$ at $r = 50$ and $\sigma_\theta = -5.55$ at $r = 60$. While the trend toward increasing compressive stress from the outside to the inside of the ring is also evident in the finite element solution

*Timoshenko, S. and J. N. Goodier, *Theory of Elasticity*, pp. 58–60.

(i.e., the compressive stress σ_θ is greater in element 2 than in element 1), the error is significant. At the centroid of the cross section ($r = 55$), for example, the elasticity solution yields $\sigma_\theta = -5.98$, whereas the average value from the finite element solution is -4.75; the error is 20 percent.

The exact radial stress at $r = 55$ is $\sigma_r = -0.568$, while the average finite element stress is $\sigma_r = -0.105$. Also, while the shear stress τ_{rz} should equal zero, the finite element solution leads to an average value of $\tau = -0.44$. Finally, the vertical normal stress σ_z should be -1.53 throughout the cross section, whereas we have computed an average value of $\sigma_z = -1.23$; the error is thus 20 percent.

The inaccuracies are, of course, related to the coarseness of the mesh for the combination of the radius and thickness of the ring selected. As the ratio of thickness to radius decreases, greater accuracy would be expected, at least for σ_θ. As the mesh is refined, all stress components would be more accurately predicted. This is demonstrated in the following example.

Example 14-8. The thick-walled cylinder, shown in Fig. 14-28(a), is axially confined between two smooth rigid plates and is subjected to an internal pressure. The stresses in the cylinder are to be determined through a finite element analysis.

The eight-element mesh shown in Fig. 14-28(b) represents a slice of the cylinder restrained against vertical displacement. Because the axial strain is zero and the (unknown) axial stress is constant for every value of z, the thickness of the slice may in principle be chosen to have any numerical value. Here the thickness is chosen somewhat arbitrarily to be 0.25 in order to maintain the cross-sectional length to width of the triangular elements to no more than 2. Numerical accuracy often is reduced when the aspect ratio of the elements becomes large (say greater than 5), because then the diagonal stiffness coefficients for the element vary greatly owing to the much greater stiffness in one direction than in the other. Finally, note that more elements are placed near the inside of the cylinder where one might expect the stress gradient to be greatest.

The analytical procedure is similar to that presented in detail in Example 14-7. Only the horizontal displacement at each node is unknown; hence the reduced system stiffness matrix $[\mathbf{K}_{ff}]$ is of order 10. Computing this matrix and the equivalent load vector at nodes 1 and 2 related to the internal pressure leads to the nodal displacements. The horizontal translations at nodes 1 and 2, for example, are found to be 1.85 and 1.87, respectively; these are not equal because the mesh is not symmetric about the horizontal centroidal axis of the slice. The horizontal translations of nodes 9 and 10 are 1.25 and 1.24, respectively. The predicted displacements are less than the exact values based on an analytical elasticity solution; the average error is, however, less than one percent.

A comparison between finite element stress components (considered to pertain to the centroids of the elements) and exact stresses is shown in Fig. 14-29. As suggested above, σ_r and σ_θ do, in fact, vary most rapidly near $r = 1$. The stresses are more accurately predicted in elements 1 through 4, whose centroids are at locations less than $r = 1.25$; the error on stress components ranges from 0.5 percent to 7.2 percent among these elements. The greatest error occurs in elements 5 and 6 which span $r = 1.25$ to $r = 1.50$; in these elements the error ranges from 4.6 percent to 17.5 percent.

Example 14-9. A 100-ft-thick soil stratum, underlain by rock, is subjected to a uniform pressure of 1 ksf acting over a circular area having a radius of 10 ft. Using

(a)

(b)

Figure 14-28

the finite element model shown in Fig. 14-30, find the settlement beneath the load and the vertical normal stress distribution in the soil.

The particular finite element model shown in Fig. 14-30 comprises 110 triangular axisymmetric elements and 69 ring nodes. Although the mesh is rather coarse, smaller elements comprise the region nearest the loading, where the stress gradients will be greatest. To reduce computation time and cost, larger elements are used where changes in stress are likely to be small.

The nodes along the centerline ($r = 0$) are constrained in the radial direction to comply with the symmetry condition on radial deformation, and they are

Figure 14-29

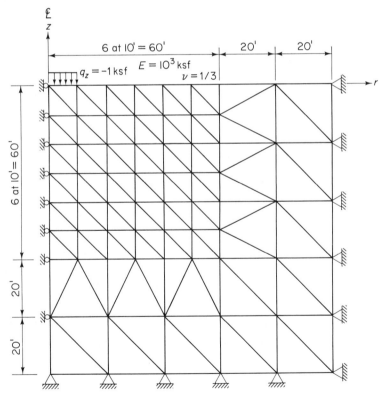

Figure 14-30

free in the vertical direction to satisfy the condition that the shear stress τ_{rz} equals zero along this line. The nodes at the base of the model must be restrained in the vertical direction to conform to the assumption that the underlying rock is rigid. These nodes also may either be free to translate or be completely restrained in the horizontal direction, depending on whether the soil-rock interface is more likely to be perfectly smooth or rough. Here the latter is chosen although, if the interface is sufficiently far from the region of applied loading, no practical difference arises between the two possible choices of boundary. Because the layer is assumed to be infinite in lateral extent, this boundary must be placed far enough from the loads so that the supports do not significantly affect the results in the region of interest. As shown subsequently, this indeed is the case for the boundary placed at $r = 100$ ft. Arbitrarily, the nodes are restrained in both the radial and vertical directions.

The system stiffness matrix $[\mathbf{K}]$ of order 138 is assembled in the usual way, in this case (because of the large size of the problem) automatically by a general purpose finite element computer program. After accounting for all the constraint conditions, we find the reduced system matrix $[\mathbf{K}_{ff}]$ to be order 108. Post-multiplying the inverse of this matrix by the equivalent load vector yields the nodal displacements.

The equivalent load vector, which could be developed using Eq. (14-72c) to account for the distributed pressure $q_y = -1$ ksf, has nonzero components only in the vertical direction at the two nodes along the top boundary nearest the center-line (at $r = 0$ and $r = 10$ ft). In fact, Eq. (14-72c) would result in a nonzero load only at the surface node at $r = 10$ ft. Because the chosen mesh is so coarse that all the applied load spans only a single element, however, we choose an alternative set of equivalent loads. The pressure acting over a circular area of radius equal to 5 ft is assumed to produce an equivalent load (-78.5^k) on the surface node at $r = 0$; the equivalent load acting on the adjacent node (-235.6^k) at $r = 10$ ft is the product of the surface pressure and the annular area between $r = 5$ ft and $r = 10$ ft. This choice is made primarily on the basis of intuition; these loads seem to be more appropriate, given the coarse mesh, than the pure ring load that would be furnished by Eq. (14-72c).

The numerical results are presented in Fig. 14-31 for the region $0 \leq r \leq 60$ ft and -30 ft $\leq z \leq 0$. The vertical displacements, shown in Fig. 14-31(a) to an exaggerated scale, are greatest on the surface at the centerline, as would be expected; they diminish with increasing depth and radial distance. The largest error* (approximately 31 percent) is associated with the surface displacement at the centerline. Displacements are more accuractely predicted at points further from the region of loading.

The resulting vertical normal stresses σ_z are shown in Fig. 14-31(b) for depths of 10 ft, 20 ft, and 30 ft. The values are the result of averaging stresses in pairs of elements that lie immediately above and below the depth of interest. Alternative means of averaging stresses, as described previously, could be employed. The attenuation of stress with increasing depth and radius is evident. Stresses are accurately predicted everywhere except in the region nearest the loading. Clearly, significantly greater accuracy would be expected if more elements were placed in the region $0 \leq r \leq 10$ ft and -30 ft $\leq z \leq 0$.

---

*Here the error is computed relative to the Boussinesq solution for a uniform circular pressure distribution applied to the surface of an elastic halfspace; see S. Timoshenko and J. N. Goodier, *Theory of Elasticity*, pp. 366–372.

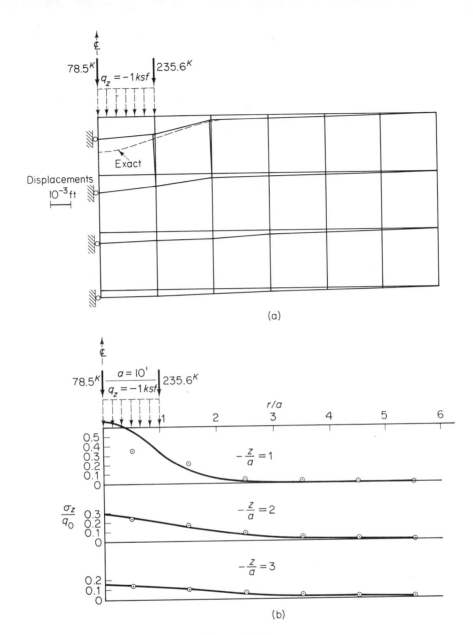

Figure 14-31

14-6 BENDING OF PLATES

A thin plate that is subjected to transverse loads, such as illustrated in Fig. 14-32, resists those loads through internal shear forces Q_x and Q_y, bending moments M_x and M_y, and twisting moments M_{xy} and M_{yx}. Because these forces and moments are inter-related and vary in two spatial directions, x and y, the behavior of thin plates is considerably more complicated than that of beams.

(a)

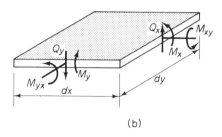

(b)

Figure 14-32

Thus, while the deflection w of a beam is related to applied distributed loading per unit length, $q(x)$, through the equation

$$\frac{d^4 w}{dx^4} = \frac{q(x)}{EI}$$

an elastic isotropic plate is governed by the equation*

$$\frac{\partial^4 w}{\partial x^4} + 2 \frac{\partial^4 w}{\partial x^2 \partial y^2} + \frac{\partial^4 w}{\partial y^4} = \frac{q(x, y)}{D}$$

in which $q(x, y)$ is applied loading per unit area and D is a measure of flexural stiffness given as for a plate of thickness h as

$$D = \frac{Eh^3}{12(1 - \nu^2)}$$

Displacement function for rectangular plate element.   We may view the finite element formulation of plate bending in a manner analogous to that of beam bending. Consider a rectangular finite element having plan dimensions a and b and thickness h, as shown in Fig. 14-33. Assuming the plate to be inextensible in its plane, we may consider the transverse displacement w of the middle plane of the plate (analogous to the neutral axis of a beam) and the

*A derivation and detailed treatment of the subject are presented by S. Timoshenko and S. Woinowsky-Krieger, *Theory of Plates and Shells*, 2nd ed., (New York: McGraw-Hill, 1959).

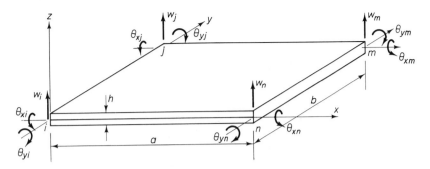

Figure 14-33

rotations θ_x and θ_y, about the x- and y-axes respectively, to represent the generalized displacements at each corner node of the plate. The rotations may be expressed as slopes of the deflected middle surface. Hence at node i, for example, the generalized coordinates are

$$\{\Delta_i\} = \begin{Bmatrix} w_i \\ \theta_{xi} \\ \theta_{yi} \end{Bmatrix} = \begin{Bmatrix} w_i \\ (\partial w/\partial y)_i \\ -(\partial w/\partial x)_i \end{Bmatrix} \tag{14-75}$$

Because the element possesses four nodes, the element displacement vector $\{\Delta\} = \{\Delta_i, \Delta_j, \Delta_m, \Delta_n\}$ has 12 rows. We wish to choose a displacement function $\{\Phi\} \equiv \{w(x, y)\}$ which will automatically satisfy the condition that the displacements and rotations at each node will be satisfied when the x, y coordinates for the node are prescribed; i.e., we require that at node i, for example,

$$w(x_i, y_i) = w_i$$
$$\partial w(x_i, y_i)/\partial y = \theta_{xi} \tag{14-76}$$
$$-\partial w(x_i, y_i)/\partial x = \theta_{yi}$$

Similar conditions are required at nodes j, m, and n. We may specify the displacement function to have the form

$$w(x, y) = \alpha_1 + \alpha_2 x + \alpha_3 y + \alpha_4 x^2 + \alpha_5 xy + \alpha_6 y^2$$
$$+ \alpha_7 x^3 + \alpha_8 x^2 y + \alpha_9 xy^2 + \alpha_{10} y^3 + \alpha_{11} x^3 y + \alpha_{12} xy^3 \tag{14-77}$$

The constants $\alpha_1, \ldots, \alpha_{12}$ then must be chosen to satisfy the conditions of Eq. (14-76) at each node. We make this choice by setting

$$w_i = \alpha_1 + \alpha_2 x_i + \alpha_3 y_i + \cdots + \alpha_{12} x_i y_i^3$$
$$\theta_{xi} \equiv \partial w(x_i, y_i)/\partial y = \alpha_3 + \alpha_5 x_i + 2\alpha_6 y_i + \cdots + 3\alpha_{12} x_i y_i^2 \tag{14-78}$$
$$\theta_{yi} \equiv -\partial w(x_i, y_i)/\partial x = -\alpha_2 - 2\alpha_4 x_i - \alpha_5 y_i - \cdots - \alpha_{12} y_i^3$$

Imposing similar conditions at nodes j, m, and n, we may then solve the resulting 12 equations for $\alpha_1, \ldots, \alpha_{12}$. After doing this, we may express the displacement function as

$$\{w(x, y)\} = [[\mathbf{N}_i], [\mathbf{N}_j], [\mathbf{N}_m], [\mathbf{N}_n]] \begin{Bmatrix} \Delta_i \\ \Delta_j \\ \Delta_m \\ \Delta_n \end{Bmatrix} \equiv [\mathbf{N}]\{\Delta\} \qquad (14\text{-}79)$$

where $\{\Delta_i\}, \ldots, \{\Delta_n\}$ take the form of Eq. (14-75) and $[\mathbf{N}_i], \ldots, [\mathbf{N}_n]$ are 1×3 matrices that represent shape functions. The matrix $[\mathbf{N}_i]$ may be most conveniently expressed in terms of the dimensionless coordinates

$$\xi = x/a \quad \text{and} \quad \eta = y/b \qquad (14\text{-}80)$$

which extend over the range 0 to 1. Then we may write

$$[\mathbf{N}_i]^T = \begin{bmatrix} 1 - \xi\eta - (3 - 2\xi)\xi^2(1 - \eta) - (1 - \xi)(3 - 2\eta)\eta^2 \\ (1 - \xi)\eta(1 - \eta)^2 b \\ -\xi(1 - \xi)^2(1 - \eta)a \end{bmatrix} \qquad (14\text{-}81)$$

The matrices $[\mathbf{N}_j], \ldots, [\mathbf{N}_n]$ have similar, but not identical, forms as $[\mathbf{N}_i]$.*

Eq. (14-79) permits us to express the transverse displacement of the plate at any location x, y (or ξ, η) in terms of the transverse displacement and rotations at the four corner nodes. This is analogous to our representation of beam elements. In fact, if we set $y = 0$ in Eq. (14-77), we obtain

$$w(x) = \alpha_1 + \alpha_2 x + \alpha_4 x^2 + \alpha_5 x^3 \qquad (14\text{-}82)$$

which agrees with the form of the displacement functions used previously for a beam element. If $\alpha_1, \alpha_2, \alpha_4,$ and α_5 are chosen to allow w and dw/dx to satisfy prescibed displacements and rotations at the ends of the beam, then Eq. (14-82) agrees with the exact solution for the beam. Unfortunately, however, Eq. (14-77) does not provide the exact solution for the transverse displacement of a plate. The consequences of this approximation are that the fourth convergence criterion (that compatibility must exist between adjacent elements) is not completely satisfied; specifically, the slope of the deflected surface in a direction normal to the side of an element may differ from the slope of an adjacent element along the same side. Thus, while all other continuity conditions are satisfied, a "kink" can occur in the deflected surface along the common edge of adjacent elements. These plate elements are, therefore, referred to as "nonconforming" elements. Despite their inherent limitations, however, nonconforming elements do satisfy all remaining convergence criteria, and associated numerical results have shown to agree well with known analytical solution for plate bending problems.

Element stiffness matrix.   We now can derive the element stiffness matrix, which relates the nodal displacements, $w_i, \theta_{xi}, \theta_{yi},$ etc., to the corresponding internal nodal transverse shear force and moments, $F_{zi}, M_{xi}, M_{yi},$ etc. (Note here that in accordance with our usual convention M_{xi} is the nodal moment (at node i) about the x-axis, whereas M_x shown in Fig. 14-32 is the bending moment

---

*For details, see J. S. Przemieniecki, *Theory of Matrix Structural Analysis*, (New York: McGraw-Hill, 1968), pp. 114–122.

along a side where x is constant and thus acts about the y-axis. This distinction, and a similar one that exists between M_{yi} and M_y, will be necessary to recall in subsequent development.) To form the element stiffness matrix, we must first express the relationships between stresses and strains and between strains and displacements; doing so will yield the matrices $[\mathbf{D}]$ and $[\mathbf{b}]$. Note, however, that the stresses and strains due to bending and twisting vary over the thickness of the plate. Therefore, the volume integral that defines $[\mathbf{k}]$ cannot be reduced to an area integral (over the plan area of the element) unless some assumption is made about the manner in which stresses and strains vary with z, the transverse distance from the middle plane.

We now assume, as we have done previously in beam theory, that the normal strains ϵ_x and ϵ_y in the x- and y-directions vary linearly with z, the perpendicular distance from the middle plane; these strains are zero at the middle plane and are maximum in tension and compression along the outer fibers at $z = \pm h/2$. In addition, we assume that the shear strains $\gamma_{xy} = \gamma_{yx}$ that act parallel to the middle plane also vary linearly with z. The distributions of ϵ_x, ϵ_y, γ_{xy}, and γ_{yx} are shown in Fig. 14-34. All other strain components (the transverse shear strains, γ_{xz} and γ_{yz}, and the normal strain ϵ_z) are considered to be negligible, just as with beam theory. If we further assume that there is no stretching of the midde plane of the plate, then we may express the strains at a fiber in terms of derivatives of the transverse displacement w. These expressions are*

$$\{\boldsymbol{\epsilon}\} \equiv \begin{Bmatrix} \epsilon_x \\ \epsilon_y \\ \gamma_{xy} \end{Bmatrix} = -z \begin{Bmatrix} \partial^2 w/\partial x^2 \\ \partial^2 w/\partial y^2 \\ 2\partial^2 w/\partial x\partial y \end{Bmatrix} \tag{14-83}$$

Note that the normal strains, ϵ_x and ϵ_y, are related to the curvatures of the plate in the x- and y-directions, respectively; the shear strain γ_{xy} is related to the twisting of the plate.

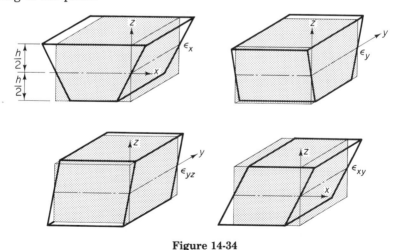

Figure 14-34

*S. Timoshenko and S. Woinowsky-Krieger, *Theory of Plates and Shells*, Chapter 2.

The strain vector may be expressed in terms of nodal displacements by recalling that

$$\{w(x, y)\} = [[\mathbf{N}_i], [\mathbf{N}_j], [\mathbf{N}_m], [\mathbf{N}_n]] \begin{Bmatrix} \mathbf{\Delta}_i \\ \mathbf{\Delta}_j \\ \mathbf{\Delta}_m \\ \mathbf{\Delta}_n \end{Bmatrix} \equiv [\mathbf{N}]\{\mathbf{\Delta}\} \qquad (14\text{-}79)$$

Hence, according to Eq. (14-83),

$$\{\boldsymbol{\epsilon}\} = -z \begin{Bmatrix} \partial^2/\partial x^2 \\ \partial^2/\partial y^2 \\ 2\partial^2/\partial x\partial y \end{Bmatrix}^T [\mathbf{N}]\{\mathbf{\Delta}\} \qquad (14\text{-}84)$$

or

$$\{\boldsymbol{\epsilon}\} \equiv \begin{Bmatrix} \epsilon_x \\ \epsilon_y \\ \gamma_{xy} \end{Bmatrix} = [[\mathbf{b}_i], [\mathbf{b}_j], [\mathbf{b}_m], [\mathbf{b}_n]]\{\mathbf{\Delta}\} \equiv [\mathbf{b}]\{\mathbf{\Delta}\} \qquad (14\text{-}85)$$

The 3×3 matrices $[\mathbf{b}_i], \ldots, [\mathbf{b}_n]$ are related to the matrices $[\mathbf{N}_i], \ldots, [\mathbf{N}_n]$ according to Eqs. (14-84) and (14-85). The matrix $[\mathbf{b}_i]$, for example, is

$$[\mathbf{b}_i] = \begin{bmatrix} (1 - 2\xi)(1 - \eta)6z/a^2 & 0 & -(2 - 3\xi)(1 - \eta)2z/a \\ (1 - \xi)(1 - 2\eta)6z/b^2 & (1 - \xi)(2 - 3\eta)2z/b & 0 \\ [1 - 6\xi(1 - \xi) - 6\eta(1 - \eta)]2z/ab & (1 - 4\eta + 3\eta^2)2z/a & -(1 - 4\xi + 3\xi^2)2z/b \end{bmatrix}$$

$$(14\text{-}86)$$

This expression and similar ones for $[\mathbf{b}_j], \ldots, [\mathbf{b}_n]$ may be found in standard references.*

As regards a constitutive relationship, we consider conditions of plane stress to prevail in planes parallel to the middle plane, i.e., σ_z is assumed to be negligibly small. Hence,

$$\begin{Bmatrix} \sigma_x \\ \sigma_y \\ \tau_{xy} \end{Bmatrix} = [\mathbf{D}] \begin{Bmatrix} \epsilon_x \\ \epsilon_y \\ \gamma_{xy} \end{Bmatrix} \qquad (14\text{-}87\text{a})$$

where

$$[\mathbf{D}] = \frac{E}{1 - \nu^2} \begin{bmatrix} 1 & \nu & 0 \\ \nu & 1 & 0 \\ 0 & 0 & (1 - \nu)/2 \end{bmatrix} \qquad (14\text{-}87\text{b})$$

To compute the element stiffness matrix $[\mathbf{k}]$, we substitute the matrices $[\mathbf{b}]$ and $[\mathbf{D}]$ into Eq. (14-29a); i.e.,

$$[\mathbf{k}] = \int_{V_e} [\mathbf{b}]^T [\mathbf{D}][\mathbf{b}] dV_e = \int_0^b \int_0^a \int_{-h/2}^{h/2} [\mathbf{b}]^T [\mathbf{D}][\mathbf{b}] dz \, dx \, dy \qquad (14\text{-}88)$$

The resulting expression for $[\mathbf{k}]$ is given in Eq. (14-89), which is shown on the next page. Note that the constants in Eq. (14-89) are as follows: $\beta = b/a$

*See J. S. Przemieniecki, *Theory of Matrix Structural Analysis*, pp. 115–125 for a more complete treatment of deriving matrix coefficients similar to those in Eqs. (14-86) and (14-89).

$$C_1 = 4(\beta^2 + \beta^{-2}) + \frac{1}{5}(14 - 4\nu) \qquad\qquad C_5 = \left[\frac{4}{3}\beta^{-2} + \frac{4}{15}(1-\nu)\right]b^2$$

$$C_2 = \left[2\beta^{-2} + \frac{1}{5}(1+4\nu)\right]b \qquad\qquad C_6 = \nu ab$$

$$C_3 = \left[2\beta^2 + \frac{1}{5}(1+4\nu)\right]a \qquad\qquad C_7 = \left[\frac{4}{3}\beta^2 + \frac{4}{15}(1-\nu)\right]a^2$$

$$C_4 = \left[2\beta^{-2} + \frac{1}{5}(1-\nu)\right]b \qquad\qquad C_8 = \left[\beta^2 - \frac{1}{5}(1-\nu)\right]a$$

$$
\begin{array}{c}
\begin{array}{ccccc}
w_i & \theta_{xi} & \theta_{yi} & w_j & \theta_{xj}
\end{array}\\[4pt]
[\mathbf{k}] = \dfrac{D}{ab}
\left[
\begin{array}{ccccc}
C_1 & & & & \\
C_2 & C_5 & & & \\
-C_3 & -C_6 & C_7 & & \\
-(C_1 - 6\beta^2) & -C_4 & C_3 - 3\beta^2 a & C_1 & \\
C_4 & -\left(\dfrac{C_5}{4} - \beta^{-2}b^2\right) & 0 & -C_2 & C_5 \\
C_3 - 3\beta^2 a & 0 & -(C_7 - 2\beta^2 a^2) & -C_3 & C_6 \\
C_1 - 6(\beta^2 + \beta^{-2}) & C_4 - 3\beta^{-2}b & C_8 & -(C_1 - 6\beta^{-2}) & C_2 - 3\beta^2 b \\
-(C_4 - 3\beta^{-2}b) & \dfrac{C_5}{4} & 0 & C_2 - 3\beta^{-2}b & -(C_5 - 2\beta^{-2}b^2) \\
-C_8 & 0 & \dfrac{C_7}{4} & C_8 - 3\beta^2 a & 0 \\
-(C_1 - 6\beta^{-2}) & -(C_2 - 3\beta^{-2}b) & -(C_8 - 3\beta^2 a) & C_1 - 6(\beta^2 + \beta^{-2}) & -(C_4 - 3\beta^{-2}b) \\
-(C_2 - 3\beta^{-2}b) & -(C_5 - 2\beta^{-2}b^2) & 0 & C_4 - 3\beta^{-2}b & \dfrac{C_5}{4} \\
C_8 - 3\beta^2 a & 0 & -\left(\dfrac{C_7}{4} - \beta^2 a^2\right) & -C_8 & 0
\end{array}
\right.
\end{array}
$$

(symmetric)

$$
\begin{array}{c}
\begin{array}{ccccccc}
\theta_{yj} & w_m & \theta_{xm} & \theta_{ym} & w_n & \theta_{xn} & \theta_{yn}
\end{array}\\[4pt]
\left.
\begin{array}{ccccccc}
C_7 & & & & & & \\
-(C_8 - 3\beta^2 a) & C_1 & & & & & \\
0 & -C_2 & C_5 & & & & \\
-\left(\dfrac{C_7}{4} - \beta^2 a^2\right) & C_3 & -C_6 & C_7 & & & \\
C_8 & -(C_1 - 6\beta^2) & C_4 & -(C_3 - 3\beta^2 a) & C_1 & & \\
0 & -C_4 & -\left(\dfrac{C_5}{4} - \beta^{-2}b^2\right) & 0 & C_2 & C_5 & \\
\dfrac{C_7}{4} & -(C_3 - 3\beta^2 a) & 0 & -(C_7 - 2\beta^2 a^2] & C_3 & C_6 & C_7
\end{array}
\right]
\begin{array}{c}
F_{zi} \\ M_{xi} \\ M_{yi} \\ F_{zj} \\ M_{xj} \\ M_{yj} \\ F_{zm} \\ M_{xm} \\ M_{ym} \\ F_{zn} \\ M_{xn} \\ M_{yn}
\end{array}
\end{array}
$$

$$(14\text{-}89)$$

Equivalent load vectors. Equivalent load vectors may be determined in the manner described in previous sections. The equivalent load for distributed transverse loading, for example, follows from the general expression

$$\{\mathbf{F}_q^E\} = \int_{A_e} [\mathbf{N}]^T \{\mathbf{q}\} dA_e$$

$$= \int_0^b \int_0^a [\mathbf{N}]^T \{\mathbf{q}\} dx \; dy = ab \int_0^1 \int_0^1 [\mathbf{N}]^T \{\mathbf{q}\} d\xi d\eta \qquad (14\text{-}90)$$

The equivalent load vector for the case where $\{\mathbf{q}\} = q_o$ (a constant load per unit area) is

$$\{\mathbf{F}_q^E\} \equiv \begin{Bmatrix} \mathbf{F}_i^E \\ \mathbf{F}_j^E \\ \mathbf{F}_m^E \\ \mathbf{F}_n^E \end{Bmatrix}_q \qquad (14\text{-}91)$$

in which

$$\{\mathbf{F}_i^E\}_q \equiv \begin{Bmatrix} F_{zi}^E \\ M_{xi}^E \\ M_{yi}^E \end{Bmatrix}_q = q_o \frac{ab}{24} \begin{Bmatrix} 6 \\ b \\ -a \end{Bmatrix} \qquad (14\text{-}92\text{a})$$

$$\{\mathbf{F}_j^E\}_q \equiv \begin{Bmatrix} F_{zj}^E \\ M_{xj}^E \\ M_{yj}^E \end{Bmatrix}_q = q_o \frac{ab}{24} \begin{Bmatrix} 6 \\ -b \\ -a \end{Bmatrix} \qquad (14\text{-}92\text{b})$$

$$\{\mathbf{F}_m^E\}_q \equiv \begin{Bmatrix} F_{zm}^E \\ M_{xm}^E \\ M_{ym}^E \end{Bmatrix}_q = q_o \frac{ab}{24} \begin{Bmatrix} 6 \\ -b \\ a \end{Bmatrix} \qquad (14\text{-}92\text{c})$$

$$\{\mathbf{F}_n^E\}_q \equiv \begin{Bmatrix} F_{zn}^E \\ M_{xn}^E \\ M_{yn}^E \end{Bmatrix}_q = q_o \frac{ab}{24} \begin{Bmatrix} 6 \\ b \\ a \end{Bmatrix} \qquad (14\text{-}92\text{d})$$

Equivalent load vectors $\{\mathbf{F}_{\epsilon_o}^E\}$ and $\{\mathbf{F}_{\sigma_o}^E\}$, which are related to initial strains and stresses, may be evaluated in a similar manner.

After combining the element stiffness matrices and equivalent element load vectors, to obtain the system stiffness matrix $[\mathbf{K}]$ and the total equivalent load vectors for the system, the stiffness equations may be solved:

$$\{\mathbf{P}\} + \{\mathbf{P}_{\epsilon_o}^E\} + \{\mathbf{P}_{\sigma_o}^E\} + \{\mathbf{P}_q^E\} = [\mathbf{K}]\{\boldsymbol{\Delta}\} \qquad (14\text{-}93)$$

As usual, $\{\mathbf{P}\}$ represents the vector of applied concentrated nodal forces, including unknown reactions. After imposing boundary constraints to reduce $[\mathbf{K}]$ to $[\mathbf{K}_{ff}]$, we may determine the unknown components of $\{\mathbf{P}\}$ and $\{\boldsymbol{\Delta}\}$ by solving Eq. (14-93).

Internal stress resultants. Once all nodal displacements have been determined, the element stiffness matrices may be used to find internal nodal forces. Thus, at node i of an element, for example, we may compute $\{\mathbf{F}_i\} \equiv \{F_{zi}, M_{xi}, M_{yi}\}$

by multiplying the three rows of $[\mathbf{k}]$ corresponding to the ith node by the displacement vector $\{\boldsymbol{\Delta}\}$. Note that M_{xi} and M_{yi} represent the internal nodal moments at node i about the x- and y-axes. Each of these nodal moments represents a combination of bending and twisting moments. In classical plate theory, however, the bending moments M_x and M_y and the twisting moment M_{xy} usually are identified individually. We may evaluate these qualities within a finite element context by first noting that they are related to the stresses by

$$M_x = \int_{-h/2}^{h/2} \sigma_x z \, dz \tag{14-94a}$$

$$M_y = \int_{-h/2}^{h/2} \sigma_y z \, dz \tag{14-94b}$$

$$M_{xy} = M_{yx} = \int_{-h/2}^{h/2} \tau_{xy} z \, dz \tag{14-94c}$$

By substituting into Eqs. (14-94) the relationships between stress and strain, Eqs. (14-87), and between strain and displacement, Eqs. (14-83), the resulting expressions may be integrated to obtain

$$\begin{Bmatrix} M_x \\ M_y \\ M_{xy} \end{Bmatrix} = -D \begin{Bmatrix} \partial^2 w/\partial x^2 + \nu \partial^2 w/\partial y^2 \\ \nu \partial^2 w/\partial x^2 + \partial^2 w/\partial y^2 \\ (1 - \nu)\partial^2 w/\partial x \partial y \end{Bmatrix} \tag{14-95}$$

For any element, the right side of Eq. (14-95) may be expressed in terms of the nodal displacement vector $\{\boldsymbol{\Delta}\}$ by differentiating Eq. (14-79). Finally, the bending and twisting moments may be expressed in terms of nodal displacements as in Eq. (14-96), which is shown on the next page. Note again that a combination of bending moment M_x and twisting moment M_{xy} at node i, for example, is designated as M_{yi}.

Example 14-10. Consider a square plate that is simply supported along all edges and is subjected to a uniformly distributed load, as shown in Fig. 14-35(a). Use the four-element model shown in Fig. 14-35(b) to find the transverse displacement and bending moments at the center of the plate.

We may take advantage of the symmetry of the plate, boundary conditions, and loading by considering only one of the square elements that comprise the plate. Thus, we construct the stiffness matrix for element 1, subject to the boundary conditions and loading conditions shown in Fig. 14-36, using in Eq. (14-89) $\nu = 0.3$ and $a = b = 1$ ft (hence $\beta = 1$). The constants $C_1, \ldots, C_8$ that appear in the element stiffness matrix are found to be

$C_1 = 10.56$ $\qquad$ $C_2 = 2.44$ ft $\qquad$ $C_3 = 2.44$ ft $\qquad$ $C_4 = 2.14$ ft

$C_5 = 1.52$ ft^2 $\qquad$ $C_6 = 0.30$ ft^2 $\qquad$ $C_7 = 1.52$ ft^2 $\qquad$ $C_8 = 0.86$ ft

While the element stiffness matrix, and hence the system stiffness matrix in this case, are of order 12×12, we may construct the reduced system stiffness matrix $[\mathbf{K}_{ff}]$ directly by accounting for those displacements that are zero. The

$$
\begin{Bmatrix}
M_{yi} \\
M_{xi} \\
\dfrac{M_{xyi}}{(1-\nu)} \\[2pt]
M_{yj} \\
M_{xj} \\
\dfrac{M_{xyj}}{(1-\nu)} \\[2pt]
M_{ym} \\
M_{xm} \\
\dfrac{M_{xym}}{(1-\nu)} \\[2pt]
M_{yn} \\
M_{xn} \\
\dfrac{M_{xyn}}{(1-\nu)}
\end{Bmatrix}
= \frac{D}{b^2}
\left[
\begin{array}{ccc|ccc|ccc|ccc}
6(\beta^2+\nu) & 4b\nu & -4a\beta^2 & -6\nu & 2b\nu & 0 & 0 & 0 & 0 & -6\beta^2 & 0 & -2a\beta^2 \\
6(\nu\beta^2+1) & 4b & -4a\nu\beta^2 & -6 & 2b & 0 & 0 & 0 & 0 & -6\nu\beta^2 & 0 & -2a\nu\beta^2 \\
\beta & b\beta & -b & -\beta & 0 & b & \beta & 0 & 0 & -\beta & -b\beta & 0 \\ \hline
-6\nu & -2b\nu & 0 & 6(\beta^2+\nu) & -4b\nu & -4a\beta^2 & 6\beta^2 & 0 & 2a\beta^2 & 0 & 0 & 0 \\
-6 & -2b & 0 & 6(\nu\beta^2+1) & -4b & -4a\nu\beta^2 & 6\nu\beta^2 & 0 & 2a\nu\beta^2 & 0 & 0 & 0 \\
\beta & 0 & -b & -\beta & b\beta & -b & \beta & -b\beta & 0 & -\beta & 0 & 0 \\ \hline
0 & 0 & 0 & -6\beta^2 & 0 & 2a\beta^2 & 6(\beta^2+\nu) & -4b\nu & 4a\beta^2 & -6\nu & -2b\nu & 0 \\
0 & 0 & 0 & -6\nu\beta^2 & 0 & 2a\nu\beta^2 & 6(\nu\beta^2+1) & -4b & 4a\nu\beta^2 & -6 & -2b & 0 \\
\beta & 0 & 0 & -\beta & b\beta & 0 & \beta & -b\beta & b & -\beta & 0 & -b \\ \hline
-6\beta^2 & 0 & 2a\beta^2 & 0 & 0 & 0 & -6\nu & 2b\nu & 0 & 6(\beta^2+\nu) & 4b\nu & 4a\beta^2 \\
-6\nu\beta^2 & 0 & 2a\nu\beta^2 & 0 & 0 & 0 & -6 & 2b & 0 & 6(\nu\beta^2+1) & 4b & 4a\nu\beta^2 \\
\beta & b\beta & 0 & -\beta & 0 & 0 & \beta & 0 & b & \beta & -b\beta & -b
\end{array}
\right]
\begin{Bmatrix}
w_i \\
\theta_{xi} \\
\theta_{yi} \\
w_j \\
\theta_{xj} \\
\theta_{yj} \\
w_m \\
\theta_{xm} \\
\theta_{ym} \\
w_n \\
\theta_{rn} \\
\theta_{yn}
\end{Bmatrix}
$$

(14-96)

(a)

(b)

Figure 14-35

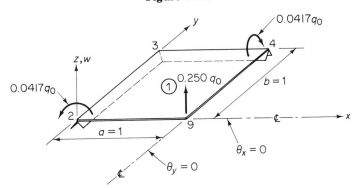

Figure 14-36

origin of the coordinate system is arbitrarily placed at node 2. The constraints along the boundaries dictate that at nodes 2, 3, and 4

$$w_2 = \theta_{x2} = 0$$

$$w_3 = \theta_{x3} = \theta_{y3} = 0$$

$$w_4 = \theta_{y4} = 0$$

Further, symmetry conditions at node 9 require that

$$\theta_{x9} = \theta_{y9} = 0$$

Thus, the only nonzero displacements are θ_{y2}, θ_{x4}, and w_9. We may therefore formulate $[\mathbf{K}_{ff}]$ of dimension 3×3 by extracting the three rows and columns from $[\mathbf{k}]$ that correspond to the unconstrained degrees of freedom. According to the chosen coordinate system, nodes 2, 4, and 9 should be regarded as nodes i, m, and n, respectively. Extracting the appropriate rows and columns from $[\mathbf{k}]$, we find

$$[\mathbf{K}_{ff}] = \frac{D}{ab} \begin{matrix} \theta_{yi} & \theta_{xm} & w_n \\ \begin{bmatrix} C_7 & 0 & -(C_8 - 3\beta^2 a) \\ 0 & C_5 & C_4 \\ -(C_8 - 3\beta^2 a) & C_4 & C_1 \end{bmatrix} & \begin{matrix} P_{myi} \\ P_{mxm} \\ P_{zn} \end{matrix} \end{matrix}$$

or

$$[\mathbf{K}_{ff}] = \frac{D}{1\ \text{ft}^2} \begin{matrix} \theta_{y2} & \theta_{x4} & w_9 \\ \begin{bmatrix} 1.52\ \text{ft}^2 & 0 & 2.14\ \text{ft} \\ 0 & 1.52\ \text{ft}^2 & 2.14\ \text{ft} \\ 2.14\ \text{ft} & 2.14\ \text{ft} & 10.56 \end{bmatrix} & \begin{matrix} P_{my2} \\ P_{mx4} \\ P_{z9} \end{matrix} \end{matrix}$$

Recall that $D \equiv Eh^3/12(1 - \nu^2)$ has units of force-length.

The equivalent load vectors for element 1 may be computed from Eqs. (14-91). Representing nodes i, j, m, n by nodes 2, 3, 4, 9, respectively, we obtain

$$\begin{Bmatrix} F^E_{z2} \\ M^E_{x2} \\ M^E_{y2} \end{Bmatrix} = q_0 \begin{Bmatrix} 0.250\ \text{ft}^2 \\ 0.0417\ \text{ft}^3 \\ -0.0417\ \text{ft}^3 \end{Bmatrix} \qquad \begin{Bmatrix} F^E_{z3} \\ M^E_{x3} \\ M^E_{y3} \end{Bmatrix} = q_0 \begin{Bmatrix} 0.250\ \text{ft}^2 \\ -0.0417\ \text{ft}^3 \\ -0.0417\ \text{ft}^3 \end{Bmatrix}$$

$$\begin{Bmatrix} F^E_{z4} \\ M^E_{x4} \\ M^E_{y4} \end{Bmatrix} = q_0 \begin{Bmatrix} 0.250\ \text{ft}^2 \\ -0.0417\ \text{ft}^3 \\ 0.0417\ \text{ft}^3 \end{Bmatrix} \qquad \begin{Bmatrix} F^E_{z9} \\ M^E_{x9} \\ M^E_{y9} \end{Bmatrix} = q_0 \begin{Bmatrix} 0.250\ \text{ft}^2 \\ 0.0417\ \text{ft}^3 \\ 0.0417\ \text{ft}^3 \end{Bmatrix}$$

Retaining the components of force associated with nonzero degrees of freedom, we obtain the generalized equivalent force vector

$$\{\mathbf{P}^E_f\} \equiv \begin{Bmatrix} P^E_{my2} \\ P_{mx4} \\ P^E_{z9} \end{Bmatrix} = \begin{Bmatrix} M^E_{y2} \\ M^E_{x4} \\ F^E_{z9} \end{Bmatrix} = q_0 \begin{Bmatrix} -0.0417\ \text{ft}^3 \\ -0.0417\ \text{ft}^3 \\ 0.250\ \text{ft}^2 \end{Bmatrix}$$

These generalized forces are shown in Fig. 14-36.

The displacements may be determined from

$$\{\mathbf{\Delta}_f\} = [\mathbf{K}_{ff}]^{-1}\{\mathbf{P}^E_f\}$$

in which

$$\{\mathbf{\Delta}_f\} \equiv \begin{Bmatrix} \theta_{y2} \\ \theta_{x4} \\ w_9 \end{Bmatrix}$$

and

$$[\mathbf{K}_{ff}]^{-1} = \frac{1}{D} \begin{bmatrix} 1.094 & 0.437 & -0.310\ \text{ft} \\ 0.437 & 1.094 & -0.310\ \text{ft} \\ -0.310\ \text{ft} & -0.310\ \text{ft} & 0.220\ \text{ft}^2 \end{bmatrix}$$

Thus, we find

$$\left\{\begin{array}{c} \theta_{y2} \\ \theta_{x4} \\ w_9 \end{array}\right\} = \frac{q_o}{D}\left\{\begin{array}{c} -0.141 \text{ ft}^3 \\ -0.141 \text{ ft}^3 \\ 0.0809 \text{ ft}^4 \end{array}\right\}$$

The bending and twisting moments may be evaluated at the nodes of the element by using the stress matrix presented in Eq. (14-96). To find these moments at the center of the plate, for example, where we have identified node 9 with node n, we may use the last three rows of the matrix and the columns corresponding to the nonzero nodal displacements, i.e.,

$$\left\{\begin{array}{c} M_{yn} \\ M_{xn} \\ \dfrac{M_{xyn}}{(1-\nu)} \end{array}\right\} = \frac{D}{b^2}\left[\begin{array}{ccc} 2a\beta^2 & 2b\nu & 6(\beta^2+\nu) \\ 2a\nu\beta^2 & 2b & 6(\nu\beta^2+1) \\ 0 & 0 & -\beta \end{array}\right]\left\{\begin{array}{c} \theta_{yi} \\ \theta_{xj} \\ w_n \end{array}\right\}$$

Hence, again using $a = b = 1$ ft, $\beta = 1$ and $\nu = 0.3$, we obtain

$$\left\{\begin{array}{c} M_{y9} \\ M_{x9} \\ M_{xy9} \end{array}\right\} = \frac{D}{1 \text{ ft}^2}\left[\begin{array}{ccc} 2 \text{ ft} & 0.6 \text{ ft} & 7.8 \\ 0.6 \text{ ft} & 2 \text{ ft} & 7.8 \\ 0 & 0 & -0.70 \end{array}\right]\left\{\begin{array}{c} \theta_{y2} \\ \theta_{x4} \\ w_9 \end{array}\right\}$$

Substitituting the previously computing displacement vector, we find

$$\left\{\begin{array}{c} M_{y9} \\ M_{x9} \\ M_{xy9} \end{array}\right\} = q_0\left\{\begin{array}{c} 0.264 \\ 0.264 \\ -0.0566 \end{array}\right\}\text{ft}^2$$

Consider the particular case of a two-foot square steel plate having a modulus of elasticity $E = 30 \times 10^6$ psi $= 4.32 \times 10^9$ psf and a thickness $h = 0.25$ in. $= 0.02083$ ft; hence $D = 3577$ lb-ft. Thus, if the load q_0 equals -100 lb/ft^2, the transverse displacement at the center of the plate is

$$w_9 = \frac{-100 \text{ lb/ft}^2}{3577 \text{ lb-ft}}(0.0809 \text{ ft}^4) = -0.00226 \text{ ft} = -0.0271 \text{ in.}$$

The corresponding bending and twisting moments are

$$\left\{\begin{array}{c} M_{y9} \\ M_{x9} \\ M_{xy9} \end{array}\right\} = \left\{\begin{array}{c} -26.4 \\ -26.4 \\ 5.66 \end{array}\right\}\text{lb-ft/ft}$$

The exact solutions for displacement and moments at the center of the plate are*

$$w_{9 \text{ exact}} = -0.0219 \text{ in.}$$

and

$$\left\{\begin{array}{c} M_{y9} \\ M_{x9} \\ M_{xy9} \end{array}\right\}_{\text{exact}} = \left\{\begin{array}{c} -19.2 \\ -19.2 \\ 0 \end{array}\right\}\text{lb-ft/ft}$$

The finite element method thus overestimates the central displacement by 25 percent and the bending moment by about 38 percent. The large error is due to the very coarse mesh. Note that because the element does not satisfy normal slope

*S. Timoshenko and S. Woinowsky-Krieger, *Theory of Plates and Shells*, pp. 113–124.

compatibility with its neighbors, the displacements can be overestimated, as illustrated by this example.

Example 14-11. Consider the same square plate as treated in the previous example, except in the present case all edges are clamped to prevent rotation, as shown in Fig. 14-37(a). Find the transverse displacement and bending moments at the center of the plate.

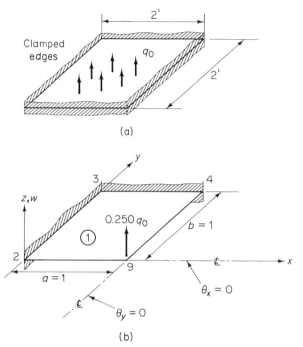

(a)

(b)

Figure 14-37

In this case the only nonzero displacement is w_9, as illustrated in Fig. 14-37(b). Therefore, the reduced system stiffness matrix is of order 1, and is simply the element in the third row and third column of the matrix $[\mathbf{K}_{ff}]$ developed in the previous example. Hence, now

$$[\mathbf{K}_{ff}] = \frac{D}{1 \text{ ft}^2}[10.56]$$

and

$$[\mathbf{K}_{ff}]^{-1} = \frac{0.0947}{D} \text{ ft}^2$$

The displacement at the center of the plate is found from

$$\{\boldsymbol{\Delta}_f\} = [\mathbf{K}_{ff}]^{-1}\{\mathbf{P}_f^F\}$$

where now

$$\{\boldsymbol{\Delta}_f\} = w_9 \qquad \text{and} \quad \{\mathbf{P}_f^F\} = P_{z9}^F = 0.250 \, q_0 \text{ ft}^2$$

The generalized force P_{z9}^E is shown in Fig. 14-37(b).

Thus,

$$w_9 = \left(\frac{0.0947 \text{ ft}^2}{D}\right)(0.250 \, q_0 \text{ ft}^2) = 0.0237\frac{q_0}{D}\text{ft}^4$$

and the internal moments at node 9 are

$$\begin{Bmatrix} M_{y9} \\ M_{x9} \\ M_{xy9} \end{Bmatrix} = \frac{D}{1 \text{ ft}^2}\begin{Bmatrix} 7.8 \\ 7.8 \\ -0.70 \end{Bmatrix}(w_9) = q_0\begin{Bmatrix} 0.185 \\ 0.185 \\ -0.0166 \end{Bmatrix}\text{ft}^2$$

For the dimensions, material properties and loading specified in the previous example,

$$w_9 = -0.00795 \text{ in.}$$

and

$$\begin{Bmatrix} M_{y9} \\ M_{x9} \\ M_{xy9} \end{Bmatrix} = \begin{Bmatrix} -18.5 \\ -18.5 \\ 1.66 \end{Bmatrix}\text{lb-ft/ft}$$

The exact solution yields*

$$w_{9 \text{ exact}} = -0.00674 \text{ in.}$$

and

$$\begin{Bmatrix} M_{y9} \\ M_{x9} \\ M_{xy9} \end{Bmatrix}_{\text{exact}} = \begin{Bmatrix} -9.24 \\ -9.24 \\ 0 \end{Bmatrix}\text{lb-ft/ft}$$

The finite element solution overestimates the central displacement by 20 percent and the bending moment by about 100 percent. In general, as a system is more highly constrained, thus reducing the number of degrees of freedom that define deformation, the accuracy decreases.

The accuracy gained by increasing the number of elements is shown in Fig. 14-38. Exact values of deflections and bending moments are compared with those associated with the foregoing one-element mesh and with a refined four-element mesh. Solutions are presented for both simply supported edges and clamped edges. For the four-element mesh, the displacement and bending moments at the center of the plate are estimated to within 10 percent of the exact values. Some displacements and moments at other locations are, however, estimated less accurately.

Example 14-12. A rectangular plate is simply supported on two opposite edges, clamped along the third edge and free on the fourth edge, as shown in Fig. 14-39(a). A concentrated transverse load is applied at the middle of the free edge. Find the deflection under the load and the bending moment at the middle of the clamped edge.

For purposes of illustration, we first consider a two-element system. Accounting for symmetry, we may reduce the system to a single element, as shown

*Ibid, p. 202.

Figure 14-38

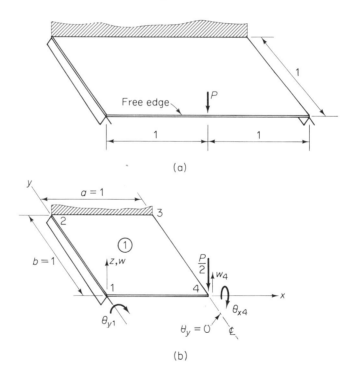

Figure 14-39

Introduction to the Finite Element Method   Chap. 14

in Fig. 14-39(b). For the nodal numbering scheme shown, the boundary conditions and loading conditions dictate that

$$w_1 = \theta_{x1} = 0$$

$$w_2 = \theta_{x2} = \theta_{y2} = 0$$

$$w_3 = \theta_{x3} = \theta_{y3} = 0$$

$$\theta_{y4} = 0$$

The only nonzero displacements are θ_{y1}, w_4, θ_{x4}.

As we have done in the previous example, we formulate the reduced system stiffness matrix directly from Eq. (14-89). Deleting rows and columns in $[\mathbf{k}]$ pertaining to the constrained degrees of freedom, and associating nodes 1, 2, 3, 4 with nodes i, j, m, n, respectively, we obtain

$$[\mathbf{K}_{ff}] = \frac{D}{ab}\begin{bmatrix} C_7 & -(C_8 - 3\beta^2 a) & 0 \\ -(C_8 - 3\beta^2 a) & C_1 & C_2 \\ 0 & C_2 & C_5 \end{bmatrix}\begin{matrix} P_{my1} \\ P_{z4} \\ P_{mx4} \end{matrix}$$

$$\begin{matrix} \theta_{y1} & w_4 & \theta_{x4} \end{matrix}$$

The dimensions of the element are $a = b = 1$ (for convenience we shall not specify units of length); hence $\beta = 1$. We also set $\nu = 0.3$. We then find

$$C_1 = 10.56 \qquad C_2 = 2.44 \qquad C_5 = 1.52$$

$$C_6 = 1.52 \qquad C_8 = 0.86$$

Therefore,

$$[\mathbf{K}_{ff}] = D\begin{bmatrix} 1.52 & 2.14 & 0 \\ 2.14 & 10.56 & 2.44 \\ 0 & 2.44 & 1.52 \end{bmatrix}$$

and hence,

$$[\mathbf{K}_{ff}]^{-1} = \frac{1}{D}\begin{bmatrix} 1.204 & -0.388 & 0.622 \\ -0.388 & 0.275 & -0.442 \\ 0.622 & -0.442 & 1.367 \end{bmatrix}$$

We recognize that

$$\{\mathbf{\Delta}_f\} \equiv \begin{Bmatrix} \theta_{y1} \\ w_4 \\ \theta_{x4} \end{Bmatrix} \quad \text{and} \quad \{\mathbf{P}_f\} \equiv \begin{Bmatrix} P_{my1} \\ P_{z4} \\ P_{mx4} \end{Bmatrix} = \begin{Bmatrix} 0 \\ -P/2 \\ 0 \end{Bmatrix}$$

Then,

$$\begin{Bmatrix} \theta_{y1} \\ w_4 \\ \theta_{x4} \end{Bmatrix} = [\mathbf{K}_{ff}]^{-1}\begin{Bmatrix} 0 \\ -P/2 \\ 0 \end{Bmatrix} = \frac{P}{D}\begin{Bmatrix} 0.194 \\ -0.138 \\ 0.221 \end{Bmatrix}$$

We may estimate the bending moment at node 3, which takes the place of node m in Eq. (14-96), i.e.,

$$\left\{\begin{matrix} M_{y3} \\ M_{x3} \\ \underline{M_{xy3}} \\ 0.7 \end{matrix}\right\} = \frac{D}{b^2}\begin{bmatrix} 0 & -6\nu & -2b\nu \\ 0 & -6 & -2b \\ 0 & -\beta & 0 \end{bmatrix}\left\{\begin{matrix} \theta_{y1} \\ w_4 \\ \theta_{x4} \end{matrix}\right\}$$

Substituting previously computed quantities, we find

$$\left\{\begin{matrix} M_{y3} \\ M_{x3} \\ M_{xy3} \end{matrix}\right\} = P\left\{\begin{matrix} 0.116 \\ 0.386 \\ 0.0976 \end{matrix}\right\}$$

Although an exact solution does not exist for the deflection, a close approximation* is $-0.168\,P/D$; on this basis, the finite element solution is too small by about 18 percent. The exact value of bending moment M_{x3} is $0.436P$; thus, the finite element method underestimates M_{x3} by about 11 percent.

The analysis is repeated with the foregoing single element being replaced by four plate elements. The deformation of one-half the plate is therefore described by 12 generalized displacements, as shown in Fig. 14-40. The displacement under the applied load, now at node 7, is found to be $-0.137\,P/D$, which is nearly the same as obtained with a single-element model. The bending moment at the center of the clamped edge, now at node 9, is $0.399\,P$; this bending moment, which is computed using the stress matrix for element 3, underestimates the exact value by about 8.5 percent.

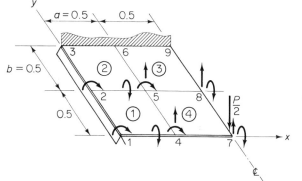

Figure 14-40

Example 14-13. The same rectangular plate considered in Example 14-12 is now reinforced with a thin beam along the free edge of the plate, as shown in Fig. 14-41(a). The beam is characterized by a moment of inertia I, Young's modulus E, and length L. Determine the deflection under the load and the bending moment at the middle of the clamped edge.

Let us again consider the plate itself to comprise two plate elements. We may then model one half the plate as a single plate element, as shown in Fig. 14-41(b), which is identical to that used in Example 14-12. Thus, for the plate alone we have

*Ibid, p. 211.

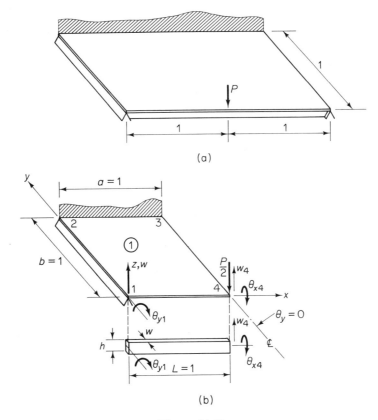

(a)

(b)

Figure 14-41

$$[\mathbf{K}_{ff}]_{\text{plate}} = D \begin{matrix} \theta_{y1} & w_4 & \theta_{x4} \\ \begin{bmatrix} 1.52 & 2.14 & 0 \\ 2.14 & 10.56 & 2.44 \\ 0 & 2.44 & 1.52 \end{bmatrix} & \begin{matrix} P_{my1} \\ P_{z4} \\ P_{mx4} \end{matrix} \end{matrix}$$

Recall that this reduced system stiffness matrix was formed from the element stiffness matrix for the plate by retaining rows and columns corresponding to nonzero generalized displacements. The plan dimensions of the element were $a = b = 1$.

We may form a similar matrix for the beam element, which must be compatible with the plate at nodes 1 and 4, as shown in Fig. 14-41(b). If, as is often the case, torsional stiffness may be neglected, then the reduced system stiffness matrix for the beam alone is

$$[\mathbf{K}_{ff}]_{\text{beam}} = \frac{EI}{L} \begin{matrix} \theta_{y1} & w_4 & \theta_{x4} \\ \begin{bmatrix} 4 & 6/L & 0 \\ 6/L & 12/L^2 & 0 \\ 0 & 0 & 0 \end{bmatrix} & \begin{matrix} P_{my1} \\ P_{z4} \\ P_{mx4} \end{matrix} \end{matrix}$$

Because the beam spans the side of the element, the beam's length is $L = a = 1$. In general, the term EI/L may be expressed as a fraction of the plate bending rigidity D. Consider now the plate's width to be $a = 1$ ft and its thickness to be $h = 0.25$ in. $= 0.02083$ ft. Suppose the beam's width is $w = 0.02083$ ft and its depth is $d = 1$ in. $= 0.0833$ ft. Then if $E = 30 \times 10^6$ psi $= 4.32 \times 10^4$ psf for both the plate and the beam and the Poisson ratio of the plate is $\nu = 0.3$, we calculate $D = 3577$ lb-ft and $(EI/L) = 1.213 D = 4339$ lb-ft. Thus we may write

$$[\mathbf{K}_{ff}]_{\text{plate}} = \frac{D}{\text{ft}^2} \begin{bmatrix} 1.52 \text{ ft}^2 & 2.14 \text{ ft} & 0 \\ 2.14 \text{ ft} & 10.56 & 2.44 \text{ ft} \\ 0 & 2.44 \text{ ft} & 1.52 \text{ ft}^2 \end{bmatrix}$$

and

$$[\mathbf{K}_{ff}]_{\text{beam}} = \frac{1.213D}{\text{ft}^2} \begin{bmatrix} 4 \text{ ft}^2 & 6 \text{ ft} & 0 \\ 6 \text{ ft} & 12 & 0 \\ 0 & 0 & 0 \end{bmatrix}$$

The reduced system stiffness matrix for the combined plate and beam is then

$$[\mathbf{K}_{ff}] = [\mathbf{K}_{ff}]_{\text{plate}} + [\mathbf{K}_{ff}]_{\text{beam}} = \frac{D}{\text{ft}^2} \begin{bmatrix} 6.373 \text{ ft}^2 & 9.420 \text{ ft} & 0 \\ 9.420 \text{ ft} & 25.12 & 2.44 \text{ ft} \\ 0 & 2.44 \text{ ft} & 1.52 \text{ ft}^2 \end{bmatrix}$$

and its inverse is

$$[\mathbf{K}_{ff}]^{-1} = \frac{1}{D} \begin{bmatrix} 0.4571 & -0.2031 \text{ ft} & 0.3260 \\ -0.2031 \text{ ft} & 0.1374 \text{ ft}^2 & -0.2205 \text{ ft} \\ 0.3260 & -0.2205 \text{ ft} & 1.0119 \end{bmatrix}$$

As in the previous example,

$$\{\mathbf{\Delta}_f\} = \begin{Bmatrix} \theta_{y1} \\ w_4 \\ \theta_{x4} \end{Bmatrix} \quad \text{and} \quad \{\mathbf{P}_f\} = \begin{Bmatrix} P_{my1} \\ P_{z4} \\ P_{mx4} \end{Bmatrix} = \begin{Bmatrix} 0 \\ -P/2 \\ 0 \end{Bmatrix}$$

Hence,

$$\begin{Bmatrix} \theta_{y1} \\ w_4 \\ \theta_{x4} \end{Bmatrix} = [\mathbf{K}_{ff}]^{-1} \begin{Bmatrix} 0 \\ -P/2 \\ 0 \end{Bmatrix} = \frac{P}{D} \begin{Bmatrix} 0.1016 \text{ ft} \\ -0.0687 \text{ ft}^2 \\ 0.1103 \text{ ft} \end{Bmatrix}$$

Comparing this displacement vector with that for the unreinforced plate treated in the previous example, we find that the presence of the beam has led to a reduction in displacement and rotations of approximately 50 percent.

Bending and twisting moments in the plate may be determined by using the element stress matrix expressed by Eq. (14-96). Using precisely the same stress matrix as employed in the previous example, we find at node 3

$$\begin{Bmatrix} M_{y3} \\ M_{x3} \\ M_{xy3} \end{Bmatrix} = P \begin{Bmatrix} 0.058 \\ 0.192 \\ 0.069 \end{Bmatrix}$$

The presence of the beam has led to a reduction of M_{x3} of approximately 50 percent as compared with the bending moment for the unreinforced plate.

The plate was reanalyzed using four elements in place of the single element for one-half the plate and two beam elements having length $L = 0.5$. The arrangement of plate elements is the same as that shown in Fig. 14-40. The displacement at the point of loading was found to be $w_7 = -0.0681$ ft$^2 P/D$ and the moment at the center of the clamped edge $M_{x9} = 0.209\ P$; the displacement and bending moment differ by less than one percent and 10 percent, respectively, from those corresponding to the single-element model.

A series of analyses was conducted in which the depth of the reinforcing beam varied from 0 to 2.0 in. The analyses were performed for both the one-element model and the four-element model of one half the plate. Figure 14-42 shows the reduction of displacement and bending moment with increasing depth of the beam.

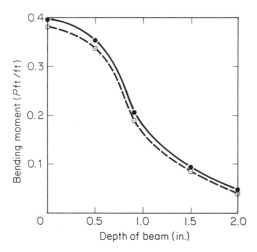

Figure 14-42

A shell may be defined as the materialization of a curved surface. A thin shell is one whose thickness is assumed to be small compared with the dimensions of its reference surface (which usually is considered to be the middle surface, analogous to that of a plate). Typical shapes include segments of cylinders, spheres and other surfaces of revolution; however, less regular curved shapes are sometimes employed. In general, shells function efficiently as structures because their shape allows them to resist applied loads primarily by internal membrane forces (forces acting tangentially to the reference surface at each point), and only secondarily by transverse shear forces and bending and twisting moments.

Any shell may be represented as an assemblage of small plate elements, each having a different orientation in order to accommodate approximately the curved surface, similar to our representing a ring in Example 14-3 by an assemblage of beam elements. If, however, the shell is axisymmetric (i.e., one that is symmetric about a line), then it may be analyzed as a series of thin ring elements. The analysis is further simplified if the loading also is axisymmetric. In this section, we shall confine our discussion to thin axisymmetric shells subjected to axisymmetric loading.

Consider the axisymmetric shell shown in Fig. 14-43(a). Axisymmetric loads will produce in a typical ring element forces and moments that are invariant with respect to θ, the circumferential coordinate. External loads will be resisted by membrane forces N_s and N_θ in the meridianal and circumferential directions, respectively, by bending moments M_s and M_θ, and by transverse forces Q_s. These internal stress resultants are shown in Fig. 14-43(b). Because of axial symmetry, no membrane shear forces, twisting moments, and transverse shear forces exist along meridians.

As the deformations of the shell's reference surface must also be axisymmetric, the transverse and meridianal displacements, w' and u', respectively (relative to the local axes n and s), may depend only on the meridianal coordinate s. Thus, the derivatives of w' and u' with respect to θ are zero; further, no displacement occurs in the circumferential direction. Note, however, that because axisymmetric deformation usually will result in a change in the radius of curvature, both the membrane strain and the bending moment in the circumferential direction usually will be nonzero.

Displacement function for axisymmetric shell element. Consider an axisymmetric shell element defined by nodes i and j and developed by a straight meridian inclined at an angle ϕ relative to the axis of symmetry, as shown in Fig. 14-44(a). The deformation of this conical element will be defined by the displacements $u'(s)$ and $w'(s)$ at each point along the meridian. Thus, we define the displacement function as

$$\{\Phi\} = \begin{Bmatrix} u'(s) \\ w'(s) \end{Bmatrix} \tag{14-97}$$

(a)

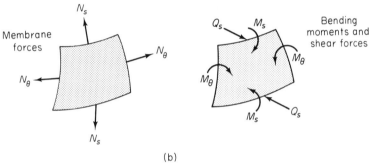

(b)

Figure 14-43

Note that the displacements $u'(s)$ and $w'(s)$ may be related to the translations and rotations at nodes i and j in precisely the same manner as in the case of a beam element. That is, we may write

$$\{\mathbf{\Phi}\} = [\mathbf{N'}]\{\mathbf{\Delta'}\} \tag{14-98}$$

in which $\{\mathbf{\Delta'}\}$, the vector of nodal displacements in the directions of local coordinates, is given by

$$\{\mathbf{\Delta'}\} = \begin{Bmatrix} \mathbf{\Delta'_i} \\ \mathbf{\Delta'_j} \end{Bmatrix} \tag{14-99a}$$

and

$$\{\mathbf{\Delta'_i}\} = \begin{Bmatrix} u'_i \\ w'_i \\ \psi'_i \end{Bmatrix} \quad \text{and} \quad \{\mathbf{\Delta'_j}\} = \begin{Bmatrix} u'_j \\ w'_j \\ \psi'_i \end{Bmatrix} \tag{14-99b}$$

where $\psi'_i = (dw/ds)_i$ and $\psi'_j = (dw'/ds)_j$.

(a)

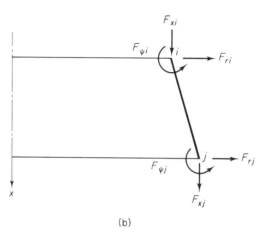

(b)

Figure 14-44

Recognizing the similarity between the deformation of the shell element and that of a beam element, we may employ Eqs. (14-1) and (14-2) which imply that u' varies linearly with s and w' varies as a cubic polynomial in s. That is

$$u' = \alpha_1 + \alpha_2 s$$

and   (14-100)

$$w' = \alpha_3 + \alpha_4 s + \alpha_5 s^2 + \alpha_6 s^3$$

We may evaluate $\alpha_1, \ldots, \alpha_6$ by imposing requirements that at $s = 0$, $u' = u_i'$, $w' = w_i'$ and $(dw'/ds) = \psi_i'$ along with similar conditions at $s = L$. Indeed, Eqs. (14-1) and (14-2) were derived in this way. Thus, defining $\xi \equiv s/L$, we may write

$$u' = (1 - \xi)u_i' + \xi u_j'$$

and   (14-101)

$$w' = (1 - 3\xi^2 + 2\xi^3)w_i' + L(\xi - 2\xi^2 + \xi^3)\psi_i' + (3\xi^2 - 2\xi^3)w_j' + L(-\xi^2 + \xi^3)\psi_j'$$

Thus,

$$[\mathbf{N}']^T = \begin{bmatrix} (1 - \xi) & 0 \\ 0 & (1 - 3\xi^2 + 2\xi^3) \\ 0 & L(\xi - 2\xi^2 + \xi^3) \\ \xi & 0 \\ 0 & (3\xi^2 - 2\xi^3) \\ 0 & L(-\xi^2 + \xi^3) \end{bmatrix} \tag{14-102}$$

We may relate the displacements u' and w' at any point of the element to the global displacements u_i, w_i, ψ_i, at node i, and u_j, w_j, ψ_j, at node j as shown in Fig. 14-44(a), by first relating the nodal global displacements to the nodal local displacements through the transformation matrix; i.e.,

$$\begin{Bmatrix} \mathbf{\Delta}'_i \\ \hline \mathbf{\Delta}'_j \end{Bmatrix} = \begin{bmatrix} [\mathbf{T}] & \vdots & [\mathbf{0}] \\ \hline [\mathbf{0}] & \vdots & [\mathbf{T}] \end{bmatrix} \begin{Bmatrix} \mathbf{\Delta}_i \\ \hline \mathbf{\Delta}_j \end{Bmatrix} \tag{14-103}$$

where

$$[\mathbf{T}] = \begin{bmatrix} \cos \phi & \sin \phi & 0 \\ -\sin \phi & \cos \phi & 0 \\ 0 & 0 & 1 \end{bmatrix} \tag{14-104a}$$

and

$$\{\mathbf{\Delta}_i\} = \begin{Bmatrix} u_i \\ w_i \\ \psi_i \end{Bmatrix} \qquad \text{and} \quad \{\mathbf{\Delta}_j\} = \begin{Bmatrix} u_j \\ w_j \\ \psi_j \end{Bmatrix} \tag{14-104b}$$

Then Eqs. (14-98) and (14-103) lead to

$$\{\mathbf{\Phi}\} \equiv \begin{Bmatrix} u' \\ w' \end{Bmatrix} = [\mathbf{N}'] \begin{bmatrix} [\mathbf{T}] & \vdots & [\mathbf{0}] \\ \hline [\mathbf{0}] & \vdots & [\mathbf{T}] \end{bmatrix} \begin{Bmatrix} \mathbf{\Delta}_i \\ \hline \mathbf{\Delta}_j \end{Bmatrix} \tag{14-105}$$

or

$$\begin{Bmatrix} u' \\ w' \end{Bmatrix} = [\mathbf{N}] \begin{Bmatrix} \mathbf{\Delta}_i \\ \mathbf{\Delta}_j \end{Bmatrix} \tag{14-106}$$

in which

$$[\mathbf{N}]^T = \begin{bmatrix} (1 - \xi) \cos \phi & -(1 - 3\xi^2 + 2\xi^3) \sin \phi \\ (1 - \xi) \sin \phi & (1 - 3\xi^2 + 2\xi^3) \cos \phi \\ 0 & L(\xi - 2\xi^2 + \xi^3) \\ \xi \cos \phi & -(3\xi^2 - 2\xi^3) \sin \phi \\ \xi \sin \phi & (3\xi^2 - 2\xi^3) \cos \phi \\ 0 & L(-\xi^2 + \xi^3) \end{bmatrix} \tag{14-107}$$

Element stiffness matrix. The element stiffness matrix relates the nodal displacements to the corresponding generalized forces shown in Fig. 14-44(b). This matrix may be determined by employing Eq. (14-29a):

$$[\mathbf{k}] = \int_{V_e} [\mathbf{b}]^T [\mathbf{D}][\mathbf{b}] dV_e \qquad (14\text{-}29\text{a})$$

As noted previously, $[\mathbf{b}]$ relates the strain and displacement vectors, while $[\mathbf{D}]$ is the elasticity matrix relating stress and strain vectors; the integration extends over V_e, the volume of the element.

Due to axial symmetry of both geometry and loading, the reference surface will undergo only normal strains. Further, if we assume that the normal strain and transverse shear strains across the thickness of the shell are negligible, then the only nonzero strains are ϵ_s and ϵ_θ, the normal strains in the meridianal (s) and circumferential (θ) directions, respectively. These strains may, to a good approximation, be assumed to vary linearly over the thickness. (We employed this assumption previously in treating beams and plates.) Each strain component may be considered to include a constant term, representing the deformation of the middle surface, plus a term that is proportional to z, the outwardly directed normal distance from the middle surface, and to the changes in curvature. (Note that while we ignored the stretching of the middle surface of the plate in Section 14-6, we account for it here.) Hence we may write

$$\epsilon_s = \epsilon_{s0} - z\chi_s \qquad (14\text{-}108)$$

and

$$\epsilon_\theta = \epsilon_{\theta 0} - z\chi_\theta$$

in which ϵ_{s0} and $\epsilon_{\theta 0}$ are the normal "membrane" strains, i.e., the normal strains of the middle surface, and χ_s and χ_θ are the corresponding curvatures. For a conical shell element ($\phi = $ constant), it may be shown that

$$\begin{aligned}
\epsilon_{s0} &= du'/ds \\
\epsilon_{\theta 0} &= (w' \cos \phi + u' \sin \phi)/r \\
\chi_s &= d^2 w'/ds^2 \\
\chi_\theta &= (dw'/ds)(\sin \phi)/r
\end{aligned} \qquad (14\text{-}109)$$

where r is the radial distance between the axis of symmetry and the middle surface.

We may employ Eqs. (14-106) and (14-107) to express the strains in Eqs. (14-108) and (14-109) in terms of nodal displacements. Hence,

$$\{\boldsymbol{\epsilon}\} \equiv \begin{Bmatrix} \epsilon_s \\ \epsilon_\theta \end{Bmatrix} = [[\mathbf{b}_i], [\mathbf{b}_j]] \begin{Bmatrix} \boldsymbol{\Delta}_i \\ \boldsymbol{\Delta}_j \end{Bmatrix} \qquad (14\text{-}110)$$

where, for example,

$$\epsilon_s$$

$$[\mathbf{b}_i]^T = \begin{bmatrix} (1/L)[-\cos \phi - 6(z/L)(1 - 2\xi) \sin \phi] \\ (1/L)[-\sin \phi + 6(z/L)(1 - 2\xi) \cos \phi] \\ 2(z/L)(1 - 3\xi) \end{bmatrix}$$

$$\overset{\epsilon_\theta}{\left[\begin{array}{l} (\sin\,\phi)(1/r)[-(1-3\xi^2+2\xi^3)\cos\,\phi + (1-\xi)\cos\,\phi - (z/L)6\xi(1-\xi)\sin\,\phi] \\ (1/r)[(1-3\xi^2+2\xi^3)\cos^2\,\phi + (1-\xi)\sin^2\,\phi + (z/L)6\xi(1-\xi)\sin\,\phi\cos\,\phi] \\ (1/r)[L\xi(1-2\xi+\xi^2)\cos\,\phi - z(1-4\xi+3\xi^2)\sin\,\phi] \end{array}\right]}\begin{array}{l}u_i \\ w_i \\ \psi_i\end{array}$$

$$(14\text{-}111)$$

The form of $[\mathbf{b}_j]$ is similar, but not identical, to that of $[\mathbf{b}_i]$.

The elasticity matrix $[\mathbf{D}]$ relates the stress and strain vectors; i.e.,

$$\{\boldsymbol{\sigma}\} = [\mathbf{D}]\{\boldsymbol{\epsilon}\} \qquad (14\text{-}112)$$

in which

$$\{\boldsymbol{\sigma}\} = \begin{Bmatrix} \sigma_s \\ \sigma_\theta \end{Bmatrix} \qquad \{\boldsymbol{\epsilon}\} = \begin{Bmatrix} \epsilon_s \\ \epsilon_\theta \end{Bmatrix} \qquad (14\text{-}113\text{a})$$

and hence,

$$[\mathbf{D}] = \frac{E}{1-\nu^2}\begin{bmatrix} 1 & \nu \\ \nu & 1 \end{bmatrix} \qquad (13\text{-}113\text{b})$$

We now may perform the integration indicated by Eq. (14-29a) over the volume of the element by recognizing that the differential volume may be expressed as

$$dV_e = (2\pi r)\,ds\,dz = (2\pi r L)\,d\xi\,dz \qquad (14\text{-}114)$$

Because $[\mathbf{b}]$ is a function of both ξ and z, and r is a function of ξ, we may write

$$[\mathbf{k}] = 2\pi L \int_0^1 \int_{-h/2}^{h/2} [\mathbf{b}]^T[\mathbf{D}][\mathbf{b}]r\,dz\,d\xi \qquad (14\text{-}115)$$

where h represents the thickness of the shell. Closed form expressions for the stiffness coefficients for orthotropic conical shell elements have been provided by Grafton and Strome.* They represent the relationship between the displacements and the total forces and moments (i.e., the integration over the nodal circumference of the relevant forces and moments per unit length), i.e.,

$$\begin{Bmatrix} F_{xi} \\ F_{ri} \\ M_{\psi i} \\ F_{xj} \\ F_{rj} \\ M_{\psi j} \end{Bmatrix} = [\mathbf{k}]\begin{Bmatrix} u_i \\ w_i \\ \psi_i \\ u_j \\ w_j \\ \psi_j \end{Bmatrix} \qquad (14\text{-}116)$$

Expressions for the element stiffness coefficients are presented in Table 14-1.

*Grafton, P.E. and D.R. Strome, "Analysis of Axi-symmetric Shells by the Direct Stiffness Method," *AIAA Journal*, Vol. 1, No. 10 (October, 1963), pp. 2342–2347.

Table 14-1 STIFFNESS COEFFICIENTS FOR CONICAL SHELL ELEMENT

$k_{11} = -k_{14} = -k_{41} = k_{44} = [C\cos^2\phi + (36/L^2)D\sin^2\phi]$

$k_{12} = k_{21} = -k_{24} = -k_{42} = (\cos\phi)[C\sin\phi - C\nu(L/2\bar{r}) - (36/L^2)D\sin\phi]$

$k_{13} = k_{31} = -k_{34} = -k_{43} = (-6D\sin\phi)[(2/L) + (r_i/\bar{r}L) - \nu(1/2\bar{r})\sin\phi]$

$k_{15} = k_{51} = -k_{45} = -k_{54} = (-\cos\phi)[C\sin\phi + C\nu(L/2\bar{r}) - (36/L^2)D\sin\phi]$

$k_{16} = k_{61} = -k_{46} = -k_{64} = (-6D\sin\phi)[(2/L) + (r_j/\bar{r}L) + \nu(1/2\bar{r})\sin\phi]$

$k_{22} = [C\sin^2\phi - C\nu(L/\bar{r})\sin\phi + C(L^2/2r_i\bar{r}) + (36/L^2)D\cos^2\phi]$

$k_{23} = k_{32} = -k_{35} = -k_{53} = (6D\cos\phi)[(2/L) + (r_i/\bar{r}L) - \nu(1/2\bar{r})\sin\phi]$

$k_{25} = k_{52} = -[C\sin^2\phi + D(36/L^2)\cos^2\phi]$

$k_{26} = k_{62} = -k_{56} = -k_{65} = (6D\cos\phi)[(2/L) + (r_j/\bar{r}L) + \nu(1/2\bar{r})\sin\phi]$

$k_{33} = (2D)[2 + 3(r_i/\bar{r}) - 2\nu(L/\bar{r})\sin\phi + (L^2/4r_i\bar{r})\sin^2\phi]$

$k_{36} = k_{63} = 8D$

$k_{55} = [C\sin^2\phi + C\nu(L/\bar{r})\sin\phi + C(L^2/2r_j\bar{r}) + (36/L^2)D\cos^2\phi]$

$k_{66} = (2D)[2 + 3(r_j/\bar{r}) + 2\nu(L/\bar{r})\sin\phi + (L^2/4r_j\bar{r})\sin^2\phi]$

where $C = \dfrac{Eh}{1-\nu^2}$　　$D = \dfrac{Eh^3}{12(1-\nu^2)}$　　$\bar{r} = \dfrac{1}{2}(r_i + r_j)$

Note: Each stiffness term must be multiplied by the factor $2\pi\bar{r}/L$.

Special forms for [k]. The case when $\phi = 0$ corresponds to a circular cylinder; the element stiffness matrix may be specialized to the following form:

$$[\mathbf{k}] = (2\pi\bar{r}/L)C \begin{bmatrix} 1 & & & & & \\ -\dfrac{\nu L}{2\bar{r}} & \left(\dfrac{L^2}{2\bar{r}^2} + \dfrac{3h^2}{L^2}\right) & & & \text{symmetric} & \\ 0 & \dfrac{3h^2}{2L} & \dfrac{5h^2}{6} & & & \\ -1 & \dfrac{\nu L}{2\bar{r}} & 0 & 1 & & \\ -\dfrac{\nu L}{2\bar{r}} & -\dfrac{3h^2}{L^2} & -\dfrac{3h^2}{2L} & \dfrac{\nu L}{2\bar{r}} & \left(\dfrac{L^2}{2\bar{r}^2} + \dfrac{3h^2}{L^2}\right) & \\ 0 & \dfrac{3h^2}{2L} & \dfrac{2h^2}{3} & 0 & -\dfrac{3h^2}{2L} & \dfrac{5h^2}{6} \end{bmatrix} \begin{matrix} F_{xi} \\ F_{ri} \\ M_{\psi i} \\ F_{xj} \\ F_{rj} \\ M_{\psi j} \end{matrix}$$

with column labels $u_i \quad w_i \quad \psi_i \quad u_j \quad w_j \quad \psi_j$

$$(14\text{-}117a)$$

This matrix may be simplified further by replacing the rotations and moments ψ_i, ψ_j, $M_{\psi i}$, and $M_{\psi j}$ by $\psi_i L$, $\psi_j L$, $M_{\psi i}/L$, and $M_{\psi j}/L$. Then all displacements have units of length and all stress resultants have units of force, resulting in a homogeneous element stiffness matrix, i.e., all coefficients possess the same units. If we define the parameters $\alpha \equiv L/\bar{r}$ and $\beta \equiv h/\bar{r}$, the element stiffness may be expressed in terms of dimensionless coefficients as follows:

$$
[\mathbf{k}] = C\frac{2\pi}{\alpha}
\begin{array}{cccccc}
u_i & w_i & \psi_i L & u_j & w_j & \psi_j L
\end{array}
$$

$$
[\mathbf{k}] = C\frac{2\pi}{\alpha}
\begin{bmatrix}
1 & & & & & \\
-\dfrac{\nu\alpha}{2} & \left(\dfrac{\alpha^2}{2}+3\dfrac{\beta^2}{\alpha^2}\right) & & \text{symmetric} & & \\
0 & \dfrac{3\beta^2}{2\alpha^2} & \dfrac{5\beta^2}{6\alpha^2} & & & \\
-1 & \dfrac{\nu\alpha}{2} & 0 & 1 & & \\
-\dfrac{\nu\alpha}{2} & -\dfrac{3\beta^2}{\alpha^2} & -\dfrac{3\beta^2}{2\alpha^2} & \dfrac{\nu\alpha}{2} & \left(\dfrac{\alpha^2}{2}+3\dfrac{\beta^2}{\alpha^2}\right) & \\
0 & \dfrac{3\beta^2}{2\alpha^2} & \dfrac{2\beta^2}{3\alpha^2} & 0 & -\dfrac{3\beta^2}{2\alpha^2} & \dfrac{5\beta^2}{6\alpha^2}
\end{bmatrix}
\begin{array}{l}
F_{xi} \\ F_{ri} \\ M_{\psi i}/L \\ F_{xj} \\ F_{rj} \\ M_{\psi j}/L
\end{array}
$$

$$(14\text{-}117\text{b})$$

The form of $[\mathbf{k}]$ given in Eq. (14-117b) is particularly convenient to use when a cylindrical shell is being represented by a set of identical elements.

In the case of $\phi = \pi/2$, the conical shell element flattens to a circular ring that may be employed to analyze circular plates. In such a case, the in-plane displacements and forces (i.e., the membrane quantities) become uncoupled from transverse displacements, forces and moments. The element stiffness matrix then may be separated into a 2×2 membrane stiffness matrix $[\mathbf{k}_m]$ and a 4×4 bending stiffness matrix $[\mathbf{k}_b]$. Note that in placing the displacements above the columns of these matrices, we have interchanged u_i and w_i (and u_j and w_j); in keeping with traditional notation, u corresponds to in-plane deformation (in the r-direction) and w corresponds to transverse displacement (now considered to be the z-direction). The matrices are then as shown by Eqs. (14-118) on p. 703. The coefficients in $[\mathbf{k}_m]$ are homogeneous, and those in $[\mathbf{k}_b]$ can be easily made so by replacing ψ_i, ψ_j, $M_{\psi j}$, by $\psi_i L$, $\psi_j L$, M_{ψ_i}/L, $M_{\psi j}/L$. Note that the second diagonal coefficient k_{22} contains a term having r_i in the denominator. Thus k_{22} becomes infinite when r_1 equals zero; however, to preserve symmetry of deformation ψ_i must equal zero when $r_i = 0$, and thus the second row and column will be deleted when this constraint condition is enforced.

Equivalent generalized nodal forces. We could employ a formal procedure to determine generalized nodal forces (including moments) that are equivalent to distributed loading. As we have noted previously, however, in most instances the elements are sufficiently numerous to replace distributed loads by concentrated ring loads associated with the lengths of elements adjacent to the rings, while ignoring an external ring moment. Thus, referring to a two-element portion of a shell subjected to internal pressures, as shown in Fig. 14-45, we evaluate the equivalent loads acting on the ring node common to the two elements to be

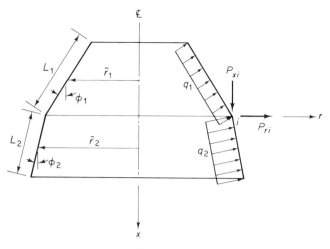

Figure 14-45

$$P_{xi}^E = -(2\pi\bar{r}_1)\frac{1}{2}q_1L_1 \sin \phi_1 - (2\pi\bar{r}_2)\frac{1}{2}q_2L_2 \sin \phi_2 \qquad (14\text{-}119a)$$

$$P_{ri}^E = (2\pi\bar{r}_1)\frac{1}{2}q_1L_1 \cos \phi_1 + (2\pi\bar{r}_2)\frac{1}{2}q_2L_2 \cos \phi_2 \qquad (14\text{-}119b)$$

Because the lengths of the elements usually are small compared with the total length of the shell, equivalent external moments usually are ignored.

Internal stress resultants. After the displacements have been determined, the internal forces acting along the rings defined by nodes i and j may be determined by premultiplying the displacement vector by the element stiffness matrix, i.e., by employing Eq. (14-116)

$$\begin{Bmatrix} F_{xi} \\ F_{ri} \\ M_{\psi i} \\ F_{xj} \\ F_{ri} \\ M_{\psi j} \end{Bmatrix} = [\mathbf{k}] \begin{Bmatrix} u_i \\ w_i \\ \psi_i \\ u_j \\ w_j \\ \psi_j \end{Bmatrix} \qquad (14\text{-}116)$$

Circumferential stress resultants, i.e., internal forces and moments acting along a meridian may be determined from the constitutive relationships, Eqs. (14-112) and (14-113), once the strains have been evaluated by Eq. (14-109). The final relationship, which has been presented elsewhere,* may be written as shown by Eq. (14-120) on p. 703, in which $C_1 = \nu C/L$ and $C_2 = 6\nu D/L^2$.

*Ibid., p. 2345.

$$[\mathbf{k}_m] = (2\pi\bar{r}/L)C \begin{array}{cc} u_i & u_j \end{array}$$

$$[\mathbf{k}_m] = (2\pi\bar{r}/L)C \left[\begin{array}{cc} \left(1 - \dfrac{\nu L}{\bar{r}} + \dfrac{L^2}{2r_i\bar{r}}\right) & -1 \\[2mm] -1 & \left(1 + \dfrac{\nu L}{\bar{r}} + \dfrac{L^2}{2r_j\bar{r}}\right) \end{array} \right] \begin{array}{c} F_{ri} \\ F_{rj} \end{array}$$

(14-118a)

$$[\mathbf{k}_b] = (2\pi\bar{r}/L)D$$

with column labels w_i, ψ_i, w_j, ψ_j and row labels F_{zi}, $M_{\psi i}$, F_{zj}, $M_{\psi j}$:

$$[\mathbf{k}_b] = (2\pi\bar{r}/L)D \left[\begin{array}{cccc} \dfrac{36}{L^2} & & & \\[3mm] -6\left(\dfrac{2}{L}+\dfrac{r_i}{\bar{r}L}-\dfrac{\nu}{2\bar{r}}\right) & 2\left(2+3\dfrac{r_i}{\bar{r}}-\dfrac{2\nu L}{\bar{r}}+\dfrac{L^2}{4r_i\bar{r}}\right) & & \\[3mm] -\dfrac{36}{L^2} & 6\left(\dfrac{2}{L}+\dfrac{r_i}{\bar{r}L}-\dfrac{\nu}{2\bar{r}}\right) & \dfrac{36}{L^2} & \\[3mm] -6\left(\dfrac{2}{L}+\dfrac{r_j}{\bar{r}L}+\dfrac{\nu}{2\bar{r}}\right) & 8 & 6\left(\dfrac{2}{L}+\dfrac{r_j}{\bar{r}L}+\dfrac{\nu}{2\bar{r}}\right) & 2\left(2+3\dfrac{r_j}{\bar{r}}+\dfrac{2\nu L}{\bar{r}}+\dfrac{L^2}{4r_j\bar{r}}\right) \end{array} \right]$$

symmetric

(14-118b)

$$\begin{Bmatrix} N_{\theta i} \\ M_{\theta i} \\ N_{\theta j} \\ M_{\theta j} \end{Bmatrix} = \begin{bmatrix} -C_1\cos\phi & C\left(\dfrac{1}{r_i}-\dfrac{\nu}{L}\sin\phi\right) & 0 & C_1\cos\phi & C_1\sin\phi & 0 \\[3mm] C_2\sin\phi & -C_2\cos\phi & D\left(-\dfrac{4\nu}{L}+\dfrac{1}{r_i}\sin\phi\right) & -C_2\sin\phi & C_2\cos\phi & -C_2\dfrac{L}{6} \\[3mm] -C_1\cos\phi & -C_1\sin\phi & 0 & C_1\cos\phi & C\left(\dfrac{1}{r_j}+\dfrac{\nu}{L}\sin\phi\right) & 0 \\[3mm] -C_2\sin\phi & C_2\cos\phi & C_2\dfrac{L}{3} & C_2\sin\phi & -C_2\cos\phi & D\left(\dfrac{4\nu}{L}+\dfrac{1}{r_j}\sin\phi\right) \end{bmatrix} \begin{Bmatrix} u_i \\ w_i \\ \psi_i \\ u_j \\ w_j \\ \psi_j \end{Bmatrix}$$

(14-120)

It should be noted that these stress resultants are per unit length along the meridian. The following examples illustrate the use of these relationships.

Example 14-14. A circular cylinder, having radius a, length $L_0 = 2a$, and thickness $h = 0.1a$, is clamped at each end and subjected to a uniform internal pressure, as shown in Fig. 14-46. Determine the radial displacements and the internal forces and bending moments, using four identical cylindrical shell elements to represent the structure.

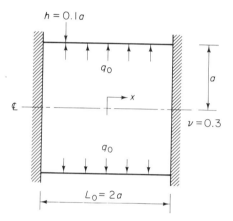

Figure 14-46

We begin by recognizing that only one-half the shell need be analyzed due to symmetry of geometry and loading about midspan, as shown in Fig. 14-47(a). (Symmetry about the longitudinal axis of the shell is required, of course, from the outset.) We may form the element stiffness matrix for each element most conveniently by using Eq. (14-117b). We set $\alpha \equiv L/\bar{r} = 0.5$, $\beta \equiv h/\bar{r} = 0.1$ and $\nu = 0.3$. Hence, for element 1, the stiffness matrix is

$$
[\mathbf{k}^{(1)}] = 4\pi C
\begin{matrix}
& u_1 & w_1 & \psi_1 L & u_2 & w_2 & \psi_2 L & \\
\begin{bmatrix}
1 & & & & & \\
-0.075 & 0.245 & & \text{symmetric} & & \\
0 & 0.06 & 0.0333 & & & \\
-1 & 0.075 & 0 & 1 & & \\
-0.075 & -0.12 & -0.06 & 0.075 & 0.245 & \\
0 & 0.06 & 0.0267 & 0 & -0.06 & 0.0333
\end{bmatrix}
&
\begin{matrix}
F_{x1} \\
F_{r1} \\
M_{\psi 1}/L \\
F_{x2} \\
F_{r2} \\
M_{\psi 2}/L
\end{matrix}
\end{matrix}
$$

The stiffness matrix $[\mathbf{k}^{(2)}]$ for element 2 is identical to $[\mathbf{k}^{(1)}]$.

The 9×9 system stiffness matrix may be formed in the usual way by combining $[\mathbf{k}^{(1)}]$ and $[\mathbf{k}^{(2)}]$. Before doing this, it is convenient to account for the

Introduction to the Finite Element Method   Chap. 14

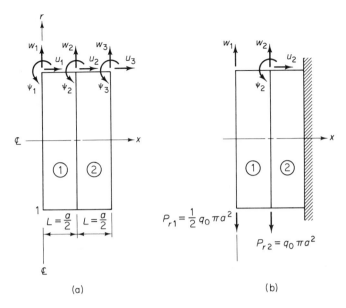

Figure 14-47

displacement constraints imposed by symmetry and by the boundary conditions. Due to symmetry we observe that

$$u_1 = \psi_1 L = 0$$

Further, the boundary conditions dictate that

$$u_3 = w_3 = \psi_3 L = 0$$

Hence, only four active degrees of freedom remain, as shown in Fig. 14-47(b). The displacement and load vectors are therefore

$$\{\Delta_f\} = \begin{Bmatrix} w_1 \\ u_2 \\ w_2 \\ \psi_2 L \end{Bmatrix} \qquad \text{and} \qquad \{\mathbf{P}_f\} = \begin{Bmatrix} P_{r1}^E \\ P_{x2}^E \\ P_{r2}^E \\ P_{m\psi2}^E/L \end{Bmatrix}$$

and the corresponding reduced system stiffness matrix, of dimension 4×4, is

$$[\mathbf{K}_{ff}] = 4\pi C \begin{matrix} & \begin{matrix} w_1 & u_2 & w_2 & \psi_2 L \end{matrix} \\ \begin{bmatrix} 0.245 & 0.075 & -0.12 & 0.06 \\ 0.075 & 2 & 0 & 0 \\ -0.12 & 0 & 0.490 & 0 \\ 0.06 & 0 & 0 & 0.0667 \end{bmatrix} & \begin{matrix} P_{r1}^E \\ P_{x2}^E \\ P_{r2}^E \\ P_{m\psi2}^E/L \end{matrix} \end{matrix}$$

and its inverse is

$$[\mathbf{K}_{ff}]^{-1} = \frac{1}{C} \begin{bmatrix} 0.5011 & -0.0188 & 0.1227 & -0.4510 \\ -0.0188 & 0.0405 & -0.0046 & 0.0169 \\ 0.1227 & -0.0046 & 0.1926 & -0.1104 \\ -0.4510 & 0.0169 & -0.1104 & 1.599 \end{bmatrix}$$

The equivalent load vector is developed using Eqs. (14-119). Because $\phi = 0$, the equivalent nodal force in the axial direction is zero. The equivalent radial loads are

$$P_{r1}^E = (2\pi a) \cdot \frac{1}{2} q_0 L = \frac{1}{2} q_0 \pi a^2$$

$$P_{r2}^E = (2\pi a) \cdot q_0 L = q_0 \pi a^2$$

Hence, as shown in Fig. 14-47(b),

$$\{\mathbf{P}_f^E\} = \frac{1}{2} q_0 \pi a^2 \begin{Bmatrix} 1 \\ 0 \\ 2 \\ 0 \end{Bmatrix}$$

The displacements are obtained from

$$\{\mathbf{\Delta}_f\} = [\mathbf{K}_{ff}]^{-1}\{\mathbf{P}_f^E\}$$

or

$$\begin{Bmatrix} w_1 \\ u_2 \\ w_2 \\ \psi_2 L \end{Bmatrix} = \frac{q_0 \pi a^2}{C} \begin{Bmatrix} 0.373 \\ -0.014 \\ 0.254 \\ -0.336 \end{Bmatrix} = \frac{q_0 a^2}{Eh} \begin{Bmatrix} 1.066 \\ -0.040 \\ 0.726 \\ -0.961 \end{Bmatrix}$$

The internal forces and moments acting on the nodal rings may be computed using Eq. (14-116). Hence, for element 1,

$$\begin{Bmatrix} F_{x1} \\ F_{r1} \\ M_{\psi1}/L \\ F_{x2} \\ F_{r2} \\ M_{\psi2}/L \end{Bmatrix}^{(1)} = 4\pi C \begin{bmatrix} 1 & & & & \text{symmetric} & \\ -0.075 & 0.245 & & & & \\ 0 & 0.06 & 0.0333 & & & \\ -1 & 0.075 & 0 & 1 & & \\ -0.075 & -0.12 & -0.06 & 0.075 & 0.245 & \\ 0 & 0.06 & 0.0267 & 0 & -0.06 & 0.0333 \end{bmatrix} \begin{Bmatrix} 0 \\ 0.373 \\ 0 \\ -0.014 \\ 0.254 \\ -0.336 \end{Bmatrix} \frac{q_0 \pi a^2}{C}$$

Thus,

$$\begin{Bmatrix} F_{x1} \\ F_{r1} \\ M_{\psi1}/L \\ F_{x2} \\ F_{r2} \\ M_{\psi2}/L \end{Bmatrix}^{(1)} = q_0 a^2 \begin{Bmatrix} -1.30 \\ 1.61 \\ -0.0726 \\ 1.30 \\ 1.44 \\ -0.160 \end{Bmatrix} \quad \text{or} \quad \begin{Bmatrix} F_{x1} \\ F_{r1} \\ M_{\psi1} \\ F_{x2} \\ F_{r2} \\ M_{\psi2} \end{Bmatrix}^{(1)} = q_0 a^2 \begin{Bmatrix} -1.30 \\ 1.61 \\ -0.0363a \\ 1.30 \\ 1.44 \\ -0.080a \end{Bmatrix}$$

Similarly, for element 2,

$$\begin{Bmatrix} F_{x2} \\ F_{r2} \\ M_{\psi2} \\ F_{x3} \\ F_{r3} \\ M_{\psi3} \end{Bmatrix}^{(2)} = q_0 a^2 \begin{Bmatrix} -1.30 \\ 1.70 \\ 0.080a \\ 1.30 \\ -0.365 \\ 0.124a \end{Bmatrix}$$

The circumferential forces and moments may be evaluated from Eq. (14-120). Noting that $\sin \phi = 1$, we may express these quantities for element 1 as

$$\begin{Bmatrix} N_{\theta1} \\ M_{\theta1} \\ N_{\theta2} \\ M_{\theta2} \end{Bmatrix}^{(1)} = \begin{bmatrix} -C_1 & C/a & 0 & C_1 & 0 & 0 \\ 0 & -C_2 & -4\nu D/L & 0 & C_2 & -C_2 L/6 \\ -C_1 & 0 & 0 & C_1 & C/a & 0 \\ 0 & C_2 & C_2 L/3 & 0 & -C_2 & 4\nu D/L \end{bmatrix} \begin{Bmatrix} 0 \\ 0.373 \\ 0 \\ -0.014 \\ 0.254 \\ -0.336/a \end{Bmatrix} \frac{q_0 \pi a^2}{C}$$

where again $C_1 = \nu C/L$ and $C_2 = 6\nu D/L^2$. Using $\nu = 0.3$, $L = a/2$ and $\nu = 0.3$, we obtain for element 1, and similarly for element 2,

$$\begin{Bmatrix} N_{\theta1} \\ M_{\theta1} \\ N_{\theta2} \\ M_{\theta2} \end{Bmatrix}^{(1)} = q_0 a \begin{Bmatrix} 1.145 \\ 0.00277a \\ 0.772 \\ 0.00013a \end{Bmatrix} \quad \text{and} \quad \begin{Bmatrix} N_{\theta2} \\ M_{\theta2} \\ N_{\theta3} \\ M_{\theta3} \end{Bmatrix}^{(2)} = q_0 a \begin{Bmatrix} 0.823 \\ 0.00057a \\ 0.0264 \\ 0.00373a \end{Bmatrix}$$

These are the stress resultants per unit length acting along a meridian of the shell.

A comparison between an exact analytical solution and the finite element solution is shown in Fig. 14-48, where the dimensionless radial displacements and longitudinal moment per unit length around the circumference (i.e., $M_{\psi i}/2\pi a$) are

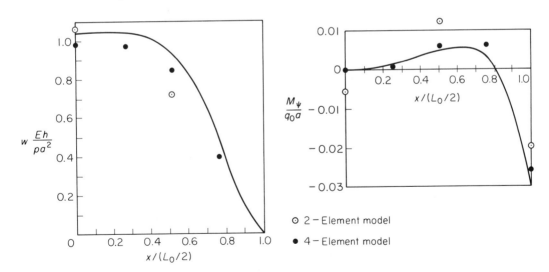

○ 2 – Element model

● 4 – Element model

Figure 14-48

plotted versus distance from midspan $(2x/L_0)$. The finite element method predicts a displacement at node 1 that is 1.7 percent too high, but at node 2 the computed displacement is 22.7 percent too low. As regards longitudinal bending moment, the error associated with nodes 2 and 3 are approximately 143 percent and -35 percent, respectively. Also shown in Fig. 14-48 are the results for a model comprising four elements of equal length. Overall, the accuracy is greatly improved; the error in displacements is within 20 percent throughout the shell, while the error related to maximum moment is approximately 16 percent. Clearly, the rapid change in bending moment near the support implies that more elements should be placed in this region to attain adequate results. Rapid change in bending moment near supports is typical of thin shell behavior.

Example 14-15. A circular plate having radius a and bending stiffness D (with $\nu = 0.3$) is simply supported and subjected to a uniform transverse load, as shown in Fig. 14-49. Determine the transverse displacements and bending moments, using two ring elements of equal width to represent the structure.

$\nu = 0.3$

a

$q = -q_0$

Simple support   **Figure 14-49**

The ring elements shown in Fig. 14-50 are formed from cylindrical shell elements by setting $\phi = \pi/2$. As only transverse forces are applied, we are interested in forming $[\mathbf{k}_b]$, the element stiffness matrices associated with bending of the plate. Thus, we employ Eq. (14-118b) with the following information:

Element	r_i	r_j	$\bar{r}$	L
1	0	$0.5a$	$0.25a$	$0.5a$
2	$0.5a$	a	$0.75a$	$0.5a$

The element stiffness matrices then may be written as

$$[\mathbf{k}_b^{(1)}] = \frac{\pi D}{a^2} \begin{bmatrix} 144 & & \text{symmetric} & \\ -20.4a & \infty & & \\ -144 & 20.4a & 144 & \\ -51.6a & 8a^2 & 51.6a & 19.4a^2 \end{bmatrix} \begin{matrix} F_{z1} \\ M_{\psi 1} \\ F_{z2} \\ M_{\psi 2} \end{matrix}$$

$$\begin{matrix} w_1 & \psi_1 & w_2 & \psi_2 \end{matrix}$$

$$[\mathbf{k}_b^{(2)}] = \frac{3\pi D}{a^2} \begin{bmatrix} 144 & & \text{symmetric} & \\ -30.8a & 8.133a^2 & & \\ -144 & 30.8a & 144 & \\ -41.2a & 8a^2 & 41.2a & 12.967a^2 \end{bmatrix} \begin{matrix} F_{z2} \\ M_{\psi 2} \\ F_{z3} \\ M_{\psi 3} \end{matrix}$$

$$\begin{matrix} w_2 & \psi_2 & w_3 & \psi_3 \end{matrix}$$

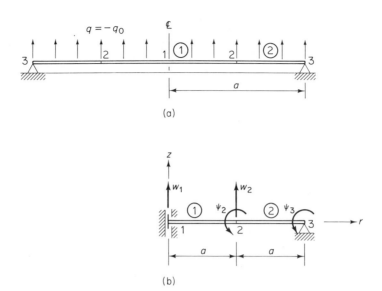

Figure 14-50

The transverse nodal displacements w_1, w_2, and w_3 and the nodal rotations ψ_1, ψ_2, and ψ_3 are designated above the appropriate columns of the matrices; the corresponding transverse forces F_{z1}, F_{z2}, and F_{z3} and bending moments $M_{\psi1}$, $M_{\psi2}$, and $M_{\psi3}$ are listed next to the rows. Note that the second diagonal term in $[\mathbf{k}_b^{(1)}]$ is infinity owing to r_i being zero for element 1. No complications arise as a result, however, because the imposed symmetry of geometry and loading requires that ψ_1 equal zero, as indicated in Fig. 14-50(b). Therefore, the row and column corresponding to ψ_2 do not appear in $[\mathbf{K}_{ff}]$; the row and column corresponding to w_3, which is zero, are also deleted.

Combining the element stiffness matrices and imposing the above-cited constraints, we obtain the reduced system stiffness matrix

$$
[\mathbf{K}_{ff}] = \frac{\pi D}{a^2}
\begin{array}{c@{}c}
\begin{array}{cccc} w_1 \quad & w_2 \quad & \psi_2 \quad & \psi_3 \end{array} & \\
\begin{bmatrix}
144 & & \text{symmetric} & \\
-144 & 576 & & \\
-51.6a & -40.8a & 43.8 & \\
0 & -123.6a & 24a^2 & 38.9a^2
\end{bmatrix}
&
\begin{array}{l} P_{z1}^E \\ P_{z2}^E \\ P_{m\psi2}^E \\ P_{m\psi3}^E \end{array}
\end{array}
$$

For convenience, $[\mathbf{K}_{ff}]$ may be made homogeneous by multiplying the rotations by a and dividing the moments by a. Then we obtain

$$
[\mathbf{K}_{ff}] = \frac{\pi D}{a^2}
\begin{array}{c@{}c}
\begin{array}{cccc} w_1 \quad & w_2 \quad & \psi_2 a \quad & \psi_3 a \end{array} & \\
\begin{bmatrix}
144 & & \text{symmetric} & \\
-144 & 576 & & \\
-51.6 & -40.8 & 43.8 & \\
0 & -123.6 & 24 & 38.9
\end{bmatrix}
&
\begin{array}{l} P_{z1}^E \\ P_{z2}^E \\ P_{m\psi2}^E/a \\ P_{m\psi3}^E/a \end{array}
\end{array}
$$

The inverse of this matrix is

$$[\mathbf{K}_{ff}]^{-1} = \frac{a^2}{\pi D} \begin{bmatrix} 0.185 & & \text{symmetric} & \\ 0.107 & 0.0691 & & \\ 0.199 & 0.106 & 0.259 & \\ 0.218 & 0.154 & 0.178 & 0.405 \end{bmatrix}$$

The equivalent generalized forces may be approximated by transverse ring loads at nodes 1 and 2, while we neglect equivalent moments applied at these nodes. This approximation is not very good when only a few elements are employed, as in the present case, but the accuracy is acceptable in most applications where many elements are used. Here, we assume that the load imposed on node 1 equals the product of the applied transverse pressure $-q_0$ and the area enclosed by $\bar{r}$ for element 1, as shown in Fig. 14-51(a). Similarly, the load imposed at node 2 equals the product of $-q_0$ and the area lying between $\bar{r}$ for element 1 and $\bar{r}$ for element 2. Hence, we compute

$$P_{z1}^E = -q_0 \pi (0.25a)^2 = -0.196 \, q_0 a^2$$

$$P_{z2}^E = -q_0 \pi [(0.75a)^2 - (0.25a)^2] = -1.571 \, q_0 a^2$$

while we assume $P_{m\psi 2}^E = P_{m\psi 3}^E = 0$. The generalized forces are shown in Fig. 14-51(b).

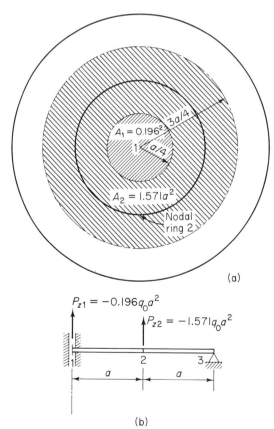

(a)

$P_{z1} = -0.196 q_0 a^2$

$P_{z2} = -1.571 q_0 a^2$

(b)

Figure 14-51

Introduction to the Finite Element Method   Chap. 14

The displacements are computed in the usual way, i.e.,

$$\{\mathbf{\Delta}_f\} = [\mathbf{K}_{ff}]^{-1}\{\mathbf{P}_f^E\}$$

where now

$$\{\mathbf{\Delta}_f\} \equiv \begin{Bmatrix} w_1 \\ w_2 \\ \psi_2 a \\ \psi_3 a \end{Bmatrix} \quad \text{and} \quad \{\mathbf{P}_f\} \equiv \begin{Bmatrix} P_{z1} \\ P_{z2} \\ P_{m\psi2} \\ P_{m\psi3} \end{Bmatrix} = -q_0 a^2 \begin{Bmatrix} 0.196 \\ 1.571 \\ 0 \\ 0 \end{Bmatrix}$$

We then find

$$\begin{Bmatrix} w_1 \\ w_2 \\ \psi_2 a \\ \psi_3 a \end{Bmatrix} = \frac{-q_0 a^4}{D} \begin{Bmatrix} 0.0652 \\ 0.0413 \\ 0.0656 \\ 0.0907 \end{Bmatrix}$$

which may be used with the element stiffness matrices to recover internal shear forces and bending moments at the nodes.

The displacements and bending moments (per unit length) for the two-element model and for a five-element are compared with the exact solution in Fig. 14-52. The two-element model overestimates the transverse displacement at the centerline by approximately 2 percent, while the five-element model provides

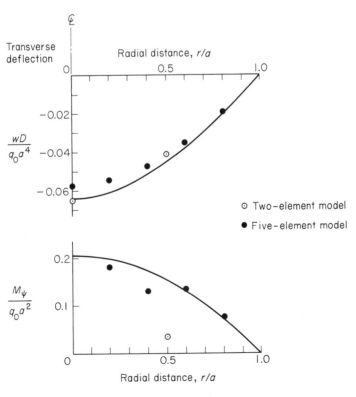

Figure 14-52

greater accuracy, of course. The bending moments M_ψ are less accurately estimated, as would be expected. Despite the ability of the two-element model to predict well the displacements, the accuracy associated with internal forces is poor. The bending moment at $r = a/2$, for example, is underestimated by a factor of four. For the five-element model, however, the maximum error for bending moment is less than 25 percent.

14-8 ADDITIONAL TOPICS

Although the preceding sections have presented the fundamental concepts of the finite element method and a sampling of applications to structural mechanics, the reader should realize that the treatment has been extremely selective. Enormously greater depth of refinement and breadth of application have been developed over the past two decades and have been reported extensively in the technical literature, including the references cited previously in this chapter. There are numerous ways in which these developments may be grouped or classified. For our purposes, perhaps the most useful way of summarizing additional topics is as follows:

• extensions of topics already discussed in previous sections
• types of structural mechanics problems that require the introduction of additional concepts
• refinements to improve accuracy
• applications beyond the realm of structural mechanics

In all our previous discussions we dealt with linearly elastic, isotropic material to treat two-dimensional (plane stress, plane strain or axisymmetric) problems. We could relax the assumption of isotropy most easily by introducing into the previous formulation a constitutive relationship that accounts for material anisotropy, while retaining the previously described displacement functions. This would lead, of course, to a different and usually more complicated stiffness matrix, but otherwise would incur no particular difficulties in the formulation; indeed, the inclusion of material anisotropy is rather standard in texts devoted to the finite element method. We also may treat nonlinear elastic problems (in which stiffness constants such as E and ν vary with strain) by solving the stiffness equations either iteratively or incrementally. With the iterative method, an estimate is made of the value of elastic constants under the prescribed loading, and displacements are computed; from the displacements are computed the strains, which then dictate the magnitude of the elastic constants. If the initial and final values of these constants are not in sufficiently close agreement, the analysis is repeated with updated constants; the iteration continues until convergence is achieved. With the incremental method, the loading is placed in small increments, and for each increment a linear analysis is performed using the elastic constants that conform to the cumulative strain incurred under the sum of previous load increments. Both methods require some computational refinements to work efficiently, but otherwise require no basic reformulation. Finally, the two-dimensional treatments may be extended. For example, axisymmetric solids and shells subjected to general asymmetric circumferential loading may be analyzed by representing both loading and displacements as harmonic functions of the angular location of a radial section. Although the formultion is more complicated and the computations are more lengthy, only a single (two-dimensional) section is analyzed and the same displacement functions described previously apply within the section. As a final example, shells of arbitrary shape may be envisioned as an assemblage of flat plate elements. Because the elements no longer lie in a single plane, element stiffness matrices must be transformed relative to a global set of axes before the system stiffness matrix may be assembled. The remainder of the analysis follows standard procedures.

Among those topics in structural mechanics that require more extensive development beyond that which we have covered previously is the treatment of problems involving yielding. These problems require a different constitutive law before and after yielding along with flow laws of plasticity. Also, the analysis of three-dimensional solids requires the formulation and introduction of three-dimensional elements, such as four-node tetrahedral elements and eight-node "brick" elements. Despite the existence of such elements for some time, the computation costs and demands on computer storage associated with three-dimensional analysis still are prohibitive for routine application. However, some special semi-analytical techniques, such as the finite strip method, help to reduce costs and storage requirements. Buckling problems also may be treated by the finite element method; these problems, however, require the deployment of the so-called geometric stiffness matrix which must be combined with the traditional elastic stiffness matrix to represent the change in geometry that is at the core of stability problems. The resulting formulation is either a nonlinear equilibrium problem for a physically imperfect system (like a crooked column subjected to an axial load) or a linear eigenvalue problem (which, for example, provides the buckling load for a perfectly straight column). Eigenvalue problems also include the free vibration of structural systems. In such cases a mass matrix, as well as a stiffness matrix, must be developed for each element and dynamical equations are solved for the system; from these emerge natural frequencies (eigenvalues) and corresponding mode shapes of free vibration. For problems involving steady-state periodic excitation, a damping matrix usually is required; this matrix is multiplied by the velocity vector and is included in the dynamical equations which are then solved for the forced response of the system. Transient problems often include stepwise integration in time; thus both the time domain and the spatial domain are discretized.

Research continues on the development of higher-order and refined elements for increasing accuracy and computational efficiency. Among existing refined elements are thick curved elements for treating thick shells, the linear-strain triangular element used in two-dimensional elasticity problems, conforming plate-bending elements, and isoparametric elements, to a name a few.

Basic theoretical issues, such as the casting of the finite element method into forms amenable to variational procedures, have been and still are important in establishing the theoretical foundations of the method. The development of general purpose, efficient, and user-friendly computer codes has continually paralleled the aforementioned topics of interest.

Finally, the finite element method has been applied to a broad spectrum of boundary-value and initial-value problems of applied mathematics far beyond the range of structural mechanics problems mentioned above. This spectrum includes, in part, field problems such as heat conduction, seepage, consolidation, fluid flow, and the distribution of electrical and magnetic potentials. Both steady-state and transient analysis have been developed and employed.

PROBLEMS

14-1. A tapered bar, having length L, area $A(x) = A_0 e^{-3x/L}$, and density ρ, is suspended from one end as shown in Figure P14-1. Find the deformation and stresses in the bar due to its self-weight by representing the member by four prismatic bar elements of equal length. Compare the finite element solution with the exact analytical solution.

Figure P14-1

14-2. Derive the element stiffness matrix for a prismatic beam element using Eq. (14-29a) along with the displacement function specified by Eq. (14-2).

14-3. The cantilever beam shown in Fig. P14-3 has a constant width w and linearly varying depth $d(x) = d_0(1 - x/L) + d_L x/L$. Compare the solutions for the displacement under the concentrated load applied at the free end using the following approaches.
  (a) a numerical version of the moment-area method,
  (b) a one-element representation using the stiffness matrix for a prismatic beam element along with an average depth for the element, and
  (c) a model comprising two prismatic finite elements.

Figure P14-3

14-4. Find the displacements and stresses in a deep cantilever beam of width t and subjected to a concentrated transverse load applied to the free end by modelling the beam as

(a) two elements, and

(b) four elements

as shown in Fig. P14-4. Assume $\nu = 0.25$. The solutions may be compared with the exact analytical solution provided by S. Timoshenko and J. N. Goodier, *Theory of Elasticity*, 2nd ed., pp. 35–39.

(a)

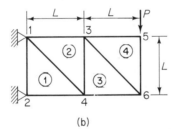

(b)   **Figure P14-4**

14-5. The thin plate described in Example 14-4 and shown in Fig. 14-15 is subjected to a uniform increase in temperature ΔT. Find the deformation and stress caused by the initial strain, $\epsilon_{x0} = \epsilon_{y0} = \bar{\alpha}\,\Delta T$, incurred by the elevated temperature, where $\bar{\alpha}$ is the coefficient of thermal expansion.

14-6. Consider a rectangular element, under conditions of plane stress, to incorporate displacement functions which have the bilinear form

$$u(x) = \alpha_1 + \alpha_2 x + \alpha_3 y + \alpha_4 xy$$

$$v(x) = \alpha_5 + \alpha_6 x + \alpha_7 y + \alpha_8 xy.$$

These functions are the counterparts of Eqs. (14-35) for a triangular element. Express the displacement functions in terms of nodal displacements $u_i, \ldots, u_n$ and coordinates $x_i, \ldots, y_n$, where the four nodes are designated as i, j, m, and n. Also show that such an element is compatible with adjacent elements of the same type.

14-7. Derive the matrix [**b**] for the rectangular element described in Problem 14-6.

14-8. Derive [$\mathbf{k}_{ii}$], the submatrix of [**k**] corresponding to node i of the rectangular element described in Problem 14-6, considering the material to be isotropic and linearly elastic.

14-9. The ring of Example 14-7 is heated enough to slip over a rigid cylinder having a radius equal to 50.5. Determine the deformations and stresses in the ring after it cools to the ambient temperature.

14-10. For a square plate having the same dimensions and elastic properties of that described in Example 14-10, use a one-element approximation to find the transverse displacement and bending moments at the center of the plate when two opposite edges are simply supported and the remaining two edges are clamped, and the transverse loading q_0 is uniformly distributed. (The exact analytical solution is $w = 0.03072\ q_0 a^4/D$, $M_x = 0.0976\ q_0 a^2$, $M_y = 0.1328\ q_0 a^2$, where a equals the length and width of the element, i.e., one-half the length and width of the plate.)

14-11. Consider a uniformly loaded square plate having all four edges supported elastically by simply supported beams. Use conditions of double symmetry to represent the plate by a single element having width and length equal to a, and find the displacement and bending moments at the center of the plate for three cases where $EI/aD = 100, 1, 0$. (Here EI is the bending stiffness of the supporting beams.) Also let $\nu = 0.3$ for the plate. Compare the solutions with that of Example 14-10.

14-12. A rectangular plate is clamped along three edges and is free along the fourth edge. The plate is subjected to a transverse hydrostatic pressure as shown in Fig. P14-12. Represent the structure by four plate elements, each having plan dimensions a by b, and determine the displacement and bending moment at the center of the free edge. (The exact analytical solution is $w = 0.0016\ q_0 a^4/D$ and $M = 0.006\ q_0 a^2$ when $\nu = 0.3$.)

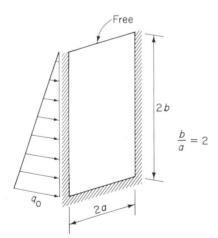

Figure P14-12

14-13. Consider the cylindrical shell of Example 14-14 to have a coefficient of thermal expansion $\bar{\alpha}$ and to be evaluated to a temperature ΔT. Estimate the deformation and internal forces and bending moments in the shell.

14-14. A circular cylindrical tank having a uniform thickness, is free at the top and clamped at the base, and is filled with a fluid having density ρ. Using a two-element model and assuming the axial deformations to be negligible, estimate the radial deflection at the top of the tank and the shear force and bending moment at the base. (Use $\nu = 0.3$.)

14-15. Consider the cylindrical shell of Example 14-14 to be reinforced at midspan by a ring having a cross-sectional area equal to $10h^2$, where h is the thickness of the shell. Find the deformations and internal stress resultants in the shell due to a uniform internal pressure.

References

1. Benjamin, J. R. *Statically Indeterminate Structures*, New York: McGraw-Hill, 1959.

2. Carpenter, S. T. *Structural Mechanics*, New York: John Wiley, 1960.

3. Charlton, T. M. *Energy Principles in Applied Statics*, London: Blackie & Son Limited, 1959.

4. Cook, R. D. *Concepts and Applications of Finite Element Analysis*, 2nd ed., New York: John Wiley, 1981.

5. Cross, H. and N. D. Morgan. *Continuous Frames of Reinforced Concrete*, New York: John Wiley, 1936.

6. Desai, C. and J. F. Abel. *Introduction to the Finite Element Method*, New York: D. Van Nostrand, 1972.

7. Gallagher, R. H. *Finite Element Analysis: Fundamentals*, Englewood Cliffs, N. J.: Prentice-Hall, 1975.

8. Gere, J. M. and W. Weaver, Jr. *Analysis of Framed Structures*, 2nd ed., D. Van Nostrand, 1982.

9. Ghali, A. and A. M. Neville. *Structural Analysis*, New York: Intext, 1972.

10. Hall, A. S. and R. W. Woodhead. *Frame Analysis*, 2nd ed., New York: John Wiley, 1967.

11. Hsieh, Y. Y. *Elementary Theory of Structures*. Englewood Cliffs, N. J.: Prentice-Hall, 1970.

12. Hoff, N. J. *The Analysis of Structures*, New York: John Wiley, 1956.

13. Ketter, R. L., G. C. Lee and S. P. Prawel, Jr. *Structural Analysis and Design*, New York: McGraw-Hill, 1979.

14. Langhaar, H. L. *Energy Methods in Applied Mechanics*, New York: John Wiley, 1962.

15. Laursen, H. I. *Matrix Analysis of Structures*, New York: McGraw-Hill, 1966.

16. Martin, H. C. *Introduction to Matrix Methods of Structural Analysis*, New York: McGraw-Hill, 1966.

17. Martin, H. C. and G. F. Carey. *Introduction to Finite Element Analysis*, New York: McGraw-Hill, 1973.

18. McGuire, W. and R. H. Gallagher. *Matrix Structural Analysis*, New York: John Wiley, 1979.

19. Meek, J. L. *Matrix Structural Analysis*, New York: McGraw-Hill, 1971.

20. Meyers, V. J. *Matrix Analysis of Structures*, New York: Harper & Row Pubs., 1983.

21. Nervi, P. L. *Structures*, Trans. G. and M. Salvadori, New York: F. W. Dodge, 1956.

22. Norris, C. H., J. B. Wilbur and S. Utku. *Elementary Structural Analysis*, 3rd ed., New York: McGraw-Hill, 1976.

23. Parcel, J. I. and R. B. B. Moorman. *Analysis of Statically Indeterminate Structures*, New York: John Wiley, 1955.

24. Przemieniecki, J. S. *Theory of Matrix Structural Analysis*, New York: McGraw-Hill, 1968.

25. Steinman, D. B. and S. R. Watson. *Bridges and Their Builders*, New York: Dover, 1957.

26. Timoshenko, S. and D. H. Young. *Theory of Structures*, 2nd ed., New York: McGraw-Hill, 1965.

27. Torroja, E. *Philosophy of Structures*, trans. J. J. Polivka and M. Polivka, Berkeley and Los Angeles: University of California Press, 1958.

28. Ural, O. *Finite Element Method*, New York: Intext, 1973.

29. Wang, C. K. *Indeterminate Structural Analysis*, New York: McGraw-Hill, 1983.

30. West, H. H. *Analysis of Structures*, New York: John Wiley, 1980.

31. White R. N., P. Gergely and R. G. Sexsmith. *Structural Engineering*, Combined edition (Vols. 1 and 2), New York: John Wiley, 1976.

32. Zienkiewicz, O. C. *The Finite Element Method*, 3rd ed., New York: McGraw-Hill, 1977.

Answers
To Selected Problems

CHAPTER 2

(All answers are in kips)

   2-2. $H_a = 70$, $H_b = 70$, $V_b = 12.5$

   2-4. $H_a = 81.4$, $H_b = 51.4$, $V_b = 60$

   2-6. $V_a = 10$, $V_b = 28.7$, $V_c = 5.3$

   2-8. $V_a = 19.3$, $H_a = 20$, $V_d = 35.7$

  2-10. $V(L_2) = 100$, $H(L_2) = 70$, $V(L_3) = 40$, $V(L_7) = 40$, $H(L_7) = 40$

  2-12. $V_a = 74.7$, $H_a = 80$, $V_c = 25.3$, $H_c = 0$

  2-14. $V_a = 50$, $H_a = 0$, $V_b = 50$, $V_c = 60$, $V_d = 10$, $H_d = 0$

CHAPTER 3

   3-4. $N_f = 5.27^k$, $S_j = 14.1^k$, $M_j = 60^{k\text{-}ft}$, $N_g = 20.6^k$, $S_g = 20.6^k$, $M_g = 85^{k\text{-}ft}$

   3-6. $M_b = -138^{k\text{-}ft}$

  3-10. $M_c = +16^{k\text{-}ft}$, $M_e = -96^{k\text{-}ft}$

  3-14. $M_c = -31^{k\text{-}ft}$

  3-16. $M_d = -480^{k\text{-}ft}$

  3-18. $M_b = +8.25^{k\text{-}ft}$

  3-20. $S_{ab} = 296(h/24)^k$, $M_c = 523(h^2/24)^{k\text{-}ft}$

  3-22. M (left support) $= -128(h^2/24)$

  3-24. Shears (multiplied by a factor $h/24$): $S_{ab} = 5.0$, $S_{bc} = 21.0$, $S_{cd} = 20.9$, $S_{de} =$

4.9, $S_{ef} = -17.9$, $S_{fg} = -33.9$; Moments (multiplied by a factor $h^2/24$): $M_b = 5.0$, $M_c = 26.0$, $M_d = 46.9$, $M_e = 51.8$, $M_f = 33.9$

3-26. $M_b = -76^{\text{k-ft}}$, $M_c = -107^{\text{k-ft}}$

3-27. At C, $F_y = -35^k$, $M_x = -357.5^{\text{k-ft}}$, $M_z = 556^{\text{k-ft}}$

3-29. $V_0 = V_2 = 57.08^k$, $V_1 = 200^k$

CHAPTER 4
(All answers are in kips)

4-2. $AB = -125$, $AC = +70$, $BC = +35.2$, $BD = -84.3$, $CD = +14.3$, $CE = +65$

4-6. $a = 0$, $b = -240$, $c = +226$

4-9. $a = -27.4$, $b = -85$, $c = +80$

4-11. $a = -14.2$, $b = -12.5$, $c = +10$

4-12. $a = -30$, $b = +50$, $c = -63.4$

4-14. $a = +5$, $b = -3.78$, $c = -2.74$

4-22. $AD = -100$, $DF = 0$, $FG = +30$, $GH = -70$, $HB = -70$, $BC = -20$, $CA = 0$, $DG = -70.7$, $DC = EG = EB = +70.7$, $EC = EH = +99$

4-24. $a = -85$, $b = 53.2$, $c = +25$

4-26. $a = +45$, $b = +112$, $c = -60$

4-28. $a = +158$, $b = -24.2$, $c = +84.2$

4-30. $a = -83.3$, $b = -17.3$, $c = -62.4$

4-31. $BC = -15.9$, $CD = -15.9$, $DE = -10.3$, $EF = +5.1$, $AF = +5.2$, $AB = -0.4$, $BE = -5.1$, $CF = +5.2$, $AD = +17.2$

CHAPTER 5

5-2. $r_c = 8'$, $r_d = 12'$, $r_c = 12'$, $T_{\max} = 256^k$

5-4. $T_{\max} = 122^k$

5-10. $a = -56^k$, $b = -31.4^k$, $c = +38^k$

5-13. M (under 200^k load) $= +3240^{\text{k-ft}}$, M (under 160^k load) $= +1640^{\text{k-ft}}$

5-15. M (under 200^k load) $= +3230^{\text{k-ft}}$, M (under 160^k load) $= +2140^{\text{k-ft}}$

5-17. $N_d = 8.47^k$, $S_d = 8.47^k$, $M_d = 175^{\text{k-ft}}$

CHAPTER 6

6-5. 1.38 in.

6-6. $-1143/EI$

6-11. At $\frac{1}{4}$ pt., $v = -72(w_0 h^4/144EI_0)$; at center, $v = -95(w_0 h^4/48EI_0)$

6-13. At center, $v = -51.47(M_0 h^2/144EI_0)$

6-15. At free end, $v = -490\ h^2/EI_0 = -1.27$ in.; at center, $v = 110h^2/EI_0 = +0.247$ in.

6-18. $u = -42,000/EI_0$, $v = 195,000/EI_0$

6-20. 4.25 in.

6-22. 7.39 in.

6-24. 1.90 in.

CHAPTER 7

7-1. $M_b = -197^{\text{k-ft}}$; $M_c = +99^{\text{k-ft}}$

7-3. $M_b = -185^{\text{k-ft}}$; $M_c = +58^{\text{k-ft}}$

7-5. $M_b = M_c = -555^{\text{k-ft}}$

7-8. $M_b = -199^{\text{k-ft}}$; $M_c = -279^{\text{k-ft}}$

7-10. $M_b = -230^{\text{k-ft}}$; $M_c = -323^{\text{k-ft}}$

7-11. 5.0′ left of B; 26.7′ left of C

7-14. 14.3′ right of B

7-15. 12.3′ left of B and 15.8′ right of B

7-19. 26.8′ right of A; 8.3′ right of B; 12.9′ right of C; 36.8′ left of D

7-21. $M_b = -233^{\text{k-ft}}$; $M_c = -200^{\text{k-ft}}$; $M_d = -300^{\text{k-ft}}$

7-24. $M_b = +668^{\text{k-ft}}$; $M_c = -924^{\text{k-ft}}$

CHAPTER 8

8-3. (a) $Y_c = 2/5$ for S_e, $Y_c = 3/5\sqrt{2}$ for S_j; (b) $Y_c = 4$ for M_e, $Y_c = 6$ for M_j

8-5. (a) $Y_a = 1.25$, (b) $Y_a = 0.25$, (c) $Y_d = 1$, (d) $Y_d = -30$, (e) $Y_d = -15$

8-7. (a) $Y_c = 1.2$, (b) $Y_c = -8.0$, (c) $Y_c = -0.2$

8-9. (a) $Y_e = -0.25$ for R_a, $Y_e = +1.25$ for R_b; (b) $Y_e = -0.25$ for S_g, $Y_e = 1$ for S_h; (c) $Y_e = -5$ for M_g and M_h

8-12. (a) $Y_g = \frac{1}{6}$, (b) $Y_g = \frac{1}{6}$, (c) $Y_g = 3$

8-16. $Y_e = \frac{2}{3}$

8-18. $U_2L_3 = 67^{\text{k}}$, $L_3L_4 = 166^{\text{k}}$

8-20. $Y_a = 1$ for V_c, $Y_a = -8/7$ for H_c, $Y_a = +8/7$ for H_d

CHAPTER 9

9-2. $PL^3/48EI$

9-5. 1.38 in.

9-10. 4.82 in.

9-12. $u = 0.77$ in., $v = 0.24$ in.

9-16. 0.303 in.

9-18. 0.618 in.

9-20. $u = 0$, $v = 0.226$ in.

CHAPTER 10

10-1. 3.77^k

10-3. $u = 0.56$ in.; $v = 1.48$ in.

10-5. 105^k

10-8. 1.90 in.

10-10. $-80^{k\text{-ft}}$

10-12. 89^k

10-13. $R_1 = (11/28)wL$; $R_2 = (8/7)wL$

10-14. $R_3 = (13/28)wL$; $M_3 = -(1/14)wL^2$

CHAPTER 11

11-1.
$$\begin{bmatrix} k_1 & -k_1 & 0 & 0 \\ -k_1 & k_1 + k_2 & -k_2 & 0 \\ 0 & -k_2 & k_2 + k_3 & -k_3 \\ 0 & 0 & -k_3 & k_3 \end{bmatrix}$$

11-3. $\Delta_1 = P_1/k_1$; $\Delta_3 = P_3/(k_2 + k_3)$
$F_1 = -P_1$; $F_2 = P_3k_3/(k_2 + k_3)$; $F_3 = -P_3k_3/(k_2 + k_3)$

11-6. $\Delta = (1/20kL^2)(6PL^2 - 4ML)$
$\theta = (1/20kL^2)(-4PL + 6M)$
$$\begin{Bmatrix} \delta_1 \\ \delta_2 \\ \delta_3 \end{Bmatrix} = \frac{1}{10kL} \begin{Bmatrix} 3PL - 2M \\ PL + M \\ -PL + 4M \end{Bmatrix}; \quad \begin{Bmatrix} F_1 \\ F_2 \\ F_3 \end{Bmatrix} = \frac{1}{10L} \begin{Bmatrix} 3PL - 2M \\ 2PL + 2M \\ -PL + 4M \end{Bmatrix}$$

11-8. (a)
$$\begin{bmatrix} k_2 + k_4 & 0 \\ 0 & k_1 + k_3 \end{bmatrix}$$

(b)
$$\begin{bmatrix} (k_1 + k_3) \sin^2 \theta + (k_2 + k_4) \cos^2 \theta & (-k_1 - k_3 + k_2 + k_4) \sin \theta \cos \theta \\ (-k_1 - k_3 + k_2 + k_4) \sin \theta \cos \theta & (k_1 + k_3) \cos^2 \theta + (k_2 + k_4) \sin^2 \theta \end{bmatrix}$$

11-10.
$$\begin{Bmatrix} F_1 \\ F_2 \\ F_3 \end{Bmatrix} = \begin{Bmatrix} -P_1 \\ -(P_1 + P_2) \\ -(P_1 + P_2 + P_3) \end{Bmatrix}; \quad \begin{Bmatrix} \delta_1 \\ \delta_2 \\ \delta_3 \end{Bmatrix} = \begin{Bmatrix} -P_1/k_1 \\ -(P_1 + P_2)/k_2 \\ -(P_1 + P_2 + P_3)/k_3 \end{Bmatrix}$$

11.12. $\Delta_2 = (P_2 + k_2\Delta_3)/(k_1 + k_2)$
$F_1 = k_1(P_2 + k_2\Delta_3)/(k_1 + k_2)$; $F_2 = -k_2(P_2 - k_1\Delta_3)/(k_1 + k_2)$

11-15.
$$[\mathbf{A}] = [\mathbf{B}]^T = \begin{bmatrix} -1 & 0 & 0 \\ 0 & 1 & 0 \\ -\dfrac{1}{2} & \dfrac{\sqrt{3}}{2} & \dfrac{1}{2} \end{bmatrix}$$

CHAPTER 12

12-1. For externally braced frame
$$\begin{Bmatrix} u_2 \\ v_2 \\ u_3 \\ v_3 \end{Bmatrix} = \frac{PL}{EA} \begin{Bmatrix} 0.6 \\ 0 \\ 1.2 \\ -0.4 \end{Bmatrix}$$

$F_1 = 0$, $F_2 = 0.6P$, $F_3 = 0.566P$, $F_4 = -0.4P$, $F_5 = -0.424P$, $F_6 = 0.424P$

12-2. $u_2 = 0.6\Delta$, $v_2 = -0.25\Delta$, $u_3 = 0.7\Delta$, $v_4 = -0.9\Delta$
$F_1 = -0.250EA\,\Delta/L$, $F_2 = 0.10EA\,\Delta/L$, $F_3 = -0.14EA\,\Delta/L$, $F_4 = 0.10EA\,\Delta/L$,
$F_5 = 0.106EA\,\Delta/L$, $F_6 = 0.247EA\,\Delta/L$

12-4. $u_5 = -0.0113$ ft, $v_5 = w_5 = 0$
$F_{1-5} = F_{4-5} = -F_{2-5} = -F_{3-5} = 20\text{k}$

12-6.
$$\begin{Bmatrix} v_2 \\ \theta_2 L \\ v_3 \\ \theta_3 L \end{Bmatrix} = \frac{-PL^3}{12EI_0} \begin{Bmatrix} 5 \\ 9 \\ 18 \\ 15 \end{Bmatrix};\quad \begin{Bmatrix} F_{y1} \\ M_{z1} \\ F_{y2} \\ M_{z2} \end{Bmatrix}^{(1)} = P \begin{Bmatrix} 1 \\ 2L \\ -1 \\ -L \end{Bmatrix};\quad \begin{Bmatrix} F_{y2} \\ M_{z2} \\ F_{y3} \\ M_{z3} \end{Bmatrix}^{(2)} = P \begin{Bmatrix} 1 \\ L \\ -1 \\ 0 \end{Bmatrix}$$

12-8.
$$\begin{Bmatrix} \theta_1 \\ \theta_2 \\ \theta_3 \end{Bmatrix} = \frac{\Delta}{2L} \begin{Bmatrix} 1 \\ -2 \\ -5 \end{Bmatrix};\quad \begin{Bmatrix} F_{y1} \\ M_{z1} \\ F_{y2} \\ M_{z2} \end{Bmatrix}^{(1)} = \frac{3\Delta EI_0}{L^3} \begin{Bmatrix} -1 \\ 0 \\ 1 \\ L \end{Bmatrix};\quad \begin{Bmatrix} F_{y2} \\ M_{z2} \\ F_{y2} \\ M_{z3} \end{Bmatrix}^{(2)} = \frac{3\Delta EI_0}{L^3} \begin{Bmatrix} -3 \\ -L \\ 3 \\ -2L \end{Bmatrix}$$

12-9.
$$\begin{Bmatrix} \theta_1 \\ \theta_2 \\ \theta_3 \\ v_3 \end{Bmatrix} = \frac{ML}{42EI_0} \begin{Bmatrix} 2 \\ -4 \\ -31 \\ -15L \end{Bmatrix};\quad \begin{Bmatrix} F_{y1} \\ M_{z1} \\ F_{y2} \\ M_{z2} \end{Bmatrix}^{(1)} = \frac{M}{L} \begin{Bmatrix} -0.286 \\ 0 \\ 0.286 \\ -0.286L \end{Bmatrix};\quad \begin{Bmatrix} F_{y2} \\ M_{z2} \\ F_{y3} \\ M_{z3} \end{Bmatrix}^{(2)} = \frac{M}{L} \begin{Bmatrix} -0.714 \\ 0.286L \\ 0.714 \\ -L \end{Bmatrix}$$

12-12.
$$\begin{Bmatrix} u_2 \\ v_2 \\ \theta_2 \\ u_3 \\ v_3 \\ \theta_3 \end{Bmatrix} = \begin{Bmatrix} 74.9 \text{ in.} \\ 0.92 \text{ in.} \\ -0.25 \\ 74.4 \text{ in.} \\ -0.92 \text{ in.} \\ -0.24 \end{Bmatrix} \times 10^{-3};\quad \begin{Bmatrix} F_{x'1} \\ F_{y'1} \\ M_{z'1} \\ F_{x'2} \\ F_{y'2} \\ M_{z'2} \end{Bmatrix}^{(1)} = \begin{Bmatrix} -2.30 \text{ k} \\ 2.51 \text{ k} \\ 163 \text{ k-in.} \\ 2.30 \text{ k} \\ -2.51 \text{ k} \\ 138 \text{ k-in.} \end{Bmatrix}$$

12-14.
$$\begin{Bmatrix} u_2 \\ v_2 \\ \theta_2^{(1)} \\ \theta_2^{(2)} \end{Bmatrix} = \begin{Bmatrix} 0.703 \text{ in.} \\ -5.27 \text{ in.} \\ -0.023 \\ -3.73 \end{Bmatrix} \times 10^{-3};\quad \begin{Bmatrix} F_{x1} \\ F_{y1} \\ M_{z1} \\ F_{x2} \\ F_{y2} \\ M_{z2} \end{Bmatrix}^{(1)} = \begin{Bmatrix} 2.08 \text{ k} \\ 1.56 \text{ k} \\ 0.928 \text{ k-in.} \\ -2.08 \text{ k} \\ -1.56 \text{ k} \\ 0 \end{Bmatrix}$$

12-16.
$$\begin{Bmatrix} u_2 \\ v_2 \\ \theta_2 \end{Bmatrix} = \begin{Bmatrix} 3.36 \text{ in.} \\ -9.28 \text{ in.} \\ -1.20 \end{Bmatrix} \times 10^{-3};\quad \begin{Bmatrix} F_{x'1} \\ F_{y'1} \\ M_{z'1} \\ F_{x'2} \\ F_{y'2} \\ M_{z'2} \end{Bmatrix} = \begin{Bmatrix} 5.23 \text{ k} \\ -0.703 \text{ k} \\ -54.4 \text{ k-in.} \\ -5.23 \text{ k} \\ 0.703 \text{ k} \\ -114 \text{ k-in.} \end{Bmatrix}$$

12-17.
$$\begin{Bmatrix} u_2 \\ v_2 \\ \theta_2 \\ v_3 \\ \theta_3 \end{Bmatrix} = \begin{Bmatrix} 0.124 \text{ in.} \\ -5.84 \text{ in.} \\ -0.56 \\ -4.11 \text{ in.} \\ 0.53 \end{Bmatrix} \times 10^{-3};\quad \begin{Bmatrix} F_{x1} \\ F_{y1} \\ M_{z1} \\ F_{x2} \\ F_{y2} \\ M_{z2} \end{Bmatrix}^{(1)} = \begin{Bmatrix} 0.620 \text{ k} \\ 9.73 \text{ k} \\ -37.2 \text{ k-in.} \\ -0.620 \text{ k} \\ -9.73 \text{ k} \\ -74.4 \text{ k-in.} \end{Bmatrix}$$

12-19.
$$\begin{Bmatrix} v_2 \\ \theta_{x2} \\ \theta_{z2} \end{Bmatrix} = \begin{Bmatrix} -217 \text{ in.} \\ 4.40 \\ -1.73 \end{Bmatrix} \times 10^{-3}$$

12-22. $-F_{1\text{-}5} = -F_{3\text{-}5} = F_{2\text{-}5} = F_{4\text{-}5} = 0.75$ k

12-24.
$$\begin{Bmatrix} u_2 \\ v_2 \\ \theta_2 \\ u_3 \\ v_3 \\ \theta_3 \end{Bmatrix} = \begin{Bmatrix} -230 \text{ in.} \\ -499 \text{ in.} \\ 3.83 \\ -230 \text{ in.} \\ -1.28 \text{ in.} \\ 3.83 \end{Bmatrix} \times 10^{-3}; \qquad \begin{Bmatrix} F_{x2} \\ F_{y2} \\ M_{z2} \\ F_{x3} \\ F_{y3} \\ M_{z3} \end{Bmatrix}^{(2)} = \begin{Bmatrix} 0 \\ -3.19 \text{ k} \\ -191 \text{ k-in.} \\ 0 \\ 3.19 \text{ k} \\ -191 \text{ k-in.} \end{Bmatrix}$$

12-26.
$$\begin{Bmatrix} u_2 \\ v_2 \\ w_2 \\ \theta_{x2} \\ \theta_{y2} \\ \theta_{z2} \end{Bmatrix} = \begin{Bmatrix} 1.80 \text{ in.} \\ -349 \text{ in.} \\ 349 \text{ in.} \\ 0 \\ -2.56 \\ -2.56 \end{Bmatrix} \times 10^{-3}; \qquad \begin{Bmatrix} F_{x2} \\ F_{y2} \\ F_{z2} \\ M_{x2} \\ M_{y2} \\ M_{z2} \end{Bmatrix}^{(1)} = \begin{Bmatrix} 4.50 \text{ k} \\ -8.15 \text{ k} \\ 8.15 \text{ k} \\ 0 \\ 360 \text{ k-in.} \\ 360 \text{ k-in.} \end{Bmatrix}$$

CHAPTER 13

13-1. $F_1 = 1.5\ F_2 = 3\ F_3 = -1.5\ F_4 = -3\ F_5 = 3\ F_7 = 3\ F_9 = 120$ k
$F_6 = F_8 = F_{10} = -56.6$ k

13-2. $F_{x'2}^{(1)} = 0,\ M_{z1}^{(1)} = 0,\ M_{z2}^{(1)} = 112.5$ k-ft, $F_{x'3}^{(2)} = -5.30$ k, $M_{z2}^{(2)} = -112.5$ k-ft, $M_{z3}^{(2)} = 0$

13-4. $F_{x'2}^{(1)} = -14.1$ k, $M_{z1}^{(1)} = 0,\ M_{z2}^{(1)} = 8.27$ k-ft, $F_{x'3}^{(2)} = -8$ k, $M_{z2}^{(2)} = -8.27$ k-ft, $M_{z3}^{(2)} = 0,\ F_{x'4}^{(3)} = -8.41$ k-ft, $M_{z3}^{(3)} = 0,\ M_{z4}^{(3)} = 0$

13-9. $F_1 = 2\ F_2 = F_3 = 0.3\ P,\ F_4 = -0.35\ P,\ F_5 = -0.335\ P,\ F_6 = 0.783\ P$

13-11. $F_1 = -F_2 = -F_3 = F_4 = 20$ k

13-13. $F_{y2}^{(1)} = -pL/16,\ M_{z2}^{(1)} = 0,\ F_{y3}^{(2)} = 15\ pL/16,\ M_{z3}^{(2)} = -7\ pL^2/16$

13-15. $F_{x2}^{(1)} = 19.3$ k, $F_{y2}^{(1)} = 2.13$ k, $M_{z2}^{(1)} = -384$ k-in., $F_{x'3}^{(2)} = 15.1$ k, $F_{y'3}^{(2)} = 9.10$ k, $M_{z'3}^{(2)} = 0,$
$\theta_1 = 0.00175,\ u_2 = 0.0116$ in., $v_2 = -0.0297$ in., $\theta_2 = -0.004,\ \theta_3 = 0.00695$

13-17. $F_{y2}^{(1)} = 2.30$ k, $M_{z1}^{(1)} = 13.6$ k-ft, $M_{z2}^{(1)} = 11.5$ k-ft, $F_{x3}^{(2)} = -2.49$ k,
$M_{z2}^{(2)} = -11.5$ k-ft, $M_{z3}^{(2)} = -11.5$ k-ft, $F_{y4}^{(3)} = -2.30$ k, $M_{z3}^{(3)} = 11.5$ k-ft,
$M_{z4}^{(3)} = 13.5$ k-ft

13-18. $F_{y2}^{(1)} = -1.66$ k, $M_{x2}^{(1)} = 20.2$ k-in., $M_{z2}^{(1)} = 24.5$ k-in., $F_{y3}^{(2)}\ 0.336$ k, $M_{x3}^{(3)} = -20.2$ k-in., $M_{z3}^{(2)} = -24.5$ k-in.
$v_2 = -0.130$ in., $\theta_{x2} = 0.000505,\ \theta_{z2} = -0.00151,\ v_3 = -0.0617$ in., $\theta_{x3} = 0.000505$ in., $\theta_{z3} = -0.000894$

13-20. $F_{x2}^{(1)} = 0.540$ k, $F_{y2}^{(1)} = 0.0270$ k, $M_{z2}^{(1)} = -4.86$ k-in., $F_{y3}^{(2)} = -0.0191$ k,
$M_{z3}^{(2)} = 0,\ F_{x'3}^{(2)} = 0.0573$ k.

13-22. $u_2 = -0.230$ in., $v_2 = -0.499$ in., $\theta_2 = 0.00383$
$u_3 = -0.230$ in., $v_3 = -0.00128$ in., $\theta_3 = 0.00383$

13-23. **(a)** stable, one degree indeterminate
(b) unstable
(c) stable, statically determinate
(d) unstable

CHAPTER 14

14-1. At free end of bar, $u = 0.228 \dfrac{\rho g L^2}{E}$ (exact), $u = 0.248 \dfrac{\rho g L^2}{E}$ (finite element).

At fixed end of bar, $\sigma = 0.317 \, \rho g L$ (exact), $\sigma = 0.326 \, \rho g L$ (finite element).

14-3. (a) $v = -0.790 \dfrac{PL^3}{EI_0}$ (using ten spatial intervals for numerical integration)

(b) $v = -1.365 \dfrac{PL^3}{EI_0}$

(c) $v = -0.666 \dfrac{PL^3}{EI_0}$ where $I_0 = w d_0^3 / 12$

14-4. (a) $v_3 = -8.96 \, P/Et$

(b) $v_5 = 13.04 \, P/Et$

14-5. $v_3 = v_4 = 12.5 \, \bar{\alpha} \, \Delta T$,

$\sigma_x = -1.25 \, \bar{\alpha} \, \Delta T, \; \sigma_y = \tau_{xy} = 0$

14-9. $u_2 = 0.466, \; u_3 = 0.462.$

In element 1, $\sigma_\theta = 8.72 \times 10^{-3}, \; \sigma_r = -0.72 \times 10^{-3}, \; \sigma_z = 2.00 \times 10^{-3}, \; \tau_{rz} = -0.16 \times 10^{-3}$

14-11. $w_9 = 0.0828 \dfrac{q_0 a^4}{D}$ for $\dfrac{EI}{aD} = 100$

$w_9 = 0.188 \dfrac{q_0 a^4}{D}$ for $\dfrac{EI}{aD} = 1$

$w_9 = 0.276 \dfrac{q_0 a^4}{D}$ for $\dfrac{EI}{aD} = 0$

14-14. At top of tank $w = 0.226 \, \rho g a^3 / C, \; \psi a/2 = 0.702 \, \rho g a^3 / C$

At midheight $w = 0.396 \, \rho g a^3 / C, \; \psi a/2 = -0.484 \, \rho g a^3 / C$

14-15.
$$\left\{ \begin{array}{c} w_1 \\ u_2 \\ w_2 \\ \psi_2 L \end{array} \right\} = \dfrac{q_0 a^2}{Eh} \left\{ \begin{array}{r} 0.276 \\ -0.010 \\ 0.532 \\ -0.248 \end{array} \right\}$$

Index

Axisymmetric shells, 694
Axisymmetric solids, 661

B

Bar chain method, 233
Bar force, 120
Beams:
   analysis by direct stiffness method, 518
   analysis by flexibility method, 574, 586
   compound, 47, 203, 323
   continuous, 259, 273, 342
   deflection, 194, 249
   differential relationships in, 77, 197
   influence lines for, 314, 323, 342
   single span, 73, 194, 247
   symmetry and antisymmetry, 555
   thermal loads and misfit, 544, 591
Bending moment, 71, 72
Bending stiffness, 192
Betti theorem, 409
Bow girder, 110
Bridge truss, 123, 124

C

Cables:
   under concentrated loads, 160
   deflection, 237
   horizontal tension, 162
   with uniform loads, 163
Cantilever method, 299
Carry-over factor, 258
Castigliano's theorems, 382, 426
Choice of redundant forces, 431, 603
Chord members of trusses, 123
Circular bow girder, 112
Circular cylinder, 704
Circular plate, 708
Complementary energy method, 370
Complementary work, 359, 387
Complex trusses, 121, 142
Compound beams, 47, 203, 323
Compound systems, 45

Compound trusses, 121, 137
Condensation, 556
Condensed stiffness matrix, 556
Conjugate beam method, 211, 233
Connectivity matrix, 625
Conservative system, 358
Continuous beams, 259, 342
Convergence criteria for finite element method, 632
Coordinates:
  generalized, 442
  global, 444
  local, 444
Criteria of statical indeterminacy, 52
Cross method, 259
Curvature, 193, 194, 203

D

Deflected shapes of structures, 58
Deflection, 189
  of arches, 227
  of beams, 194, 200, 204, 210, 214
  of cables, 237
  of nonlinear elastic systems, 387
  of rigid frames, 218, 222
  of trusses, 228
Deflection influence coefficients, 445
Deflection theory, 22
Degrees of freedom:
  active, 445, 471, 481
  master, 556
  nodal, 415
  slave, 556
Degrees of kinematic indeterminacy, 415
Degrees of statical indeterminacy, 52
Degrees of redundancy, 52
Design specifications, 13, 14
Designer's sign convention, 71, 435
Differential relationships in beams, 77, 197
Direct stiffness method, 455, 469, 491, 568
  for beams subjected to concentrated loads, 519
  for beams subjected to distributed loads, 526
  for frames, 530
  for trusses, 508
Displacement, 22, 189

Displacement function, 625
Displacement method, 403, 415, 449, 475
Displacement vector, 445
Distribution factor, 259
Dummy unit load method, 375

E

Elastic curve, 190
Elastic theory, 22
Elastic weight method, 210, 233
Elasticity matrix, 628
Element stiffness matrix, 450
Energy relations in structural systems, 358
Equilibrium, 34
Equivalent load vectors, 680
Equivalent nodal forces, 528, 630
Equivalent static loads, 8

F

Factor of safety, 12, 13
Factor of serviceability, 12
Finite element formulation, 623
Finite element method, 619
Finite element modeling of:
  axisymmetric shells, 694
  axisymmetric solids, 651
  plane stress and plane strain, 639
  plates, 673
Fixed end moments, 252, 253, 254, 271, 527
Fixed end reactions, 253, 254
Fixed end shears, 527
Flexibility coefficients, 404, 445
Flexibility matrix:
  for bar elements, 579
  global (system), 445, 481
  member, 480
  for planar beam elements, 580
  relation to stiffness matrix, 446, 487
Flexibility method, 403, 475, 483, 570
  for direct computation of reactions, 606
  for statically determinate structures, 476, 572
  for statically indeterminate structures, 477, 583

Influence lines (*cont.*)
  for girders supporting floor beams, 327
  for simple trusses, 336
  for three-hinged arches, 330
  for two-hinged arches, 349
  as virtual displacement diagrams, 314
Internal forces, 21
Internal nodal forces, 458
Internal stress resultants, 680
International system (SI) of units, 18
Irregular loadings, 99

J

Joint rotation, 256, 263, 271
Joint translation, 256, 268, 271

K

Kinematic indeterminacy, 415
Kinematic stability, 34, 36, 39

L

Large deflection theory, 22
Least work, theorem of, 426
Load factor, 13
Loads, 7
Local coordinate system, 444
Long span trusses, 125

M

Matrix, partitioning of, 456
Matrix of member flexibilities, 480
Matrix of member stiffnesses, 453
Matrix methods, 438, 491, 570
Matrix notation and operations, 438
Matrix representation of linear equations, 441
Maxwell-Betti's theorem, 345, 409
Maxwell's theorem of reciprocal displacements, 345, 408, 446
Member flexibility matrix, 480

Twisting moment, 22
Two-hinged arch, 349

U

Unbalanced moment, 260, 263, 269
Uniform stress form, 23

V

Varying stress form, 23
Virtual displacement, principle of, 373
Virtual force, principle of, 373
Virtual work, method of, 378
Virtual work, principle of, 372, 375, 629

W

Web members of trusses, 123